BIOLOGY

TEACHER'S EDITION

SEPUP **SCIENCE & GLOBAL ISSUES**

BIOLOGY

TEACHER'S EDITION

SCIENCE EDUCATION
FOR PUBLIC UNDERSTANDING
PROGRAM

UNIVERSITY OF CALIFORNIA, BERKELEY
LAWRENCE HALL OF SCIENCE **LHS**

INCORPORATED

This material is based upon work supported by the National Science Foundation under Grant No. ESI-0352453. Any opinions, findings, and conclusions or recommendations expressed in this material are those of the authors and do not necessarily reflect the views of the National Science Foundation.

For photo and illustration credits, see pages 795–799, which constitute an extension of this copyright page.

The CD accompanying this book contains masters for student sheets and transparencies.

The preferred citation format for this book is
SEPUP. (2011). Science and Global Issues: Biology. Teacher's Edition. Lawrence Hall of Science, University of California at Berkeley. Published by Lab-Aids ®, Inc., Ronkonkoma NY

SEPUP
Lawrence Hall of Science
University of California at Berkeley
Berkeley CA 94720-5200
e-mail: sepup@berkeley.edu
Website: www.sepuplhs.org

Published by:
LaB-aiDS INCORPORATED
17 Colt Court
Ronkonkoma NY 11779
Website: www.lab-aids.com

Acknowledgments

SCIENCE AND GLOBAL ISSUES PROJECT

Barbara Nagle, Ph.D., *Project Director*

Sara Dombkowski Wilmes, *Project Coordinator*

Maia Willcox, *Field Test and Publications Coordinator*

SEPUP SCIENCE AND GLOBAL ISSUES DEVELOPMENT TEAM

Janet Bellantoni

Sara Dombkowski Wilmes

John Howarth

Christopher Keller

Laura Lenz

Barbara Nagle

Maia Willcox

UNIT AUTHORS

Sustainability
Janet Bellantoni, Maia Willcox, and Sara Dombkowski Wilmes

Ecology: Living on Earth
Maia Willcox, John Howarth, and Sara Dombkowski Wilmes

Cell Biology: World Health
Laura Lenz, Barbara Nagle, and John Howarth

Genetics: Feeding the World
Sara Dombkowski Wilmes, Maia Willcox, and Barbara Nagle

Evolution: Maintaining Biodiversity
Laura Lenz, Barbara Nagle, and John Howarth

OTHER CONTRIBUTORS

Kristin Nagy Catz

Raquel Gomes

Christopher Keller

Patty Kreikemeier

Donna Parker

CONTENT AND SCIENTIFIC REVIEW

Sustainability

Brent Boscarino, Ph.D., *Department of Natural Resources, Cornell University, Ithaca, New York*

Marianne Krasny, Ph.D., *Department of Natural Resources, Cornell University, Ithaca, New York*

Jasquelin Peña, *Department of Civil and Environmental Engineering, University of California at Berkeley, Berkeley, California*

Mark Spencer, Ph.D., *Department of Environmental Science and Policy Management, University of California at Berkeley, Berkeley, California*

Ecology: Living on Earth

Brent Boscarino, Ph.D., *Department of Natural Resources, Cornell University, Ithaca, New York*

Greg Goldsmith, *Department of Integrative Biology, University of California at Berkeley, Berkeley, California*

Alan Shabel, *Department of Integrative Biology, University of California at Berkeley, Berkeley, California*

Brody Sandel, *Department of Integrative Biology, University of California at Berkeley, Berkeley, California*

Cell Biology: World Health

Jennifer Chua, Ph.D., *National Institute of Health/National Institute of Child Health and Human Development, Bethesda, Maryland*

Raquel Gomes, Ph.D., *iGEM, University of California, San Francisco, California*

Jonathan Knight, Ph.D., *Department of Biology, San Francisco State University, San Francisco, California*

Genetics: Feeding the World

April Blakeslee, Ph.D., *Marine Invasions Ecology Lab, Smithsonian Environmental Research Center, Edgewater, Maryland*

Andrew Kramer, Ph.D., *Odum School of Ecology, University of Georgia, Athens, Georgia*

Sonal Singhal, *Department of Integrative Biology, University of California at Berkeley, Berkeley, California*

Evolution: Maintaining Biodiversity

Kefyn Catley, Ph.D., *Department of Biology, Western Carolina University, Cullowhee, North Carolina*

Nicholas J. Matzke, *Department of Integrative Biology, University of California, Berkeley, California*

PRODUCTION

Copyediting: Trish Beall

Index: Dick Evans

Design, illustration, photo research and composition: Seventeenth Street Studios

Administrative Assistance: Roberta Smith and Anna Vorster

FIELD TEST CENTERS

The following centers participated in field testing *Science and Global Issues: Biology*. We are extremely grateful to the center directors, teachers, and their students for their significant contributions to the development of this course.

REGIONAL CENTER, IOWA

Phyllis Anderson and Christopher Soldat, *Center Directors*

Anthony Brack, Jason Cochrane, Dawn Posekany

REGIONAL CENTER, WESTERN NEW YORK

Kathaleen Burke and Tammy Martin, *Center Directors*

Elizabeth Brunn, Nathan Kahler, Christen LaBruna, Heather Maciewjeski, Julie Sek, Susan Wade

BALTIMORE, MARYLAND

Keely Brelsford, *Center Director*

Dana Johnson, Aubrey Melton

BOULDER VALLEY, COLORADO

Kristin Donley, *Center Director*

Eliza Bicknell, Martina Kastengren, Kelly Ksiazek, Alberto Real

DUBLIN, OHIO

Donna Parker, *Center Director*

Chuck Crawford, Henry Lee, Heather Moore, Becky Saylor

GRAND RAPIDS, MICHIGAN

William Smith, *Center Director*

Jackie Billingsley, Abby Velie

LOS ANGELES, CALIFORNIA

Tammy Bird, *Center Director*

Brandie Borges, Elisa de la Pena-Nagle

NEW YORK, NEW YORK

Marc Siciliano, *Center Director*

Jared Fox, Leah McConaughey, Patrick Whelton

TUCKER, GEORGIA

Lisa Martin-Hansen, *Center Director*

Jeb Fox, Kelly Voss

WAKE COUNTY, NORTH CAROLINA

Michael Tally, *Center Director*

Jennifer Morrison, Tracey Myer, Tina Robinette, Rebecca Townsend, Susanne Turley

WHITTIER, CALIFORNIA

Tara Barnhart, *Center Director*

Jeff Varney

INDEPENDENT

Alameda, California: Patricia Williamson

Floyd, Kentucky: Angela King

Hartford, Connecticut: Angela Kumm

Hickory, North Carolina: Linda Culpepper

Oakland, California: Sam Tsitrin

Parkersburg, West Virginia: Nathan Alfred

Contents

Ecology: Living on Earth   69

Cell Biology: World Health 249

Genetics: Feeding the World   405

Evolution: Maintaining Diversity 619

How to Use *Science and Global Issues*

READING ALL THE way through the teacher pages that accompany an activity will prepare you to teach it effectively and smoothly. Much of the information contained in these pages is essential for successfully supporting students in completing the activity.

Number of class sessions is based on 50-minute periods.

Quantities provided assume the 4-2-1 model is being used. See Teacher Resources I: Course Essentials.

Location of blackline masters, safety precautions, and any required advance preparation will be noted after the Materials list.

Activity types used in SGI: Biology are: Investigation, Laboratory, Modeling, Project, Reading, and Talk It Over.

✓ *indicates a QuickCheck assessment opportunity. Full assessments are indicated with the name of the assessment variable. QuickCheck and full assessments are noted in the teaching summary, corresponding teaching suggestion, and sample responses.*

Numbered teaching suggestions correspond with specific points in the activity.

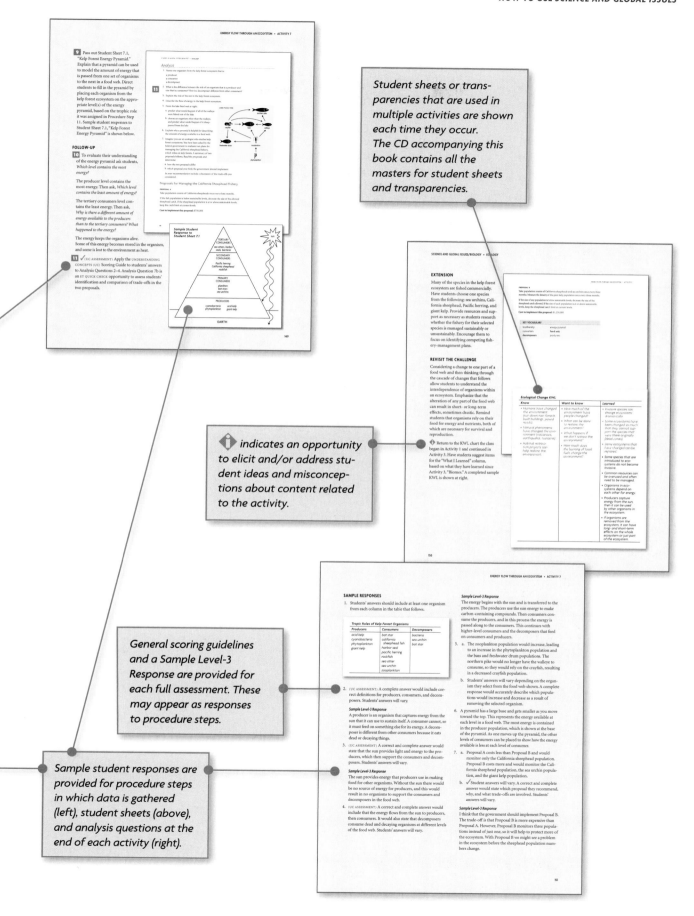

Student sheets or transparencies that are used in multiple activities are shown each time they occur. The CD accompanying this book contains all the masters for student sheets and transparencies.

ⓘ indicates an opportunity to elicit and/or address student ideas and misconceptions about content related to the activity.

General scoring guidelines and a Sample Level-3 Response are provided for each full assessment. These may appear as responses to procedure steps.

Sample student responses are provided for procedure steps in which data is gathered (left), student sheets (above), and analysis questions at the end of each activity (right).

Science and Global Issues: Biology Course Overview

To **HELP YOU** plan your lessons, the table below summarizes the units in the course. Unit overviews, which begin on the next page, give more detailed information about each activity in the units.

TITLE	MAIN SCIENCE CONTENT	ESTIMATED TIME
Sustainability	Ecological systems resiliency, resource use and availability, ecological footprint, making sustainable decisions	8 to 14 teaching periods (2 to 3 weeks)
Ecology: Living on Earth	Flow of energy through ecosystems, global ecosystems, population ecology, photosynthesis and respiration	29 to 45 teaching periods (6 to 9 weeks)
Cell Biology: World Health	Structure and function of animal and plant cells, cell specialization, basic biochemistry, disease-causing microbes	26 to 40 teaching periods (6 to 8 weeks)
Genetics: Feeding the World	Phenotype, genotype, traits, DNA replication, mutations, protein synthesis, gene expression, mitosis, meiosis, genetic engineering	29 to 42 teaching periods (6 to 9 weeks)
Evolution: Maintaining Biodiversity	Levels of biodiversity, introduction to phylogeny, evolutionary processes and natural selection, speciation, evidence for natural selection	19 to 34 teaching periods (4 to 7 weeks)

UNIT OVERVIEWS

Sustainability

Listed below is a summary of the activities in this unit. Note that the total teaching time is listed as 8 to 14 periods of approximately 45 to 50 minutes (approximately 2 to 3 weeks). Since this unit sets the context for the whole course by introducing various aspects of sustainability, it is recommended that at the very least all students should complete activities 1 to 3.

	ACTIVITY DESCRIPTION	KEY CONCEPTS AND PROCESSES	ADVANCE PREPARATION	ASSESSMENT	TEACHING PERIODS
1	**INVESTIGATION: Our Global Community** Students investigate the use of resources across regions of the world by manipulating indicator data.	indicator, sustainability, resource use LITERACY	Assemble pie charts	AQ2b: ET (Quick check)	1–2
2	**INVESTIGATION: Life in Other Countries** Students further investigate indicators of four countries and analyze the current sustainability challenges facing those communities.	indicator, sustainability	Gather resources on countries	Proc: GI	1–2
3	**READING: Sustainability Case Studies** Students read about two communities that took steps to improve their resource use of energy, water, and land.	product life cycle, land degradation, sustainable practice, indicator LITERACY			1–2
4	**INVESTIGATION: Ecological Footprint** Students complete an on-line survey that estimates their ecological footprint and then compares the results with averages for the United States, other countries, and the world.	ecological footprint, resource use, sustainable practice	Students complete survey at home before class		1–2
5	**LABORATORY: Jaffrey City's Problem** Students act in the role of scientists testing for contaminants in the lake water of fictitious Jaffrey Lake.	evidence, claims and reasoning, eutrophication, correlation and causality LITERACY		Proc: OD, AD, CS AQ4: AD	2–3
6	**TALK IT OVER: Jaffrey City's Master Plan** Students propose a master plan for dealing with the contamination of Jaffrey Lake in a way that is satisfactory to the stakeholders in the community.	making sustainable decisions, evidence and trade-offs, stakeholders		Proc: CS AQ1: ET	2–3

Ecology: Living on Earth

Listed below is a summary of the activities in this unit. Note that the total teaching time is listed as 29 to 45 periods of approximately 45 to 50 minutes (approximately 6 to 9 weeks).

	ACTIVITY DESCRIPTION	KEY CONCEPTS AND PROCESSES	ADVANCE PREPARATION	ASSESSMENT	TEACHING PERIODS
1	**TALK IT OVER: Ecosystems and Change** Students investigate case studies of ecosystem changes and the impacts on organisms.	human impacts on ecosystems, sustainability, indicators LITERACY		Proc: GI	2–3
2	**LABORATORY: A Population of Duckweed** Students monitor and analyze the growth of a population of duckweed plants for an eight-week period.	populations, communities, invasive species		Proc: OD AQ 1: AD	3–4 (over a period of 8 weeks)
3	**INVESTIGATION: Biomes** Students investigate characteristics of biomes and types of organisms in biomes.	biomes, human impacts on ecosystems, invasive species, sustainability, indicators LITERACY		AQ 5 & 6: UC	2–3
4	**INVESTIGATION: Invasive Species** Students investigate characteristics that make it likely for a species to become an invasive and examine case studies of invasive species introductions	human impacts on ecosystems, invasive species, sustainability, indicators LITERACY		AQ 4: ET	2–3
5	**MODELING: The Tragedy of the Commons** Students investigate how fishing limits impact the sustainability of a fishery.	sustainability, population dynamics, human impacts on ecosystems LITERACY	Purchase fish crackers in yellow and orange; count crackers into plastic bags	Proc: GI AQ 11b: ET	2
6	**INVESTIGATION: Producers and Consumers** Students observe plankton and investigate the link between plankton productivity and sustainable fisheries.	plankton, consumers, producers	Order live specimens Optional: Obtain local freshwater plankton sample	AQ 5: AD	1–2
7	**INVESTIGATION: Energy Flow Through an Ecosystem** Students explore the relationships that exist among organisms in a kelp forest and use a food web they construct to predict the impact of different events on the kelp forest ecosystem.	food webs, trophic roles, consumers, producers, decomposers, energy pyramids, invasive species, human impacts on ecosystems LITERACY		AQ 2, 3, & 4: UC AQ 7b: ET (Quick check)	2
8	**INVESTIGATION: Carbon Cycle** The class models the movement of carbon through the natural carbon cycle, and compares this to the impact of human activities on the movement of carbon in carbon cycle.	carbon cycle, nitrogen cycle, human impact on cycles	Arrange for computers with Internet access; check that computers have updated browsers to run simulation; bookmark simulation URL if appropriate	AQ 3: UC	1–2

Ecology *(Continued from previous page)*

	ACTIVITY DESCRIPTION	KEY CONCEPTS AND PROCESSES	ADVANCE PREPARATION	ASSESSMENT	TEACHING PERIODS
9	**INVESTIGATION: The Photosynthesis and Cellular Respiration Shuffle** Students determine the cycle of photosynthesis and cellular respiration by organizing a series of statements into a sequence.	photosynthesis, cellular respiration LITERACY	Set up equipment to project video clip; arrange for computers with Internet access; check that computers have updated browsers to run simulation; bookmark simulation URL if appropriate	AQ 3 & 6: UC	1–2
10	**LABORATORY: Respiring Beans** Students investigate cellular respiration in beans. Students develop their own variable and test conditions.	cellular respiration LITERACY	Germinate beans 3–4 days in advance; determine test conditions available for laboratory	Proc: DI AQ 4: AD AQ 6: UC	2–3
11	**LABORATORY: Respiration and Photosynthesis in Plants** Students observe underwater plants in various conditions to determine if plants respire and photosynthesize. Students develop their own variable and test conditions.	photosynthesis, cellular respiration LITERACY	Order live specimens; determine test conditions available for laboratory; determine where experimental setups will be left overnight	Proc: DI Proc: OD (Quick check) AQ 5, 6, & 8: UC	2–3
12	**INVESTIGATION: Too Much Life** Students use yeast to model population dynamic, cellular respiration & eutrophication.	cellular respiration, population dynamics, eutrophication LITERACY	Set up equipment to project video clip; purchase skim milk; prepare yeast solution approximately 15 minutes before each class	Proc: GI AQ 3: UC (Quick check) AQ 7: UC	1–2
13	**INVESTIGATION: Symbiotic Relationships** Students use descriptions of inter-species interactions to determine different symbiotic relationships.	symbiosis, parasitism, mutualism, commensalisms	Set up equipment to project video clip	AQ 3: UC	1–2
14	**INVESTIGATION: Investigating Population Growth Rates** An online simulation is used to investigate the effect of birth rate and carrying capacity on the growth rate of a population.	populations, population growth rates, birth rates, carrying capacity	Arrange for computers with Internet access; check that computers have updated browsers to run simulation; bookmark simulation URL if appropriate	AQ 6, 7, & 8: AD (Quick check)	1–2
15	**MODELING: Changes Due to Population Growth** Students examine the effect of a salmon farm on wild salmon population growth.	population dynamics, carrying capacity, effects of aquaculture on ecosystems		Proc: OD AQ4: ET (Quick check)	1–2
16	**INVESTIGATION: Ecosystems Out of Balance** Students examine graphs of different populations effected by fisheries and try to determine what the whole ecosystem effect has been.	inter-species relationships, carrying capacity, human effects on marine ecosystem	Set up equipment to project video clip	Proc: AD AQ 1: UC AQ 5: AD	1–2

Ecology (Continued from previous page)

	ACTIVITY DESCRIPTION	KEY CONCEPTS AND PROCESSES	ADVANCE PREPARATION	ASSESSMENT	TEACHING PERIODS
17	**READING: Ecosystem Change and Resiliency** Students read about primary and secondary succession and how that is affected by ecosystem resiliency.	succession, ecosystem resiliency LITERACY		AQ 1 & 2: UC	1–2
18	**TALK IT OVER: Fishery Case Studies** Students analyze case studies and predict how fishery management strategies might impact the sustainability of Bayside and the Purple-spotted Flatfish fishery.	food webs, carrying capacity, population dynamics, inter-species relationships, human impacts on ecosystems		Proc: ET (Quick check)	1–2
19	**INVESTIGATION: Making Sustainable Fishery Decisions** Students analyze indicator data to determine the impact of a fishery management strategy on the sustainability of Bayside and the Purple-spotted Flatfish fishery.	food webs, carrying capacity, population dynamics, inter-species relationships, human impacts on ecosystems LITERACY	Separate indicator cards	Proc: ET AQ 3: UC	**2**

Cell Biology: World Health

Listed below is a summary of the activities in this unit. Note that the total teaching time is listed as 26 to 40 periods of approximately 45 to 50 minutes (approximately 6 to 8 weeks).

	ACTIVITY DESCRIPTION	KEY CONCEPTS AND PROCESSES	ADVANCE PREPARATION	ASSESSMENT	TEACHING PERIODS
1	**TALK IT OVER: World Health and Sustainability** Students look at world health data and examine factors of sustainability tied to disease	indicators, sustainability LITERACY		PROC: GI AQ 1: AD (Quick check)	2–3
2	**LABORATORY: Cells and Disease** Students observe normal red blood cells, sickled red blood cells, and blood infected with Plasmodium in order to determine the cause of two patients' symptoms. Students begin to think about cell structure and function.	microbes, abnormal cells and disease LITERACY		AQ 4: UC AQ 5: ET (Quick check)	1–2
3	**LABORATORY: What is a Cell?** Students prepare a drawing of a cell as a formative assessment and write their ideas about cells. Then they examine using a light microscope the similarities and differences in various types of living cells and fixed cells.	cell structure and function LITERACY		AQ 4: UC (Quick check) AQ 5: UC	2–3
4	**INVESTIGATION: What Do Cells Do?** Students learn about common cells structures and functions.	cell structure and function LITERACY	Arrange for computers with Internet access; check that computers have updated browsers to run simulation; bookmark simulation URL if appropriate	AQ 2: UC	1–2

Cell Biology (Continued from previous page)

	ACTIVITY DESCRIPTION	KEY CONCEPTS AND PROCESSES	ADVANCE PREPARATION	ASSESSMENT	TEACHING PERIODS
5	**INVESTIGATION: What Do Specialized Cells Do?** Students investigate the different numbers and types of organelles required for specialized plant and animal cells.	cells structure and function, cell differentiation	Arrange for computers with Internet access; check that computers have updated browsers to run simulation; bookmark simulation URL if appropriate	AQ 1: UC	2
6	**READING: Cell Structure and Function** Students read about the history of the development of the cell principle, and cell structures and functions.	cell principle, cell structure and functions, cell cycle, cell differentiation LITERACY		AQ 4: UC	1
7	**MODELING: A Model Membrane** Students investigate several models of the cell membrane in order to observe properties of the cell membrane.	cell structure and function, cell membrane LITERACY	Prepare bubble solution	AQ 6: AD (Quick check)	1–2
8	**LABORATORY: The Cell Membrane and Diffusion** Students investigate the properties of the cell membrane and osmosis and diffusion by using dialysis tubing models using water, glucose, starch and iodine.	cell structure and function, cell membrane LITERACY	Prepare sucrose solutions Prepare two balloons for demonstration	AQ 1, 2: AD AQ 6: ET (Quick check)	2–3
9	**READING: Cell Membrane Structure and Function** Students read about the cell membrane's functions and the fluid mosaic model.	cell structure and function, diffusion, osmosis, passive transport, active transport LITERACY		AQ 3, 5, 6: UC	1–2
10	**RESEARCH PROJECT AND PRESENTATION: Functions of Proteins in Cells** Students research one type of protein and present the information to the class in order to learn the diverse functions of proteins in cells.	cell structure and function, proteins, enzymes LITERACY		AQ 3: UC Proc: CS	2–3
11	**LABORATORY: Investigating Enzyme Function** Students design an experiment to test the effects of pH and temperature on the function of an enzyme.	Enzymes LITERACY	Prepare lactase and glucose solutions; prepare yeast solutions	Proc: GI Proc: DI AQ 4: AD Proc: OD (Quick check)	2–3
12	**READING: Photosynthesis and Cellular Respiration** Students complete a computer simulation of the processes of photosynthesis and cellular respiration and then complete a reading about the two processes.	chloroplasts, mitochondria, light and dark reactions, Calvin cycle, glycolysis, electron transport chain, anaerobic fermentation LITERACY	Arrange for computers with Internet access; check that computers have updated browsers to run simulation; bookmark simulation URL if appropriate	AQ 7: UC (Quick check) AQ 8: UC	1–2
13	**INVESTIGATION: The Cell Cycle** Students investigate the cell cycle including mitosis and cytokinesis	cell cycle, mitosis, cytokinesis LITERACY	Prepare portions of clay so that each group of four receives one half-full cup of each of the four colors	Proc: GI AQ 5: UC (Quick check)	1–2

Cell Biology (Continued from previous page)

	ACTIVITY DESCRIPTION	KEY CONCEPTS AND PROCESSES	ADVANCE PREPARATION	ASSESSMENT	TEACHING PERIODS
14	**INVESTIGATION: Stem Cell Differentiation** Students use a set of colored chips to investigate the steps in which embryonic stem cells become specialized cells.	cell differentiation			1
15	**TALK IT OVER: Stem Cell Research** Students discuss a set of questions surrounding the stem cell research debate, and examine why it is not useful for addressing infectious diseases.	cell differentiation, stem cells LITERACY			1
16	**INVESTIGATION: HIV/AIDS Infection and Cell Organelles** Students investigate how HIV uses the endomembrane system during infection of a human cell.	cell structure and function, virus infection of cells LITERACY		AQ 6: UC (Quick check)	1–2
17	**TALK IT OVER: Disease Interventions** Students summarize the disease mechanism for six diseases, examine various interventions for the six diseases and their trade-offs	abnormal cells and disease, disease interventions, diseases and sustainable development LITERACY		Proc: GI AQ 2: UC (Quick check)	2–3
18	**TALK IT OVER: World Health Proposal** Students write a world health proposal to address the problems of disease and vote on which to fund when funding is limited.	abnormal cells and disease, disease interventions, diseases and sustainable development		AQ 2: ET	2–3

Genetics: Feeding the World

Listed below is a summary of the activities in this unit. Note that the total teaching time is listed as 29 to 42 periods of approximately 45 to 50 minutes (approximately 6 to 9 weeks).

	ACTIVITY DESCRIPTION	KEY CONCEPTS AND PROCESSES	ADVANCE PREPARATION	ASSESSMENT	TEACHING PERIODS
1	**INVESTIGATION: A Genetically Modified Solution?** Students consider the use of Genetically Modified Organisms by looking at it from the perspective of a country trying do decide if they should grow Bt corn.	benefits and risks of genetic modification, trade-offs LITERACY	Set up equipment to project video clip;	AQ 4: ET	1–2
2	**LABORATORY: Creating Genetically Modified Bacteria** Students investigate the conditions necessary for genetically modified bacteria to express an inserted gene.	genetic modification, *E. coli*, plasmid, bacterial transformation, gene expressions LITERACY	Order live specimens; prepare bacteria starter plates; prepare $CaCl_2$ tubes; prepare containers of ice	Proc: GI	3–4

6

Genetics *(Continued from previous page)*

	ACTIVITY DESCRIPTION	KEY CONCEPTS AND PROCESSES	ADVANCE PREPARATION	ASSESSMENT	TEACHING PERIODS
3	**MODELING: Mitosis and Asexual Reproduction** Students view online computer animations and construct a narrated sketch of the phases of meiosis. Students show how an gene inserted into a genetically modified organism can be passed on to a daughter cell through the process of asexual reproduction.	chromosomes, mitosis, asexual reproduction	Arrange for computers with Internet access; check that computers have updated browsers to run simulation; bookmark simulation URL if appropriate	Proc: UC	1–2
4	**INVESTIGATION: Breeding Corn** Students observe the phenotypes of several ears of corn and use their observations and Punnett squares to determine the genotypes of the parents used to produce the resulting corn ears.	genotype, phenotype, ratios, crosses, Punnett squares, sex cells LITERACY	Optional: laminate corn ears	Proc: GI Proc: AD AQ 4: UC	1-2
5	**READING: Genes and Traits** Students read about basic genetics concepts as they relate to the heredity of traits.	genotype, phenotype, Mendel's work, alleles, inheritance of traits, simple dominance, incomplete dominance, codominance LITERACY			1
6	**MODELING: Breeding Corn for Two Traits** Students use Punnett squares to predict the outcome of a cross between corn plants for two traits. Students create a plan to determine the genotype of a parent based on observing the results of crosses for two traits.	phenotype, genotype, dihybrid Punnett squares, crosses for two traits, Law of independent assortment, simple dominance LITERACY	Optional: laminate corn ears	Proc: GI	1–2
7	**MODELING: Breeding Better Rice** Students use Allele Cards to apply their knowledge of genetics to the breeding of a desirable strain of rice.	genotype, phenotype, patterns of inheritance, Punnett square, independent assortment of traits, selective breeding, traits LITERACY	Separate and sort allele cards		1–2
8	**INVESTIGATION: Interpreting Pedigrees** Students trace traits in pedigrees to determine their mechanism of inheritance.	pedigrees, sex-linked traits, co-dominance			1–2
9	**LABORATORY: DNA Isolation** Students compare DNA isolated from spinach to DNA from various other samples to investigate the universal structure of DNA.	DNA, isolation, cell lysis	Chill DNA precipitation solution; have students bring in samples for DNA isolation	Proc: GI	2
10	**MODELING: Modeling DNA Structure** Students work with several different representations and a model of DNA to learn about its molecular structure.	DNA, nucleotide, sugar-phosphate backbone	Separate DNA model pieces into bags	Proc: UC (Quick check)	2

Genetics *(Continued from previous page)*

	ACTIVITY DESCRIPTION	KEY CONCEPTS AND PROCESSES	ADVANCE PREPARATION	ASSESSMENT	TEACHING PERIODS
11	**READING: Genomics** Students read about the history of genomics and how the science is developing.	genomics, Human Genome Project LITERACY			1
12	**INVESTIGATION: DNA Replication** Students use online simulation & DNA model to gather evidence to support one of three hypothesis of DNA replication –conservative, semi-conservative, or dispersive-- in a historical exploration of the DNA replication experiments conducted by Meselson and Stahl.	DNA, semi-conservative replication	Arrange for computers with Internet access; check that computers have updated browsers to run simulation; book-mark simulation URL if appropriate	AQ 1: UC (Quick check)	1–2
13	**MODELING: Meiosis and Sexual Reproduction** Students view computer simulations to investigate how chromosomes divide during meiosis. Students use their understanding of meiosis to explore the question, "What is the chance an inserted gene will be passed onto a daughter cell through the process of sexual reproduction?"	chromosomes, meiosis, crossing over, gametes, sexual reproduction LITERACY	Arrange for computers with Internet access; check that computers have updated browsers to run simulation; book-mark simulation URL if appropriate		1
14	**READING: Genes and Chromosomes** Students read about the passing of chromosomes from the parents to offspring during the process of sexual and asexual reproduction.	genes, chromosomes, asexual reproduction, sexual reproduction, karyotypes, independent assortment, crossing over LITERACY		AQ 1: UC AQ 2 & 7: UC (Quick check)	1
15	**PROJECT: Evaluating Genetically Modified Organisms** Student produce informational posters that highlight the development of and issues related to a genetically modified organism. Information gained through a poster session is used to develop criteria to evaluate GM organisms that will be used in the final activity.	genetically modified organisms, trade-offs, genes, DNA LITERACY	Determine organisms to be researched; determine resources available for research; set project time-line; determine poster presentation methods and acquire appropriate materials	Proc: GI Proc: CS AQ 2: ET (Quick check)	4–6
16	**MODELING: Protein Synthesis: Transcription and Translation** Students work through the stages of protein synthesis. Then they work through a model to show the steps involved at each stage.	genes, DNA, transcription, translation, protein synthesis, DNA mutations LITERACY	Arrange for computers with Internet access; check that computers have updated browsers to run simulation; book-mark simulation URL if appropriate	Proc: UC	2–3
17	**INVESTIGATION AND MODELING: Cell Differentiation and Gene Expression** Students explore gene expression combinations and explore the impact of gene expression and repression on cell phenotype.	genes, DNA, chromosomes, gene expression, gene repression LITERACY			1–2

8

Genetics (Continued from previous page)

	ACTIVITY DESCRIPTION	KEY CONCEPTS AND PROCESSES	ADVANCE PREPARATION	ASSESSMENT	TEACHING PERIODS
18	**LABORATORY: Which Corn is Genetically Modified?** Students run and interpret a DNA electrophoresis gel to determine which corn samples contain genetically modified corn.	genetically modified corn, DNA, genes, DNA electrophoresis LITERACY	Prepare buffer and gels	AQ 2: CS	2
19	**READING: Biopharming Edible Vaccines** Students read about the engineering of plants that are genetically modified to produce proteins that induce a vaccine response in humans.	genetic modification, DNA, DNA electrophoresis, gene expression, bacterial transformation, DNA constructs, selectable markers LITERACY			1
20	**TALK IT OVER: Are GMOs the Solution?** Students use information gathered from different research studies to determine if they want to use a genetically modified crop to help solve a sustainability challenge.	genetic modification, genes, DNA, chromosomes, evaluation of research proposals, trade-offs LITERACY		Proc: AD Proc: ET	1–2

Evolution: Maintaining Diversity

Listed below is a summary of the activities in this unit. Note that the total teaching time is listed as 19 to 34 periods of approximately 45 to 50 minutes (approximately 4 to 7 weeks).

	ACTIVITY DESCRIPTION	KEY CONCEPTS AND PROCESSES	ADVANCE PREPARATION	ASSESSMENT	TEACHING PERIODS
1	**TALK IT OVER: Biodiversity and Sustainability** Students play a game in which they manage one ecosystem on an island to learn about how biodiversity and sustainability are connected.	biodiversity and sustainability			1–2
2	**TALK IT OVER: Human Activities and Biodiversity** Students read scenarios that describe various human activities that affect the diversity of ecosystems, species, and populations.	human impacts on species LITERACY		PROC: GI	1–2
3	**MODELING: Geologic Time** Students convert geologic time to the scale of a football field and place key events along the timeline.	geologic time, deep time, diversity of life LITERACY	If you do not have a football field, mark off 100 yards on a playing field on school property, in the school gymnasium, or in a hallway; Make poster-sized signs for the geologic eras, periods, and epochs	AQ1: UC, CS	1–2

9

Evolution (Continued from previous page)

	ACTIVITY DESCRIPTION	KEY CONCEPTS AND PROCESSES	ADVANCE PREPARATION	ASSESSMENT	TEACHING PERIODS
4	**READING: Darwin and the Development of a Theory** Students read about Charles Darwin and how his ideas were emerging from others' and led to the theory of evolution by natural selection.	evolution by natural selection, sexual selection, artificial selection LITERACY			1–2
5	**INVESTIGATION: Using Fossil Evidence to Investigate Whale Evolution** Students examine illustrations of whale fossils and stratigraphic representations to trace the evolution of whales.	natural selection over large time-span, fossil record, strata, scientific argumentation LITERACY		AQ4: UC (Quick check)	1–2
6	**READING: Evidence from the Fossil Record** Students read about how scientists interpret evidence from the fossil record, including the use of stratigraphy and radiometric dating to determine the age of fossils.	natural selection, stratigraphy, strata, radiometric dating, fossil record evidence, macroevolution, transitional forms LITERACY			1–2
7	**INVESTIGATION: The Phylogeny of Vertebrates** Students use a matrix of shared derived characters to create an evolutionary tree for a group of vertebrates, and use additional evidence to support a tree hypothesis.	common ancestry, evolutionary trees, shared characters		AQ 3 & 4: UC (Quick check)	1–2
8	**INVESTIGATION: Studying Hominids** Students examine fossil and molecular data to hypothesize the evolutionary relationships between apes, and extinct and modern humans.	common ancestry, evolutionary trees, shared characters, human evolution, fossils LITERACY		AQ 1: UC	2–3
9	**INVESTIGATION: Studying Lineages for Conservation** Students read about Madagascar and investigate an evolutionary tree of lemurs in order to rank four areas on the island for conservation priority.	common ancestry, evolutionary trees LITERACY		AQ 1: ET	1–2
10	**INVESTIGATION: What is a Species?** Students use the biological species concept as one piece of information about where new species are in the process of separation from existing species. Students also investigate the factors that lead to reproductive isolation of species.	biological species concept, speciation, reproductive isolation, geographic isolation		PROC: GI AQ 2 & 3: UC	3–4
11	**MODELING: Natural Selection** Students work with a computer simulation to investigate the processes of adaptive radiation and extinction.	genetic variation due to mutation and recombination, natural selection, adaptive radiation	Arrange for computers with Internet access; check that computers have updated browsers to run simulation; bookmark simulation URL if appropriate		1–2

Evolution (Continued from previous page)

	ACTIVITY DESCRIPTION	KEY CONCEPTS AND PROCESSES	ADVANCE PREPARATION	ASSESSMENT	TEACHING PERIODS
12	**MODELING: The Genetic Basis of Adaptation** Students use a model to investigate changes in gene frequency in a population of mice after an environmental change occurs.	genetic variation due to mutation and recombination, natural selection, adaptation	Prepare cups for each group with 8 D cards and 8 d cards	PROC: OD (Quick check) AQ 1: UC (Quick check)	1–2
13	**READING: The Processes and Outcomes of Evolution** Students read about the concepts of microevolution, adaptation, speciation, macroevolution, and extinction.	species, microevolution, macroevolution, common ancestry, adaptation, homologous, analagous, vestigial structures, natural selection LITERACY		AQ 2: UC (Quick check)	1–2
14	**TALK IT OVER: Ideas About Evolution** Students reexamine the thinking they have done in the unit about the statements describing scientific concepts related to evolution.	species, common ancestry, adaptation, natural selection		AQ 1: UC, CS	2–3
15	**TALK IT OVER: Conservation on an Island Biodiversity Hotspot** Students read about four forest areas being considered for conservation on a fictitious island, and use phylogenetic data and other evidence to make their recommendation.	biodiversity, ecosystem services, protected area, phylogeny, trade-offs LITERACY		AQ 1: ET, CS	1–2

Sustainability

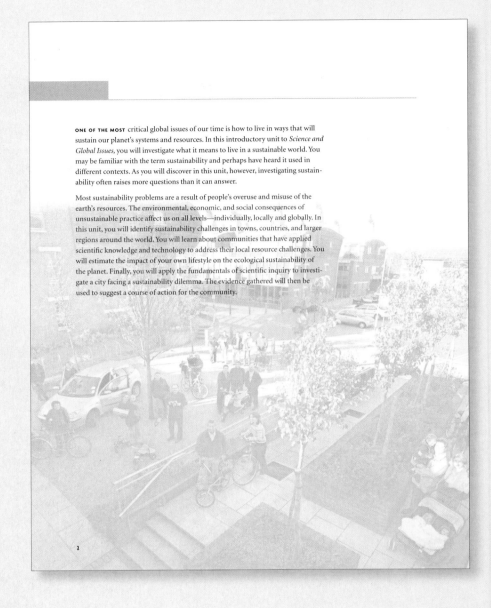

ONE OF THE MOST critical global issues of our time is how to live in ways that will sustain our planet's systems and resources. In this introductory unit to *Science and Global Issues,* you will investigate what it means to live in a sustainable world. You may be familiar with the term sustainability and perhaps have heard it used in different contexts. As you will discover in this unit, however, investigating sustainability often raises more questions than it can answer.

Most sustainability problems are a result of people's overuse and misuse of the earth's resources. The environmental, economic, and social consequences of unsustainable practice affect us on all levels—individually, locally and globally. In this unit, you will identify sustainability challenges in towns, countries, and larger regions around the world. You will learn about communities that have applied scientific knowledge and technology to address their local resource challenges. You will estimate the impact of your own lifestyle on the ecological sustainability of the planet. Finally, you will apply the fundamentals of scientific inquiry to investigate a city facing a sustainability dilemma. The evidence gathered will then be used to suggest a course of action for the community.

2

1 Our Global Community

INVESTIGATION • 1–2 CLASS SESSIONS

OVERVIEW

In this activity, students investigate resource use across the world by examining regional statistical data. The concepts of sustainability and indicators are introduced. Students conclude the activity with a discussion of a slide presentation that summarizes global indicator data.

KEY CONTENT

1. A community is sustainable if it meets its present needs without compromising the ability of future generations to meet their own needs.

2. An indicator is an observation or calculation that shows the presence or state of a condition or trend.

3. Certain indicators reveal quality of life and natural resources consumption in a community.

KEY PROCESS SKILLS

1. Students describe trends and relationships shown by data.

2. Students make calculations using data.

3. Students develop conclusions based on evidence.

4. Students evaluate the source, quality, and quantity of evidence.

5. Students identify and describe trade-offs.

MATERIALS AND ADVANCE PREPARATION

Because many activities in this unit require the teacher to use an overhead or data projector, make sure that one is always available.

For the teacher
slide presentation, "Planet 100"

For the class
set of 9 large Indicator Pie Graphs
set of region signs
small magnets*

For each student
calculator*

Not supplied in kit

Masters for Science Skills Sheets are in Teacher Resources II: Diverse Learners. Masters for Literacy Skills Sheets are in Teacher Resources III: Literacy.

Use magnets for fastening the graphs to a magnetic board. Determine how you will display the graphs one at a time.

TEACHING SUMMARY

Getting Started

• Introduce the concept of a sustainable community.

Doing the Activity

• Conduct a class demonstration to show the distribution of resources across world regions.

• (LITERACY) Introduce the use of a science notebook.

• Students convert regional data total amounts to per-capita amounts.

• Students discuss how the data are presented in the activity.

• Students watch a brief presentation on global statistics.

Follow-Up

• Students consider the role of indicator data in evaluating sustainability.

BACKGROUND INFORMATION

The term sustainability, in the context of human development, was coined in the 1980s. In 1987, the United Nations World Commission on Environment and Development (WCED) reported, "Humanity has the ability to make development sustainable—to ensure that it meets the needs of the present without compromising the ability of future generations to meet their own needs." The words sustainable and sustainability now appear in many contexts, with many interpretations, but without a universally accepted definition.

There are, however, three generally accepted dimensions to sustainability: environmental, social, and economic. These are represented with three overlapping circles, as shown on the left in the diagram below. While this model is useful, it does not adequately show that societies and economies are fundamentally dependent on the natural world. The diagram on the right below attempts to improve the first diagram by showing that economy and society are constrained by environmental limits. The concept of living within environmental constraints has lead to an alternative definition of sustainability, as stated by the International Union for Conservation of Nature (IUCN), which is to "improve the quality of human life while living within the carrying capacity of supporting ecosystems."

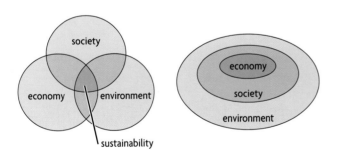

Despite the imprecision of the term sustainability, there is now abundant scientific evidence to indicate that humankind is living in an unsustainable way. The combination of the population explosion in the developing world and increased consumption of resources in the developed world have created a formidable challenge to the future of the planet. Turning humans' consumption of natural resources to within sustainable limits requires a full-scale international effort.

Measuring the environmental, social, and economic status of sustainability involves analysis of indicators, benchmarks, audits, indexes, and accounting and reporting systems at local, regional, and global levels.

REFERENCES

International Energy Agency (IEA) Statistics Division. 2006. *Energy balances of OECD countries and energy balances of non-OECD countries.* Retrieved November 2009 from earthtrends.wri.org/.

International Union for Conservation of Nature. 1991. *Caring for the earth: A strategy for sustainable living.* Retrieved November 2009 from data.iucn.org/ dbtw-wpd/edocs/CFE-003.pdf.

United Nations Environment Programme—World Conservation Monitoring Centre. 2006. *World database on protected areas.* Retrieved November 2009 from earthtrends.wri.org/.

United Nations Statistics Division. 2002, 2004. *Millennium development goals database.* Retrieved November 2009 from data.un.org/.

United Nations World Commission on Environment and Development. 1987. *Report of the world commission on environment and development: Our common future.* Retrieved October 2009 from www.un-documents.net/ wced-ocf.htm.

United States Government, Central Intelligence Agency. 2005, 2007, 2008, 2009. *The world factbook.* Retrieved November 2009 from www.cia.gov/library/publications/ the-world-factbook/.

GETTING STARTED

1 Before students begin this activity, make clear to them that this unit is an introduction to a science course, and is not an advocacy-oriented endeavor. Students will analyze data in this unit and make their own decisions about the magnitude of, and possible solutions to, sustainability issues. In this activity, they look at life in different regions of the world to get a sense of the global community we live in. When talking about sustainability at this time, elicit students' ideas about sustainability, but do not focus on the definition given in the introduction, as they will revisit that later in the activity.

Before beginning the procedure, discuss the meaning of the words *environmental, economic,* and *social,* which are used throughout the unit. Review the concept of an indicator, which is defined in the introduction. Cite an everyday example, such as the number of robberies in a town as an indicator of how safe the town is for residents.

---

1 Our Global Community

1 **P**EOPLE ACROSS the world share the same basic needs, despite many differences. Food, water, energy, and shelter sustain our human communities. Any group of people with a common interest living in a particular area—from the smallest village to the largest country—is a community. All the people of the world form a global community, with diverse governments, environments, and cultures. A community is **sustainable** if it meets its present needs without compromising the ability of future generations to meet their own needs. Sustainable activities do not press nature beyond its capacity to regenerate. A sustainable solution to a difficult situation must consider the environmental, economic, and social impacts on the community.

In this course, *Science and Global Issues,* you will explore ways science helps people to understand and develop solutions to sustainability challenges. You will begin this activity by analyzing some statistical indicators from around the globe. An **indicator** is an observation or calculation that shows the presence or state of a condition or trend. By looking at a set of indicators, you will explore the sustainability of human activities in populated regions of the world.

Challenge

▶ What do indicators tell us about regions of the world?

Researchers tag a lemon shark in the Bahamas (left). Students study marine life on the coast of Vancouver Island (above).

3

DOING THE ACTIVITY

2 For this activity countries were sorted into regions based on a combination of geographical location and culture. A complete list of countries by region is shown at the end of the activity in this Teacher's Edition. For any country that can be considered part of more than one region, its placement was based on its cultural identity. If students investigate data sets that do not appear in this activity, tell them to be aware that composition of regions varies from source to source and indicator to indicator.

3 Depending on the number of students in the class, some calculations will show numbers of people in fractions. Discuss and decide with students how to represent these numbers for the activity. For those with populations of less than one, it helps to run the activity with a representative in that region anyway. The table below shows population ratios and an example for a class of 24 students and one teacher.

SCIENCE & GLOBAL ISSUES/BIOLOGY • SUSTAINABILITY

MATERIALS

FOR THE CLASS
set of large Indicator Pie Graphs
set of region signs
small magnets

FOR EACH STUDENT
calculator

Procedure

Part A: World Data

2 1. On the world map below, identify the eight geographical regions of the world this activity focuses on:

3

2. Your teacher will designate eight locations in the classroom—one for each region of the world. A sign at each location labels the region.

3. As a class, look at the large Indicator Pie Graph for world population. In this procedure your class represents the entire population of the world. Use the percentages for each region to calculate how many people in your class represent each region.

4. Assign everyone in the class to a region based on the results of the calculation in the previous step. Have each person move to his or her "region" in the classroom.

Sample Class response: Procedure Step 3

Region	Population percent (%)	Class proportions (people)
Asia	53	13
Sub-Saharan Africa	12	3
Europe and Eurasia	11	3
Greater Middle East	10	2
North America	6.5	1
South America	6	1
Central America and the Caribbean	1	1
Australia and Oceania	0.5	1

4 Make sure students interpret the data on the pie pieces properly. For example, the pie piece with the region, "Sub-Saharan Africa," the title, "HIV deaths," and the quantity, "73%," means that 73% of the world's deaths due to HIV were in Sub-Saharan Africa. It does not mean that 73% of Sub-Saharan Africans have died from AIDS.

Indicator Key

INDICATOR	ICON	EXPLANATION
CO₂ emissions		An estimate of the amount of carbon dioxide released into the atmosphere based on United Nations (UN) data.
Energy consumption		The amount of primary energy consumed, on average, by each person living in a particular country or region in a year. All primary sources of energy, such as coal and coal products, oil and petroleum products, natural gas, nuclear power, and hydroelectric power, are included. Energy losses from transportation, friction, heat, and other inefficiencies are included in these totals.
GDP	$$$$$$$$	The gross domestic product (GDP) is the value of all final goods and services produced within a nation in a given year. It is provided here at purchasing-power-parity (PPP) exchange rates valued at prices prevailing in the United States. This is the measure most economists cite when looking at per-capita wealth and when comparing living conditions or resource consumption across countries.
HIV deaths	HIVHIVHIVHIVHIVHIV	An estimate of the number of adults and children who died of AIDS during a given calendar year.
Internet users		The number of users within an area who access the Internet. Statistics vary from country to country and range from those who access the Internet at least several times a week to those who access it only once in a period of several months.
Malnutrition		The total undernourished population is calculated as the number of people who consume less than a minimum food-energy requirement, which is estimated by sex and age group by a reference body weight. This minimum energy requirement varies by country, but typically averages 1,750–2,030 calories per person daily.
Population		US Census Bureau's International Programs estimates based on population censuses, sample surveys of vital-statistics-registration systems pertaining to the recent past, and assumptions about future trends.
Protected area		The total protected area is the area of land especially dedicated to the protection and maintenance of biological diversity and natural resources. Protected areas include nature reserves, wilderness areas, national parks, natural monuments, habitat-and-species-management areas, protected landscapes and seascapes, and managed-resource areas. The data in this activity excludes marine and intertidal areas.
Threatened species		Critically endangered, endangered, and vulnerable species, including mammals, birds, reptiles, amphibians, fishes, mollusks, insects, and plants.

4

6. As a class, choose the next indicator to examine. Read aloud the definition of the indicator from the graph. Each piece of the pie represents the region's portion of the world's total for that indicator (not a portion of the regional total).

7. Again, send a representative to get and bring back the appropriate pie piece from the Indicator Pie Graph.

8. Repeat Steps 6–7 until your region has collected all the Indicator Pie Graph pieces.

9. As a class, walk around the room and review the data for each region. Compare

   • the amounts of the indicators relative to other regions

   • how the indicators relate to the population of each region

5 Follow this procedure to introduce the use of science notebooks in the *Science and Global Issues* course. Explain to students that as they conduct activities they will record data, observations, hypotheses, conclusions, and thoughts in their notebooks. Decide how you would like them to record their work in each of the activities in this unit. For recommendations and more information see "Science Notebooks" in the Literacy section of Teacher Resources II: Diverse Learners.

6 Categorizing the indicators is somewhat subjective, and some may fall into more than one category. The following shows a sample student response:

> **Economic:** *energy, GDP, malnutrition*
>
> **Environmental:** *CO_2 emissions, protected area, threatened species*
>
> **Social:** *HIV deaths, population, Internet access*

7 Make sure the class understands the meaning of the term *per capita*. The table at right shows expected student responses. To provide more calculation practice, you may want to require students to perform the per capita calculations for all the regions, not just their own.

5

10. With those in your region, categorize the nine indicators into three groups: economic, environmental, and social. Record the groups, and explain your choices in your science notebook.

6

7

11. Using the data on the pie graphs and in the table below, calculate both the gross domestic product (GDP) in U.S. dollars, and the carbon dioxide (CO_2) emissions *per capita* for your region. A sample calculation is shown below the table.

World Data	
INDICATOR	WORLD TOTAL
Population (people)	6,705,900,000
Gross domestic product (US dollars)	69,490,000,000,000
CO_2 emissions (metric tons, per year)	27,246,000,000

SAMPLE CALCULATION: NORTH AMERICA

$$\text{GDP per capita} = \frac{\text{(world total GDP) (North America \% of world total GDP)}}{\text{(world total population) (North America \% of world population)}}$$

$$= \frac{(\$69,490,000,000,000)\,(.25)}{(6,705,900,000 \text{ people})\,(.065)}$$

$$= \$39,856/\text{person}$$

12. Share the per-capita data for all the regions with the class. When the data have been reviewed, discuss
- how perceptions can change when the data are presented differently
- what other ways the data could be presented
- what the indicators in the activity show
- what the indicators don't show
- how indicators could be used to evaluate sustainability

Part B: Planet 100

8

13. Watch the slide presentation "Planet 100." During the presentation, record any
- information that is surprising.
- questions the presentation raises for you.

9

14. When the presentation is over, share your notes according to your teacher's instructions. Discuss what the presentation shows about the sustainability of the global community if the world continues on its current path.

6

Sample Student Response: Procedure Step 11

Region	GDP/capita (US dollars)	CO_2 emissions/capita (metric tons per year)
North America	39,856	16.2
Europe and Eurasia	25,435	8.5
Australia and Oceania	20,725	8.1
Central America and the Caribbean	10,363	4.1
Greater Middle East	7,254	3.2
Asia	6,061	2.8
South America	10,363	2.0
Sub-Saharan Africa	1,727	0.7

FOLLOW-UP

8 Show the slide presentation, "Planet 100," to summarize the findings from Part A. Students may be surprised at the proportions of those who "have" and those who "have not." They may notice any one of a number of surprising points, such as the high numbers of people without basic sanitation, with little money, and with little opportunity for education. You may want to review the population growth slide, and note that the increase in population is not linear because each year the base number rises. Population numbers were estimated on an exponential scale. Emphasize that the presentation shows yet another way to present indicator data.

9 Before discussing this issue, review the definition of sustainability that appears in the introduction. Let students know this definition came from work by the United Nations in the late 1980s. If appropriate for your students, you may want to further discuss some of the information provided in the Background Information. You may want to conduct this discussion in pairs, groups of four, or as a class.

Students may argue on either side about whether the indicators in this activity have shown that the world's population is sustainable economically, environmentally, and socially. Some may argue that the indicators only show a slice of time and not trends. Similarly, the data do not show all factors related to the indicators. For example, the data show the emissions of CO_2 for a region, but not the rate at which that area absorbs the CO_2, which can vary greatly. Others may think the indicators show that the amount of environmental harm (from CO_2 emissions, for example) is far beyond what future generations can bear, and that no more information is needed to make a reasonable conclusion.

10 ✓ Analysis Question 2b is a Quick Check assessment to monitor students' ability to identify trade-offs in their decisions, which is a component of the EVIDENCE AND TRADE-OFFS (ET) Scoring Guide. For more information on Quick Checks and the Scoring Guide refer to Teacher Resources III: Assessment. Although students apply data in their responses for this and the next activity, they are not formally introduced to the term *evidence* until Activity 5, "Jaffrey City's Problem." The concepts of evidence and trade-offs are emphasized in Activity 6, "Jaffrey City's Master Plan." In those activities, you will again use the EVIDENCE AND TRADE-OFFS (ET) Scoring Guide from the SEPUP Assessment System for a summative assessment.

The goals of *Science and Global Issues* related to evidence and trade-offs are to teach students that

- decisions often involve trade-offs.

- identifying trade-offs involves analyzing evidence.

Explain to students that in this activity they will identify trade-offs when choosing a method for showing data. In a decision involving trade-offs, something is given up to gain something else. Since many decisions involve trade-offs, it is important for students to understand that a perfect choice is often not possible. It is possible, however, to recognize and analyze the trade-offs associated with each decision. For example, when asked, "Paper or plastic?" at a store checkout counter, most shoppers make the choice quickly. But there are several trade-offs attached to choosing paper or plastic. A shopper who chooses paper may do so to avoid generating plastic waste or using up hydrocarbon resources. In requesting the paper bag, though, the shopper is contributing to other environmental problems, such as increased water and energy usage, and the higher amounts of solid waste and

CO$_2$ emissions associated with making paper bags. Neither choice is particularly beneficial for the environment, and both choices have a downside. Identifying the trade-offs helps clarify the reasoning behind a decision, and the strength of the evidence relevant to making the most informed decision. To further explore trade-offs, brainstorm with the class a list of decisions they make every day. Choose one, and talk through the associated trade-offs of deciding one way or another. This practice will familiarize students with ways of identifying and considering trade-offs for this and subsequent activities.

11 This box lists the key vocabulary developed in this activity. When words are formally defined in an activity, they appear in bold type in the list. Non-bolded words refer to previously

---

Analysis

1. Did calculating indicators per capita significantly change your perception of the sustainability of a region? Explain why or why not.

2. Indicator levels can vary from country to country within a region. For example, Botswana (population two million) and Ethiopia (population 85 million) are both in Sub-Saharan Africa. However, 95% of the people in Botswana have improved drinking water, compared to 22% of Ethiopians. The average of people with improved drinking water for all countries in Sub-Saharan Africa is 66%.

   a. Use this example to explain how data can be misleading.

   10 b. Do you think it is better to rely on regional data or data from individual countries when looking at global trends? Support your answer using the example above, and identify the trade-offs of the choice you made.

3. According to the United Nations, South America consumes 4% of the energy generated in the world every year and generates 0.02% of the waste. However, only one country in South America (Brazil) reported its figures to the United Nations.

   a. Make a list of possible reasons why some world data collected by the United Nations is not reported or is underreported.

   b. Describe some consequences of unreported or underreported data.

4. Give an example of at least one potentially useful indicator that was NOT presented in this activity and what it could show about sustainability.

5. Who is responsible for protecting the following resources?

   a. air

   b. water

   c. soil

   d. fossil fuels

11 KEY VOCABULARY

indicator	sustainable

7

introduced vocabulary. Encourage students to use these words when answering the Analysis Questions. Also, during informal and formal discussions listen for these words and see if students are applying them correctly. Decide how you will support students' understanding of the vocabulary—perhaps with a student glossary, or setting up a class word wall. For more suggestions on ways to develop students' understanding of and proficiency with scientific vocabulary, see the Vocabulary section of Teacher Resource III: Literacy.

SAMPLE RESPONSES

1. The per-capita calculations made countries like the United States and Europe look less sustainable, particularly in the areas of energy consumption and pollution. The same calculations made Asia look more sustainable because, while it uses a large portion of the resources, it also has a larger population.

2. a. The data can be misleading because it is incomplete. Percentages do not provide the sample size, and so the total number of people without improved drinking water doesn't account for the number of people in each country. For example, 22% of 85 million Ethiopians is 18.7 million, whereas 95% of 2 million is 1.9 million. So the higher-percentage country actually has fewer people without improved water. Likewise, an average doesn't provide an accurate description because it does not represent any one population. For example, the average for Africa is 66%, but that does not portray either Botswana or Ethiopia.

   b. ✓Answers may vary. Students' answers should work with the example provided and explain the trade-offs of their choices. Some students may think regional data is not as helpful as country data when looking for global trends. This is because the country data shows a more complete picture. The trade-off is that the country data can be overwhelming. In the example provided, it may be difficult to generalize when faced with the data of all the African countries. Other students may think that regional data alone provides adequate detail, especially if comparing them to other regions. The trade-off is that if there are large differences between countries, the regional data do not show that. In the example provided, regional data would not show areas where few have improved water, and those populations would be overlooked.

3. a. Possible reasons data is not properly reported:
   - Hard to measure waste
   - Do not have trained staff in that country to collect data
   - Countries don't want others to know about their waste treatment
   - Leaders don't allow the data to be collected
   - Data is lost
   - No money to conduct study

   b. Underreported data can change the results of regional data. The situation could be much different than the indicators show. This could mean people's efforts to help things globally are not effective if it isn't clear where the problems are located.

4. Answers may vary. Some responses are as follows:
   - Sanitation—shows potential for disease
   - Infant mortality—shows general health
   - Educational level—shows quality of life
   - Oil reserves—shows economic and political status

5. Answers will vary, but the following show convention:
   a. Everyone, emitters are responsible
   b. Everyone, water agencies, governments are responsible
   c. Individuals, companies, or governments are responsible on a case-by-case basis
   d. Individuals, governments, and companies—everyone is responsible for their use

REVISIT THE CHALLENGE

Students should be able to articulate that regional indicator data can help to make comparisons, such as comparing GDP or energy use to get an impression of the state of the world. These comparisons reveal many inequities and sustainability challenges in the global community.

WORLD REGIONS
Asia: 27 countries

Bangladesh, Bhutan, Brunei, Cambodia, China, India, Indonesia, Japan, Kazakhstan, Kyrgyzstan, Laos, Malaysia, Maldives, Mongolia, Myanmar, Nepal, North Korea, Philippines, Singapore, South Korea, Sri Lanka, Taiwan, Tajikistan, Thailand, Turkmenistan, Uzbekistan, Vietnam

Australia and Oceania: 15 countries
Australia, East Timor, Fiji, Kiribati, Marshall Islands, Federated States of Micronesia, Nauru, New Zealand, Palau, Papua New Guinea, Samoa, Solomon Islands, Tonga, Tuvalu, Vanuatu

Central America and the Caribbean: 20 countries
Antigua and Barbuda, The Bahamas, Barbados, Belize, Costa Rica, Cuba, Dominica, Dominican Republic, El Salvador, Grenada, Guatemala, Haiti, Honduras, Jamaica, Nicaragua, Panama, Saint Kitts and Nevis, Saint Lucia, Saint Vincent and the Grenadines, Trinidad and Tobago

Europe: 48 countries
Albania, Andorra, Armenia, Austria, Belarus, Belgium, Bosnia and Herzegovina, Bulgaria, Croatia, Cyprus, Czech Republic, Denmark, Estonia, Finland, France, Georgia, Germany, Greece, Hungary, Iceland, Ireland, Italy, Kosovo, Latvia, Liechtenstein, Lithuania, Luxembourg, Macedonia, Malta, Moldova, Monaco, Montenegro, Netherlands, Norway, Poland, Portugal, Romania, Russia, San Marino, Serbia, Slovakia, Slovenia, Spain, Sweden, Switzerland, Ukraine, United Kingdom of Great Britain and Northern Ireland, Vatican City

Greater Middle East (includes Middle East, the Gulf, North Africa and parts of Western Asia): 23 countries
Afghanistan, Algeria, Azerbaijan, Bahrain, Egypt, Iran, Iraq, Israel, Jordan, Kuwait, Lebanon, Libya, Morocco, Oman, Pakistan, Qatar, Saudi Arabia, Somalia, Syria, Tunisia, Turkey, United Arab Emirates, Yemen

North America: 3 countries
Canada, Mexico, United States of America

South America: 12 countries
Argentina, Bolivia, Brazil, Chile, Colombia, Ecuador, Guyana, Paraguay, Peru, Suriname, Uruguay, Venezuela

Sub-Saharan Africa: 48 countries
Angola, Benin, Botswana, Burkina Faso, Burundi, Cameroon, Cape Verde, Central African Republic, Chad, Comoros, Republic of the Congo, Democratic Republic of the Congo, Cote d'Ivoire, Djibouti, Equatorial Guinea, Eritrea, Ethiopia, Gabon, The Gambia, Ghana, Guinea, Guinea-Bissau, Kenya, Lesotho, Liberia, Madagascar, Malawi, Mali, Mauritania,* Mauritius, Mozambique, Namibia, Niger, Nigeria, Rwanda, Sao Tome and Principe, Senegal, Seychelles, Sierra Leone, South Africa, Sudan, Swaziland, Tanzania, Togo, Uganda, Zambia, Zimbabwe

sometimes considered to be in Intra-Saharan Africa

2 Life in Other Countries

INVESTIGATION • 1–2 CLASS SESSIONS

OVERVIEW

In this activity, students look more closely at indicator data for four selected countries. They compare the profiles of the four countries to that of the United States and make inferences about life in those countries. Then students further investigate one of the countries. In groups, students analyze the current sustainability challenges facing those countries.

KEY CONTENT

1. A community is sustainable if it meets its present needs without compromising the ability of future generations to meet their own needs.

2. An indicator is an observation or calculation that shows the presence or state of a condition or trend.

3. Certain indicators reveal quality of life and natural resources consumption in a community.

4. Sustainability problems of a community might be environmental, economical, or social.

KEY PROCESS SKILLS

1. Students describe trends and relationships shown by data.

2. Students develop conclusions based on evidence.

3. Students make accurate interpretations, inferences, and conclusions from text.

MATERIALS AND ADVANCE PREPARATION

For the teacher

Transparency 2.1, "Country Comparison"

Scoring Guide: GROUP INTERACTION (GI)

Group Interaction Student Skills Sheet 2, "Developing Communication Skills" (optional)

For each pair of students

computer with internet access (optional)*

For each student

Scoring Guide: GROUP INTERACTION (GI) (optional)

Not supplied in kit

Masters for Science Skills Sheets are in Teacher Resources II: Diverse Learners. Masters for Literacy Skills Sheets are in Teacher Resources III: Literacy. Masters for Scoring Guides are in Teacher Resources IV: Assessment.

Decide how much time you want students to spend investigating other countries. If you are providing students with information, decide on the amount and format. This part of the procedure provides an opportunity for differentiated instruction. For most classes the research portion of the Procedure is not intended to be a full project, but rather a portion of or one class period. If students do not have computer access, provide some resources for them or find some time outside of the classroom for students to complete the assignment. The resources listed in the References below can be a starting place for students and teachers.

TEACHING SUMMARY

Getting Started

- Elicit students' ideas about how life in other countries compares to life in the United States.

- (GI ASSESSMENT) Introduce the GROUP INTERACTION (GI) Scoring Guide.

Doing the Activity

- Students examine statistics for four countries.

- Students further investigate life in one of these countries.

- Students identify economic, environmental, and social issues in all the countries considered.

Follow-up

- Students reflect on how data reveals a country's sustainability challenges.

BACKGROUND INFORMATION

The countries in this activity were chosen to be somewhat representative of a region, have a relatively large population, and illustrate a range of global diversity. They confront a variety of economic, social, and environmental sustainability issues. They also span the range of the Human Development Index (HDI). The HDI is a United Nations index that ranks countries by level of "human development," which usually also implies whether a country is categorized as developed (high), developing (medium), or underdeveloped (low). The HDI combines normalized measures of life expectancy, literacy, educational attainment, and per-capita GDP. It is a common means of measuring well-being and quality of life.

REFERENCES

BBC News. 2009. *Country profiles.* Retrieved November 2009 from news.bbc.co.uk/2/hi/country_profiles/default.stm.

Center for Environmental Systems Research, University of Kassel, 2000. Retrieved November 2009 from www.nationmaster.com/.

United Nations Statistical Division. 2006, 2007. Retrieved November 2009 from www.data.un.org/.

United States Government, Central Intelligence Agency. 2005, 2007, 2008, 2009. *The world factbook.* Retrieved November 2009 from www.cia.gov/library/publications/the-world-factbook.

World Bank, World Development Indicators Database. 2002, 2004. Retrieved November 2009 from www.nationmaster.com/.

GETTING STARTED

1 Introduce the activity by asking students to share their experiences of other countries. Some may have come from, have family connections to, or have visited other parts of the world. Let students know that in this activity they will look more closely at life in four other countries and compare it to life in the United States. As in the previous activity, they will examine various indicators to gain an understanding of the challenges each country faces.

Throughout this unit students will engage in small-group work and discussions. Good group communication skills will help them gain a better understanding of content and more meaningfully discuss what they are learning. You may wish to use Group Interaction Student Skills Sheet 2, "Developing Communication Skills," which gives suggestions for communicating well in a group. For more information, see the Facilitating Group Interaction section of Teacher Resources II: Diverse Learners.

Provide all students a copy of the GROUP INTERACTION (GI) Scoring Guide, and ask them to keep it with their science notebooks, as they will refer to it several times in *Science and Global Issues*. Let them know that you will use this at specific times to provide feedback on their work in their groups of four and with their partners. Take this opportunity to explain your expectations for group effort, and to discuss as a class what successful group work looks like. For more information on scoring how students work together, see Teacher Resources IV: Assessment.

DOING THE ACTIVITY

2 **Do not reveal the names of the countries until Procedure Step 3.** This allows students to make conclusions based on the data and not on their preconceptions.

---

2 Life in Other Countries

1 IN THE LAST activity you compared indicator data across regions of the world. Within each region, every country and community is unique. Each country has a distinct economy, environment, and society. In this activity you will examine the profiles of four countries. Based on the indicator data provided, you will identify each country's greatest sustainability challenges. You will also explore life in one of the countries by conducting further research.

Challenge

▶ What can indicators reveal about the sustainability challenges facing different countries?

Procedure

2 1. Assign each of the four countries shown on the following pages to a member of your group. Carefully examine the indicators for your assigned country. Indicators for the United States are also provided for comparison.

2. Think about what the indicator data say about life in your assigned country as compared to life in the United States. Make at least one statement regarding how you think people in your assigned country live. Record your statement in your science notebook. Then, share your ideas with your group.

3 3. After learning the name of the country you selected, investigate aspects of the country's environment, economics, culture, and history. Record your findings in your science notebook. Make sure to compare life in your assigned country to life in the United States using the following kinds of indicators:

- economic
- environmental
- social

4. Evaluate the statement or statements you made in Step 2 and determine what evidence from your investigation supports it.

8

Remind students to look carefully at the units for the amounts provided, and to keep in mind which ones are estimates and which are not. The definitions for each indicator are shown at the end of the activity in this Teacher's Edition.

3 Provide students the names of the countries shown in the table on the following page. Students' investigations of these countries should not extend to a full research project (see Advance Preparation). Provide students with a time goal or work guideline for this step. Students can begin their search on the SEPUP website, *sepuplhs.org/sgi*. You may want to discuss with your class the need for cultural sensitivity when looking at lifestyles of people from other countries. Students should keep in mind that lifestyles vary considerably depending on socioeconomic status.

4 Encourage students to refer to their research to re-evaluate their own claims and make them more complete and accurate. Emphasize the need for scientists to continually gain information and re-evaluate conclusions. The following example of data interpretation illustrates the point that data often only show part of the story: Ask the students, *If I told you that 50% of the people in this room ate olives at least once yesterday, what would that indicate to you about people's olive-eating habits?*

Answers may include that olives are a very popular food. Next ask the students, *Now what if I told you that those people were all at the same party last night. Would that change your answer?*

Answers should include yes or maybe; reasons will vary. Next ask the students, *Now I will give you a third piece of data: only 5% of the people in this room ate olives last month. What does that indicate to you about the other data we just discussed? Are your conclusions about people's olive-eating habits the same as before?*

Answers should include that olives are not as popular as they originally hypothesized and that they have changed their conclusions based on the new data.

5 The table on the following page shows some of the information that students may find. Information in parentheses shows direct reference to the indicator data provided in this activity.

When reviewing what students found in constructing their tables, discuss what conclusions they were able to draw, and what other information they felt they needed to gain a fuller understanding of the sustainability of each country. During the discussion, if students do not bring it up, be sure to point out that what seem to be indicators of sustainability may

---

An Inuit hunter catches dinner with a fish spear (left). A European woman shops for a meal in a supermarket (above).

4

5. Compare the indicator data provided with the information you collected. Describe how the indicators do or do not adequately show the sustainability issues in that country.

6. Present a summary of life in the country you researched to the others in your group. Be sure to include economic, environmental, and social challenges facing that country.

5

7. As a group, make a table that shows the most urgent economic, environmental, and social challenges for each country, including the United States. You will need this information to answer the Analysis Questions.

9

---

also show a poor quality of life. Students should come to the conclusion that while some countries may appear sustainable, more data might indicate that when the quality of life is poor, the population cannot sustain itself. Because of this correlation, some sustainability experts say a key aspect of sustainability is social justice, in that a sustainable community makes sure people have equal access to the resources that they need to have a decent quality of life. Students may agree or disagree with this idea, but they should discuss the concept of equitable access to resources and what it means that some countries are using more resources than others.

Sample Student Response: Procedure Step 7

Challenge	Country A: Brazil	Country B: India	Country C: Japan	Country D: Nigeria	USA
Economic	High inflation; large gap between rich and poor; a lot of foreign debt	Large portion of population is in poverty; very large and growing population (1.2 billion); must import more commodities than it produces (by $67 billion US)	Has to import over half its food because it cannot provide it; large aging population; government has massive debt; 20% of the world's big earthquakes occur there; imports more oil than it exports (by 5,230,000 barrels per day)	Half of residents live in poverty; struggles to get foreign investments because of corruption and mismanagement; lacking infrastructure, i.e., roads and electricity; foreign debt	Growing gap between rich and poor; aging population; rapidly rising medical expenses; increased pension costs; large budget deficits; imports more oil than it exports (by 12,545,000 barrels per day); foreign debt
Environmental	Endangered species as a result of deforestation in Amazon basin; land degradation from improper mining and farming methods; wetland degradation; oil spills; illegal wildlife trade; air pollution (average 28 microgram/m^3); water pollution in cities; lack of basic sanitation (50% without)	Deforestation; soil erosion; overgrazing and desertification; water pollution from raw sewage and runoff of agricultural pesticides; air pollution from industry; undrinkable tap water; huge and growing population taxes resources; 80% of area has water shortage; poor air quality (average 72 microgram/m^3)	Air pollution from power plant emissions (average 31 microgram/m^3); acidification of lakes; poor water quality; threatened aquatic life; depletion of tropical timber; depletion of fish	Rapid urbanization; soil degradation; deforestation, air pollution (average 67 microgram/m^3); water and air pollution; desertification	Air pollution from fossil fuels (average 23 microgram/m^3); largest carbon dioxide emitter in the world; water pollution from pesticides and fertilizers (19.3 million metric tons/year); limited natural fresh water (water shortage in 31% of area); land degradation
Social	Large slum populations in cities; rain forest exploitation; widespread cocaine abuse and trafficking	Majority of rural population is illiterate and impoverished; caste system has strict social hierarchy; constant conflict with Pakistan; large opium trade; high infant mortality (57 deaths/1,000 births)	Limited immigration law; very dense population	Political instability; ongoing ethnic and religious fighting; massive poverty and unemployment; land disputes; cocaine and heroin trafficking; only 3 doctors/10,000 people; high infant mortality (99 deaths/ 1,000 births)	Racial tensions; urban crime; largest consumer of cocaine, heroin, and marijuana

⬧ This symbol represents an opportunity to elicit students' experiences or ideas so that the subsequent instruction can build on or modify their understanding. Sometimes you will uncover ideas that are inconsistent with scientific explanations but may seem logical in the everyday world. The Teaching Suggestions often provide strategies that you can use to address these misconceptions.

⬧ One common misconception students have is that all African countries are underdeveloped and rural. Nigeria, however, has large cities and developed infrastructure in its urban locations. If this doesn't show up in students' work, be sure to comment on it as related to the nature of "average" discussed in the last activity. Another common misconception students have is that the United States is typical in regard to resource use. This and the previous activity should show how atypical the United States is compared to other countries.

FOLLOW-UP

6 For the purposes of this course, emphasize the environmental challenges and the important role of science. For example, scientific understanding of air and water systems is central to overcoming the challenge of cleaning up those parts of the ecosystem. In the next activity, students will focus further on environmental issues within a community.

7 Transparency 2.1, "Country Comparison," shows all the indicator data in one table and may be helpful to project while making direct comparisons during class.

SAMPLE RESPONSES

1. Answers will vary. Some of the alarming statistics are: the high infant mortality rates of India and Nigeria; the relatively high amounts of oil imports and water shortage in the United States; the poor air quality in India; and the low basic sanitation rates in Brazil and Nigeria.

2. Answers will vary. Some useful indicators that students may have encountered are: waste generation; water quality; biodiversity of species; percent of population that is urban vs. rural; employment rate; literacy of the population; leading causes of death; amount of renewable energy used; amount of time spent commuting; or any of the indicators that have recently and dramatically increased or decreased.

3. Answers will vary. Student responses may include:

   Brazil: deforestation, destruction of the habitat, unstable economy, large poor population, drug abuse and trafficking

   India: deforestation, desertification, pollution, huge population, poverty, war, illiteracy, drug trade

   Japan: air pollution, CO_2 emissions, poor water quality, huge debt, earthquakes, has to import food

   Nigeria: deforestation, soil degradation, pollution, poverty, government corruption, poor infrastructure, religious fighting, drug trafficking

   USA: air pollution, high energy use and CO_2 emissions, water pollution, lack of freshwater resources, economic inequities, expensive medical and pension costs, large deficit, drug abuse

4. Answers will vary. From a purely environmental perspective, none of the countries are truly sustainable. All the countries have utilized nature beyond its capacity to renew and regenerate.

   a. The indicators provided point to Brazil as the most sustainable overall, despite having only 50% basic sanitation. Socially, students are likely to choose the USA

Analysis

1. Which indicator data that were provided were surprising? Describe the data, and explain what they tell you.

2. What other indicator data did you find useful in understanding daily life in other countries? Explain.

6 3. Look at the economic, environmental, and social challenges in your table from Procedure Step 7. What are the most urgent challenges for each country?

7 4. Of the countries in the activity, which one(s) have a lifestyle you think is the

   a. most sustainable in the future?

   b. least sustainable in the future?

   Explain the evidence or indicators that support your choices.

5. Suppose representatives from the five countries in this activity came together to discuss improving the sustainability of the planet. Think of the sustainability issues that the countries would want to address by first answering these questions:

   a. Which sustainability challenges might they have in common?

   b. Which sustainability challenges might they NOT have in common?

   c. What challenges does the group face while working together to improve the sustainability of the planet?

6. You find the following posting about the future of the planet on a message board:

   Global Sustainability:
   One challenge
   One solution

   Do you think this should be the slogan for a meeting of world leaders who are trying to improve the environment? Include information from this activity to support your response.

7. How can science contribute to improving the sustainability of the world?

KEY VOCABULARY	
indicator	sustainability

10

---

as the most sustainable, but a closer looks shows that Japan has a lower infant mortality rate and longer life expectancy. Economically, Nigeria may seem most sustainable because it exports more than it imports. However, the population is generally very poor, which is not sustainable.

b. Nigeria may seem the most unsustainable because of its low life expectancy, meager sanitation, and relatively few physicians. However, India appears unsustainable in that it has a large water shortage and relatively low life expectancy. Lastly, students might evaluate the USA as the least sustainable because of the huge imbalance between imports and exports and oil imports and exports.

5. Answers will depend on research results, but general conclusions should be similar. A sample response is shown here:

a. Some of the common problems are poverty, drug trafficking and/or abuse, air and water pollution.

b. Some of the problems not in common are CO_2 emissions, urbanization, improper mining, fertilizer use, overconsumption, extreme poverty, dense populations, racial tensions, military conflict, land degradation, energy use, and natural resource use.

c. In general, the questions above show that countries have more uncommon problems than common ones. This makes the conversation difficult if each place has a different priority. For example, in Nigeria the high infant mortality rate and poverty are probably more important issues than deforestation. In contrast, in the USA, CO_2 emissions may be of higher priority than soil erosion, making the cooperation of these two countries a challenge.

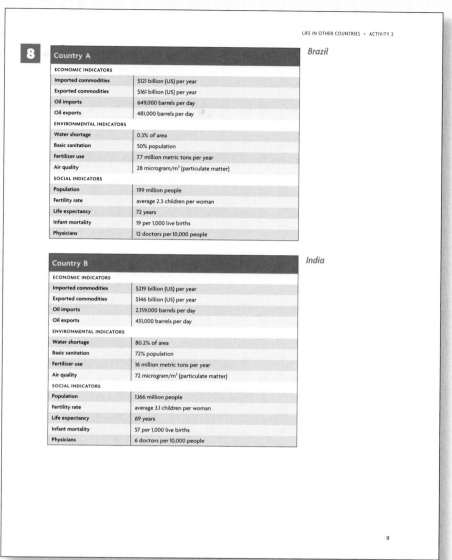

8 **Country A** — *Brazil*

ECONOMIC INDICATORS

Imported commodities	$121 billion (US) per year
Exported commodities	$161 billion (US) per year
Oil imports	649,000 barrels per day
Oil exports	481,000 barrels per day

ENVIRONMENTAL INDICATORS

Water shortage	0.3% of area
Basic sanitation	50% population
Fertilizer use	7.7 million metric tons per year
Air quality	28 microgram/m^3 (particulate matter)

SOCIAL INDICATORS

Population	199 million people
Fertility rate	average 2.3 children per woman
Life expectancy	72 years
Infant mortality	19 per 1,000 live births
Physicians	12 doctors per 10,000 people

Country B — *India*

ECONOMIC INDICATORS

Imported commodities	$219 billion (US) per year
Exported commodities	$146 billion (US) per year
Oil imports	2,159,000 barrels per day
Oil exports	451,000 barrels per day

ENVIRONMENTAL INDICATORS

Water shortage	80.2% of area
Basic sanitation	72% population
Fertilizer use	16 million metric tons per year
Air quality	72 microgram/m^3 (particulate matter)

SOCIAL INDICATORS

Population	1,166 million people
Fertility rate	average 3.1 children per woman
Life expectancy	69 years
Infant mortality	57 per 1,000 live births
Physicians	6 doctors per 10,000 people

11

6. Students might agree or disagree with this statement. Their investigations into the four countries profiled in this activity should show that each community has a unique combination of challenges, making the slogan inaccurate. However, there are common problems that are faced by many communities. For example, Japan and the USA have CO_2 emissions as a major sustainability challenge, whereas Brazil, India, and Nigeria are facing major land-degradation issues with deforestation and desertification. Therefore, others may think that, despite the differences between countries, sustainability has more commonalities than dissimilarities, making the unifying slogan appropriate. Those students may assert that the planet is one ecosystem that has to be sustainable for all

in order to be sustainable for some. The key point to be brought out here is that sustainability challenges do not stop at borders, and global cooperation is critical.

7. Science can contribute to developing a sustainable world in many ways. First, scientists collect accurate, reliable, and complete data on which to base decisions. Second, scientists study relationships within the ecosystem and the effects humans have on it. Third, they develop technology to overcome or mitigate some of the challenges.

REVIST THE CHALLENGE

This challenge is answered in Analysis Question 6 where students identified some commonalities and differences in the problems the countries in this activity face. Reinforce the idea that when countries discuss sustainability, each country comes to the table with its own sustainability priorities. This idea foreshadows the concept of stakeholders, which is introduced in the last activity.

8 **Definitions**

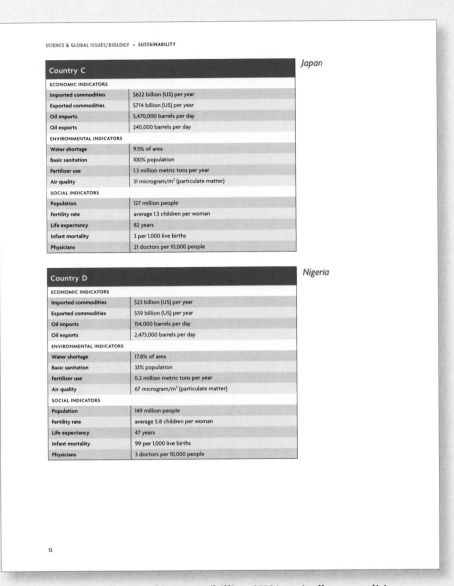

Japan

Country C	
ECONOMIC INDICATORS	
Imported commodities	$622 billion (US) per year
Exported commodities	$714 billion (US) per year
Oil imports	5,470,000 barrels per day
Oil exports	240,000 barrels per day
ENVIRONMENTAL INDICATORS	
Water shortage	9.5% of area
Basic sanitation	100% population
Fertilizer use	1.3 million metric tons per year
Air quality	31 microgram/m³ (particulate matter)
SOCIAL INDICATORS	
Population	127 million people
Fertility rate	average 1.3 children per woman
Life expectancy	82 years
Infant mortality	3 per 1,000 live births
Physicians	21 doctors per 10,000 people

Nigeria

Country D	
ECONOMIC INDICATORS	
Imported commodities	$23 billion (US) per year
Exported commodities	$59 billion (US) per year
Oil imports	154,000 barrels per day
Oil exports	2,473,000 barrels per day
ENVIRONMENTAL INDICATORS	
Water shortage	17.8% of area
Basic sanitation	33% population
Fertilizer use	0.2 million metric tons per year
Air quality	67 microgram/m³ (particulate matter)
SOCIAL INDICATORS	
Population	149 million people
Fertility rate	average 5.8 children per woman
Life expectancy	47 years
Infant mortality	99 per 1,000 live births
Physicians	3 doctors per 10,000 people

12

Population (millions of people): adults and children as estimated from census data.

Fertility rate (births per woman): the average number of children a woman will have during her lifetime.

Life expectancy (years): the average number of years a newborn infant would live if current patterns of mortality at the time of its birth were to stay the same throughout its life.

Infant mortality rate (deaths/1,000 live births): the number of deaths of infants under one-year old in a given year per 1,000 live births in the same year.

Physicians (doctors/10,000 people): medical doctors who are graduates of a school of medicine and who are working in the country in medical practice, teaching, or research.

Total imports (billion $US/year): all commodities—does not include products brought back into a country after being made from exported raw materials.

Total exports (billion $US/year): all commodities—does not include products exported again after being imported.

Oil imports (barrels/day): total oil imported per day, including both crude oil and oil products.

Oil exports (barrels/day): total oil exported per day, including both crude oil and oil products.

Water shortage (% area): the estimated area where water consumption exceeds 40% of the water naturally available at that location.

Basic sanitation (% population):
those who live in structures with a
connection to sewer, septic system,
or improved pit latrine.

**Fertilizer use (million metric tons/
year):** the quantity of plant nutrients
used per unit of arable land. Fertilizer products cover nitrogenous,
potash, and phosphate fertilizers, but
do not include traditional nutrients
such as animal and plant manures.

**Air quality, particulate matter
(microgram/m³):** concentrations of
fine suspended particulates that can
penetrate deep into the respiratory
track. The estimates represent
the average annual exposure level of
the average urban resident to out-
door particulate matter.

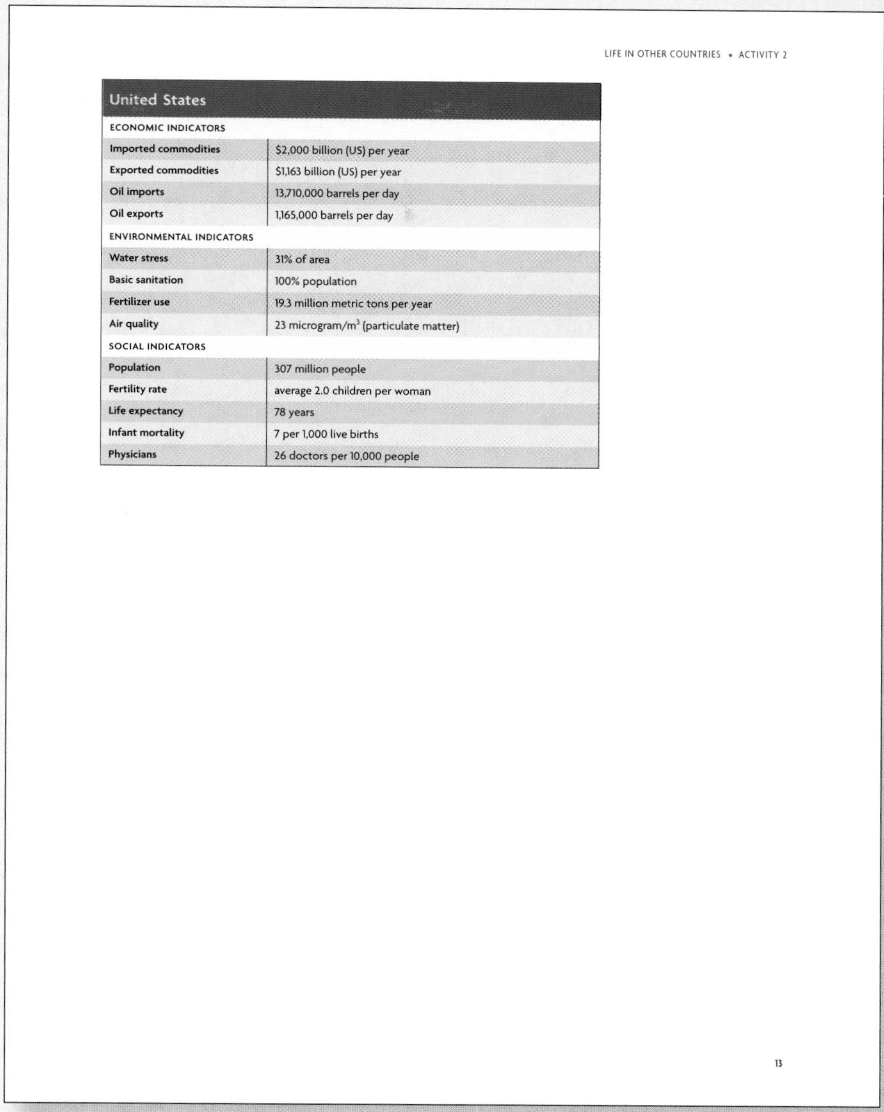

United States

ECONOMIC INDICATORS

Imported commodities	$2,000 billion (US) per year
Exported commodities	$1,163 billion (US) per year
Oil imports	13,710,000 barrels per day
Oil exports	1,165,000 barrels per day

ENVIRONMENTAL INDICATORS

Water stress	31% of area
Basic sanitation	100% population
Fertilizer use	19.3 million metric tons per year
Air quality	23 microgram/m³ (particulate matter)

SOCIAL INDICATORS

Population	307 million people
Fertility rate	average 2.0 children per woman
Life expectancy	78 years
Infant mortality	7 per 1,000 live births
Physicians	26 doctors per 10,000 people

13

3 Sustainability Case Studies

READING • 1–2 CLASS SESSIONS

OVERVIEW

Students read about two communities that took steps to reduce their use of energy and water and improve land resources. Two literacy strategies accompany the text to support reading comprehension.

KEY CONTENT

1. Sustainability problems have adverse environmental, economical, and social impacts on communities.

2. A product's life cycle describes the amounts of resources and energy it takes to make the product, the length of the product's usefulness to the consumer, and how the product is disposed of, recycled, or reclaimed when it is no longer needed.

3. Desertification happens when land-use practices cause healthy land to lose nutrients and water-holding capacity.

4. Some solutions to sustainability challenges are technologically, economically, and socially viable.

KEY PROCESS SKILLS

1. Students make accurate interpretations, inferences, and conclusions from text.

MATERIALS AND ADVANCE PREPARATION

For each student

Student Sheet 3.1, "Summary Sheet: Sustainability Case Studies"

Student Sheet 3.2, "Three-Level Reading Guide: Sustainability Case Studies"

TEACHING SUMMARY

Getting Started

- The class reviews the sustainability challenges they investigated in previous activities.

Doing the Activity

- (LITERACY) Students read about actions taken by two communities to address sustainability issues.

- (LITERACY) Students identify specific sustainability challenges facing communities.

Follow-up

- ✓ Students evaluate the success of actions taken to address the sustainability issues.

BACKGROUND INFORMATION

Product Life-cycle Analysis

Life-cycle analysis, also called life-cycle inventory or life-cycle assessment, involves collecting data about the resources spent and environmental harm incurred from the first step of making a product to its final fate. It runs from the mining of the raw materials for the product to its transportation to the consumer to the effects of its use, to re-use, recycling, or eventual disposal. Only by assessing all the data involved in its "life," can we form a conclusion about a product's full impact on the environment. Life-cycle analysis is a potentially powerful decision-making tool for regulators, manufacturers, and scientists, and enables consumers to make more informed choices.

Unfortunately, reliable methods for measuring and evaluating all phases of the life cycle do not yet exist. Comparisons are difficult because of the assumptions that are used. For example, in food packaging one cannot assume that all containers are the same size, made of the same kind or amount of material, or that the energy that made the packages came from a coal-burning plant. As a result, analyses have reached different and sometimes contradictory conclusions about similar products. The more dissimilar the products, the more assumptions need to be made. However, business people, economists, and environmentalists are currently contributing a great deal of work toward standardizing a method of collecting and interpreting relevant data.

Land Degradation

Land degradation is the decline in the overall quality of soil, water, or vegetation and is caused by human activities or natural processes and events. The decline diminishes the function of the land within an ecosystem. Such major examples of land degradation as the Aral Sea and the Dust Bowl have occurred on every continent of the world and throughout history.

Desertification is a specific kind of land degradation that occurs in arid, semi-arid, and dry sub-humid areas and results from various factors, including climate change and human activities. The immediate cause is often the removal of vegetation in dry conditions. Additionally, overgrazing destroys valuable plant species, leaving mostly undesirable ones. Unproductive soils cause biodiversity loss and ecological deterioration, changes in natural resources, and increasing poverty and severe strain for human populations. The poor in developing countries are especially hard-hit by desertification because they depend directly on agriculture to fill many basic needs.

REFERENCES

Bioregional Development Group. 2009. *BedZED seven years on: The impact of the UK's best known eco-village and its residents.* Retrieved March 2010 from www.bioregional.com.

World Resource Institute (WRI) in collaboration with United Nations Development Programme, United Nations Environment Programme, and World Bank. 2005. *World resources 2005: The wealth of the poor—Managing ecosystems to fight poverty.* Washington, DC: WRI.

GETTING STARTED

1 ◆ Ask students to recall the sustainability challenges they identified in the previous activity. Ask the student groups to discuss and list responses to the following question: *What sustainability challenges do you think residents of the United Kingdom face in comparison to those in India?*

If students are unfamiliar with the profile of the UK, where one of the case studies in the reading is located, equate it to living in the United States. From the previous activity, students should be able to identify fossil fuel consumption as a problem facing developed countries like the United States and the United Kingdom. Likewise, they should be able to recall that in India, deforestation and desertification are among the biggest environmental concerns.

DOING THE ACTIVITY

2 (LITERACY) The literacy strategies for the readings in this book help improve students' performance in reading comprehension, particularly of informational text. In this activity, Student Sheet 3.1, "Summary Sheet: Sustainability Case Studies," supports students' comprehension of the reading by providing some structure to process the information presented. Student Sheet 3.2, "Three-Level Reading Guide: Sustainability Case Studies," gives students statements representing three levels of understanding: literal, interpretive, and applied. They are then asked to determine which statements are supported by the text.

Possible responses to the reading guide are shown at the end of the activity in this Teacher's Edition. Note that the statements under number 3 (applied) do not have a single correct response. Students may interpret information differently and agree or disagree with each statement. Regardless of their perspectives, it is important for students to be able to explain and support their positions.

---

3 Sustainability Case Studies

1 **C**OMMUNITIES AROUND THE world face a variety of sustainability challenges. Even though the challenges differ from one community to the next, there is often one similarity: many sustainability issues are a result of overuse of the earth's resources. In this activity, you will read about two communities that have taken steps toward more sustainable use of resources.

Challenge

▶ What steps have communities taken to live in ways that are more sustainable?

MATERIALS

FOR EACH STUDENT
Student Sheet 3.1, "Summary Sheet: Sustainability Case Studies"
Student Sheet 3.2, "Three-Level Reading Guide: Sustainability Case Studies"

Procedure

2
1. As you complete the reading, fill out Student Sheet 3.1, "Summary Sheet: Sustainability Case Studies."

2. When you have finished the reading, complete Student Sheet 3.2, "Three-Level Reading Guide: Sustainability Case Studies."

Reading

EVERYDAY DECISIONS

Every day people make personal decisions about transportation, food, and use of water and other resources. On an individual level, these decisions seem to have little impact on the world. However, when the effects are multiplied by large numbers of people, the results are significant. The sum of many individuals' actions can increase or decrease the sustainability of the community. Here are the true stories of two places where the actions of individuals made a difference in the sustainability issues facing their communities.

BEDDINGTON ZERO FOSSIL ENERGY DEVELOPMENT, ENGLAND

Beddington Zero Fossil Energy Development (BedZED) is one of a handful of developments, or "ecovillages," in the world that were designed and built to encourage people to live using fewer resources. Completed in 2002 near London,

14

BedZED has 100 living and work spaces. A team of scientists, engineers, and architects designed the community, with help from the local government.

One of the primary goals of BedZED was to reduce the amount of fossil fuels burned for energy. Our continued reliance on fossil fuels is releasing more and more carbon dioxide into earth's atmosphere. A growing body of evidence shows that, as a result, climates around the world are changing—often in harmful ways. Developed countries, in particular, such as England and the United States, give off relatively high amounts of carbon dioxide emissions.

To build BedZED the designers chose cost-effective materials that had a life cycle with a smaller ecological impact than standard products. The **product life cycle** describes the amounts of resources and energy it takes to make a product, the length of the product's usefulness to the consumer, and how the product is disposed of, recycled, or reclaimed when it is no longer needed. In general, a more sustainable product is made from relatively more reclaimed material and less raw material, and requires less energy to produce and transport it.

BedZED is one of the world's best-known eco-villages.

15

3 Note that on the product life cycle diagram, transportation of goods (as shown by the truck icon) has its own life cycle that is not shown in its entirety. The energy input and waste of transportation are shown on the diagram because they are common to both life cycles.

The life cycle of this wood waste could be extended if it were recycled or repurposed instead of being placed in a landfill.

For example, the life cycle of a wooden board includes the energy and resources used in cutting the tree, transporting it to the mill, cutting the board, shipping it to a distributor, and transporting it to the construction site. The "life" of the wooden board continues for however long it is part of the constructed house. The useful life of the board is likely to end when the house is torn down or remodeled. Since construction debris usually ends up in a landfill or is incinerated, more energy is consumed to transport the board to a landfill or incinerator, its final destination. The "life" of the board, however, goes on because there are both economic and environmental costs to maintain it in the landfill or burn it in an incinerator.

Sometimes a board does not go to the landfill or incinerator but is, instead, reused or recycled. Then the materials would be put back into the "cycle," whether to become part of another house or go into another product. In either event more energy and resources go into this next "life." In this way, a product's life cycle is never really a closed loop. The term "cycle" can be misleading because the life cycle of a product does not necessarily mean the resources in the products are reclaimed and continually cycled through different states.

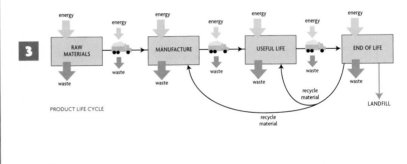

PRODUCT LIFE CYCLE

As well as selecting materials that have a lighter ecological impact, BedZED's builders designed the complex so that residents would rely less on energy and water in their daily routines. For example, the apartments have energy-efficient refrigerators, washers, dryers, and other appliances. Rooms and windows are placed to maximize the amount of sun to heat the house during the day. Water meters are installed at eye level in the kitchens, rather than being put outside of or under the homes, so that residents can monitor the amount of water they use. A community composting and recycling system begins with a built-in waste collection center in each kitchen. Recycling goes even further with a special office-paper recycling plan in which all used paper is recycled and returned to BedZED for reuse.

One of BedZED's goals is to provide alternatives to private car travel.

BedZED's electrical power was originally generated by solar panels and a biofuel power system. The biofuel power system generated energy by burning recycled garden waste instead of fossil fuels. The biofuel power system supplied electricity and heat to the community. Unfortunately, there were problems with the system. Residents had to use gas-powered water heaters, and a majority of their electricity came from the regional power plant.

Since transportation contributes to carbon dioxide emissions, BedZED was designed to help its residents reduce trips outside the community. For example, there are on-site workspaces, exercise facilities, a community center, and a bicycle repair shop. When residents travel, they do so by taking advantage of BedZED's car-sharing program, electric cars, nearby bus and subway lines, and bicycles. Although BedZED residents travel less frequently by car, they tend to fly more often. As a result, they have a slightly higher than average overall transportation impact.

Having so many resources within BedZED also has the effect of maintaining a strong social community. About 84% of the residents feel that the community is an improvement on their previous neighborhood. On average, they know more than twice as many neighbors as those in the surrounding area. Since the apartments are desirable places to live in, the sale price of a BedZED apartment is higher than similar nearby apartments.

After the project was completed, data from water and energy indicators were collected. In comparison to the average Londoner, BedZED residents use less energy in the home, consume less water, and drive fewer miles.

17

Some of the indicators, measured five years after project ompletion, are shown in the table below.

BedZED Data			
INDICATOR	AVERAGE IN ENGLAND	BEDZED GOAL	2007 BEDZED AVERAGE
Energy consumption			
Electricity consumption at home (kWh/person/day)	4.5	3.0 (33% reduction)	3.4
Heat consumption, space and water heating (kWh/person/day)	21.2	2.1 (90% reduction)	5.2
Total energy consumption (kWh/person/day)	25.7	5.1 (80% reduction)	8.6
Water consumption (liters/person/day)	150	100.0 (33% reduction)	72 + 15 recycled or rain water
Carbon emissions (kg CO$_2$/person/day)	25	0 (100% reduction)	1.4
Personal fossil fuel car mileage (km/person/year)	6,344	3,172.0 (50% reduction)	2,318

SOURCE: BioRegional, 2009

While BedZED has met its goal of reducing residential energy consumption, it has experienced its share of challenges. Energy consumption has not been reduced as much as planned. The cost to build BedZED ran higher than expected. Critics claim BedZED is a failure because it relies on some fossil fuel for energy. Supporters say BedZED is still successful because it took fewer resources to build than other living complexes, and residents use less water and energy than they would in traditional homes.

The photovoltaic solar panels at BedZED provide electricity and help shade the house in warm weather.

DAREWADI WATERSHED RESTORATION PROJECT, INDIA

Darewadi is a rural village of about 2,500 people located in India, east of the city of Mumbai. The residents of Darewadi are primarily farmers and herders, who make their living raising crops and animals to sell in nearby communities.

Although the region receives little rainfall each year, the local resources had supported the village population for many years. However, by the early 1980s, overfarming, overgrazing, and population growth caused changes to the local ecosystem. As a result, less arable land was available because farming had exhausted the soil. To create more farmland the residents began clear-cutting the natural landscape, removing trees and shrubs that held water in the ground. This dried out the soil even further. The villagers faced a crisis in the mid-1990s when there was no longer enough water and arable land to support the residents of the village. Not wanting to abandon their homes, the residents of Darewadi had to find ways to support themselves. Many traveled for months on end to neighboring villages and cities to find work. For those who stayed, water was brought in by truck during the extremely dry summer months.

The Darewadi villagers' everyday activities, over the years, had caused their land to degrade. **Land degradation** is the decline in the overall quality of soil, water, or vegetation caused by human activities or natural events. Land degradation caused by human activities is not unique to Darewadi—it occurs all over the world.

In 1996, a nonprofit group together with the Indian and German governments started the Indo-German Watershed Development Project. The project depended on the knowledge of scientists that specialized in agriculture, forestry, and the movement of water. The goal of the project was to restore the Darewadi watershed and land to a condition that could once again support the population.

First, the project convinced Darewadi residents to change their approach to the land and trained them in skills that would restore the ecosystem. Working with the leadership in the village, specialists taught sustainable farming practices, and residents learned how to build trenches and dams to harvest rainwater and underground water. The villagers made a difficult choice when they agreed to stop raising and herding grazing animals. This ban protected the land from further harm and gave it time to recover. To encourage regrowth, the villagers planted native trees and grasses, and prohibited the cutting of all trees and shrubs for five years. In addition, a community board made up of members from every social group was set up to oversee the project. Some indicator data for the project is shown on the next page.

FOLLOW-UP

4 1 hectare $= 10{,}000\ \mathrm{m}^2$
$\qquad\quad = 2.47$ acre

5 Discuss with students how each case study affected the sustainability of an individual, a community, and the world. For example, the people who lived in BedZED are individually contributing to the reduction of energy and water use because their personal consumption is smaller than that of the average resident in England. On a community level, BedZED is contributing fewer greenhouse gas emissions, which might help curb climate change. The changes that BedZED made at the personal and community level, if replicated worldwide, can eventually lead to a positive global effect.

The project in Darewadi had positive effects for the individuals who recovered their farming jobs, and the community as a whole was saved. The changes also improved the water quality in the region. This can have a positive effect on global sustainability by providing an example for other communities to overcome similar sustainability problems.

6 ⓘ Students may have the misconception that technology makes life less sustainable because it causes more pollution, and requires more energy and resources. This activity, however, shows that, in some cases, technology does help reduce environmental impact.

7 ✓ Analysis Question 3c assessment monitors students' ability to identify trade-offs in their decisions, which is a component of the EVIDENCE AND TRADE-OFFS (ET) Scoring Guide.

SAMPLE RESPONSES

1. a. In the BedZED case study, mostly environmental indicators (water use, electricity use, and miles traveled) were monitored. Home prices were also measured, which is a social and economic indicator.

SCIENCE & GLOBAL ISSUES/BIOLOGY • SUSTAINABILITY

The Darewadi Watershed Restoration Project Data

INDICATOR	BEFORE PROJECT, 1996	AFTER PROJECT, 2001	JANUARY 2005
Months requiring delivery of drinking water by truck	February to June	none	none
Active wells (number)	23	63	67
Livestock	1,507	780	1,007
Agricultural employment (months per year)	3–4	9–10	9–10
Agricultural wage rate (rupees per day)	20–30	40–50	40–50
Kitchen gardens	0	30	30
Televisions	3	76	76
Bicycles	2	122	122
Waste land area (hectares)	167	17	15
Cropped area (hectares)	800	107	1,085

SOURCE: Watershed Organization Trust, 2005

Within five years positive effects were seen in the Darewadi community. The volume of water in the watershed increased, and it was no longer necessary to truck in water. Grasses and trees grew back. Rather than relying on a single grain crop, millet, farmers grew a variety of new crops, including vegetables. More residents were able to stay and farm year-round in Darewadi. Villagers learned to maintain the local resources by using different methods of tending to the soil.

SOLVING SUSTAINABILITY CHALLENGES

These two case studies show the changes communities can make by applying science and technology to improve their lives and maintain natural resources for future generations. In both BedZED and Darewadi, scientific knowledge contributed to improving the economic, environmental, and social lives of the communities. These examples show how science and technology can play an important part in solving sustainability issues.

Analysis

1. For each of the two case studies explain:
   a. What kind of indicators were monitored—economic, environmental, and/or social?
   b. What do the indicators show about the effects of the changes that were made?

2. What specific science- and technology-related changes did the communities make that lowered their
   a. energy use?
   b. water use?

20

Home prices increased, indicating the economic and social situation of this ecovillage is desirable, but it was not directly measured in the data provided. In Darewadi, the indicators fell into all three categories. Things like number of active wells, amount of plant life, and number of kitchen gardens were environmental. Employment and number of televisions and bicycles were social and economic.

b. The indicators in the BedZED case showed that residents indeed used fewer resources. The indicators from Darewadi showed improvement also. The number of wells, increased employment, and decreased trucked-in water show they were able to restore the resources. This was a more sustainable practice that improved the environmental, social, and economic situations.

2. a. In BedZED, knowledge of science and technology was applied in the construction of the homes, such as the design of the electrical and heating systems and the placement of water meters.

    b. In Darewadi, scientists knew ways to help the villagers gain water, such as building trenches and reducing the overgrazing.

        In BedZED, the technology was advanced in comparison to Darewadi. In Darewadi the knowledge and technology was not cutting edge, but the application of scientific knowledge in both cases was significant.

3. a. Answers will vary. One common example of an unsustainable lifestyle choice is people driving inefficient cars, or driving them more than they need to, leading to more CO_2 emissions. Another is inefficient appliances at home. Students also may be familiar with local water- or land-use issues. They may refer to data from Activity 1 or 2 or their own research as evidence that the lifestyle is not sustainable.

    b. Students may suggest doing the activity less, such as by carpooling to school, taking the bus, or watering the garden less often.

    c. ✓ Trade-offs associated with their choices usually involve more expenditure in either money or time. Examples might be that the bus takes longer to get to school, or some non-native plants might die if not watered regularly.

    d. In these two examples, indicators that show rate or total consumption are useful, like the number of days taking the bus versus driving the car, or a change in a water bill.

---

3. Give an example of a potentially unsustainable practice involving natural resources in your community.

    a. Use indicator data to show how it is not sustainable.

    b. Propose alternatives to this activity that might be more sustainable. Explain why your choice(s) are more sustainable.

    7 c. What are the trade-offs you would have to consider when deciding whether or not to adopt the alternatives?

    d. What indicators would you use to determine if the alternative was sustainable?

KEY VOCABULARY	
indicator	**product life cycle**
land degradation	sustainability

21

REVISIT THE CHALLENGE

Both Darewadi Village and BedZED provided examples of positive actions taken to bring a community closer to sustainable living. Some of those steps included organized group efforts, individual changes, economic incentives, and the implementation of technology.

Summary Sheet: Sustainability Case Studies

BedZED

Challenges Faced by Community	Type of Challenge (economic, environmental, social)	Solution to Challenge
Dependence on fossil fuels	Environmental	Consume less, use renewable energies, use products with minimal life cycle, recycle, and reuse
High water use	Environmental	Prominent water meters
Transportation	Environmental	Reduce miles traveled
Energy costs	Economic	Reduce consumption by using high-efficiency appliances
Construction costs	Economic	Use recycled products in construction of houses
Attracting residents	Social	Make low cost of operations appealing to residents
Community formation	Social	Locate work and residential facilities close together

Darewadi Village

Challenges Faced by Community	Type of Challenge (economic, environmental, social)	Solution to Challenge
Overgrazed land	Environmental	Reduce livestock grazing
Land degradation	Environmental	Reduce deforestation, plant more crop varieties, reduce farm area
Job loss	Economic, social	Restore land so farm employment increases
Availability of water	Economic, environmental	Reduce deforestation, reclaim rainwater, replant areas
		Restore ecosystem so water is stored locally

Three-Level Reading Guide: Sustainability Case Studies

1. Place a check next to the statements below that you believe agree with what the reading says. Sometimes, the exact words found in the reading are used. At other times, other words may be used to communicate the same meaning.

    ☑ **a.** Over-farming and overgrazing changed the ecosystem in Darewadi.

    ❑ **b.** Land degradation is a problem only in Darewadi village.

    ☑ **c.** A goal of the BedZED project was to create a community that uses less energy and water.

2. Place a check next to the statements below that you believe represent the intended meaning of the reading.

    ☑ **a.** The life cycle of a product or material is not really a "cycle."

    ❑ **b.** The quality of life for Darewadi Village residents decreased at the completion of the Watershed Development Project.

    ❑ **c.** No one wanted to live in BedZED after it was built.

3. Place a check next to the statements below that you agree with, and support your choices with ideas from the reading and from your own knowledge and experience.

    ❑ **a.** Sustainability challenges are easy to solve.

    Students are likely not to agree with this because sustainability issues are multi-faceted and involve simultaneously solving social, environmental, and economic problems. However, some may feel that the reading shows communities that took successful actions, despite unforeseen problems in the projects.

    ❑ **b.** Individuals can affect the ecosystem of the planet.

    Those who agree with this statement think people can improve the environment one person at a time and feel that the world's sustainability is up to individual people. Those who disagree may feel like the efforts of larger groups, such as governments and multinational projects, can have the largest positive impact.

    ❑ **c.** It is never too late to restore an ecosystem.

    Those who agree with this statement hope that communities don't feel like it is too late to try and that all efforts are worthy. Those who disagree may understand that there is indeed a point at which the ecosystem has been harmed to the point of no return. Restoration efforts need to be started before a "tipping point" is reached.

    ❑ **d.** It is possible to live an "average" life in the United States without fossil fuels.

    Those who agree with this statement have a vision of no fossil-fuel use through the implementation of renewable energies and reduced consumption. Those who disagree may feel that the American lifestyle is hugely energy-demanding and that renewable energies will not be enough to sustain our expected quality of life.

4 Ecological Footprint

INVESTIGATION • 1–2 CLASS SESSIONS

OVERVIEW

Students complete an on-line survey that estimates the individual environmental impact of their lifestyles—their ecological footprint—and compare their results with averages for the United States, other countries, and the world.

KEY CONTENT

1. The earth has a finite amount of resources.
2. Each individual has an impact on the ecosystem and that impact can, in many cases, be reduced.

KEY PROCESS SKILLS

1. Students make predictions.
2. Students develop conclusions based on evidence.
3. Students employ technology in their investigations and communications.

MATERIALS AND ADVANCE PREPARATION

For each student

Student Sheet 4.1, "Ecological Footprint Homework"
computer with Internet access*

not included in kit

Have students collect information on their family's electric, gas, and fuel oil bills for the online survey before they fill it in in class. The information for students to gather from home is listed on Student Sheet 4.1, "Ecological Footprint Homework." If students are unable to complete it at home, or are uncomfortable sharing that information, you may want to provide average numbers for your community.

Review the Extension and decide if you would like students to record their carbon footprint data in addition to their ecological footprint data. If so, discuss the Extension with students before they start the Procedure.

TEACHING SUMMARY

Getting Started

- Introduce the concept of a person's individual ecological footprint.
- Students work with family members to prepare for the survey.

Doing the Activity

- Students complete an online electronic survey about their personal ecological footprint.
- Students discuss and generate ideas for reducing an individual's ecological footprint.

Follow-up

- The class discusses the ecological impacts of daily life.

BACKGROUND INFORMATION

Ecological Footprint

An ecological footprint is a quantitative measurement that estimates the amount of resource consumption and waste production of an individual, community, population, or manufactured product. An ecological footprint is expressed in terms of land and sea area (acres or hectares) needed to sustain the resource consumption and absorb the wastes produced. Ecological footprints are generally calculated estimates based on the answers to a series of questions and known data. The known data is collected from such large fact-finding organizations as the United Nations, the Energy Information Association, and the World Health Organization. An actual measurement for an individual person could only be obtained with strict monitoring, documentation, and technologically advanced equipment.

The terms *ecological footprint* and *ecological footprint analysis* were first presented by ecologist William Rees and Mathis Wackernagel in 1998 in their book, *Our Ecological Footprint: Reducing Human Impact on the Earth*. The book explores the idea that every aspect of one's lifestyle contributes to one's ecological footprint, and that the footprint can be measured and reduced. Since its introduction, ecological footprint analyses have become much more sophisticated and accurate. Despite their increased accuracy, however, they are still subject to assumptions, such as the idea that every area of resource consumption and waste production can be converted to the same unit and thus compared.

Carbon Footprint

Ecological footprint and carbon footprint are two different quantities, but a carbon footprint is a subset of an ecological footprint. The term *carbon emission* is a measurement of the total mass of greenhouse gas emissions caused directly and indirectly by a person, community, population, or a manufactured good. Since there are greenhouse gases besides carbon dioxide, these other gases are converted to a "carbon dioxide equivalent" that is determined by their influence on the greenhouse effect. Carbon footprint is the estimated amount of land and sea area that would be needed to completely absorb one person's carbon emissions.

People can have large ecological footprints and not use a drop of fossil fuels. In fact, the story of the collapse of the population on Rapa Nui (Easter Island) in the 1700s shows what can happen when a community, in part, uses resources at a rate faster than the ecosystem can generate. Conversely, it is rare to have a relatively large carbon footprint and a small ecological footprint because a carbon footprint is a subset of an ecological footprint.

REFERENCES

Diamond, J. 2005. *Collapse: How societies choose to fail or succeed*. New York: Penguin Group.

Rees, W. E., Wackernagel, M., & Testemale, P. 1998. *Our ecological footprint: Reducing human impact on the earth*. Gabriola Is., British Columbia: New Society Publishers.

Venetoulis, J., & Talberth, J. 2009. *Redefining progress*. Retrieved Aug 2010 from www.myfootprint.org/en.

GETTING STARTED

1 Let students know that this activity focuses on the environmental impact of daily life on the ecosystem, as opposed to the economic or social aspects of sustainability. Have the class read the introduction to the activity, and then discuss the concept of an ecological footprint. Remind students that a footprint, in the general sense of the word, means leaving an impression or a mark that alters the surface you have walked on. Ask the class, *How does an ecological footprint differ from a regular footprint?*

Answers should include that an actual footprint is a physical image impressed on a surface that generally doesn't do any harm, whereas an ecological footprint is a complex calculation of environmental harm due to resource use. Ask further, *What information could you use to measure your ecological footprint?*

Answers may include how many miles they drive each week, how much garbage they produce, if they use household chemicals, how much food they eat, types of products they buy, and how much electricity they use. Connect their responses to the idea that each piece of information indicates an amount of a particular resource they are using or an amount of something they are putting into the environment. It is related to a product life cycle in that the ecological footprint estimates, in part, the ecological price of the life cycle of a product, a person, or an organism.

4 Ecological Footprint

1 **E**VERY HUMAN ACTIVITY involves resources from the earth. An "ecological footprint" is the term often used to describe the impact of an activity on the environment. An **ecological footprint** is a quantitative measurement that estimates the amount of resources consumed and waste produced by an individual, a community, a population, or even a manufactured product. This complicated calculation combines the effects of various environment-related activities, which are measured in different units, into a single indicator of environmental sustainability. It shows the impact in terms of the land area of the earth that is required to sustain the activity.

For an example consider a typical bowl of breakfast cereal. Here is a list of some of the resources involved in getting that bowl of cereal to your table:

- The ingredients in the cereal came from plants, and to get these plants to grow a farmer needed a tract of land, water, soil, and usually, fertilizer.

- Processing and transporting the ingredients required energy (likely fossil fuels) and materials, such as trucks, each of which has its own footprint.

- Your bowl and spoon were made from raw materials that were mined somewhere on earth, and manufactured somewhere.

- The milk in the bowl of cereal came from a cow, which needed space to live, grass or feed to eat, and likely, electrical energy to run the machines that milked the cow. Transporting, pasteurizing, and packing the milk involved

To calculate the ecological footprint of your breakfast cereal, include the cultivation, transportation, and processing of the wheat and other ingredients.

22

more land for roads, factories, and grocery stores. More natural resources were used to make the container (trees or fossil fuels).

• The milk had to be kept cool in a refrigerator, and refrigerators require electrical energy. Electricity is often produced by burning fossil fuels, which must be extracted from the earth, transported, and refined, and which release carbon dioxide when burned.

• Eventually you will throw away or recycle the cereal box and milk container, which will take up space in a landfill or be subject to more resource consumption at a recycling plant.

The many components in the life cycle of the bowl of cereal include the raw materials, the energy used, and land needed. All of the components require space on and resources from the earth. The ecological footprint of the bowl of cereal shows the land area it takes to sustain the entire life cycle of the bowl. In comparison, the ecological footprint of the bowl of cereal is likely to be larger than a bowl of fresh fruit from the same location that was not as heavily processed. This is because the fresh food requires fewer raw materials, less processing, and less energy.

Challenge

▶ Can the earth's ecosystems sustain our current use of resources?

MATERIALS

FOR EACH STUDENT
    Student Sheet 4.1, "Ecological Footprint Homework"
    computer with Internet access

Every day choices, such as whether to hang clothes or put them in the dryer, affect the size of a person's ecological footprint.

23

2 Students will find that some of the survey questions ask for information beyond their general knowledge. These questions are consolidated onto Student Sheet 4.1, "Ecological Footprint Homework," that students should fill in with their family members before completing the survey in class. Review each question with students and clarify any unfamiliar terms, such as offset for carbon, secondhand, green-design, and sustainably harvested.

DOING THE ACTIVITY

3 Before beginning the survey, review the concept of an "average" person, and the fact that this represents average amounts for a group made up of very different people with different lifestyles. You may want to give students an analogy, such as the heights of students in the class versus the average height of the class. Also be sure to explain that any result they get in this activity is an estimate, and that to get a truly accurate footprint they would have to document and monitor their daily activities much more closely. Explain to the class that each of them will likely get different results based on the responses they give to the online footprint estimators. Make clear that the results are not a grade, and students should focus on being as accurate as possible in order to generate valid results.

Students may fill in the survey questions in any order, and they may go back and change their answers. There is an initial screen that gives participants the option of sharing their e-mail addresses, as well as the results of their survey with the survey developers. You may instruct your students to skip this screen, which will not affect the results of their survey or their ability to access the rest of the website.

SCIENCE & GLOBAL ISSUES/BIOLOGY • SUSTAINABILITY

Procedure

2

1. Collect the necessary information listed on Student Sheet 4.1, "Ecological Footprint Survey Questions," with your family, and bring the information to class.

3

2. Go to the SEPUP *Science and Global Issues* website at *sepuplhs.org/sgi*, and follow the links to the ecological footprint survey. Answer the questions as accurately as you can.

3. After completing the survey, record your "footprint in global acres" and the "number of planets" in your science notebook.

4

4. Share your results with your group. Compare your ecological footprint to those of others in the group, to average Americans, and to average individuals in the other countries shown in the table below.

Ecological Footprint by Country		
COUNTRY	AVERAGE AREA NEEDED TO SUSTAIN ACTIVITY (ACRES/PERSON)	AREA NEEDED IF THE WORLD POPULATION LIVED LIKE THIS (NUMBER OF PLANETS)
Nigeria	8.8	0.2
India	16.4	0.4
Brazil	31.6	0.8
Japan	123.3	3.2
United States	246.4	6.3

5. Predict what would happen if you changed one quantity—the answer to one question—in the survey. Write your prediction in your science notebook.

6. Go back to the on-line survey, and test your prediction from Step 5. Once you make the change in your survey responses, the effect appears on the screen. Record the change you made and the result in your science notebook.

7. Repeat Step 6 until you have figured out what changes most reduced your ecological footprint.

5

8. As a group, discuss three ways in which you might significantly change your daily activities to lower your ecological footprint. Record these ideas in your science notebook.

24

---

4 Identify the ecological footprint data as yet another indicator of sustainability that shows something about the countries studied in Activity 2. Students will be asked in the Analysis Questions to reflect on whether the ecological footprints make sense, based on their previous investigations of the countries. If students don't notice, point out that Japan was identified in the previous activity as having a quality of life comparable to the United States, but it has only half the ecological footprint.

You may also want to relate this activity to Activity 3 by discussing the average ecological footprint of residents of BedZED, which is 2.6 planets. This does not meet the United Kingdom's goal of "one planet living," or an ecological footprint result of 1.0 planets.

FOLLOW-UP

5 ◆ Encourage students to be creative in their discussions and to go beyond routine ideas for reducing ecological impacts. Typically the actions that lower the footprint are traveling fewer miles (by car or plane), and reducing energy consumption in homes. Discuss the everyday strategies they came up with for reducing their ecological footprints. Make them aware of other strategies that they might not have considered, such as eating less meat, changing their food sources, or composting garbage. Encourage students to look up data to demonstrate how and why these actions would change their footprints. You may want to create a class list that can be posted in the room for students to revisit as the unit continues.

6 This is a fundamental question in the unit. By this point, students have seen enough data to use as evidence to form and support a point of view. Make sure to review students' ideas from this question in a discussion, and ask them to reflect on what they know at this point compared to the first activity.

Analysis

1. How did your ecological footprint compare to that of an average person in the United States? Explain why you think your ecological footprint is or is not different from the average person's.

2. Are the footprints of the average person in other countries consistent with what you investigated about life in other countries in previous activities? Support your answer with the indicator data presented in previous activities.

3. What are the characteristics of a lifestyle that is
   a. more ecologically sustainable?
   b. less ecologically sustainable?

4. a. What questions do you think are missing from the ecological footprint survey?
   b. Explain why they might not have been included.

5. What are the strengths and weaknesses of using "number of planets" as an indicator for measuring the environmental impact of someone's lifestyle?

6. When the ecological footprint of every person on earth is considered, it requires 1.5 earths to sustain the global community indefinitely at the current population and rate of consumption.
   a. Is the population of the world ecologically sustainable at the current rate of consumption?
   b. If the world's population continues this level of consumption, what do you think will happen in the future?

KEY VOCABULARY

ecological footprint	sustainability

25

EXTENSION

As students answer the survey questions, record the "carbon footprint" from the results. A carbon footprint is the part of an ecological footprint that relates only to the use of fossil fuels and greenhouse gas emissions. In this survey, the carbon footprint is the estimated amount of area needed to absorb the CO_2 emissions. Ask students to:

a. Compare their carbon footprints to those of the average person in the United States and of other countries, as shown in the table at right.

b. Compare the relationship between the carbon footprint and ecological footprint shown on the previous page, and summarize any noticeable trends.

Carbon Footprint for the Average Person

COUNTRY	CARBON FOOTPRINT (ACRES)
Nigeria	2.5
India	4.9
Brazil	7.5
Japan	34.6
United States	91.4

Students' carbon footprints are likely to fall in a range of 30 to 100 acres. When they compare their carbon footprints to the ecological footprint, they should see that they show a trend. That is, a large carbon footprint usually means a large ecological footprint because it is a subset of the ecological footprint. Make clear that they are different, however, because they do not have the same definition and do not always correlate. For example, the land degradation in Darewadi had a large ecological impact, but the farmers did not use fossil fuel to cause it and thus their farming practices had only a small carbon footprint. The data tables of students who complete the Extension may be similar to the table at right.

Sample Student Response: Extension

Country	Average carbon footprint per capita (acres)	Average ecological footprint per capita (acres)	Percentage of ecological footprint that is carbon (%)
Nigeria	2.5	8.8	28
India	4.9	16.4	30
Brazil	7.5	31.6	23
Japan	34.6	123.3	28
USA	91.4	246.4	37

SAMPLE RESPONSES

1. Answers will vary. Because students' footprints will vary, usually ranging between three and seven planets, they may either be above or below average. Typically, their results are higher than for all the other countries, with the possible exception of Japan. Students often explain the difference as a quality-of-life difference between the United States and other places. However, students should be aware by this point that, on average, USA use of resources is not as efficient as it is in other countries.

2. ✓ Yes, the results from this activity are consistent with data presented previously. For example, the indicator data in Activity 2 stated that the amount of total imports, which roughly approximates consumption level, was the greatest for the United States ($2,000 billion). This is followed by Japan ($622 billion), India ($219 billion), Brazil ($121 billion), and finally Nigeria ($23 billion). This is the same order as the ecological footprints of an average person from those countries.

3. a. A lifestyle that is more sustainable is characterized by a smaller ecological footprint involving less energy and water use, more recycling, buying unprocessed foods, and driving less.

   b. A lifestyle that is less sustainable is characterized by a larger ecological footprint involving more energy consumption, particularly fossil fuels. This is indicated by more driving, electricity consumption, and water use.

4. a. The survey did not ask questions about how often a person uses an item, buys secondhand items, or doesn't buy them at all.

   b. Questions about use of items probably weren't asked because it would be hard to measure the impact, or it might be overwhelming to ask about all items. Many everyday questions are not asked because, relative to the other issues on the survey, the impact is smaller. An example might be whether a person asks for new paper or plastic bags at the store or brings old ones to use again.

5. The strength of "Number of planets" is that it allows direct comparison and the consequences are obvious. However, a weakness is that it is awkward to talk about more or less than one planet. Another weakness is that the estimation to calculate the footprint, although reasonable, is complicated.

6. a. Based on the ecological footprint model in this activity, the world population is not ecologically sustainable at its current rate of consumption. This activity did not calculate how long it will take before we might run out of resources.

   b. Students' responses will vary, but should predict that resources will become very hard to obtain, expensive, or could eventually push the earth's resources to the point where there is not enough to sustain the population.

REVISIT THE CHALLENGE

Based on the survey, the average resource use for the world is beyond what can be sustained because it requires an area the size of 1.5 earth surfaces. For a global lifestyle to be sustainable, its ecological footprint has to cover only one planet or less.

5 Jaffrey City's Problem

LABORATORY • 2–3 CLASS SESSIONS

OVERVIEW

Students act the role of scientists testing for contaminants in the lake water of fictitious Jaffrey Lake. They analyze the data collected to determine the source of the nitrogen- and phosphorus-containing compounds and construct a report that communicates their results to the community.

KEY CONTENT

1. Concentrations of solutions can be measured in units of parts per million (or parts per billion).

2. A small concentration of a contaminant can have a large effect on water quality.

3. Human activity can have negative effects on water quality.

4. A correlation is a relationship between one event or action and another.

5. A causal relationship between two correlated events is when one event (called cause) and another event (called effect) are related by the latter being a direct consequence of the former. In a causal relationship, the cause(s) alone produces the effect.

KEY PROCESS SKILLS

1. Students make predictions.

2. Students take measurements and record data.

3. Students formulate explanations based on data.

MATERIALS AND ADVANCE PREPARATION

For the class
40 dropper bottles of Jaffrey Lake water (locations 1–40)

For the teacher
Scoring Guide: ORGANIZING DATA (OD)
Scoring Guide: ANALYZING DATA (AD)
Scoring Guide: COMMUNICATING SCIENTIFIC IDEAS (CS)
transparency of Student Sheet 5.1, "Jaffrey Lake Water Testing"
transparency of Literacy Transparency 2, "Reading Scientific Procedures" (optional)

For each group of four students
Chemplate®
dropper*
set colored pencils*

For each pair of students
12 phosphate- or nitrate-test strips
phosphate or nitrate color-comparison chart
cup with rinse water*
paper towels*
white scrap paper*

For each student
Student Sheet 5.1, "Jaffrey Lake Water Testing"
safety goggles*
Scoring Guide: ORGANIZING DATA (OD) (optional)
Scoring Guide: ANALYZING DATA (AD) (optional)
Scoring Guide: COMMUNICATING SCIENTIFIC IDEAS (CS) (optional)
Literacy Student Sheet 3, "Writing Review" (optional)
Not supplied in kit

Masters for Science Skills Sheets are in Teacher Resources II: Diverse Learners. Masters for Scoring Guides are in Teacher Resources IV: Assessment.

Decide how much time you want students to spend investigating nitrates and phosphates and how much information you will provide for them. For most classes the research portion of the Procedure is not intended to be a full project but rather a portion of one class period. If students do not have computer access, provide some resources for them or find some time outside of the classroom for students to complete the assignment.

Students work in pairs to create a concentration map for one of the two substances. If you want each student to have a concentration map for both substances, prepare an additional copy of Student Sheet 5.1, "Jaffrey Lake: Water Testing," to distribute when they share their data in groups of four.

SAFETY

The lake samples in the kit are a mixture of potassium nitrate (KNO$_3$), and a buffer solution. Have students wear safety eyewear and avoid skin contact with the solutions.

Check your local regulations for guidelines on disposing of the lake samples. Most local regulations allow the lake samples to be put down the drain without pretreatment, if the drains are connected to a sanitary sewer system with a water treatment plant operating on the effluent. Do not pour the lake samples down the drain if it empties into groundwater through a septic system or into a storm sewer.

TEACHING SUMMARY

Getting Started

- Introduce the concept of parts per million as it applies to pollution.
- Review the term *scientific evidence*.

Doing the Activity

- Introduce the SEPUP 4-2-1 cooperative learning model.
- Introduce the SEPUP Assessment System.
- (OD ASSESSMENT) (LITERACY) Students test Jaffrey Lake water and share their data.
- Students further investigate the sources and effects of nitrate and phosphate contamination.
- (AD, CS ASSESSMENT) (LITERACY) Students write reports on the contamination.

Follow-up

- (AD ASSESSMENT) Students analyze data for correlations and causal relationships.

BACKGROUND INFORMATION

Nitrates

Nitrates and nitrites are families of chemical compounds containing atoms of nitrogen and oxygen. Nitrates contain a nitrogen atom joined to three oxygen atoms, while nitrites are joined to two. In nature, nitrates are readily converted to nitrites and vice versa. Nitrates are critical to the continuation of life on earth, since they are one of the main sources from which plants obtain the element nitrogen. This element is required for the production of amino acids, which, in turn, are needed for the synthesis of proteins in both plants and animals.

The development and increased reliance on synthetic fertilizer in the past 100 years has spread abnormal amounts of nitrates into rivers, lakes, and marine coastline waters all over the world. Because all nitrates are soluble, most of the fertilizer that is not taken up by plants in the field is washed away into the watershed. In lakes and coastal marine areas, nitrates become food sources for algae and other plant life, sometimes resulting in the formation of algal blooms. Such blooms are usually the first step in the eutrophication of a pond or lake (see eutrophication below). Additionally, nitrates in drinking water are a health hazard to young children and cause blue-baby syndrome, in which the oxygen-carrying capacity of blood is reduced.

Phosphates

Phosphorus is also essential to the growth of organisms, for both their metabolism and photosynthesis. In bodies of water it occurs naturally, mainly in the form of phosphate. Many phosphate compounds are not very soluble in water, and so much of the phosphate in natural systems exists as a solid. Some, however, is released into solution, and soil, water, rivers, and lakes usually contain low concentrations of dissolved phosphates.

Phosphates are classified as orthophosphates (the simplest phosphate PO$_4^{3-}$), polyphosphates (complex molecules with two or more phosphorus atoms, oxygen atoms, and in some cases, hydrogen atoms), and organically bound phosphates (phosphate that is bound to plant or animal tissue). Farmers and others apply orthophosphates and polyphosphates to agricultural or residential land as fertilizers, and from there some of it is carried into surface waters by storm runoff and snowmelt. Both orthophosphates and polyphosphates are added to detergent and cleaning products and can be ultimately discharged into lakes and rivers. Because phosphorus is essential for metabolism, organic phosphate is found in all animal waste. Therefore, phosphate runoff is an issue if there is a body of water near cattle feedlots, hog farms, dairies, or barnyards. Additionally, orthophosphates enter the water through untreated human sewage or wastewater effluent that has not had the phosphate removed. Only very high levels of phosphates are toxic to people and animals.

Nutrient pollution

Excessive levels of phosphate or nitrate cause pollution in a body of water and are typically a result of human activities. Phosphate pollution is often a result of a point-source discharge from factories, agriculture, wastewater-treatment plants, underground mines, oil wells, and oil tankers. Typically, nitrogen pollution comes from point and non-point sources. Since non-point sources cannot be traced to a single site of discharge, it is hard to control. The nature of the non-point source makes it very difficult to hold individuals or organizations accountable.

Eutrophication

Eutrophication, the dramatic increase in available nutrients resulting in an increase in plant growth, occurs in aquatic environments around the world. Recent surveys have shown that up to 54% of lakes in Asia are eutrophic, as are 53% in Europe, 48% in North America, 41% in South America, and 28% in Africa. While eutrophication occurs naturally, for example in seasonal floodplains, it is generally caused by human activities, such as the runoff of fertilizers from agricultural areas, and pollution from untreated sewage. In freshwater systems phosphorus is problematic, as it is the limiting factor in many of those ecosystems, while nitrogen is the limiting factor in most marine environments.

Eutrophication affects primary productivity first, causing an increase in the biomass of phytoplankton, often referred to as an algal bloom. Sometimes the phytoplankton are toxic or inedible (e.g., causing red tides, ciguatera, paralytic shellfish poisoning); other times they simply cause a large fluctuation in the dissolved oxygen available to the ecosystems. The increase in biomass also provides increased nutrients for different bacteria, which can deplete the dissolved oxygen in the ecosystem. This can cause dead zones, where species other than the algae and bacteria are unable to survive. It can also provide opportunities for invasive species to take over an area, by reducing the biodiversity and competition for specific resources within the dead zone.

Cleanup of the excess nutrients, prevention of nutrient and pollution input, and restoration of ecosystems has been successful in some areas to reverse the eutrophication, but other areas have been unable to recover. Many factors affect the recovery, including the extent of the eutrophication, how long it has been occurring, the location, and how easily organisms can migrate back into the area from surrounding ecosystems. A good example of recovery from eutrophication is Lake Erie, which now has a rapidly improving and resilient ecosystem that responded to cleanup efforts.

GETTING STARTED

1 After reviewing the scenario described in the introduction, let students know that they will be testing Jaffrey Lake water and measuring results that are parts per million (ppm). Introduce the concept of parts per million by asking, *What is something you think of in terms of millions?*

Responses may include money, dollars, or the number of people in a city. Ask the class, *If I had a million dollars, and I gave away one dollar, would it make a difference to me?*

Students should say no because one dollar is a very small amount of money relative to a million. Let them know that the dollar in question is one part per million. An everyday example that is similar to the activity experiments is chlorine in a swimming pool, which is also measured in parts per million. A chlorine level of 1 ppm (a typical concentration for public pools) means for every kilogram of water, there is 1 milligram of chlorine. Some other common examples of parts per million are:

- one minute in two years
- one second in 12 days
- one penny of $10,000
- one grain of salt in two pounds of potato chips
- one inch in 16 miles
- one postage stamp on a basketball court

Sometimes small concentrations make a big difference. Some everyday examples are:

- Lead and nicotine are fatal at levels less than 1 ppm in the bloodstream.
- Most people can detect ammonia in the air at 5 ppm or stronger.
- Healthy adult humans have approximately 1.5 ppm of copper in their bodies.

---

5 Jaffrey City's Problem

1 **JAFFREY CITY IS** a sprawling community located on the shores of Jaffrey Lake. The area has grown considerably in the past 20 years, which has been good for the local economy. But recently Jaffrey residents have noticed that Jaffrey Lake, which used to be clean, full of wildlife, and a great place to swim, has changed. Slimy, green algae floats on the surface, and the water has turned murky. People are finding dead fish on the shore, and everyone is afraid they'll get sick if they swim in the lake. Preliminary water tests found higher-than-normal levels of two substances: phosphates and nitrates. The Jaffrey City Council decided that the lake is in danger, and it ordered more tests on the lake water.

In this activity, you will take the role of scientists testing water from Jaffrey Lake to determine the levels of phosphate and nitrate. This data will provide **evidence,** information used to refute or support a claim, about the water quality. Based on the evidence, you will identify the likely source or sources of the contamination.

26

It is important that the students understand why ppm is a relevant unit for water-quality issues. In some instances, contaminants pose a threat at the ppm, ppb, or even ppt level. Let students know they will measure small amounts of phosphate and nitrate in Jaffrey Lake water and that even low concentrations are important. For a hands-on activity that develops the concept of parts per million, see SEPUP's *Issues and Physical Science* activity on serial dilution called "Parts Per Million."

ℹ️ Students may have the misconception that water that is clear is not polluted. This activity shows that some forms of pollution are not readily apparent to the naked eye.

Review the definition of scientific evidence provided in the introduction. Explain that in this activity, students will collect information and then apply their test results from Jaffrey Lake to support or refute the claim that the water is contaminated. The consideration of evidence is a key step in decision-making. Throughout this unit, and throughout *Science and Global Issues*, students will collect and analyze information to use as evidence to support or refute claims.

2 To reduce confusion, it is best to use colors that are similar to the colors that students will observe in their tests. This is straightforward for the distinct colors used in the phosphate test. However, representing the coloring of the pink continuum for nitrate can be more challenging. Here is a suggested coloring scale for the pencil sets provided in the kit:

Phosphate

0–0.19 ppm (orange)

0.2–0.49 ppm (yellow)

0.5–2.5 ppm (green)

> 2.5 ppm (blue)

Nitrate

0–1.9 ppm (black)

2.0–4.9 ppm (brown)

5.0–25 ppm (purple)

> 25 ppm (red)

3 In this activity the test for nitrate is an authentic test that approximates the concentration of nitrate in the form of KNO_3 in the water. In consideration of cost and efficiency, however, the phosphate PO_4 test is simulated using pH.

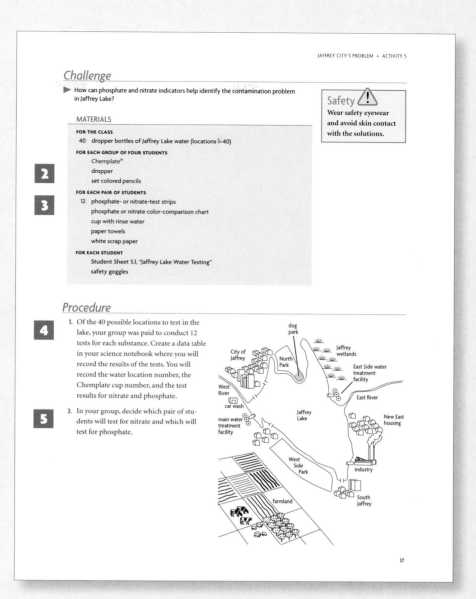

Challenge

▶ How can phosphate and nitrate indicators help identify the contamination problem in Jaffrey Lake?

Safety ⚠️
Wear safety eyewear and avoid skin contact with the solutions.

MATERIALS

FOR THE CLASS
40 dropper bottles of Jaffrey Lake water (locations 1–40)

FOR EACH GROUP OF FOUR STUDENTS
Chemplate®
dropper
set colored pencils

FOR EACH PAIR OF STUDENTS
12 phosphate- or nitrate-test strips
phosphate or nitrate color-comparison chart
cup with rinse water
paper towels
white scrap paper

FOR EACH STUDENT
Student Sheet 5.1, "Jaffrey Lake Water Testing"
safety goggles

Procedure

1. Of the 40 possible locations to test in the lake, your group was paid to conduct 12 tests for each substance. Create a data table in your science notebook where you will record the results of the tests. You will record the water location number, the Chemplate cup number, and the test results for nitrate and phosphate.

2. In your group, decide which pair of students will test for nitrate and which will test for phosphate.

DOING THE ACTIVITY

4 The ORGANIZING DATA (OD) Scoring Guide can be applied to students' written work from the Procedure to assess students' growth. This is as an opportunity to introduce students to the SEPUP assessment system. Provide all students with an ORGANIZING DATA (OD) Scoring Guide, and ask them to keep it with their science notebooks, as they will refer to it several times and throughout the *Science and Global Issues* course. Explain to the class that you will apply the ORGANIZING DATA (OD) Scoring Guide to provide feedback on the quality of their work and that you will use their writing from the Procedure to model how the scoring guide works.

Begin by pointing out the scoring levels 0 to 4, and review the criteria for each score. Explain that the scores are based on the completeness and quality of their responses and do not correspond to letter grades. A Level-3 response is a complete and correct response. A Level-4 response signifies that the student has both achieved and exceeded the acceptable level of response. At first, many students will write Level-2 responses, and they should strive to achieve Level-3 responses. Let students know that you would like them to strive to improve by at least one level in later activities.

As a class, discuss what a Level-3 response would include. For example, their data tables should be clearly labeled and show all the data from their groups. You may develop a Level-3 exemplar with the class or share with students the Level-3 response shown on the last page of this activity as part of the student report. Point out the elements that make the example a Level-3 response, and discuss how a Level 1 and a Level 2 are different. Ask students for ideas about how to improve the Level-3 response to make it a Level 4.

---

3. With your group, look at Student Sheet 5.1, "Jaffrey Lake Water Testing," and select three of the locations numbered 1–40 on the map to test first. Choose locations you think will most likely contain high concentrations of the substances. Record in your notebook why you predicted these locations.

4. To begin the testing, take your Chemplate to the "lake area" and find the three bottles with the matching location numbers. Place 5 drops from each location in separate Chemplate cups and bring it back to your table. Record the location numbers and the corresponding Chemplate cup numbers in your data table.

5. Test the three waters for your substance, as described in the testing procedure below. Record the data in your table.

TESTING PROCEDURE:

a. Place the white paper on top of the paper towel.

b. Label the test strip with the location number.

c. Put one drop of location water on the end of the test strip.

d. For the phosphate test, compare the test strip to the color chart. For the nitrate test, wait one minute before comparing.

e. Record the result in your table.

f. Rinse out the dropper with water in the rinsing cup.

6. Using the results from your tests, begin to complete Student Sheet 5.1, "Jaffrey Lake Water Testing." Choose different colored pencils to represent the levels of each substance, and fill in the key using the scales shown on the color-comparison chart. Identify your map as either "nitrate" or "phosphate" concentrations, depending on the substance you are testing.

7. Share your data with the other pair in your group. As a group, choose three additional locations to test that are based on the results.

8. Repeat Steps 4–7 until you have tested 12 locations.

6 9. Compare maps and look for any patterns in the concentration levels and locations of the substances. Compare your data to the county standards shown below:

Phosphate in Jaffrey Lake	
NATURAL CONCENTRATION (PPM)	LOCAL LIMIT (PPM)
0.05	0.1

Nitrate in Jaffrey Lake	
NATURAL CONCENTRATION (PPM)	LOCAL LIMIT (PPM)
<2	10

28

---

5 Activities in *Science and Global Issues* use a 4–2–1 cooperative learning model. Groups of four students share certain materials, pairs of students in the groups work together and discuss issues, and each student is responsible for recording ideas, observations, and thoughts. In this activity, students choose the lake locations to test in their groups of four, but perform the separate substance tests in pairs. Encourage students to work within their groups, with their partners, and with the other pair in their group to solve problems and answer questions. Collaboration is essential for developing new ideas and gaining a better understanding of scientific concepts. If necessary, be sure to explain to students your expectations for successful group effort. If students need support working through the procedure of this activity, consider projecting Literacy Transparency 2, "Reading Scientific Procedures," found in Teacher Resources III: Literacy.

6 If you want each student to have a concentration map for both substances (see Advance Preparation), then provide an additional copy of Student Sheet 5.1, "Jaffrey Lake Water Testing," to each student.

If students have trouble seeing a pattern in their data, have groups or the class combine data. For completed maps of the contamination, refer to the last page of this activity. You may want to project Transparency 5.1, "Jaffrey Lake Water Testing," and color in results with the class.

Note: It is not necessary to show students the results from all the water samples for them to successfully complete this and the next activity. In fact, withholding that information makes the experience more authentic for students. The maps are provided on the last two pages of this activity for your reference.

Students' data should show that phosphorus levels are highest near two of the storm drains on the west side of the lake and near the City. Also, there is a higher concentration of phosphates near the dog park in North Park. There are lower concentrations near the car wash, the new east housing development, and the east side of the lake. Nitrates are more diffuse in the lake, but in general, higher concentrations are found near the city and on the west side of the lake. Jaffrey wetlands, new east housing, and the east side of the lake have lower concentrations.

Note: The variation and distribution of concentrations provided for this activity are somewhat exaggerated to show the entry points of the nutrients. Depending on the lake's physical properties, nitrate and phosphate concentrations would typically be elevated near the zones of greatest loading. It may be difficult, however, to determine if they are indeed non-point sources because concentrations could be fairly uniform around the surface waters of the lake.

In this activity, students' tests measure only these two quantities. However, in actuality, there are many measurements related to nutrient loading that are commonly taken. Other possible ways of measuring nitrogen and phosphorous quantities include measuring orthophosphate, total dissolved phosphorous, nitrite, and ammonia nitrogen. When investigating your local and state results, keep in mind that precise reporting of what quantity was measured is, at times, unclear and the actual substance that is measured varies.

7 Students can begin their search at the *Science and Global Issues* page of the SEPUP website *(sepuplhs.org/sgi)*. The focus for this step is not to conduct an exhaustive research project with formal findings, but to gather enough information to complete the next procedure step accurately. Adjust your expectations for the research work based on time available and curriculum expectations.

8 The ANALYZING DATA (AD) and the COMMUNICATING SCIENTIFIC IDEAS (CS) Scoring Guide can be applied to students' work in Procedure Step 11 to assess students' growth. Optionally, provide each student an AD and a CS Scoring Guide, and explain to the class that you will use the guides to provide feedback on the quality of their work. Then discuss the specific expectations you have for their reports. If appropriate, you may want to have students work together to generate one report per pair of students or per group of four. A Level-3 response appears at the end of the activity in this Teacher's Edition. Students' responses should include accurate scientific explanation, clearly displayed data, and logical conclusions based on their test results.

After they have written their reports, but before you score them, have students participate in a peer writing review. A peer writing review presents a series of questions by which students evaluate each other's writing. It can be especially helpful in guiding them to write a complete and coherent response. Students can compare others' responses to the review questions to improve or revise their own writing. Literacy Student Sheet 3, "Writing Review," lists questions and includes space for students to respond. If students need more writing support in the initial stages of composing, consider using a writing frame, which provides a structure by which students can articulate a response. See Teacher Resources III: Literacy for more information on writing frame strategies.

7

10. Investigate both phosphate and nitrate and the environmental effects of these substances in high amounts.

8

11. Prepare a formal report for the Jaffrey City Council that includes the following:

- A statement about the typical natural and man-made sources and amounts of phosphate and nitrate.
- Information on the effects of high levels of phosphate and nitrate.
- An explanation of the role of phosphate and nitrate in the eutrophication in the lake. **Eutrophication** is a dramatic increase of available nutrients in the water, resulting in an increase in plant growth.
- Your group's test results and map.
- Your group's conclusion about the likely source(s) and severity of the contamination.
- A recommendation, if any, for future testing.

Analysis

1. What evidence is there that indicates Jaffrey Lake has a contamination problem?

2. It is estimated that nearly 50% of the lakes in North America have high phosphate or nitrate levels. Estimates for other regions of the world range from 30% (Africa) to 54% (Asia). How might these indicators inform decisions about our current and future water-treatment systems?

3. Suppose there is another lake in another city located farther down the East River.

   a. How might the city that is further down the river be affected by the contamination in Jaffrey Lake?

   b. If it is determined that the contamination in the other lake is partly a result of discharge from the East River, whose responsibility is it to clean that lake?

29

Discuss the reports and students' findings. Students should have found some areas of Jaffrey Lake to have elevated levels of both contaminants, and that the concentrations are high enough to be significant. Their research should reveal some of the following common sources for nitrates and phosphates:

Nitrate sources

fertilizers

septic tanks

untreated wastewater

decaying plant debris

geological formations

animal feedlots

Phosphate sources

human and animal waste

fertilizers

soil erosion

untreated wastewater

pulp and paper industry

chemical fertilizer manufacturing

detergents

Students should agree that the main entry points for the contaminants to enter the lake are on the west side near the West Side Park and the main water-treatment plant. For phosphates, locations #3 and #8 were the highest and measured greater than 2.5 ppm. Additional entry points are the untreated storm drains near Jaffrey City. The dog park had a high concentration of phosphates, but not nitrates. For nitrates, the west side was also the highest with concentrations greater than 25 ppm, but the contaminant was more evenly distributed in the lake. Some places that students may have thought were discharging pollutants, such as the car wash and the industrial site, were not entry points for high levels of contaminants to enter the water.

Discuss with students whether the lake is sustainable at the measured levels of nitrate and phosphate. Students should be able to definitively say from their test results and the appearance of the lake that it is not sustainable.

9

4. Look at the graph below, showing the average concentrations of four indicators in a lake over 60 years. Based on the graph data only, decide if you agree or disagree with the three statements below, and explain why. The following definitions may help you evaluate the claims:

A **correlation** is a relationship between one event or action and another. A positive correlation means that as one event or action becomes large, the other also becomes large, and vice versa. A negative correlation means that when one event or action becomes larger, the other becomes smaller, and vice versa.

A **causal relationship** between two correlated events is when one event (called the cause) directly produces another event (called the effect). In a causal relationship, the cause(s) alone produce the effect.

a. *There is a strong negative correlation between the phosphate concentration and the fish population. In other words, the phosphate concentration increased while the fish population decreased.*

b. *There is a strong positive correlation between the nitrate concentration and the algae concentration. In other words, after the nitrate concentration rose, the algae concentration increased in a similar way.*

c. *The increased nitrate concentration is causing the increased algae concentration. There is a causal relationship between the two.*

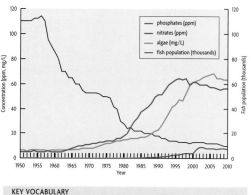

KEY VOCABULARY	
correlation	evidence
causal relationship	indicator
eutrophication	

30

FOLLOW-UP

9 This question introduces the concepts of correlation and causality. Remind students that the data provided are not from Jaffrey Lake, but a sample lake used for the purpose of illustrating the difference between correlation and causality. Explain the difference with the following simple example.

Imagine a town where the murder rate has increased at the same rate that ice-cream sales have risen. The correlation between the events is strong. However, it would be incorrect to imply causality, that is, to claim that ice-cream consumption causes murders or that fear of murder causes people to eat more ice cream. The missing explanation is that murders occur more often in summertime, when the weather is warmer. Emphasize to students that causality can only be determined after appropriate studies all have consistent results. In the ice cream–murder scenario, one could test causality by removing ice cream from all stores for a summer to see if the murder rate is affected. There must be a body of evidence to show causality. This example illustrates the importance of logical reasoning of plausible explanations when constructing claims based on evidence. The discussion of correlation and causality relates to the students' inquiry because their concentration data alone are not enough to determine likely causes of contamination in Jaffrey Lake. Only by sharing data from others' tests and researching common sources of contamination can they gain enough evidence to make this determination.

The ANALYZING DATA (AD) Scoring Guide can be used to score students' responses in Analysis Question 4 about correlation and causality. Look for responses saying that the statement in part 4c is the only possibility for causality because the graphs show nearly identical curves, although the graph alone is not enough evidence. For more on the SEPUP Assessment System, see Teacher Resources IV: Assessment.

EXTENSION

Find out the recommended and actual amounts of phosphate and nitrates for lakes and/or marine ecosystems in your state. Start your search at the SEPUP website, *sepuplhs.org/sgi*.

SAMPLE RESPONSES

1. The evidence is from those locations that have concentrations of phosphate and nitrate that were higher than the natural and local limits. For phosphate, about half of the locations had concentrations well above the limit of 0.1 ppm, and the other half had concentrations that may be above the limit. For nitrate, all locations tested higher than the natural level of the lake, and about half had values greater than 25 ppm.

2. That half of the lakes in North America have high nitrate or phosphate concentrations indicates that our current water-treatment processes need to be improved. The indicator of ppm concentration is valuable to evaluate water regularly to see if improvements are made.

3. a. The community downstream from Jaffrey Lake is affected by the contamination because it may enter their own lake via the East River.

   b. Students may think that the lake in another city is the problem of the other city. However, the upstream community that is responsible for part of the pollution is typically responsible for at least that portion. If this idea is applied to other resources, such as air pollution, it shows how difficult it can be to hold a community or country in one part of the world liable for effects that have manifested in a community on the other side of the globe.

4. *Sample Level-3 Response*

   a. Yes, there is a negative correlation between the fish population and the phosphate concentrations. The evidence in the graph does not support a causal relationship because the fish population started declining sharply in 1960, well before phosphate levels increased in the 1990s.

   b. Yes, there is a strong correlation between nitrate concentration and the algae concentration because the shape of the curves is nearly identical.

   c. Although it is likely that there is causality here (as has been researched and shown) the data *on this graph alone* do not prove causality. To a scientist, the strong correlation would be evidence for further study.

REVISIT THE CHALLENGE

Students should be able to articulate that monitoring concentrations of contaminants is vital in determining

1. the source or sources of pollution.

2. if future sustainability efforts are effective.

SAMPLE STUDENT RESPONSE: Procedure Step 11

Sample Level-3 Response

(AD, CS ASSESSMENT) Nitrates and phosphates naturally occur in nature. Phosphates are often found in soil, depending on the geography, and nitrates are part of the nitrogen cycle. Both are nutrients that are ordinarily found in small amounts in fresh water. Nitrates are usually 0–10 ppm and phosphates are 0–0.1 ppm naturally in fresh bodies of water. Due to animal wastes, industry, and fertilizers, the levels of nitrates and phosphates have risen in many rivers, lakes, and marine coastal waters. High nitrate level in drinking water can affect babies. They can turn bluish and have trouble breathing since their bodies are not getting enough oxygen. High phosphate levels do not have any direct health effects, but cause algae to grow in the water.

Eutrophication is when a lake or marine coast has a big increase in nutrients, usually from human activity, which increases plant growth. As a result of the nutrient-rich water, the phytoplankton population increases, and when they die and sink it increases the amount of organic matter for bacteria to grow on. The bacteria deplete the surrounding water of oxygen, which means many organisms must migrate or die. The dead and decaying organic matter can eventually fill the lake, making it more shallow and then, eventually, a swamp. Sometimes, however, a lake that has accelerated eutrophication due to human activity can recover and avoid disaster if the nutrients are decreased.

Our test results show that there is a serious problem on the west side of the lake, most likely a result of excess nutrient input to the lake. There was both more phosphate and more nitrate there than on the east side. The contaminants seem to be coming mostly from the old sewage plant, the storm drains there and near the city, and the dog park. We suspect there is some run-off coming from the farmland. Our test results are shown in the table at right and the map on the following page.

We recommend further testing at the same sites in six months to see if the problem persists. After Jaffrey City comes up with a solution, the water should continue to be tested every six months. Also, if there is enough money, other sites that other groups found to have high concentrations, such as locations #2, #8, and #21, should also be tested.

Phosphate and Nitrate Results

Testing round	Location number	Phosphate level (ppm)	Nitrate level (ppm)
1	1	0–0.19	2–4.9
	3	> 2.5	> 25
	4	0.2–0.49	> 25
2	12	0.2–0.49	> 25
	18	0.5–2.5	5.0–25
	22	0–0.19	5.0–25
3	24	0–0.19	2.0–4.9
	29	0–0.19	2.0–4.9
	32	0–0.19	> 25
4	33	0–0.19	5.0–25
	39	0.2–0.49	> 25
	40	0–0.19	5.0–25

Jaffrey Lake Water Testing: (Nitrate) Phosphate (CIRCLE ONE)

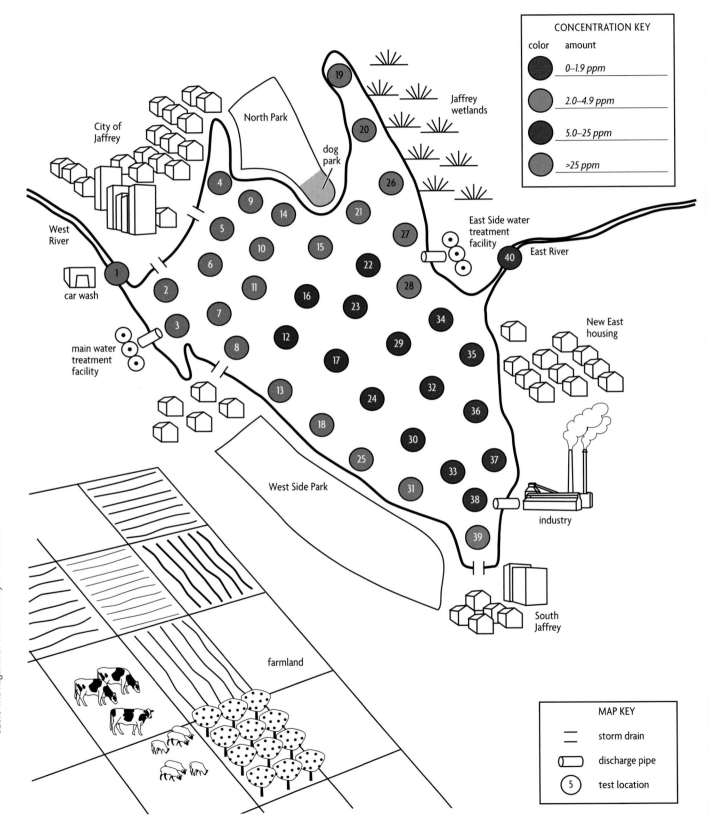

CONCENTRATION KEY

color	amount
●	0–1.9 ppm
●	2.0–4.9 ppm
●	5.0–25 ppm
●	>25 ppm

MAP KEY

— storm drain

▭ discharge pipe

(5) test location

Jaffrey Lake Water Testing: _Nitrate_ (_Phosphate_) (CIRCLE ONE)

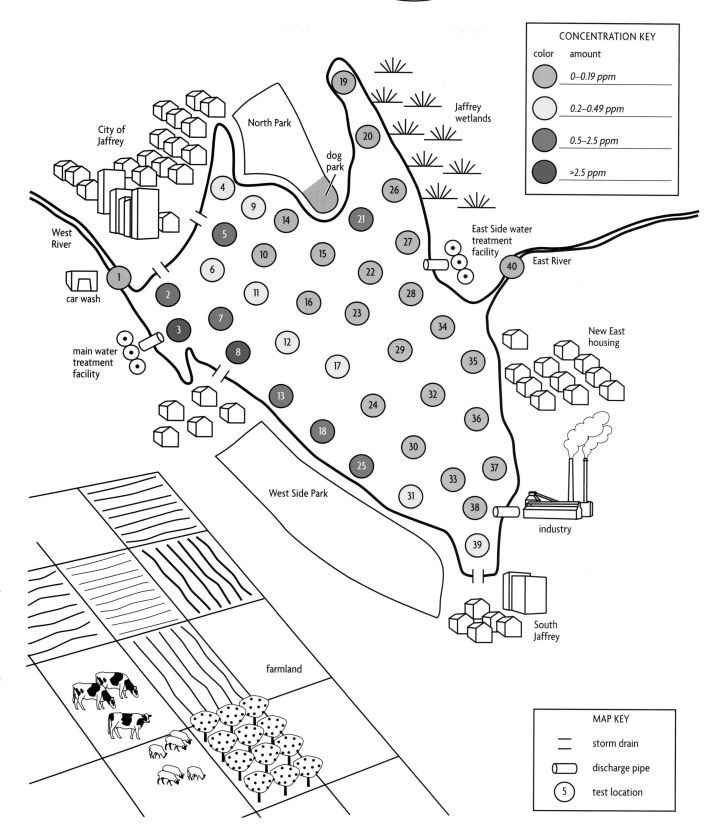

6 Jaffrey City's Master Plan

TALK IT OVER • 2–3 CLASS SESSIONS

OVERVIEW

Students propose a master plan for dealing with the contamination of Jaffrey Lake in a way that builds consensus among the stakeholders in the community.

KEY CONTENT

1. Successful decision-making takes into account all stakeholders.

2. Trade-offs must be made when seeking viable solutions to sustainability problems.

3. Sustainability problems have adverse environmental, economical, and social impacts on the community.

KEY PROCESS SKILLS

1. Students use evidence to make a decision.

2. Students identify and describe trade-offs.

3. Students consider and evaluate multiple perspectives.

MATERIALS AND ADVANCE PREPARATION

For the teacher
Scoring Guide: EVIDENCE AND TRADE-OFFS (ET)

Scoring Guide: COMMUNICATING SCIENTIFIC IDEAS (CS)

transparency of Student Sheet 5.1, "Jaffrey Lake Water Testing"

For each group of four students
set of 9 Proposal Idea Cards

For each student
Scoring Guide: EVIDENCE AND TRADE-OFFS (ET) (optional)

Scoring Guide: COMMUNICATING SCIENTIFIC IDEAS (CS) (optional)

Masters for Scoring Guides are in Teacher Resources IV: Assessment.

TEACHING SUMMARY

Getting Started
- Review the results from the previous activity.

Doing the Activity
- Students consider the positions of various stakeholders.
- (ET, CS ASSESSMENT) Students work in groups to create a proposal for Jaffrey Lake.
- Students vote on a Master Plan for Jaffrey Lake.

Follow-up
- (ET ASSESSMENT) The class discusses the decision-making process used in Jaffrey City.

BACKGROUND INFORMATION

Wastewater Treatment and Nutrient Removal

Historically, wastewater-treatment plants did not remove significant amounts of phosphates and nitrates. Greater environmental awareness, however, has led to advanced treatment processes that effectively remove most of those nutrients. Nonetheless, new treatment plants are not necessarily a perfect solution because the advanced systems are relatively expensive to build and operate, and maintaining effluent quality requires precise supervision of the process and the equipment.

Most wastewater-treatment processes remove nutrients from wastewater in the third phase of treatment. Phosphates are usually removed by precipitation, where chemicals are added to wastewater, or with a biological treatment. Nitrate removal, unlike phosphate removal, does not involve generating additional sludge. Nitrates are usually removed biologically by converting the nitrates into nitrogen gas, which is then released into the atmosphere.

GETTING STARTED

1 As a class, review the evidence gathered in the previous activity, and examine the current state of Jaffrey Lake. Project the transparency of Student Sheet 5.1, "Jaffrey Lake Water Testing," that shows the results from students' water tests and ask students to summarize the problem areas where phosphate and nitrates enter the lake.

Introduce the term *stakeholders* and discuss their roles in the Jaffrey Lake community. When reviewing the concept of trade-offs, revisit the explanation of evidence and trade-offs provided in Teaching Suggestion 10 for Activity 1 in this Teacher's Edition.

---

6 Jaffrey City's Master Plan

1 **THE PEOPLE OF** Jaffrey City have decided that in its current state Jaffrey Lake is not sustainable, and they are committed to reducing the contamination. There is some evidence that if no more phosphates are added to the lake, the affected ecosystem may recover. They want to stop the algae growth and reduce any health hazards from the nitrates. The City Council's goals to make the lake sustainable are to

- protect wildlife
- improve water quality
- prevent future pollution

Jaffrey City has a budget of $2 million per year to spend on cleaning up the lake.

In this activity, you will use the test results from the previous activity to create a master plan for Jaffrey Lake. When developing such a plan, it is important to consider the needs and interests of all of the stakeholders. **Stakeholders** are individuals or groups who are affected by or involved in a decision. To get enough stakeholders to support and implement a plan, **trade-offs**, or outcomes given up to gain other outcomes, may have to be made.

Protecting wildlife is one part of maintaining a sustainable ecosystem.

31

55

DOING THE ACTIVITY

2 Explain that the students' job in Part A of this activity is to create a Master Plan that is satisfactory to all the stakeholders in the community. If it is not, those stakeholders are likely to vote against the proposal. Let students know they will take the role of one of the stakeholders in Part B of the activity.

3 Point out to students, if they don't figure it out, that the $2 million budget is a yearly budget so that proposal ideas could potentially be paid for over several years. Information on total cost and how long it would take to implement each proposal is included on the Proposal Idea Cards.

Storm drains often discharge run-off directly into lakes and streams.

Challenge

▶ How can a sustainability plan be developed for Jaffrey Lake that will balance the interests of all of the stakeholders?

MATERIALS

FOR EACH GROUP OF FOUR STUDENTS
set of 9 Proposal Idea Cards

Procedure

Part A: Developing a Proposal

2 1. In your group, read the summary of the perspectives of each stakeholder on the next pages. Use the summaries to identify the priorities for each stakeholder in the community during the decision-making process.

3 2. Review each of the Proposal Idea Cards. Discuss the pros and cons of each suggestion with your group.

32

4 For Procedure Step 3 use the COMMUNICATING SCIENTIFIC IDEAS (CS) Scoring Guide to assess students' growth. For more on the SEPUP Assessment System, see Teacher Resources IV: Assessment. Provide all students with a CS Scoring Guide, and ask them to keep it with their science notebooks, as they will refer to it several times in this unit and throughout the *Science and Global Issues* course. Explain to the class that you will use it to provide feedback on the quality of their work. Then discuss the specific expectations you have for their reports. If appropriate, you may want to have students work together to generate one report per pair of students or per group of four. A Level-3 response appears in this Teacher's Edition at the end of this activity. Responses should clearly and completely report the work of the group and the decisions they made.

5 Randomly assign each student a new role as one of 10 stakeholders. You may want to have groups of students with the same stakeholder role get together and discuss their perspectives, or students may consider their roles individually. Emphasize to students that they "change hats" in Part B of the activity when they assume the role of a stakeholder. They are no longer part of the proposal team from Part A, and they have to look out for the interests of their new stakeholder role during the discussion and voting.

FOLLOW-UP

6 ◆ Before voting on the proposals, decide with students what kind of vote the class will participate in, such as a simple majority, two-thirds, or another type of margin needed to pass the plan. Also clarify what happens in the case of a tie, such as a run-off or revote. After the vote has determined which plan will be implemented, discuss the roles of the stakeholders in the decision-making process

---

4

3. Keeping the $2 million budget per year and the stakeholders' interests in mind, create a sustainability proposal for Jaffrey Lake. Your group's solution should include:

   • The Jaffrey City idea(s) you would adopt and the evidence from the previous activity that supports your choice.

   • Indicators that will measure the success of your proposal in the future.

   • A three-part explanation of the likely impact of your proposal:

     · Economic—explain what money will be spent, and when, in the next 5–10 years.

     · Environmental—predict what will happen to the phosphate and nitrate levels in Jaffrey Lake, and how any changes will affect the lake environment.

     · Social—explain how the community will be affected and predict which stakeholders will support your proposal.

4. Present your group's proposal to the class with the goal of convincing your classmates to choose your plan over the other proposals.

5. As a class, discuss the strengths and weaknesses of each proposal.

Part B: Voting for a Master Plan

5

6. Your teacher will assign you a role as one of the stakeholders. Cast your vote on which proposal should be implemented in Jaffrey Lake *as you believe the stakeholder would vote.*

6

7. Tally the votes of the stakeholders to see which proposal will become the Master Plan for Jaffrey Lake.

33

---

of Jaffrey City. Ask students, *If the Environmentalist alone made the decision on which proposal ideas to follow, how do you think the vote would have turned out?*

Students should realize that a group decision is often different than an individual's choice and that a scientist might have priorities other than those of many of the stakeholders. Other stakeholders might not like the environmentalist's priorities, which in this case are similar to those of an environmental scientist, because it did not account for their needs. Emphasize with students that solving sustainability problems, like the one facing Jaffrey City, involves balancing as much as possible the priorities of many and the economic realities of the community.

Jaffrey Lake Stakeholders

Jaffrey City resident

- Does not spend time at the lake or depend on it
- Doesn't want to pay more in taxes or fees
- Is concerned about industry discharging pollutants into the lake

SUPPORTED PROPOSAL IDEAS

Awareness Campaign, Phosphate and Nitrate Ban

OPPOSED PROPOSAL IDEAS

New Main Water-treatment Plant, Septic-tank Upgrades

Car-wash Owner

- Upgraded discharge system in the past five years and is still in debt for it
- Feels he has already done his part, and so the City needs to clean up the lake without raising his cost of doing business
- Does not want to be blamed for contamination problem in the lake

SUPPORTED PROPOSAL IDEAS

Awareness Campaign, Agricultural Incentives

OPPOSED PROPOSAL IDEAS

Phosphate and Nitrate Ban, New Main Water-treatment Plant

New East Housing Representative

- Spent a lot of money to put in a local sewage-treatment system
- Wants to continue to be steward of the lake
- Wants to maintain property values
- Cannot carry additional cost of new city treatment plant

SUPPORTED PROPOSAL IDEAS

Lakefront-protection Plan, Phosphate and Nitrate Ban, Awareness Campaign, Septic-tank Upgrades, Agricultural Incentives, Lake Research

OPPOSED PROPOSAL IDEAS

New Main Water-treatment Plant

Farmer

- Has always used fertilizer to grow strong crops
- Feels that his farming practice can improve with better technology
- Has applied to get some federal money to improve his farming but application is stalled
- More costs are likely to put the farm out of business

SUPPORTED PROPOSAL IDEAS

Lakefront-protection Plan

OPPOSED PROPOSAL IDEAS

Agricultural Incentive, Phosphate and Nitrate Ban, New Main Water-treatment Plant

35

Environmentalist

- Wants to act now before it is too late to restore the lake ecosystem
- Willing to spend whatever money it takes
- Wants stricter regulations and better enforcement for protecting the marsh area and wildlife

SUPPORTED PROPOSAL IDEAS

Lake Research, Lakefront Protection Plan, Agricultural Incentives, New Main Water-treatment Plant with phosphate and nitrate removal, Septic-tank Upgrades

OPPOSED PROPOSAL IDEAS

none

Fertilizer-plant Owner

- Pleased that demand continues to rise and business is doing very well
- Uses nitrate and phosphate sources that are reclaimed from nature when possible
- Interested in cheaper and quicker ways to reclaim material rich in nutrients from water
- Is aware that people think she is discharging into the lake and wants to convince them that her plant is clean

SUPPORTED PROPOSAL IDEAS

New Main Water-treatment Plant with phosphate and nitrate removal, Agricultural Incentives, Lake Research

OPPOSED PROPOSAL IDEAS

Phosphate and Nitrate Ban

Fisherman

- Fifth-generation fisherman and very proud of work
- Worried about the future of his profession since fish population has significantly declined
- Worried about the decline in cleanliness of the lake
- Has low profit and cannot pay additional fees or taxes

SUPPORTED PROPOSAL IDEAS

New Main Water-treatment Plant with phosphate removal, Lake Research

OPPOSED PROPOSAL IDEAS

Lakefront Protection Plan

City Councilor

- Wants to please as many stakeholders as possible so as to ensure re-election
- Needs a legal and fair solution
- Doesn't want to raise taxes or fees
- Doesn't want to put the city into debt

SUPPORTED PROPOSAL IDEAS

New Main Water-treatment Plant, Agricultural Incentives, Phosphate and Nitrate Ban, Awareness Campaign

OPPOSED PROPOSAL IDEAS

Lakefront Protection Plan

Land Developer

- Developed New East Housing area and wants to develop the marsh area
- Wants fewer regulations on building
- Has a history of being a responsible builder who is a good leader for businesses
- Wants cost of doing business to be as low as possible

SUPPORTED PROPOSAL IDEAS

Phosphate and Nitrate Ban, Awareness Campaign

OPPOSED PROPOSAL IDEAS

Lakefront Protection Plan

Wastewater Plant Manager

- Knows that wastewater can be completely cleaned, for a price and with proper equipment
- Wants clean water standards to be met
- Wants to upgrade the plant but doesn't have the money to do so
- Doesn't want liability for poor plant because City has thus far not supported improving it

SUPPORTED PROPOSAL IDEAS

New Main Water-treatment Plant with phosphate and nitrate removal, Septic-tank Upgrades, Lake Research

OPPOSED PROPOSAL IDEAS

Lakefront Protection Plan

7 Apply the EVIDENCE AND TRADE-OFFS (ET) Scoring Guide to students' written work for Analysis Question 1 to assess their growth. You may want to provide all students with an ET Scoring Guide, and ask them to keep it with their science notebooks, as they will refer to it several times in this unit and throughout the *Science and Global Issues* course. Explain to the class that you will use it to provide feedback on the quality of their work. Then discuss the specific expectations you have for their responses. Students' responses should identify the evidence that led to their decisions and the trade-offs they made while developing their plans.

8 Analysis Questions 6 and 7 are important because they help connect the issues of Jaffrey Lake to those faced by other countries and the global community.

SAMPLE RESPONSES

1. (ET ASSESSMENT) Answers will vary. Look for students' responses to identify their evidence as found in concentration levels from the previous activity.

Sample Level-3 Response

We proposed to build the New Main Water-treatment Plant with phosphate removal and to use the Agricultural Incentives. The evidence that was the most influential in making this decision was the phosphate levels at testing locations on the west side of the lake. The high levels were measured right where the old water-treatment plant and the storm drain empties into the lake, which means the phosphates are not being removed before going into Jaffrey Lake. Also, the high phosphate concentration near the West Side Park shows it is likely that there is a lot of runoff from the animals and fertilizers at the farm.

There is one major trade-off in our decision. We chose the most expensive option, building the New Main

Water-treatment Plant. This trade-off means we have to accept an increase in water rates for customers in exchange for an effective solution. We thought that the New Main Water-treatment Plant might not be approved because of the high cost compared to other proposals. We risk having stakeholders not vote for an expensive plan, but we think it is the best way to prevent future nutrient pollution in the lake.

2. a. Answers will vary. Students should refer to the descriptions of the Jaffrey Lake stakeholders and cite individual positions.

   b. Answers will vary. Students should refer to the descriptions of the Jaffrey Lake stakeholders and cite individual positions.

Analysis

7

1. Describe the Proposal Idea you voted for in Procedure Step 6 and state the major evidence that most influenced your choice. Then describe the trade-offs of the proposal. The trade-offs should include the social, economic, and environmental impacts on the community.

2. Which stakeholder is most likely to
   a. support your proposal?
   b. oppose your proposal?
   Explain why he or she would support or oppose your proposal.

3. Should each stakeholder's interests have equal weight in the City Council's decision? Why or why not?

4. What could the residents of Jaffrey City do if the indicators from the Master Plan showed the health of Jaffrey Lake had not improved five years after your Master Plan was implemented?

5. Assume that many residents of Jaffrey City were aware of the dangers of phosphate and nitrate in the lake. For many years, the community knew of the likely sources of the contaminants. What are some of the possible reasons action was not taken to improve the lake before now?

8

6. How do you think a local situation like the one at Jaffrey City might be similar and different from what might happen
   a. in other countries around the world?
   b. in a lake that shares boundaries with more than one country?

7. There are many places in the world where sewage receives minimal treatment or is discharged directly into the environment. This has an effect on the water, soil, and the health of the nearby population. In the statistics shown below, "basic sanitation" means those who live in a structure with a connection to a sewer, septic system, or improved pit latrines. Basic sanitation does not necessarily include removal of phosphates, nitrates, or other contaminants.

Basic Sanitation					
INDICATOR	USA	JAPAN	INDIA	BRAZIL	NIGERIA
Basic sanitation (% population)	100	100	72	50	33

   a. For the countries above that do not have basic sanitation, what are some of the economic, social, and environmental challenges to overcoming this sustainability problem?
   b. What ideas do you have that could help overcome these challenges?

39

Explanations to a and b should show students' understanding of the various perspectives of the stakeholders.

3. Answers will vary. Some students may support the idea that all stakeholder interests are weighed equally. However, others may see that each stakeholder makes different contributions to the city and that, in real life, they are often not weighed equally.

4. Answers will vary. Some students will suggest that more testing can be done, some may want to spend more money on a new Master Plan, and others may want to stop spending money on it all together. All of these things reflect what has happened in real communities when projects are planned.

5. Answers will vary. Perhaps Jaffrey City did not have the money to deal with the problem, perhaps a group of stakeholders blocked any efforts, or perhaps the leadership was not organized enough to find a solution. Again, this reflects what sometimes happens in real communities that are facing serious sustainability problems.

6. a. The Jaffrey City problem is similar to the issues in other countries because it has to do with water quality, which is an issue around the world. The decision-making process is also similar in that there are many kinds of stakeholders in any country that need to work together to solve problems. It is different in that each country has its own environmental, political, and economic situations.

   b. It would be similar in that there would be various interests and stakeholders, but different in that there would be more than one government. Since it is harder to work together across borders (as shown in Activity 2), the cleanup process would be more challenging.

---

8. How do you think each of the following are involved in sustainable decision-making:
   a. science and technology
   b. individuals
   c. government

9. Identify a problem(s) in your own community that relates to the sustainability of the environment. Then identify what scientific knowledge would be needed for developing a plan to improve the situation.

KEY VOCABULARY

evidence	sustainability
indicator	**trade-off**
stakeholder	

---

7. a. Some of the challenges with this issue are: lack of infrastructure, limited allocated money, and political and cultural challenges.

   b. Some ideas might be: improved awareness, more funding for the problem, more understanding of local cultures, and a global discussion about improving water quality.

8. a. Scientists can provide better understanding of the effects of human activity on the ecosystem, which would be helpful in making decisions. The development of cheap and accessible technologies can help get solutions to communities.

   b. Individuals can contribute by reducing their own impact on the environment, and by encouraging groups to discuss and make sustainable decisions.

c. Government plays an important role in sustainable decision-making because policy has the potential to have a large impact. Responsible governing needs to take into account the sustainability of decisions made for large groups of people.

9. Answers will vary, but common issues relate to water quality, ecosystem loss and degradation, land use, and urbanization.

REVIST THE CHALLENGE

Students may have found that it is difficult to please all the stakeholders who are affected by public decisions. However, seeking input from all stakeholders often increases the chances for a decision that is at least satisfactory to most people.

SAMPLE STUDENT RESPONSE: Procedure Step 3

Sample Level-3 Response

(CS, ET ASSESSMENT) Our proposal is to build the New Main Water-treatment Plant with phosphate-removal and to implement the Agricultural Incentives. We chose these options because they address the two largest sources of contamination in Jaffrey Lake: sewage and agricultural runoff. This is based on the water testing evidence that showed the highest levels of nitrate and phosphate at the water treatment plant and just downhill of the farmland. The other proposals might be worthy, but these two will have the most effect right at the source. We did not choose the nitrogen-removal component because it is not shown to be completely effective.

Economic Prediction

The treatment plant will cost $8 million, but increased water rates will cover $2 million of that cost. The remaining $6 million cost for nutrient removal and the agricultural incentives will be spread out over three additional years. Our five-year budget is shown in the following table.

Year(s)	Project	Money spent
1-3	New Main Water-treatment Plant	$6 million
4	New Main Water-treatment Plant Addition: phosphate removal	$2 million
5	Agricultural Incentives	$2 million

Although the cost of the plant is one of the higher-priced Proposal Ideas, the cost-benefit of this plan is high. Namely, there will be money saved on future cleanups.

Environmental Prediction

We predict that this proposal will be very effective in reducing the phosphate level in the lake, thus slowing the eutrophication of Jaffrey Lake. This is because the biggest sources will be reduced and so the levels of contaminants will have to get smaller. We predict there will be more fish and plants and a healthier ecosystem as a result of this plan.

Social Prediction

This proposal will clean up the lake, which will improve the quality of life for everyone in the community. Although this proposal may not be popular with residents of Jaffrey City or farmers who will pay higher water rates, it will be socially unacceptable for the residents if people are not able to use the lake because it is contaminated. There are many stakeholders who will support it, like the environmentalists, the fishermen, and the City Councilors, and so we think they will convince others. The farmers may also not like the Agricultural Incentive plan because it imposes more rules and requirements. So although our proposal may not have really popular ideas like the Awareness Campaign, we think that people will realize that this plan does the most for reducing the nutrient level in the lake.

We propose that the indicators to be measured are phosphate levels, nitrate levels, and amount of algae. Testing will only be done occasionally because there is no money in the budget for more.

Unit Review: Sustainability

Sustainability

A community is sustainable if it meets its present needs without compromising the ability of future communities to meet their own needs. Sustainability problems have adverse environmental, economical, and social impacts on communities. The consequences of unsustainable practices affect us at all levels—individually, locally, and globally.

To evaluate the sustainability of a human activity scientists identify the kinds of data that indicate problems or absence of problems. Some of these indicators reveal information on the quality of life in relation to natural resources consumption in a community. Measured nutrient levels in lake water, for example, identify contaminants that are having an effect on water quality and the ecosystem.

KEY VOCABULARY

sustainability

indicator

Natural Resources

One of the challenges for our global community is to agree on ways to sustain our planet's finite natural resources and, where necessary, to change the way we now live. Human activities that severely degrade land and water quality are usually a result of international, national, local, or individual choices. A community's policies can encourage or mandate individuals and industries to alter their practices to prevent further abuse of resources.

One tool for estimating an individual's role in the depletion of resources is the ecological footprint calculator. This is a computer model that estimates the area of the earth that is required to sustain an activity. An ecological footprint calculator helps an individual voluntarily take action to reduce his or her own ecological impact. Another way to analyze the environmental impact of daily life is to outline the life cycles of the products we each use. The product life cycle describes the resources and energy involved in making the product, the length of its usefulness, the environmental impact of the product, and how it is disposed of, recycled, or reclaimed when it is no longer useful.

KEY VOCABULARY	
ecological footprint	land degradation
eutrophication	product life cycle

Making sustainable decisions

Successful decision-making takes into account evidence and the interests of all stakeholders. Solutions to sustainability challenges are technologically, environmentally, economically, and socially viable. However, a community often must accept some trade-offs when seeking a sustainable response to a community problem.

KEY VOCABULARY	
evidence	stakeholder
trade-off	

Inquiry and the Nature of Science

Collecting and analyzing relevant data allows scientists to identify relationships between human activity and the resulting ecological, environmental and social impacts. Further research can determine if there is a causal relationship between two correlated events.

Models are useful for representing complex environmental phenomena. Information from models, and other types of evidence, inform decision-making that affects sustainability.

KEY VOCABULARY
correlation
causal relationship

Ecology: Living on Earth

REMINDER

Order live materials for Activities 2 and 6, following the instructions in your materials kit. Leave ample time for specimen delivery.

OUR WORLD HOLDS an amazing variety of organisms living in all sorts of environments. Organisms affect their environments, and in turn the environment affects them. Understanding the complex web of relationships within ecosystems is essential to understanding their sustainability.

Humans interact with ecosystems in many ways. We rely on ecosystems to supply us food, shelter, energy, and the oxygen we breathe. As we consume resources and discard our wastes, however, we change ecosystems and sometimes threaten their sustainability.

In this unit you will examine a variety of ecological issues including the impact of human activities on ecosystems. You will see what can happen when people cause pollution in an area vital to nonhuman and human organisms. You will learn about invasive species and their impacts on established ecosystems. You will also investigate how different management strategies affect the sustainability of fisheries. Finally, you will suggest actions humans can take to help sustain ecosystems for the future.

44

1 Ecosystems and Change

TALK IT OVER • 2–3 CLASS SESSIONS

OVERVIEW

In this activity, students examine case studies that describe the impacts of various kinds of changes on four ecosystems. Students are asked to predict what will happen to these ecosystems in 50 years if the situations continue as described. The concepts of ecosystem sustainability, resiliency, and biodiversity are introduced.

KEY CONTENT

1. Ecosystems involve interactions between communities of living things and those living things with their physical environment.

2. Ecological changes can stress ecosystems in many ways. When the ecosystem is able to recover from or accommodate stress it is demonstrating resiliency.

3. Biodiversity is related to the number of species in an ecosystem.

4. Increasing biodiversity (e.g., by adding an invasive species) does not necessarily increase the sustainability of an ecosystem.

5. Reducing biodiversity, especially reducing native species, can make an ecosystem less sustainable.

KEY PROCESS SKILLS

1. Students make accurate interpretations, inferences, and conclusions from the text.

2. Students make predictions.

MATERIALS AND ADVANCE PREPARATION

Because many activities in this unit require the teacher to use an overhead or data projector, make sure that one is always available.

For the teacher
Scoring Guide: GROUP INTERACTION (GI)

Group Interaction Student Sheet 1, "Evaluating Group Interaction"

Literacy Transparency 3, "Read, Think, and Take Note"

transparency of Literacy Student Sheet 5, "KWL"

transparency of a short newspaper article on any topic*

For each student
3 sticky notes*

Student Sheet 1.1, "Case Study Comparison"

Literacy Transparency 3, "Read, Think, and Take Note" (optional)

Scoring Guide: GROUP INTERACTION (GI) (optional)

Group Interaction Student Sheet 1, "Evaluating Group Interaction" (optional)

Not supplied in kit

Masters for Science Skills Student Sheets are in Teacher Resources II: Diverse Learners. Masters for Literacy Skills Sheets are in Teacher Resources III: Literacy. Masters for Scoring Guides are in Teacher Resources IV: Assessment.

TEACHING SUMMARY

Getting Started

- Students share their ideas about ways in which they think ecosystems change.

Doing the Activity

- (LITERACY) (GI ASSESSMENT) Introduce the GROUP INTERACTION (GI) Scoring Guide.

- (LITERACY) Each student in a group of four is assigned to read a case study.

- Students summarize their case studies for members of their group.

- Groups record the similarities and differences between the four case studies.

- Groups predict what might happen in each case study 50 years from now.

Follow-up

- The class discusses the environmental, economic, and social aspects of sustainability and how these are related to biodiversity and resiliency of ecosystems.

BACKGROUND INFORMATION

One of the main reasons to study ecology is to develop an understanding of how natural systems work. It is important to do so not only to satisfy human curiosity, but because of the unique nature of man's impact on the environment. Human decisions affect ecosystems directly and indirectly, in large and small ways, and in the long- and short-term. A solid understanding of ecology forms a basis for informed decisions and accurate predictions of responses to environmental change.

Ecosystems are always subject to stress. Sometimes an ecosystem can react to the stress in such a way as to maintain the status quo. Different factors provide resistance to stress on an ecosystem. For example, an invasive species might not be successful in an ecosystem where there is a species that preys heavily on it. Other times, a stressor can cause a series of gradual changes that eventually alter the entire nature of the ecosystem (see Activity 17, "Ecosystem Change and Resiliency"). However, on occasions the stress is so severe that an ecosystem cannot recover. In such cases the effects of the stress exceed the resiliency of the ecosystem, and the impact is permanent and negative. Such changes can be quick and dramatic, as with a chemical spill, or slow as with climate change. Although the causes of severe stress may be natural— for example, volcanic eruptions, in many instances they are the result of human activity.

While there is not a straightforward linear relationship between biodiversity and sustainability, the sustainability of an ecosystem is reduced when the number of species in it falls below a critical point. Consequently, the level of biodiversity is often a useful indicator of the degree of sustainability of an ecosystem. Note, however, that the introduction of invasive species can increase the biodiversity of an ecosystem while reducing the sustainability.

GETTING STARTED

1 ◆ This symbol represents an opportunity to elicit students' experiences or ideas so that the subsequent instruction can build on or modify their understanding. Sometimes you will uncover ideas that are inconsistent with scientific explanations but may seem logical in the everyday world. The Teaching Suggestions often provide strategies that you can use to address these misconceptions.

As a class, begin a KWL chart for ecological change. The letters KWL refer to the three sections of the reading strategy that ask, "What do I **K**now? What do I **W**ant to Know? What did I **L**earn?" KWLs help students process and apply the information that they encounter in the reading. For more information on this strategy, refer to Teacher Resources III: Literacy. Ask the class to list changes that they have seen in the environment as they have grown up, what they think has caused those changes, and what they want to know about ecological change and its causes. There is a sample KWL shown below. Students will fill in the third column in Activities 3 and 7.

Consider showing a video clip or images that illustrate environmental change in your locality, if possible. For suggestions go to the *Science and Global Issues* page of the SEPUP website *(sepuplhs.org/sgi)*. Introduce the term ecosystem. Have the class brainstorm the types of changes that could affect an ecosystem and in what ways. Pose the open question, *Is ecological change good or bad—or neither?*

Accept all answers, but each time ask students to include supporting examples. There is no correct answer to the question, but it may stimulate thought and illustrate students' grasp of environmental issues. Explain to the class that they are going to read about how human activities and interventions have affected (and are still affecting) four different ecosystems.

---

1 Ecosystems and Change

ECOLOGY is the study of how organisms interact with one another and the environment. With an understanding of ecology, people can make informed decisions about environmental issues. Take, for example, a gardener who is considering how to deal with an insect that is destroying her tomatoes. To apply an insecticide she would need to know how that chemical would affect other organisms in the yard and what would happen if the insecticide got into the water or the soil.

A community of various organisms interacting with each other within a particular physical environment is known as an **ecosystem.** Ecosystems are constantly changing—sometimes in gradual and hardly noticeable ways and sometimes rapidly and dramatically. Change that occurs in one part of an ecosystem will affect other parts of the ecosystem. One of the most critical aspects of any change that occurs in an ecosystem is how it affects the ecosystem's **sustainability.** An ecosystem is **sustainable** if it can support its diversity and ecological processes through time.

Challenge

▶ How does change affect ecosystems?

Wildlife and humans live together in many ecosystems.

Ecological Change KWL

Know	Want to know	Learned
• Humans have changed the environment (cut down rain forests, built buildings, paved roads). • Natural phenomena have changed the environment (volcanoes, earthquakes, tsunamis). • Habitat restoration projects can help restore the environment.	• How much of the environment have people changed? • What can be done to restore the environment? • What happens if we don't restore the environment? • How much does the burning of fossil fuels change the environment?	

DOING THE ACTIVITY

2 (LITERACY) (GI ASSESSMENT)
Introduce the GROUP INTERACTION (GI) Scoring Guide. Discuss with the class your expectations for group work, and review Group Interaction Student Sheet 1, "Evaluating Group Interaction." More information on the SEPUP assessment system is in Teacher Resources IV: Assessment. If your students worked through the "Sustainability" unit, they will be familiar with the use of science notebooks in this course. If not, explain that as they conduct activities, they will record data, observations, hypotheses, conclusions, and thoughts in their notebooks. Keeping a science notebook helps students track data, note questions as they arise in investigations and discussion, and build science-writing skills. Decide how you would like students to record their work in each of the activities in this unit. For recommendations and more information on science notebooks, see Teacher Resources III: Literacy.

3 Use a jigsaw to form groups of four students. A jigsaw has students split into groups to learn about a specific topic, in this instance to read a case study. Then they return to their regular groups of four and teach each other what they have just learned. Explain that there are four case studies in this activity and that it is important for all students to be familiar with all four. However, each student in a group will take responsibility for one of the case studies—reading it with a student from another group, and reporting on the case to his or her own group members. Allow a couple of minutes for groups to decide (or assign, if necessary) which case study each student in a group will read.

---

a

b

Some examples of the diverse ecosystems found on the earth include islands and atolls (a) and hot springs (b).

MATERIALS

FOR EACH STUDENT
3   sticky notes
Student Sheet 1.1, "Case Study Comparison"

Procedure

2 1. In your group, assign one student to each case study in this activity.

3 2. Following your teacher's directions, partner with someone from another group who is reading the same case study.

4 3. You and your partner will silently read your assigned case study. As you read, use the "Read, Think, and Take Note" strategy. To do this:

  • Stop at least three times during the reading to mark on a sticky note your thoughts and questions about the reading. Use the list of guidelines below to start your thinking.

Read, Think, and Take Note: Guidelines

As you read, from time to time, write one of the following on a sticky note:

• Explain a thought or reaction to something you read.

• Note something in the reading that is confusing or unfamiliar.

• List a word that you do not know.

• Describe a connection to something you learned or read previously.

• Make a statement about the reading.

• Pose a question about the reading.

• Draw a diagram or picture of an idea or connection.

46

---

4 (LITERACY) All of the readings in this course provide an opportunity to improve students' reading ability and comprehension through various strategies. Model the strategy "Read, Think, and Take Note" for students as you read a newspaper article. "Read, Think, and Take Note" is an opportunity for students to record thoughts, reactions, or questions on sticky notes as they read. The notes serve to make concrete the thoughts arising in their minds and then serve as prompts to generate conversation or write explanations. Throughout this unit and the rest of *Science and Global Issues* you will see multiple opportunities for students to employ and become comfortable with this strategy. Explain to students that through these literacy strategies they are learning the ways in which proficient readers think while reading. Display the guidelines shown on Literacy Transparency 3, "Read, Think, and Take Note," in your classroom for students to refer to. Look for additional occasions for students to apply this strategy when reading text. For more information on "Read, Think, and Take Note," see Teacher Resources III: Literacy.

Pair up students from different groups who are reading the same case study. Give each pair sufficient time to read their assigned case study, while applying the "Read, Think, and Take Note" literacy strategy. After students have finished reading, have them compare sticky notes, discuss what they wrote, and answer each other's questions if they are able to. Then, pass out Student Sheet 1.1, "Case Study Comparison," and ask students to complete the appropriate column. Ask each pair of students to make a diagram that shows the changes and the effects of the changes that were described in the case study. Although there is no right or wrong way to draw such a diagram, it may help to show one or two examples of possible diagrams to the class.

SAMPLE CAUSE-AND-EFFECT DIAGRAM FOR CASE STUDY 1

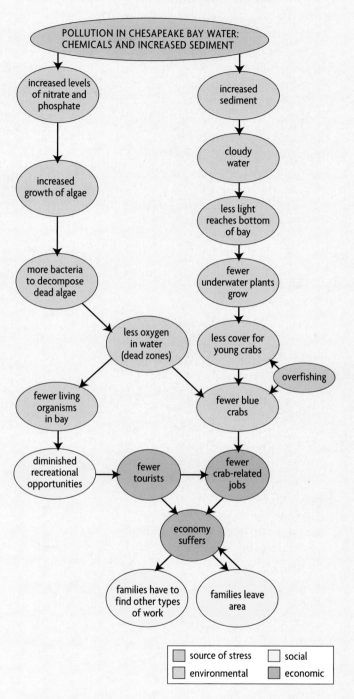

5 Have students return to their original groups, and allow sufficient time for them to each briefly summarize their assigned case study for their other group members. Students should refer to their cause-and-effect diagrams to help with their summaries. After hearing each summary, all group members should have the opportunity to ask clarifying questions and then complete the column on Student Sheet 1.1 for that case. A sample of this sheet appears at the end of this activity.

FOLLOW-UP

6 Use the discussions of the case studies, predictions from Procedure Step 9, and the Analysis Questions to help students understand that change can affect ecosystems in many different ways. With input from the class, develop a list of types of changes that can affect an ecosystem. Make sure that the list includes, or can be grouped into, sudden or gradual change, large- or small-scale change, single- or multi-source causation, and natural or human causation. Illustrate each of these changes with examples from the case studies and other sources.

7 To help students understand the concepts of combined stresses as part of the answer to Analysis Question 3 consider presenting the analogy of an ill person. A particular disease may be acute or chronic, and both types can be equally serious but manifest themselves differently. Sometimes when a person is sick a secondary infection can have devastating consequences. This is similar to the effects of the combined stresses that are present in the coral reef and Chesapeake Bay situations.

- After writing a thought or question on a sticky note, place it next to the word, phrase, sentence, or paragraph in the reading that prompted your note.

4. Discuss with your partner the thoughts and questions you had while reading.

5. Discuss with your partner the causes of ecosystem changes in your study, and each fill in the column on your case study on Student Sheet 1.1, "Case Study Comparison."

6. Follow your teacher's directions to complete a diagram that shows the connections between the events described in the case study you read.

5 7. Return to your original group and summarize for the other members of your group what you have learned from the case study. Show the diagram you drew and Student Sheet 1.1, "Case Study Comparison," to help you with your summary.

8. Use the information provided by your group to complete the remaining columns on Student Sheet 1.1, "Case Study Comparison."

9. For each of the case studies, develop a prediction of what might happen in 50 years if nothing is done to further influence the situation described. Write your prediction in your science notebook. Include the reasoning behind your prediction.

6 10. Follow your teacher's directions in sharing your prediction with the rest of the class.

Analysis

1. For each case study, write one to three sentences that summarize the changes that occurred in each ecosystem.

2. Group the causes of the changes you listed in Question 1 as "naturally occurring" or "human-caused."

7 3. According to the information the case studies provide, what types of changes seem to make an ecosystem less sustainable? Explain your answer.

4. Use the predictions that were developed in Procedure Step 9 to infer how the diversity of organisms might change over the next 50 years in the locations described in each case study. Explain your answer.

8
KEY VOCABULARY	
ecology	sustainability
ecosystem	sustainable

47

8 This box lists the key vocabulary developed in this activity. When words are formally defined in an activity, they appear in bold type in the list. Encourage students to include these words when answering the Analysis Questions. Also, during informal and formal discussions listen for these words and see if students are applying them correctly. Decide how you will support students' understanding of the vocabulary—perhaps with a student glossary, or setting up a class word wall. For more suggestions on ways to develop students' understanding of and proficiency with scientific vocabulary, see the Vocabulary section of Teacher Resource III: Literacy.

SAMPLE RESPONSES

1. **Case Study 1: The Crab Jubilee**
   Increased crab harvesting along with pollution have decreased the blue crab population in Chesapeake Bay. This decrease has caused job losses in traditional industries, such as crab fishing, and economic hardship.

SCIENCE & GLOBAL ISSUES/BIOLOGY • ECOLOGY

CASE STUDY 1

The Crab Jubilee

IMAGINE WALKING ALONG the Chesapeake Bay shoreline in Maryland or Virginia and looking for crabs to catch. To your surprise you come across hundreds, maybe thousands, of crabs crowded together in shallow water and on the shore.

You will eat well tonight! Locals call this a "crab jubilee," and it is an event that people have witnessed many times in the past. Probably Native Americans saw this phenomenon thousands of years ago. As the human population of the region has increased, so has the frequency of the "crab jubilees." This may sound good if you like to eat crab, but in fact, it is a sign of problems in Chesapeake Bay.

The name Chesapeake is derived from a Native American word meaning "great shellfish bay," and shellfish have always been an important food source for the people in the area. The blue crab (*Callinectes sapidus*) has been harvested commercially in the bay

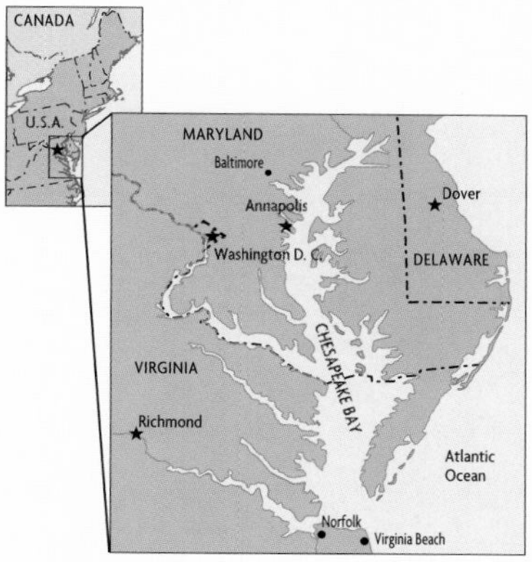

A "crab jubilee" on the shore of Chesapeake Bay

48

since the mid-1800s. Over the years more and more crabs have been harvested, with 1993 having a record catch—347 million crabs worth $107 million. Since that time, however, the number of crabs harvested has declined. In 2007 the number had dropped to 132 million, with a value of $52 million. In 1999, more than 11,000 people in the area had crab-related jobs, but in 2006, fewer than 7,000 were involved in the crab industry. The effect on the regional economy was so severe that in 2008 the U.S. Department of Commerce declared a commercial fishery failure.

One of the factors thought to have contributed to the failure of the blue crab fisheries is overfishing. To keep the crab populations stable a certain minimum number of egg-producing crabs must survive each year. Scientists have estimated that the crab population would not decline as long as the number of crabs harvested each year did not exceed 46% of the total crab population. However, over the past decade it is estimated that an average of 62% of all of the blue crabs in the bay were caught each year.

The other problem is pollution of the bay's waters from chemicals and sediment that have washed into the bay from such sources as farms, sewage treatment plants, suburban lawns, and golf courses. Nitrogen- and phosphorus-containing chemicals from these sources have increased the growth of algae in the bay. The algae and the sediment make the waters

cloudy enough to limit the amount of sunlight that reaches the bottom and to impede the growth of underwater plants. Eelgrass, in particular, is crucial to crab populations because tiny crab larvae blend in with the grass and are less visible to predators. Without the grass fewer of the young crabs reach maturity.

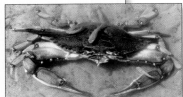

Blue crab (Callinectes sapidus)

When the algae die they fall to the bottom of the bay. As bacteria decompose the dead algae, they remove much of the oxygen from the water. These oxygen-deprived areas cannot support life, and organisms that cannot move elsewhere die, creating dead zones. Crabs moving out of the dead zones may end up in great numbers on land where the oxygen levels are higher. This is the reason for the "crab jubilees." Although dead zones can develop as the result of natural phenomena, such as changes in ocean current patterns, scientists believe that dead zones indicate that human activities are increasing the frequency of "crab jubilees," and are ultimately affecting the sustainability of the crab population. ■

49

Case Study 2:

The March of the Toads

Once introduced into Australia, cane toads quickly acclimated to various environments and spread rapidly. In some cases the increase in cane toad populations has decreased the populations of native animals significantly.

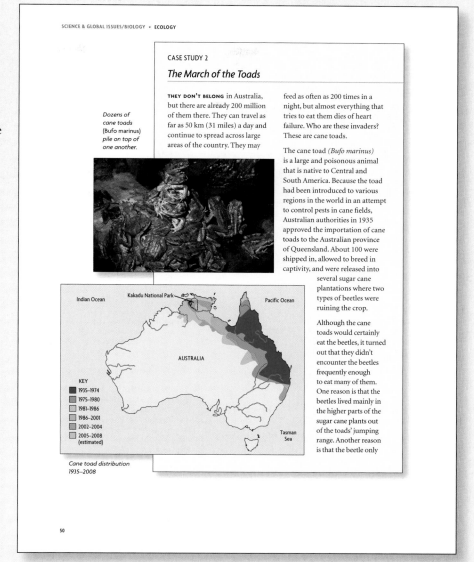

SCIENCE & GLOBAL ISSUES/BIOLOGY • ECOLOGY

CASE STUDY 2

The March of the Toads

Dozens of cane toads (Bufo marinus) pile on top of one another.

THEY DON'T BELONG in Australia, but there are already 200 million of them there. They can travel as far as 50 km (31 miles) a day and continue to spread across large areas of the country. They may feed as often as 200 times in a night, but almost everything that tries to eat them dies of heart failure. Who are these invaders? These are cane toads.

The cane toad *(Bufo marinus)* is a large and poisonous animal that is native to Central and South America. Because the toad had been introduced to various regions in the world in an attempt to control pests in cane fields, Australian authorities in 1935 approved the importation of cane toads to the Australian province of Queensland. About 100 were shipped in, allowed to breed in captivity, and were released into several sugar cane plantations where two types of beetles were ruining the crop.

Although the cane toads would certainly eat the beetles, it turned out that they didn't encounter the beetles frequently enough to eat many of them. One reason is that the beetles lived mainly in the higher parts of the sugar cane plants out of the toads' jumping range. Another reason is that the beetle only

Indian Ocean

Kakadu National Park

Pacific Ocean

AUSTRALIA

KEY
- 1935–1974
- 1975–1980
- 1981–1986
- 1986–2001
- 2002–2004
- 2005–2008 (estimated)

Tasman Sea

Cane toad distribution 1935–2008

50

invaded the sugar cane fields at the time of year when the cane toads didn't go there because of the lack of protective plant cover. In addition, the beetles were most active during the day, but the cane toads fed mainly at night. The toads didn't go hungry though, as they ate pretty much anything that would fit into their mouths—including insects, frogs, small reptiles, mammals, and birds—eventually diminishing the biodiversity of the areas they were invading.

A female cane toad can produce around 35,000 eggs every time she mates, which can happen several times a year. They lay their eggs in almost any body of water, large or small, fresh or salt. Because cane toads can survive in a wide range of conditions, they adjusted well to the environment in Queensland and began to spread to other parts of Australia. Australia has no natural predator that can control the cane toad populations, but the cane toad has made its mark on populations of many other animals. The cane toad adult has poison glands in its skin, and the tadpoles are highly toxic to most animals. Most of the Australian predators that eat them die of heart failure. Even crocodiles are not immune, and since 2005, after cane toads invaded the Victoria River district of Australia's Northern Territory, there has been a 77% decline in the freshwater crocodile population.

Also, where cane toads are present, local populations of northern quoll have disappeared. Rabbit-sized marsupials that eat a wide variety of prey, quoll often die from eating cane toads. The population of northern quoll is particularly vulnerable to extinction because the males die after mating when they are one year old. When this natural loss is accelerated by the losses caused by the cane toads, quoll populations quickly become unsustainable.

Cane toads are causing yet other problems. They are suspected in reducing the numbers of animals that aboriginal bushmen traditionally rely on as food sources. The toads are known to eat pet food and feces, the latter leading them to carry diseases, such as salmonella. In 2001 the cane toads reached the carefully conserved Kakadu National Park, raising fears that the toads will disturb the delicate balance of species in the park and reduce its biodiversity. Local economies may be affected if tourism suffers as a result of changes to the park. ■

Northern quoll (Dasyurus hallucatus) (left) often die from eating poisonous cane toads. This crocodile (below) will likely die from the poison in the cane toad it is eating.

Case Study 3:

The Bleaching of the Reefs

Coral reefs, which are home to millions of organisms, have been damaged by unsustainable fishing practices and by changes in the oceans. Higher water temperatures in particular have caused bleaching of large areas of coral reefs.

CASE STUDY 3

The Bleaching of the Reefs

CORAL REEFS OCCUPY a small fraction, about 0.2%, of the earth's ocean floor. Yet it is estimated that 25% of all marine organisms live in or around coral reefs and that nearly one million different species can be found there. Coral reefs support fishing and provide building materials for local communities. They also act as natural breakwaters, protecting coastal areas. They have great potential in providing ingredients for new medicines and are a major attraction for tourists. These benefits, however, also mean that coral reefs around the world are under threat.

Coral reefs are made up of millions of small animals called polyps. Polyps are invertebrates that flourish in warm and shallow parts of oceans. These tiny animals rely on even smaller organisms—algae—for their survival. These algae are single-celled, photosynthesize in the presence of sunlight, and live in the tissues of the polyps. Most polyps themselves live inside a hard external framework that they have made from minerals in the seawater. Large colonies of polyps and their limestone skeletons form the coral reefs, some of which are so large that they can be seen from space.

Scientists estimate that in the past 50 years more than a quarter of the world's reefs have been destroyed. Today there are no signs that this

Coral reef with
a diversity of fish

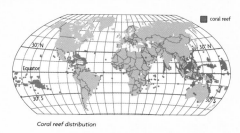

Coral reef distribution

destruction is slowing down. One source of coral reef damage is human-generated—in the form of unsustainable and illegal fishing practices, such as when fishermen drop dynamite onto the reefs to help them kill and catch fish.

Fishing can also harm coral indirectly. For example, it plays a role in increasing populations of the coral-eating sea star called the crown of thorns. Normally the number of sea stars living in a reef is low, as several species of reef organisms prey on the young sea stars. However, when too many of these predators are caught by fishermen, many more sea stars survive to become adults and eat up much more of the reef—up to 90% in some cases.

Another major threat to coral reefs is climate change, which is a global problem. Coral reefs are sensitive to changes in ocean temperatures, and many are in areas where the temperature is already close to the upper limit in which a reef can survive. A water temperature increase of as little as 1°C can decrease the ability of the coral algae to photosynthesize. It can sometimes cause the polyps to expel the algae. In both situations the coral loses its color and looks "bleached" or white, indicating that it is under stress.

Warmer ocean temperatures also favor the growth of bacteria that cause diseases in the coral reefs. Compounding those problems, the increase of carbon dioxide gas in the atmosphere is making the world's

oceans more acidic. This reduces the concentration of some of the chemicals that the polyps use to build the limestone skeletons and further weakens the coral reefs.

In 1997 and 1998, coral reefs all over the world suffered extensive bleaching. More than 50% of the Great Barrier Reef in Australia was affected and at least 50% of the reefs in Palau in the South Pacific were killed. The following year tourism in Palau was down 10%. Coral reefs hold the largest biodiversity in the oceans and are estimated to contribute more than $20 billion to local economies around the world. All ecosystems, fortunately, have a certain level of resiliency, and, provided the tipping point isn't reached, change does not always have to have permanent negative effects. Should the ocean temperature go back down, some of the coral might recover. However, to reverse the ocean warming will require tremendous human effort, and it will be expensive. Can the world, however, afford to continue losing its coral reefs and the biodiversity within them? ■

Crown of thorns (Acanthaster planci) sea stars (top) can severely damage coral reefs.

This coral (above) has "bleached," likely due to fluctuation in water temperature.

Case Study 4:

The Yellowstone Fires of 1988

The 1988 fires, natural and human-caused, affected large areas of Yellowstone National Park. Although many plants were burned and a number of animals were killed, the area has recovered. Beneficial effects of the fire included allowing certain seeds to germinate, enriching the soil, and creating space for new plants to grow.

2. See the sample chart below. Students may list other changes, some of which they might consider natural. For example, they may suggest that the impact of the crown of thorns sea star on coral reefs is natural since the reef is a natural food source for the crown of thorns. Acknowledge that this, and other changes they suggest, might be natural but that the problems described in the case study occur when humans disrupt the balance of these natural relationships. For example, humans are the cause of the overfishing of sea star predators, which leads to an overabundance in the number of sea stars. The presence of more sea stars results in larger areas of a reef being consumed.

SCIENCE & GLOBAL ISSUES/BIOLOGY • ECOLOGY

CASE STUDY 4

The Yellowstone Fires of 1988

Fires sweep through Yellowstone in 1988.

OVER SEVERAL DAYS in August 1988, many towns close to Yellowstone National Park experienced smoke so thick that drivers had to turn on their headlights in the middle of the day. People were advised to stay indoors to avoid breathing the smoke-filled air. Some communities in and around the park were temporarily evacuated as the worst fires ever recorded in Yellowstone burned out of control. By the fall of 1988, more than

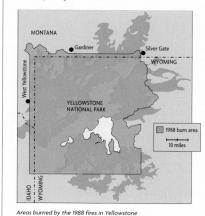

Areas burned by the 1988 fires in Yellowstone

54

Sample Student Response to Analysis Question 2

Natural	Human-caused
• lightning-caused fires	• fires
	• introduction of cane toads
	• coral reef damage caused by certain fishing practices and changes to the oceans
	• pollution in Chesapeake Bay
	• overfishing of blue crabs

3. The changes that were caused by humans seem to have had the most severe negative effects and would therefore make an ecosystem less sustainable. Sometimes the change was rapid, such as the introduction of cane toads. Other times the change was more gradual but the negative effects were greater. In two of the four case studies, the sustainability of the ecosystems was lowered due to a combination of changes (fishing practices and changes in the oceans for coral reefs, pollution and overfishing in Chesapeake Bay).

4. Exact answers will vary, depending on students' predictions. The biodiversity, however, will likely decrease in all of the situations except Yellowstone. In case studies 1, 2, and 3 both the number and types of organisms are decreasing. Specifically, the cane toad study mentions local extinctions of the northern quoll and large reductions in the number of freshwater crocodiles. The reef article describes large reductions in the sizes of coral reefs and mentions the vast number of species that are typically found near and in reefs. Some, perhaps many, of these species would decline as the reefs decline. The crab article notes the decrease in eelgrass as well as the blue crabs, and it refers to dead zones where nothing lives.

REVISIT THE CHALLENGE

The sustainability of an ecosystem is influenced by humans' environmental, economic, and social considerations. Ecosystems may gradually or suddenly undergo permanent change, or they may exhibit resiliency by responding in a way that minimizes the change. Sustainability is threatened when the damage is greater than the resiliency of the ecosystem. There seems to be a biodiversity threshold in an ecosystem below which the likelihood of recovery from adverse change is highly diminished.

Ask students to describe changes they may have seen or heard about in an ecosystem. To help prompt a class discussion consider having several resources available, such as relevant newspaper, magazine, and online articles. (*National Geographic* is a good place to start.) Alternatively, you might ask students to find and present relevant articles.

Finally, remind students that this is an introductory activity and that they will explore each concept further as they progress through the unit.

25,000 firefighters had worked on controlling the fires and over one third of Yellowstone National Park had burned.

Yet at the start of the summer of that year there were few indications of the scale of what was to come. The previous six summers and the spring of 1988 had all been wetter than normal, and fire activity had been low. The lack of fire had led to a buildup of old trees and underbrush in the forests of Yellowstone. This was fuel that was ready to burn if the conditions were right. The summer of 1988 turned out to be the driest in the park's history. By the middle of July, 8,500 acres of the area had burned.

Within two weeks the area affected by fire had increased by a factor of 10 and on August 20 winds of about 130 km/h (80 mph) helped to double the size of the fires in a single day. Lightning caused most of the fires, but humans caused three of the largest. The first snows in September significantly dampened the fires, and they were all extinguished before winter arrived. Concern was expressed across the country about the impacts of the fires on wildlife, vegetation, tourism, and local economies. There was much discussion about whether the fires should have been put out earlier when they were still small.

Nearly all of Yellowstone's plant communities have burned at some time in the past. Scientists think that fires in Yellowstone naturally burn at intervals varying from 20 to 300 years, depending on the location and type of vegetation. While fire can be a destructive force, it also stimulates growth in the park. Soil receives nutrients from burned plant materials, and when forests burn, more sunlight reaches the ground. Both of these processes help plants to grow. Studying the Yellowstone fires and other fires has provided scientists with evidence that allowing periodic fires, instead of always preventing them, can benefit ecosystems. Periodic fires both prevent the build up of woody debris that can make fires much larger and stimulates growth in the forest.

Over hundreds of years the burned areas will progress through a variety of stages as they recover.

(Continued on next page)

This area is beginning to recover after the Yellowstone fires.

55

(Continued from previous page)

This process is called succession. Wildflowers, grasses, and sagebrush may be the first to grow, but soon aspen trees will begin to sprout. Aspen has a thin bark and burns readily in a fire. But while the part of the tree aboveground is damaged or destroyed, the extensive underground network of roots is protected from the heat of the flames by the soil, so it isn't long after the fire is out before shoots begin to grow. Unlike the aspen, Douglas fir trees have very thick bark that insulates most of the tree from the heat. Such trees are very resilient and can often survive fires. Lodgepole pine, which makes up 80% of the forests of Yellowstone, has thin bark and the trees burn readily in fires, but it also benefits from fire. This tree produces cones that are glued shut by resin. Only the heat of a fire is enough to melt the resin and allow the cone to open for the seeds inside to disperse. Since the seeds will be produced after the ground has been cleared and enriched by fire, they are more likely to grow.

Scientists found that 345 elk died as a direct result of the fires, which is less than 1% of the elk population. During the winter following the fire, thousands of elk died from lack of food, but the numbers of elk had recovered completely within five years. The fires also killed some fish, 36 deer, 12 moose, 6 black bears, 9 bison, and possibly 1 grizzly bear. The carcasses of these animals provided food for other animals, such as coyotes, bears, and some birds. Dead trees provided more places for birds like woodpeckers and bluebirds to find holes in which to build their nests. Overall there does not seem to have been a significant long-term negative effect on animal populations. The fires did have an effect on tourism while they were occurring, but the influx of firefighters and the media made up for this to some degree. There was no decrease in the number of tourists who visited the region the following year. ∎

—*Adapted from National Park Service,*
"Wildland Fire in Yellowstone."

Case Study Comparison

	The Crab Jubilee	The March of the Toads	The Bleaching of the Reefs	The Yellowstone Fires of 1988
Local causes of changes	overfishing increase in human population	introduction of cane toads to sugar cane fields	fishing practices, such as overfishing and use of dynamite	human activity buildup of old trees and underbrush lightning
Global causes of changes	increase in human population pollution	none	global climate change causing warmer ocean temperatures and increased ocean acidity	changing weather patterns that led to very dry conditions
Environmental effects	cloudier water less eelgrass less protection for young crabs low oxygen levels dead zones loss of biodiversity	many organisms eaten by cane toads some local populations became extinct loss of biodiversity	fewer reefs weaker reefs bleaching of coral increased bacterial growth/disease loss of biodiversity	fire, smoke, lack of food lethal/harmful for some animals enriched soil and more sunlight on soil—more plant growth some increased germination
Economic effects	fewer crabs to catch fewer jobs related to crabs—fishing, tourism, restaurants, etc.	possible loss of money from reduced tourism money spent trying to control the cane toad populations and on treating affected organisms	less protection for coastal communities less money from tourism reduced fishing both locally and farther away	short-term loss of jobs and money from tourism increased business from firefighters
Social effects	some families that have relied on crab-related jobs must find different work families move from the region	loss of traditional food sources for aboriginal bushmen	some families that have traditionally relied on the reefs have to find new jobs or move to different places loss of beauty of reefs	short-term change in numbers of jobs (e.g., fewer tour guides, etc.) concerns about living where there might be another large fire human health impact (makes asthma worse) loss of beauty of landscape

2 A Population of Duckweed

LABORATORY • 3–4 CLASS SESSIONS (OVER A PERIOD OF 8 WEEKS)

OVERVIEW

Students monitor the growth of a population of duckweed plants for approximately eight weeks. They use the population data they collect to discuss population growth rates and the carrying capacity of an ecosystem.

KEY CONTENT

1. Populations grow at varying rates, depending on conditions.

2. Some species are better suited to certain environmental conditions than others.

3. Some conditions can lead to exponential population growth for certain species.

4. Population growth is limited by the resources available.

5. Ecosystems have a carrying capacity based on the current resources available, which determines how large a population the ecosystem can support.

KEY PROCESS SKILLS

1. Students take measurements, and collect and record data.

2. Students graph and analyze data.

MATERIALS AND ADVANCE PREPARATION

For the teacher
transparency of Student Sheet 2.1, "Class Duckweed Population Data"
Scoring Guide: ORGANIZING DATA (OD)
Scoring Guide: ANALYZING DATA (AD)

For each group of four students
permanent marker*

For each pair of students
clear plastic cup*
piece of masking tape*
bacteriological loop
source of spring water*
duckweed plants

For each student
Student Sheet 2.1, "Class Duckweed Population Data"
2 sheets of graph paper*
Science Skills Student Sheet 3a and 3b, "Scatterplot and Line Graphing Checklist" (optional)
Scoring Guide: ORGANIZING DATA (OD) (optional)
Scoring Guide: ANALYZING DATA (AD) (optional)

Not supplied in kit

Masters for Science Skills Student Sheets are in Teacher Resources II: Diverse Learners. Masters for Scoring Guides are in Teacher Resources IV: Assessment.

SAFETY NOTE

Be sure that students do not wash any plants or partial plants down the drain. Duckweed is considered an invasive species in many areas worldwide. Check with your county or state agencies on proper disposal methods. In many places, it is sufficient to allow the plants to dry out and then throw them into the trash. You may wish to set up a strainer lined with several layers of cheesecloth or coffee filters, and ask students to filter the materials from their experiments.

TEACHING SUMMARY

Getting Started

• Introduce population dynamics.

Doing the Activity

• Students set up a population of duckweed and track its growth for eight weeks.

• (OD ASSESSMENT) The class constructs a population graph with data collected over eight weeks.

Follow-up

• (AD ASSESSMENT) The class discusses the relationship between population growth and sustainability.

BACKGROUND INFORMATION

Duckweed

Duckweed generally refers to a family of plants, Lemnaceae, that grows throughout the world in still or slow-moving freshwater. In this activity your students work with the species *Lemna minor*. Duckweed grows and reproduces rapidly and is often the subject for studies on plant development, genetics, and population growth. It has also become a food source in freshwater fish farming. It grows particularly well in areas where there are elevated levels of nitrogen and phosphorus, as would be found where there is agricultural or sewage runoff. It often outcompetes native aquatic plants for resources.

Duckweed grows well in spring water, and must have access to sunlight or fluorescent grow lights. It does not grow well in distilled water and some tap water. To increase the growth of duckweed in your classroom you or your students might

a) add chelated iron, obtained from liquid plant fertilizers available at nurseries and garden supply centers.

b) use fresh pond water.

c) treat the tap water as you would for a freshwater aquarium to remove chlorine and other chemicals.

d) regularly replace the water in the cups, instead of just adding to it, as evaporation of water from the cups may increase the salt concentration.

GETTING STARTED

1 Read the introduction in the Student Book with the class. If students are unfamiliar with the term *organism,* explain to them that it is a general term for living things, whether animals, plants, fungi, or microorganisms (e.g., bacteria). Refer back to the cane toad case study in the previous activity to help distinguish the terms population and community, particularly as they are used in an ecological context. This is especially important if you have English-language learners in your class. Explain that ecologists investigate the factors that affect populations and communities. Because this activity will continue for the length of the unit, students need not delve deeper into population dynamics at this point.

2 A Population of Duckweed

1 THROUGHOUT THIS UNIT you will be studying populations of organisms. A **population** is a group of individuals of the same species that live in the same general area and are able to reproduce. For example, all of the rainbow trout living in one stream would be a population, if they were able to mate and have live offspring. Studying species' populations in an ecosystem helps scientists determine the stability of that ecosystem.

The population of bannerfish (Heniochus diphreutes), shown at left, lives near a coral reef.

In the community shown below, bannerfish, several species of coral, and other fish species all live near a coral reef.

57

89

DOING THE ACTIVITY

2 Assign groups of students different initial numbers of plants, such as 10, 15, 20, 25, or 30. No initial population, however, should be smaller than 10 plants. Be sure students choose healthy and whole plants for their initial population. Discuss with the class which variables will be held constant for all of the duckweed setups (the amount of water, sunlight, and size of the container), and which variable will differ (the starting population size). Review the concepts of independent and dependent variables if necessary.

3 Check students' data table designs. If necessary, discuss the important points of the data table, including the time intervals at which students will check population growth and the number of columns students will need for recording the data.

You will also study the interactions of several species. Ecologists, scientists who study ecology, describe populations of multiple species living in the same area as a **community**. In a stream the biological community might include populations of rainbow trout, mosquitoes, aquatic plants, snails, and tadpoles. As you saw in the previous activity, it is communities of organisms, along with nonliving factors, that make up an ecosystem.

The plant you will study in this activity, duckweed *(Lemna minor)*, grows well in a range of conditions. While it flowers and reproduces sexually, it can also reproduce without flowering, via asexual reproduction. In some regions, duckweed is considered an invasive species, much like the cane toads are invasive in Australia. If enough duckweed grows on the surface of a pond, it uses up the dissolved carbon dioxide in the pond, preventing the native aquatic plants from obtaining carbon dioxide. This decreases the aquatic plants' oxygen production. Without enough oxygen the fish and other organisms living in the pond will die.

In this activity, you will collect data from a growing population of duckweed over several weeks to learn about populations and how they grow.

Challenge

▶ How quickly can a population grow? How does the size of a population change through time?

MATERIALS

FOR EACH GROUP OF FOUR STUDENTS
    permanent marker

FOR EACH PAIR OF STUDENTS
    clear plastic cup
    piece of masking tape
    bacteriological loop
    source of spring water
    duckweed plants

FOR EACH STUDENT
    Student Sheet 2.1, "Class Duckweed Population Data"
  2 sheets of graph paper

4 Introduce Science Skills Student Worksheets 3a and 3b, "Scatterplot and Line Graphing Checklist." Ask students to return to their prediction graphs and add in any key characteristics that they did not include. Students will refer back to this worksheet as they graph data throughout the unit. Introduce the ORGANIZING DATA (OD) Scoring Guide that you will use to assess students' graphing abilities. Clarify your expectations for Level-3 and Level-4 responses. Pass out a copy of the guide to each student, and direct them to keep it for subsequent graphs in the coming weeks. We suggest that you have students score each other's graphs using the Scoring Guide, and provide time for them to adjust their graphs before you collect their work. See the sample student graph lower right.

5 If possible, have students store their duckweed in an easily accessible and sunny location. Ideally, students will count their duckweed population twice a week for eight weeks. Minimally they should count the populations once a week. Students must check and replenish the water regularly, depending on the evaporation rate in your classroom. If the plants have adequate light and water, you can expect that the duckweed populations will increase the most rapidly in the first two to three weeks. Then the population numbers will continue to increase, but at a slower rate, until the population reaches carrying capacity. If your classroom is cold or has low light levels, you may wish to have students add liquid plant fertilizer—the same amount for each population. If you do this be sure to discuss its effect on the experiment with the class.

A whole duckweed plant resembles the plant in this picture. Be sure you are only counting whole plants in your data collection.

Procedure

Part A: Establishing a Baseline

To track the growth of your duckweed population you need to set a baseline, or starting point, for your population. Having a baseline allows you to monitor population changes.

1. Write your names and the date on the masking tape, and affix it to the plastic cup.

2. In your science notebook, create a data table to record and track your population two times each week for eight weeks. Count and record how many plants your teacher has given you.

3. In your science notebook, sketch a graph predicting what will happen to the number of plants in your duckweed population over the next eight weeks. Beneath the graph explain how you made your prediction.

4. Fill your plastic cup to approximately two-thirds full with spring water.

5. Carefully transfer your duckweed plants into your plastic cup using the bacteriological loop. Make sure the plants are completely in the water.

   Caution: Duckweed plants are fragile. Be sure to handle them gently when transferring them with the loop so that you do not break the leaves or roots.

6. Place your duckweed population in the location designated by your teacher.

Safety ⚠

Because duckweed is invasive, be careful not to pour any down the drain. Your teacher will provide disposal instructions at the end of the experiment. Check your hands and equipment for pieces of duckweed plants before using the sink.

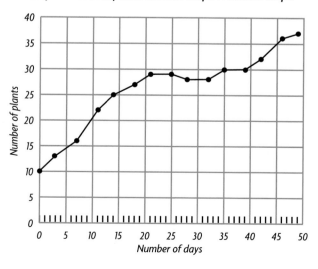

Sample Level-3 Response: Student Graph Procedure Step 9

Number of plants (y-axis: 0, 5, 10, 15, 20, 25, 30, 35, 40)

Number of days (x-axis: 0, 5, 10, 15, 20, 25, 30, 35, 40, 45, 50)

FOLLOW-UP

6 (OD ASSESSMENT) Pass out Student Sheet 2.1, "Class Duckweed Population Data." Project a transparency of the student sheet, and ask student groups to record their data on it, as well as on their student sheets. Discuss what the data show. You may also wish to have students compare their population graphs, either on butcher paper, or on individual overheads to share with the class. Discuss why it is not scientifically accurate to pool the data. Use the ORGANIZING DATA (OD) Scoring Guide to evaluate the students' graphs and give them feedback. It is helpful to show students a variety of sample responses for any assessment opportunity to give them concrete examples for the scoring levels. There are a number of exemplars in Teacher Resources IV: Assessment.

7 (AD ASSESSMENT) As the class discusses the relationship between population growth and sustainability, students should specifically discuss the concepts of carrying capacity and growth rates as they apply to the duckweed experiment. **Note:** Students will not address the Analysis Questions until the eight-week period is completed, and the concepts contained in many questions may be unfamiliar until they are introduced in Activity 14, "Investigating Population Growth Rates." Analysis Question 1 is an opportunity for you to assess students' ability to analyze data, particularly by questioning the characteristics of data (i.e., Is the source objective and reliable? Are there inconsistencies? and Have sources of error been identified?) and by recognizing trends and relationships between variables.

Students' written work from Analysis Question 1 can be scored with the ANALYZING DATA (AD) Scoring Guide. This is as an opportunity to introduce the SEPUP assessment system. Provide each student with an AD Scoring Guide, and ask them to keep it with their science notebooks, as they will refer to it several times in this unit and

---

Part B: Tracking the Population

(To be done over several weeks)

7. Carefully count the number of live plants present in your population, and update your data table. Do not count plants that have turned completely brown or white.

8. Add water to your population as necessary or according to your teacher's instructions. If the water in your cup is evaporating too quickly, you may need to add water between data-collection points. Check with your teacher for instructions on how and when to do this.

6 9. At the end of the data-collection period, use graph paper to plot a line graph of population size versus time lapsed for your duckweed population.

Analysis

7 1. Interpret your graph by answering the following questions.
   a. What happened to your duckweed population over the study period?
   b. Why do you think your population changed the way it did?

2. Do the data you collected agree with your prediction from Procedure Step 3? Explain.

3. How is your graph different from other students' population graphs? Why do you think the graphs are different?

Duckweed overtakes a lake in Iowa.

60

---

throughout the *Science and Global Issues* course. Explain to the class that you will use the AD Scoring Guide to provide feedback on the quality of their work. Let them know that you will use their writing from Analysis Question 1 to model how the scoring guide works.

Begin by pointing out the scoring levels 0–4, and review the criteria for each score. Explain that the scores are based on the quality of their responses and do not correspond to letter grades. A Level-3 response is a complete and correct response. A Level-4 response signifies that the student has both achieved and exceeded the acceptable level of response. Let students know that you would like them to strive to improve by at least one level in later activities. At first, many students will write Level-2 responses, and they should strive to achieve Level-3 responses.

As a class, discuss what a Level-3 response would include. A Level-3 response should include a description of the graph and any overall trends, as well as a reasonable explanation for why the trend occurs. You may develop a Level-3 exemplar with the class or share with students the Level-3 response shown in the Sample Response to Analysis Question 1. Point out the elements that make the example a Level-3 response, and discuss how a Level 1 and a Level 2 are different. Ask students for ideas about how to improve the Level-3 response to make it a Level 4. After students have answered Analysis Questions 6 and 7, use their responses to discuss with the class the relationship between population growth and sustainability.

SAMPLE RESPONSES

1. (AD ASSESSMENT) Students' answers will vary. A complete and correct response will include a description of the data and any trends, and an interpretation of why the trends occurred.

    Sample Level-3 Response

    a. The graph showed that our population grew at a faster rate in the first three weeks than in the last five weeks, and then it began to level off. Overall the population increased.

    b. I think this happened because there were a lot of resources available for the population to grow rapidly at first, and as it grew there were less resources available so the growth leveled off.

2. Answers will vary and should include a comparison of their graph produced in Procedure Step 9 to their graph for Procedure Step 3. Make sure that students' answers include an explanation of how their initial thinking, represented by the graph from Procedure Step 3, changed after constructing the graph in Procedure Step 9.

3. Answers will depend on which graphs they chose to compare. Students should note that they were working with very small populations over a relatively short period of time, and so they would not see growth patterns as quickly, particularly exponential growth patterns.

4. In this activity the factors affecting the carrying capacity of the duckweed habitat include the size of the cup, the volume of water the cup can hold, and the amount of sunlight available to the duckweed. The most important factor is likely to be the size of the plastic cup (the duckweed habitat). If the activity had continued longer than eight weeks, the duckweed would continue to grow until they run out of space.

---

4. What environmental limiting factor do you think is most important in setting the carrying capacity for duckweed in this activity? Explain your reasoning.

5. What effect do you think each of the following would have on the population:

   a. placing the population in a lake where other duckweed is already present

   b. introducing an organism that eats duckweed

   c. introducing a duckweed disease

   d. adding fertilizer to the duckweed habitat

6. The graph below shows the global human population growth over the past 2,000 years. Compare this graph to the graph of your duckweed population. What similarities and what differences are there?

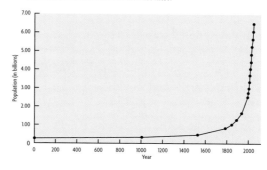

7. How does what you have learned about population growth and carrying capacity relate to sustainability?

KEY VOCABULARY

carrying capacity	limiting factor
community	organism
ecosystem	**population**
invasive species	population growth rate

61

93

5. a. If a lot of duckweed is introduced, the other population might die. If the introduced population stays small, it will have almost no effect on the lake population.

 b. The duckweed population would decrease if an organism that eats duckweed were introduced, unless that organism started eating other types of plants, like the cane toads that did not eat the organism they were supposed to eat.

 c. The duckweed population would decrease if a duckweed disease were introduced.

 d. The duckweed population would increase if fertilizer were added because of the increased nutrients made available by the fertilizer. But then the population would reach a new carrying capacity and would remain constant.

6. Answers will vary based on the shape of the class duckweed graph. Both graphs show a rapid increase in population at some point. Answers are likely to include that the overall shape is different in that the duckweed population grew rapidly at first, and then, once carrying capacity was reached, the rate of growth slowed. In comparison, the Historical World Population Growth Graph shows that the world population rose slowly until 1600, when the rate of growth increased dramatically.

7. We have learned that populations continue to grow as long as there are resources to support them. But eventually they may reach a limit, due to the finite nature of resources. This limit is called the carrying capacity of the ecosystem. If resources become too depleted, the ecosystem will no longer sustain the population. This is the correlation to sustainability for this population.

REVISIT THE CHALLENGE

Discuss how the duckweed populations changed, as well as other populations students have looked at during the unit. Encourage them to compare the duckweed results to the different population graphs you looked at in Activity 14, "Investigating Population Growth Rates."

3 Biomes

INVESTIGATION • 2–3 CLASS SESSIONS

OVERVIEW

In this activity, students are introduced to biomes. They examine climate graphs for 16 locations around the world and group the graphs by similarities to create eight pairs. They then match these to the written descriptions of eight biomes. Finally, students read information about eight plants and determine which biome would be most suitable for each plant.

KEY CONTENT

1. A biome is a region with characteristic climate, geography, and ecological communities of plants and animals.

2. The world can be grouped into a number of distinct biomes.

3. Because biomes are a human construct, there is not perfect agreement on the number and types of biomes found on earth. This unit includes the following biomes: tropical rain forest, desert, savanna, chaparral, temperate grassland, taiga, temperate deciduous forest, and tundra.

4. The abiotic (nonliving) factors in an environment include light, temperature, precipitation, soil, rocks, and minerals.

5. The biotic factors in an environment are related to living things and include organisms, their interactions, and their waste.

6. Some traits are useful in helping an organism survive in a habitat. If the conditions in an environment change sufficiently, or if the organism moves to an entirely different environment, the trait(s) may no longer be useful and the organism will not be as well suited to the conditions.

KEY PROCESS SKILLS

1. Students make accurate interpretations, inferences, and conclusions from text.

2. Students graph and analyze data.

MATERIALS AND ADVANCE PREPARATION

For the teacher

transparency of Student Sheet 3.1, "Climate Information for Locations"

Scoring Guide: UNDERSTANDING CONCEPTS (UC)

Literacy Student Sheet 5, "KWL," partially filled out in Activity 1, "Ecosystems and Change"

For each pair of students

set of 8 Biome Organism Cards

pair of scissors*

container of white glue or roll of transparent tape*

For each student

Student Sheet 3.1, "Climate Information for Locations"

Student Sheet 3.2, "Biomes Match"

Scoring Guide: UNDERSTANDING CONCEPTS (UC) (optional)

*Not supplied in kit

Masters for Science Skills Student Sheets are in Teacher Resources II: Diverse Learners. Masters for Literacy Skills Sheets are in Teacher Resources III: Literacy. Masters for Scoring Guides are in Teacher Resources IV: Assessment.

TEACHING SUMMARY

Getting Started

- Introduce biomes, and biotic and abiotic factors.

Doing the Activity

- Introduce the UNDERSTANDING CONCEPTS (UC) Scoring Guide.

- Groups of two students work to organize the climate graphs into similar pairs.

- Groups match the climate graph pairs to descriptions of biomes.

- Groups match each organism card to the biome that it seems most suited to.

Follow-up

- (UC ASSESSMENT) The class discusses how regions of the world share certain similarities and that the native species found in a region are adapted to the conditions there.

BACKGROUND INFORMATION

Biomes are regions of the world that share similarities on biotic and abiotic levels. Since the abiotic conditions (especially climate and soil) within a biome fall within a certain range, the traits that help a plant or animal to survive in one location will also help it survive in the same type of biome in a different part of the world. However, having certain traits does not guarantee that an organism can be successfully relocated to the same biome in another part of the world, as such factors as exposure to disease and presence of predators will also have an impact. Because the species in different geographic locations evolved in different ways, the types of species found in different locations vary, even if the biome is the same type. For example, the anaconda is found in parts of the Amazon rain forest, but the python is found in the rain forests of Borneo. Although they are different species, these snakes have similar characteristics (good swimmers, constrictors, can go for long periods without food, need warmth and humidity) and occupy similar habitats in their environments. Both are adapted to the conditions found in the tropical rain forest biome.

The biomes described in this activity represent one way of categorizing ecological regions of the world. Other systems can be found in reference books and through the Internet. Some are more specific and have more biomes, others combine categories in different ways. Since biomes are a human construct, there is not absolute agreement on the definitions and numbers of biomes. However, the concept of biomes is useful in the study of ecology.

Biomes often only include terrestrial ecosystems. Freshwater and marine ecosystems are not always considered by scientists to be part of biome classifications, but are also helpful in the study of ecology and will be addressed in later activities.

Note: The values shown for monthly average temperatures for each location, A through P, are the average of the monthly average high and low temperatures.

GETTING STARTED

1 ⬧ Use the first paragraph in the Introduction in the Student Book to pose the question: *If the cane toad in the case study in Activity 1, "Ecosystems and Change," had been introduced in Anchorage or Las Vegas would you expect results similar to those seen in Australia?*

The class may need some assistance to come to the conclusion that the climates of these two locations are not like that of Queensland. For example, you may need to describe the climate of Queensland for the students—warm to hot, with moderate to high rainfall. Lead students to the idea that for an organism to stand a chance of establishing itself in a location it must be suited to the environment there, including the climate. Have students suggest examples of suitable and unsuitable climates for species—for example, ferns do not live in the desert. Proceed to the next paragraph of the introduction and discuss the definition of a biome. Discuss the difference between biotic and abiotic factors, using precipitation and temperature as examples of abiotic factors. You may want to show your students a variety of world biome maps. For suggestions go to the *Science and Global Issues* page of the SEPUP website (*sepuplhs.org/sgi*).

2 Review the definition of evidence. Evidence is information that supports or refutes a claim. Explain that scientists collect information (data) using various tools and strategies, including observation and experimentation. Tell students that in this activity, they will work with climate graphs and biome descriptions to match locations to biomes and organisms to biomes. The consideration of evidence is a key step in decision-making. Throughout this unit and *Science and Global Issues*, students will collect and analyze information, which they may then apply as evidence to support or refute claims.

---

3 Biomes

1 **A**s you saw in Activity 1, "Ecosystems and Change," around 100 cane toads were introduced in the 1930s to Queensland in Australia. The current number of cane toads in Australia is more than 200 million. Would such a dramatic increase have occurred if the cane toad had been introduced to Anchorage, Alaska, or Las Vegas, Nevada?

For an organism to exist in an ecosystem it has specific traits that permit it to survive in that ecosystem. If an organism moves to a location that is similar to its native environment, it is more likely to survive than if it moved to a place entirely different, because its traits are likely to still be helpful to it in this new environment. The environment where an organism lives is influenced by both **biotic** (living) and **abiotic** (nonliving) factors. Abiotic factors include climate and type of soil. Across the world are regions with similar abiotic conditions, which are referred to as **biomes**. A biome features a range of conditions, and therefore various locations in the same biome will be similar but not identical. There is not complete agreement among scientists as to the exact number and types of biomes in the world.

2 In this activity you will examine several sets of information. You will then use these as evidence to identify the particular biomes of a variety of locations around the world. **Evidence** is information used to support or refute a claim. You will also use evidence to match a selection of organisms to these biomes.

Hungarian steppes (left) and Montana prairie (above) have very similar biotic and abiotic factors, even though they are on two separate continents.

62

DOING THE ACTIVITY

3 Introduce the UNDERSTANDING CONCEPTS (UC) Scoring Guide, and tell the class your expectations for satisfactory work.

4 The pairing for graphs A, E, J, and K may initially be hard to distinguish (see note below). The correct combinations of climate graphs and biomes are shown below:

Biomes and Climate Graph Matches

Biome	Locations
Tropical rain forest	D and H
Desert	L and O
Savanna	G and N
Chaparral	F and P
Temperate grassland	E and K
Taiga	C and M
Temperate deciduous forest	A and J
Tundra	B and I

Note: Students may have trouble distinguishing temperate deciduous forest from temperate grassland, which both have similar temperate climates. The biome information for temperate grasslands states that precipitation tends to be higher in late spring and summer, whereas in the temperate deciduous forest precipitation is more even throughout the year. Graphs E and K show more of a spike in precipitation in late spring/early summer than graphs A and J and therefore are better to group with temperate grasslands. It is not critical that students see clear distinctions in these four graphs. The difficulty they encounter in trying to correctly group these biomes reinforces the fact that biomes are not determined solely by climate, but also by such factors as soil conditions, predominant vegetation types, and specific adaptations of species.

Challenge

▶ How do the characteristics of a biome determine the types of organisms found there?

MATERIALS

FOR EACH PAIR OF STUDENTS
set of 8 Organism Cards
pair of scissors
container of glue or roll of transparent tape

FOR EACH STUDENT
Student Sheet 3.1, "Climate Information for Locations"
Student Sheet 3.2, "Biomes Match"

3 ## Procedure

1. Student Sheet 3.1 shows climate information for 16 locations around the world. Each graph contains two sets of data, average temperature and average precipitation per month. Cut the sheet into 16 separate climate graphs.

4

2. With your partner organize the climate graphs into eight groups by pairing each location with the one that has the most similar climate.

5

3. Read the descriptions of types of terrestrial biomes on the following pages. Write a short summary of each biome in your science notebook, leaving enough room between them to paste in the climate graphs when you are finished.

4. From the climate descriptions match each biome to one of the pairs of locations that you created in Step 2.

5. In your science notebook, paste each climate graph next to your summary of its corresponding biomes.

6. Using the information on the Organism Cards, match each organism to the biome in which the organism might be found. Match each organism to only one biome. Record your matches on Student Sheet 3.2, "Biomes Match," and make sure that all biomes are matched with one organism.

6

7. In your science notebook include your reasons for matching each organism with the particular biome you chose.

---

5 After spending time reviewing the pairings with the class—especially the two temperate biomes— ask the students to read the description of each biome in the Student Book and to write summary notes for each in their science notebooks. Be sure students leave at least a half page between each biome summary so that they can affix the appropriate pair of climate graphs in that space.

6 Check that students have correctly matched the climate graphs and the biome descriptions. Hand out the Organism Cards, and allow students to match the organisms (in this case, plants) to the biomes where they seem most suited. Although several plants might survive in multiple biomes, students are asked to make the best match and to only match one plant to one biome. Student Sheet 3.2, "Biomes Match," will help in this process. If students have difficulty matching the plants, suggest that they first make the more obvious matches and then follow a process of elimination.

See the sample completed Student Sheet 3.2 at the end of this activity for the correct matches.

Tropical Rain Forest

A tropical rain forest is warm and humid all year. Temperatures are fairly constant in the 20°C–30°C (68°F–86°F) range. Total rainfall per year can vary from 2,000–4,000 mm (about 80–160 inches). In many tropical rain forests there is no dry season. The soil has limited nutrients, but the warm temperatures and abundant water support a wide variety of organisms. Plants can grow quickly, and dead matter decays rapidly. Trees can become very tall, and many are evergreen and do not shed their leaves. Plants compete for light. Many of these forests are found near the equator where daylight length is about 12 hours throughout the year. ▪

Desert

Deserts have low precipitation of 15–300 mm (about 0.5–12 inches) per year. The low humidity allows temperatures to become cold at night. Hot deserts experience temperature variations from an average of about 10°C (50°F) in winter to 35°C (95°F) or more in the summer. The soil is often poor in nutrients but rich in minerals. To survive in the desert, plants and animals must be able to conserve water. Desert plants generally provide very little shade, and there are very few trees. ▪

64

Savanna

The savanna has warm temperatures, generally around 25°C–35°C (77°F–95°F) year round. Temperatures are not as constant throughout the year as are those in the tropical rain forest. Total rainfall varies from 500–1,500 mm (about 20–60 inches) per year but is not evenly distributed. There is a long dry season and a rainy season. Trees are scattered, and grasses grow quickly when it rains. The soil is shallow and drains quickly. Fires can occur during the dry season and are important in maintaining biodiversity. When the fires kill small animals, the bodies of the dead animals provide food for other animals, such as birds. Other organisms survive the fires by running away, burrowing underground, or having deep roots. The parts of the plants that burn above ground nourish the soil. ∎

Chaparral

The chaparral receives most of its precipitation as rain during the winter months. Rainfall totals vary from about 200–700 mm (about 8–28 inches) per year. Winter, spring, and fall are generally cool and mild with average temperatures between 10°C and 15°C (50°F–59°F). Summers are warm with average temperatures around 25°C (77°F) although on some days the temperature may rise as high as 40°C (104°F). Some areas of chaparral experience frost at certain times of the year, but there are usually six months or more of frost-free days. The dry summers often cause drought conditions and increase the chance of fires. Vegetation is diverse

and sometimes dense. Shrubs, wildflowers, and grasses are common. There are a wide variety of small animals, including amphibians, birds, reptiles, insects, and small mammals. ∎

65

Temperate Grassland

Temperate grassland experiences a wide range of temperature and precipitation through the year. Precipitation is moderate with a yearly average of 500–900 mm (about 20–35 inches). Most rain falls in late spring and in summer. The winter is cold, with average temperatures well below freezing, while summer temperatures average around 25°C (77°F). Five to six months of the year are frost-free. The soil is often fertile and dominated by tall grasses that have adapted to the cold winter temperatures, occasional summer droughts, and periodic fires. The

roots of these grasses help to hold the soil together. Many large mammals graze in these grasslands. ∎

Taiga

Taiga is an area of extensive forests where the ground is frozen for much of the year. The winters are long and cold with average temperatures around –15°C (5°F). Precipitation ranges from 300–850 mm (about 12–34 inches) per year. Summers are short, moist, and generally mild enough that the ground thaws. Average temperatures in the summer are around 15°C (59°F), but daily maximum temperatures occasionally rise as high as 30°C (86°F). About three months of the year are frost-free. The range of types of plants that grow here is quite narrow because many plants cannot access the nutrients in the frozen soil. Most of the trees are evergreen conifers. Many different types of mammals live in the taiga, including some very large ones. ∎

Temperate Deciduous Forest

Temperate deciduous forests experience four distinct seasons with a total annual precipitation of 700–2,000 mm (about 28–80 inches) that is spread throughout the year. Temperatures vary a lot over the year and between locations. There are about 140–200 frost-free days each year, depending on the location. Average winter temperatures usually fall to below freezing, and summer averages are around 25°C (77°F). The generally fertile soil, year-round precipitation, and approximately six-month growing period support a wide diversity of plants. Most trees lose their leaves before winter, and some animals hibernate or migrate during the winter months. ■

Tundra

Very cold temperatures and low precipitation, with yearly totals between 120 and 250 mm (about 5–10 inches), are characteristic of tundra. Winters are long with average temperatures of –30°C (–22°F) or lower. The soil is thin and covers a permanently frozen layer of subsoil called permafrost. The permafrost makes it difficult for plants to extend roots deep into the ground. The permafrost also prevents water from seeping deep into the ground during the short summer when the soil at the surface thaws. Animals usually have fat and fur to help cope with the cold temperatures. Some animals hibernate to survive the harsh winters, and some migrate. Average summer temperatures can reach 10°C (50°F). The growing season for plants is very short with only about two months of the year being frost-free. Plants that do well in tundra tend to grow close to the ground. ■

FOLLOW-UP

7 It is intentional that the term "extreme conditions" has not been defined for the students. The purpose of Analysis Question 1 is to stimulate a discussion about what "extreme" might mean when considering an organism's needs. The discussion should include the importance of acclimating to an environment.

8 (UC ASSESSMENT) It may be necessary to help students with part b of Analysis Question 3 if they are unfamiliar with the seasonal differences in the Northern and Southern hemispheres. To do this you might ask them when summer and winter would occur in the location designated in the data table and to examine how the patterns in the climate graphs they have already looked at differ from this climate graph.

Analysis Questions 5 and 6 are UNDERSTANDING CONCEPTS (UC) assessment questions.

Analysis

7

1. Which biome has the most extreme conditions? Explain your answer.

2. Which biome has the most constant conditions over the course of the year? Explain your answer.

8

3. Make a climate graph using the data in the table below.

Climate Data for Location Q

MONTH	AVG. TEMP. (°C)	AVG. PRECIP. (mm)
January	29	37
February	28	41
March	25	31
April	20	17
May	16	19
June	12	14
July	12	14
August	14	9
September	19	8
October	23	21
November	26	29
December	28	38

   a. Which biome is Location Q likely to be in? Explain your choice of biome.

   b. What else do the climate data indicate about where Q might be? Explain your answer.

4. **Biodiversity** is the number of species found in a given ecosystem or area. Based on what you learned in this activity, why do you think levels of biodiversity differ from biome to biome?

5. Review the description of *Monarda fistulosa* from Procedure Steps 6 and 7 in your student notebook. In which other biome could *Monarda fistulosa* most likely be found? Explain your answer.

6. *Cyclorana platycephala* is a frog that is found in Australia. Like all frogs, it needs to keep its skin moist. During periods of drought it digs a chamber in the ground and lines it with mucous, which hardens and seals the chamber from water loss. The frog settles into the chamber, its metabolism slows down, and it becomes inactive. The frog can survive in this state for up to five years. Describe how this trait will determine the types of biome that the frog might live in.

68

---

9 Review the biome descriptions in the Student Book, and point out the following:

- There is a second type of tropical forest called tropical dry forest. Unlike the rain forest where there is year-round precipitation, tropical dry forest has a dry season for several months of the year. These forests, found in India, Mexico, Bolivia, Indochina, and other countries have more deciduous trees than do rain forests, and these trees lose their leaves prior to the start of the dry season.

- Desert environments are not always hot and dry. The following are also deserts:

- Semiarid deserts, where the summers are warm to hot, quite long, and dry, but the winters bring some precipitation. Examples include parts of Utah, Nevada, and Montana.

- Coastal deserts where the summers are warm and the winters cool. Precipitation is low but not as low as in the semiarid desert. An example is the Atacama of Chile.

- Cold deserts, where the temperatures are very cold in winter and the summers are short, warm, and moist. Winter precipitation includes snow. Two examples are Greenland and the Antarctic.

- Tundra includes alpine tundra, which is found at high altitudes. Here the temperatures can be cold, especially at night. The growing season lasts about six months; plant growth rates tend to be very slow and most growth occurs underground. This tundra occurs above the tree line and can be found in such areas as Mt. Rainier National Park in Washington.

Use the discussion of the investigation and the Analysis Questions to reinforce the concept of biomes and that organisms are acclimated to the environment where they are found. Emphasize that there isn't universal agreement

---

7. How might ecologists use the frog described in Question 6 as an indicator for change within a biome?

9 8. What might be two of the reasons that scientists do not agree about the number and types of biomes that exist in the world?

KEY VOCABULARY	
abiotic	biotic
biodiversity	ecosystem
biomes	evidence

69

---

on definitions of specific biomes. Further, make sure that students understand that biomes are a generalization, and within biomes, particularly in different regions of the world, there is great diversity of ecosystems.

SAMPLE RESPONSES

1. Students' responses will vary. Some may decide that the term "extreme conditions" means very hot or very cold, in which case they would choose desert or tundra as the most extreme biomes. If they looked at temperature variation over the course of a year, they may choose tundra or possibly temperate grassland. If they choose the biome with the most variation in rainfall, they would select savanna.

2. Students' responses will vary. Some will say that, overall, the tropical rain forest probably has the most stable climate, because there was very little variation in temperature over the course of the year. Although the exact quantity of rainfall in the rain forest varied from month to month, it never decreased to low values. It is also reasonable for students to choose chaparral or desert as having the least variation. Be sure to check their reasoning.

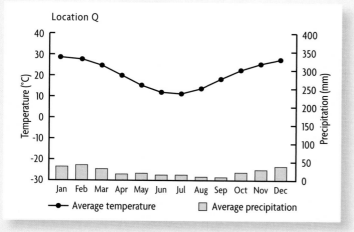

3. a. Location Q is probably in the desert biome because it always has a low amount of precipitation with moderate to hot temperatures.

   b. Location Q is probably in the Southern Hemisphere because the warmest time of the year is in December and January.

4. Some biomes might be "easier" to live in than other biomes, so a wider range of organisms could survive there. In other biomes fewer organisms are able to survive.

5. (UC ASSESSMENT) *Monarda fistulosa* is found in temperate deciduous forests. It could probably also be found in temperate grasslands as the climate conditions are very similar in both biomes.

6. (UC ASSESSMENT) The trait allows the frog to survive in a wider range of biomes, including those that have little rainfall or periodic droughts.

7. Scientists could count the number of active and inactive frogs throughout the year. If the environment became drier, it would be expected that fewer frogs would be active. If it became wetter, more frogs would be active.

8. Students' answers will vary. They may include the following responses:

   • Some of the biomes have quite similar characteristics and therefore could be classified in various ways.

   • The conditions within a biome can vary considerably, and so there are not distinct boundaries that define a biome.

   • Some scientists might divide a biome into smaller regions that they consider sufficiently different to be classified as separate and distinct biomes.

   • Human classification systems are always open to interpretation.

REVIST THE CHALLENGE

Make sure that students understand that certain traits of organisms enable them to live in the environment where they are found. Emphasize that some organisms may be able to live in a variety of biomes (for example, rats) while others are more restricted in their range (for example, cacti). In addition, conditions in some biomes are more complex and require specialized traits for survival. Through technology humans have also created microclimates, such as the lush green desert environments in Las Vegas, or cacti grown in a school in Alaska.

Return to the KWL chart the class began in Activity 1. Have students suggest items for the "What I Learned" column based on what they have learned in the first three Activities. You will revisit this chart again in Activity 7, "Energy Flow Through an Ecosystem." A sample KWL appears below.

Ecological Change KWL

Know	Want to know	Learned
• Humans have changed the environment (cut down rain forests, built buildings, paved roads). • Natural phenomena have changed the environment (volcanoes, earthquakes, tsunamis). • Habitat restoration projects can help restore the environment.	• How much of the environment have people changed? • What can be done to restore the environment? • What happens if we don't restore the environment? • How much does the burning of fossil fuels change the environment?	• Invasive species can change ecosystems dramatically. • Some ecosystems have been changed so much that they cannot support the species that were there originally (dead zones). • Some ecosystems that have changed can be repaired.

Biomes Match

Organism	Ideal growing conditions and other information				Best biome match
	Temperature	Precipitation	Soil	Other	
Picea mariana	as low as −60°C at least 60 frost-free days	380 to 760 mm	poor, thin soil		taiga
Sorghastrum nutans	needs warm and cold seasons	300 to 800 mm	many types of soil	needs warm soil for root growth, winter for seeds, can survive droughts	temperate grassland
Encelia farinosa	no frost	less than 250 mm		grows least in summer, stores water, can survive droughts	desert
Carex saxatilis	at least 2 months frost free	less than 300 mm	poor, thin soil	grows most in summer	tundra
Chloris gayana	as low as −22°C at least 6 months frost free	750 to 1,500 mm	shallow soil	grows mainly in spring and summer, survives droughts	savanna
Monarda fistulosa	as low as −35°C at least 6 months frost free	700 to 1,500 mm needs year-round precipitation	thin soil		temperate deciduous
Rafflesia arnoldii	year-round warm temperatures	year-round precipitation		parasitic, lives on a vine	tropical rain forest
Heteromeles arbutifolia	can survive high and low temperatures	200 to 700 mm needs little water, especially in the summer	well-drained soils	survives droughts, resistant to fire	chaparral

4 Invasive Species

INVESTIGATION • 2–3 CLASS SESSIONS

OVERVIEW

In this activity students examine several invasive species that have become problems in regions of the United States. They record the species' effects on the economy, environment, and human health and identify the characteristics that make each of these species a threat. Finally, they take opposing roles in assessing a proposal to introduce a nonnative species into a location.

KEY CONTENT

1. Native species are those that are naturally found in an ecosystem. Since it is impossible for humans to know exactly which species are "natural" to an environment, it is generally considered that a species is native if it is thought to have existed in an environment for thousands of years.

2. An introduced species is one that has been brought into an environment in which it does not naturally occur. Such species are also referred to as nonnative, exotic, or nonindigenous.

3. Not all introduced species succeed in a new environment. If one can easily acclimate to the new environment, it is more likely to become established.

4. If a nonnative species causes harm to the environment, the economy, or human health, it is considered invasive.

5. If a nonnative species displaces a native species from its habitat, it is considered invasive.

KEY PROCESS SKILLS

1. Students make accurate interpretations, inferences, and conclusions from text.

2. Students communicate and defend a scientific argument.

3. Students identify evidence.

4. Students identify and weigh trade-offs when making a decision.

MATERIALS AND ADVANCE PREPARATION

For the teacher
Scoring Guide: EVIDENCE AND TRADE-OFFS (ET)

For each student
Student Sheet 4.1, "Invasive Species Information"

Literacy Student Sheet 4, "Discussion Web" (optional)

Literacy Student Sheet 2a, "Writing Frame—Evidence and Trade-offs" (optional)

Literacy Student Sheet 3, "Writing Review" (optional)

Scoring Guide: EVIDENCE AND TRADE-OFFS (ET) (optional)

Masters for Science Skills Student Sheets are in Teacher Resources II: Diverse Learners. Masters for Literacy Skills Sheets are in Teacher Resources III: Literacy. Masters for Scoring Guides are in Teacher Resources IV: Assessment.

TEACHING SUMMARY

Getting Started

• Introduce the term habitat by discussing with the class the differences between native, nonnative, and invasive species.

Doing the Activity

• (LITERACY) Each student in a group of four reads a different case study of an invasive species.

• Students look for similarities as they compare their notes on four invasive species.

• Groups develop a list of characteristics that increase the likelihood that a species will become invasive.

• Groups analyze two perspectives as they examine a proposal to stop the decline of oysters in Chesapeake Bay.

Follow-up

- (LITERACY) Summarize how a species might become invasive, and discuss the risks and possible benefits of intentionally introducing a nonnative species into an environment.

- (LITERACY) The class conducts a walking debate to discuss the introduction of nonnative oysters into Chesapeake Bay.

- (LITERACY) (ET ASSESSMENT) Students weigh evidence to make a recommendation for or against the introduction of nonnative oysters into Chesapeake Bay.

BACKGROUND INFORMATION

There are many well-publicized examples of invasive species. Species that are considered invasive in the United States include zebra mussels, kudzu, tiger mosquitoes, purple loosestrife, northern snakehead, brown snake, Asian longhorn beetle, and thousands more. (See the *Science and Global Issues* page of the website—*sepuplhs.org/sgi*—for links to more information.) Nonnative species are introduced intentionally or accidentally into new areas in many ways. Once introduced, a species may eventually die out or it may become established if its traits are advantageous to its living in the new environment and if there is an available habitat. If the species grows and reproduces rapidly, has a mechanism to spread (by flying, wind or water dispersal, attached to boats, etc.), can tolerate a variety of environmental conditions, and can find plenty of food, it is likely to have a significant impact on its new environment. Organisms that are able to outcompete native species by exploiting available resources are likely to displace other organisms, disrupt the balance of the ecosystem, and possibly reduce the biodiversity and sustainability of the area.

Whether a potentially invasive species becomes established doesn't depend solely on its characteristics; it is also determined by factors within the environment, such as the types and number of other organisms present, limited resources, competition from other species, predators, and disease.

GETTING STARTED

1 Begin the class by having students examine their duckweed populations. Ask them what warning was included in the Student Book as part of Activity 2, "A Population of Duckweed." Elicit suggestions as to why the warning to not rinse duckweed down the drain is so important. Ask students if they have ever seen duckweed growing naturally in the community. Explain that duckweed is native to Australia and Southeast Asia, and ask what might happen if the duckweed is released into the environment near the school. Make sure that students understand that not all nonnative species become invasive. To be classified as invasive there must be harm to the environment, economy, or human health. Discuss examples of what such harm might look like in each of these three areas.

4 Invasive Species

1 SPECIES ENTER NEW areas in several ways. In the case of the cane toads, people intentionally introduced them to Australia for pest control. In some cases an organism is carried accidentally with cargo that is being transported from one place to another. In other cases, organisms are carried on the wind and on currents in rivers, lakes, and oceans. If a species is introduced to an area where it is not naturally found, it is referred to as **nonnative**, and is also known as *exotic* or *non-indigenous*. The specific location where an organism lives within an ecosystem is its **habitat**. This is different from an ecosystem, which refers to all of the biotic and abiotic factors interacting in one location. Within an ecosystem, the population of a native species may decline, and even become locally extinct when an introduced species begins to take over the same role in a habitat. This, in turn, decreases the native biodiversity of the area.

Many crops and animals currently found in the United States are nonnative, including wheat, potatoes, soybeans, honeybees, cows, sheep, and goats. In fact there are approximately 50,000 nonnative species of organisms in the United

Many species commonly found in the United States are nonnative and invasive, such as the brown tree snake (a), honey bees (b), ice plant (c), and eucalyptus trees (d).

70

DOING THE ACTIVITY

2 Divide the class into groups of four students and pass out Student Sheet 4.1, "Invasive Species Information." Sample answers appear in this Teacher's Edition at the end of this activity.

3 Allow time for each student in the group to share the information about their species that they wrote on the student sheet.

4 Allow a short time for groups to use the similarities to develop a list of characteristics that seem to increase the chance that a nonnative species will become invasive in a new environment. Then, as a class discussion, ask the groups to pool all of their information and develop a list of characteristics and conditions that allow a species to become invasive. This list should include:

- The ability for the population to increase rapidly

- Ample nourishment (either because the food source is plentiful in the new environment or because the organism can eat a wide variety of foods)

- Traits well suited to the new environment

- Acclimation

- Adequate defense mechanism against potential predators

- Absence of predators.

States today, of which about 4,300 are regarded as invasive. For a nonnative species to be considered **invasive,** it must cause harm to the economy, the environment, or human health. Invasive species often diminish the sustainability of an ecosystem by consuming resources and upsetting the typical interactions between species.

Challenge

▶ How do certain characteristics increase the likelihood that a nonnative species becomes an invasive species?

MATERIALS

FOR EACH STUDENT
Student Sheet 4.1, "Invasive Species Information"
Literacy Student Sheet 6, "Discussion Web"

Procedure

Part A

2
1. On the following pages are four case studies of particular invasive species. Decide in your group who will read each case study.

2. Use the information from the case studies to complete Student Sheet 4.1, "Invasive Species Information," as you read about your assigned species.

3
3. Compare your results with those of the members in your group who studied the other three invasive species. In your science notebook, write down any similarities that you see among the case studies.

4. As a group, use these similarities to develop a list of characteristics that you think increase the potential of a nonnative species to become invasive. Write the list in your science notebook.

4
5. Follow your teacher's directions on when and how to share your group's thinking with the rest of the class. As a class, decide on the characteristics that increase the likelihood that a nonnative species will become invasive.

71

CASE STUDY 1

The Round Goby

THE ROUND GOBY is a freshwater fish that grows to between 10 and 25 cm in length. Originally from central parts of Eurasia, it was discovered in the Great Lakes in the 1990s and is thought to have been accidentally discharged in the ballast water from oceangoing cargo ships visiting ports in the Great Lakes. The goby is no longer limited to the Great Lakes and is spreading throughout the region's rivers and canals.

Round goby (Neogobius melanostromus)

The round goby is an aggressive fish, especially when protecting its spawning grounds. It consumes great quantities of food and can eat clams, mussels, plankton, large invertebrates, fish eggs, small fish, and insect larvae. The round goby can feed in total darkness due to a well-developed sensory system that allows it to detect water movement.

It can also feed in fast-moving water by attaching itself to the bottom of a stream or river with a suction-like disk on its underside.

The round goby is capable of rapid population growth and spawns repeatedly during the summer months, with the female producing up to 5,000 eggs each time. It can live in a variety of habitats and compete with native species for food and space. Often the round goby is the only fish that fishermen see in a section of water. This can make many riverbank or lake-front towns less appealing to visiting sport fishermen, who are trying to catch such fish as trout and salmon. One positive side effect is that the round goby eats another invasive species, the zebra mussel. Native predatory fish, such as the walleye, eat round gobies. ■

The top map shows locations where the round goby was documented in 2000. The bottom map shows data from 2009.

CASE STUDY 2

The Indian Mongoose

Indian Mongoose (Herpestes javanicus)

THE INDIAN MONGOOSE grows to around 60 cm (24 inches) and lives as long as 13 years, although 3–4 years is more common in the wild. It is fast moving, and although it mainly eats insects, it will also eat crops, fruits, seeds, birds, eggs, small cats, snakes, frogs, and crabs. Usually solitary creatures, they sometimes live in groups, and their habitat ranges from scrubland to different types of forest to areas where humans live. They breed rapidly, with males able to father offspring when they are only four months old. Each female can produce two to five pups every year.

Seventy-three Indian Mongooses were intentionally introduced to the Hawaiian Islands in 1883. They were imported to eat rats that were destroying the sugar cane crops. However, rats tend to be most active during the night, whereas mongooses are most active during the day, so the plan did not work very well. The Indian Mongoose is suspected in causing the extinction of at least one species of bird in Hawaii, and it has killed significant numbers of other native species. As do many other animals, mongooses can carry rabies and leptospirosis. Leptospirosis is a bacterial disease that causes symptoms ranging from rashes to kidney and liver failure. Mongooses may transfer it to humans if the animals' urine mixes with water supplies. ∎

Leptospirosis can be passed on to humans.

CASE STUDY 3

Zebra Mussel

ZEBRA MUSSELS are native to Eastern Europe. They generally live for four to five years and grow to 5 cm (about 2 inches) in length. The females can reproduce at around two years old and are capable of producing up to one million eggs per year. Adults survive out of water for several days if the temperature is low and humidity is high. Young zebra mussels swim freely and are spread easily by water currents. Adult mussels spread when they attach themselves to objects that have hard surfaces, such as hulls of boats. When the object is moved to a different location, the zebra mussels move with it.

Zebra mussels first appeared in the Great Lakes in 1988, most likely having been flushed into the lakes when ocean going cargo ships discharged ballast water. Zebra mussels feed by filtering algae and plankton from water, with each mussel filtering up to one liter per day. In areas where there are millions of zebra mussels, two major changes to the ecosystem have occurred: the water has become clearer, which is beneficial for some organisms but not others; and the food for native larval fish has decreased. The clearer water can benefit plants that live on the bottom of the lakes because they

Zebra mussels (Dreissena polymorpha) can clog the insides of pipes.

have more access to light and thus grow more. Fish that prefer this type of habitat have actually increased in the Great Lakes. The decrease in food for native larval fish causes fewer of the larval fish to survive, creating a food shortage for the animals that feed on these fish. Zebra mussels also attach themselves to native mussels, clams, crayfish, and turtles, sometimes in such great numbers that these organisms have trouble functioning. Several native species of fish eat zebra mussels, but not enough of them to keep the mussel populations down. Sometimes the colonies block water-intake pipes, restricting water flow and causing problems at power plants and water-supply facilities. ■

CASE STUDY 4

Giant Salvinia

*Giant salvinia
(Salvinia molesta)*

GIANT SALVINIA IS an aquatic plant native to South America that was first found in the United States in 1995. It forms mats as it floats freely on the surface of slow-moving or still freshwater and reproduces asexually when fragments break off to form clones. The plant can double in size in as little as two days, and its mass can double in a week. As the mats grow they form layers as much as a meter thick. The buds of giant salvinia can withstand dry conditions, and the plants can tolerate freezing air temperatures—but not ice—on the surface of the water where they grow.

Giant salvinia can spread on moving water or by clinging to boats and other recreational craft. A single plant can spread over an area of more than 100 sq km (about 40 sq mi) within a three-month period.

The floating mat formed by giant salvinia blocks sunlight from the water and prevents oxygen mixing at the surface. This change in conditions reduces the number and variety of microorganisms living in the water, which in turn means less food for the organisms that feed on them. The rapid spread of giant salvinia can threaten crops, such as rice, and clog irrigation and drinking-water lines. The thick mats can clog waters to the extent that swimming, boating, and fishing become impossible. The mats are also breeding grounds for mosquitoes. ■

This pond has been taken over by a population of giant salvinia.

75

5 One of the goals of *Science in Global Issues* is to teach students that:

1. decisions often involve trade-offs.
2. identifying trade-offs involves analyzing evidence.

Explain to students that in this unit they will make several decisions about fisheries and ecosystem change. In this activity students review the trade-offs involved in the possible introduction of a nonnative species to aid in the recovery of a collapsed oyster fishery. In a decision involving trade-offs, something is given up to gain something else. Since many decisions involve trade-offs, it is important for students to understand that a perfect choice is often not possible. It is possible, however, to recognize and analyze the trade-offs associated with each decision. For example, when asked, "Paper or plastic?" at a store checkout counter, most shoppers make the choice quickly. But there are several trade-offs attached to choosing paper or plastic. A shopper who chooses paper over plastic may do so to avoid generating plastic waste or using up petroleum resources. In requesting the paper bag though, they are contributing to other environmental problems such as increased water and energy usage, and the higher amounts of solid waste and CO_2 emissions associated with making paper bags. Neither choice is particularly beneficial for the environment, and both choices have a downside. Identifying the trade-offs helps clarify the reasoning that is being applied to make a decision, and the strength of the evidence relevant to making the most informed decision.

SCIENCE & GLOBAL ISSUES/BIOLOGY • ECOLOGY

Part B

5 In this section you will read about the benefits and risks of the possible introduction of a nonnative species to try to replenish a fishery. The balance between these benefits and risks is known as a trade-off. A **trade-off** is an exchange of one thing in return for another, giving up something that is a benefit or an advantage, in exchange for something that may be more desirable.

6. Read the summary of a report about the possible introduction of nonnative oysters into Chesapeake Bay.

6 7. Use a Discussion Web to analyze the statement "nonnative oysters should be introduced into Chesapeake Bay as soon as possible." In the Discussion Web, make sure to discuss the characteristics of invasive species the class listed in Step 5. For the Discussion Web, have two members of your group take the role of fishermen who make their living from harvesting oysters in the Bay, and two should act as conservationists who wish to return the Bay to its original state.

7 8. When you have completed the Discussion Web, with your same-role partner, compare your comments and conclusions with the members of your group who took the other role. In your science notebook, write down any questions that you would want answered before making a final decision on whether to introduce the nonnative oyster species into the Bay.

8 9. Under your teacher's direction, discuss as a class the questions that you recorded for Step 8.

Oysters are growing on floats in a creek near Chesapeake Bay as part of an aquaculture education project.

76

To further explore trade-offs, brainstorm with the class a list of decisions they make every day that involve trade-offs. Choose one and talk through the associated trade-offs of deciding one way or another. This practice will familiarize students with ways of identifying and considering trade-offs for this and subsequent activities.

6 (LITERACY) Instruct students to complete Student Sheet, 4.2, "Discussion Web: Oysters in Chesapeake Bay." This literacy strategy provides a framework for students to discuss and organize their ideas about introducing nonnative oysters to Chesapeake Bay. Encourage students to focus on applying evidence from the activity or the unit as they fill out the student sheet. For more information on discussion webs, see Teacher Resources III: Literacy. Each member of the group should first read the summary of the Chesapeake Bay oyster situation in the Student Book. The groups then split into pairs with two students taking the role of conservationists and the other two adopting the role of fishermen. Each pair should complete the Discussion Web based on the perspective that would be associated with their role. In the center box they write the question, "Should nonnative oysters be introduced?" On the left side the heading should be "Conservationists" and on the right "Fishermen." Students list evidence on the appropriate side. A sample completed discussion web is shown below.

7 Members of each group share their completed Discussion Webs within their groups and generate a list of questions they have about the proposal to introduce the nonnative oysters into the bay. Questions from Procedure Step 8 might include what the likelihood is of these nonnative oysters bringing disease into the bay, how likely the oysters are to spread outside the bay, whether the oysters would crowd out and eventually replace the native oysters, and if steps have been taken to reduce the habitat destruction and to improve water quality. Allow time to discuss these, and other questions, with the class. Bring up the dilemma of waiting until all questions have been answered, which could be so long that the bay could suffer irreversible damage, or acting before the problem and potential solution are fully understood. Remind students about the problems that the Indian mongooses and cane toads were supposed to solve. The proposal to introduce nonnative oysters to Chesapeake Bay was in fact rejected in the middle of 2009 after eight years of study. So as to avoid influencing the students, share this information with the class only after the discussion and debate has taken place.

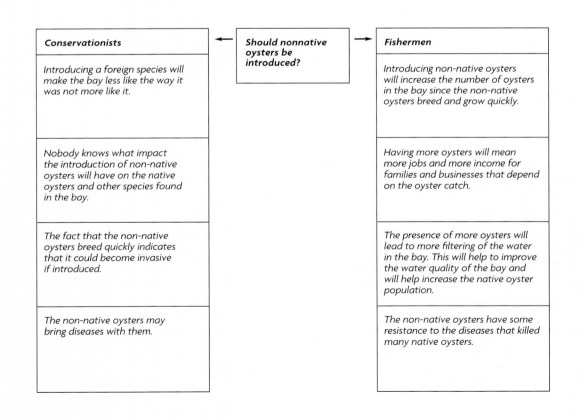

Conservationists	Should nonnative oysters be introduced?	Fishermen
Introducing a foreign species will make the bay less like the way it was not more like it.		Introducing non-native oysters will increase the number of oysters in the bay since the non-native oysters breed and grow quickly.
Nobody knows what impact the introduction of non-native oysters will have on the native oysters and other species found in the bay.		Having more oysters will mean more jobs and more income for families and businesses that depend on the oyster catch.
The fact that the non-native oysters breed quickly indicates that it could become invasive if introduced.		The presence of more oysters will lead to more filtering of the water in the bay. This will help to improve the water quality of the bay and will help increase the native oyster population.
The non-native oysters may bring diseases with them.		The non-native oysters have some resistance to the diseases that killed many native oysters.

8 (LITERACY) You can extend the debate and prepare students for the written assessment by conducting a walking debate. See Teacher Resources III: Literacy for more information. Designate one corner of the room as "introduce nonnative oysters" and a second area of the room as "do not introduce nonnative oysters." Have students stand in the place that they believe is the best action. (If most of the students already agree on a particular option, you may want to assign some of them to the other options to foster the skills of debate and evidence analysis.)

Have students in each area talk among themselves to create a convincing, evidence-based argument that will bring students from the other areas to their own area. They can also develop questions to ask the other groups. Have each group present their argument and respond to any questions. After all groups have spoken, each student individually decides which was the most convincing argument by moving to the area that represents his or her final position.

Possible evidence students may include in their responses for each position is shown in the table at right.

Sample Student Evidence

Conservationists (do not introduce nonnative oysters)	Fishermen (introduce nonnative oysters)
• nonnatives do not grow well when competing with other species • might outcompete native oysters and prevent their recovery	• grow more rapidly than native oysters • can survive a wide range of conditions • are resistant to diseases that kill native oysters • filter the water

Students may include additional evidence from other activities or outside sources as appropriate.

FOLLOW-UP

9 (LITERACY) (ET ASSESSMENT) Use the Analysis Questions to check that students have understood the difference between native, nonnative, and invasive species, and why some nonnative species become invasive while others don't. Use Analysis Question 4 to introduce the EVIDENCE AND TRADE-OFFS Scoring Guide, and discuss with the class what would be required for a Level-3 response to this question. This question is particularly suited to assessing students on their analyses of options and perspectives, and on supporting a position. To help students with this question you may wish to pass out Literacy Student Sheet 2a, "Writing Frame—Evidence and Trade-Offs." This sheet provides a literacy strategy that gives students a structure for communicating their ideas. It helps students organize their ideas into coherent written responses. More information about the use of the writing frame literacy strategy is in Teacher Resources III: Literacy. A sample student Level-3 response is shown under Sample Responses item 4 at the end of this activity.

After students have written their responses, but before you score them, have students participate in a peer writing review. A peer writing review presents a series of questions by which students evaluate each other's writing. It can be especially useful in guiding them to write a complete and coherent response. Students can compare others' responses to the review questions or revise their own writing. Literacy Student Sheet 3, "Writing Review," lists questions and includes space for students to respond. See Teacher Resources III: Literacy for more information on the peer review.

Analysis

1. What characteristics increase the likelihood that a nonnative species will become an invasive species?

2. What conditions in an ecosystem are likely to allow a species to become invasive there? How might scientists use biomes to study this?

3. Biological control involves the introduction of a natural enemy to control the spread of an organism that is considered a pest. What are the trade-offs in introducing a nonnative species to control an established invasive species?

9 4. Summarize the position taken by either the fishermen or the conservationists about the oysters in Chesapeake Bay. Include the evidence that supports that position. Weigh the evidence to make a recommendation for or against the introduction of the nonnative oysters into Chesapeake Bay. Include at least two trade-offs associated with your recommendation.

KEY VOCABULARY	
ecosystem	**invasive species**
evidence	**nonnative species**
habitat	**trade-off**

77

EXTENSION

Explain that invasive species are a concern for every state in the United States and for all countries around the world. Every year hundreds of millions of dollars are spent on prevention and treatment programs and on dealing with the consequences of invasive species. Have students research what the scope of the invasive species problem is in their own state.

SAMPLE RESPONSES

1. Invasive species tend to tolerate a wide range of conditions, breed rapidly, and consume large quantities of food, sometimes eating a wide variety of food sources.

2. If an ecosystem were similar to the native ecosystem of a species, it would probably be easier for it to invade. Scientists might refer to descriptions of biomes to predict where a species might become invasive. For example, if the species is found in a new location that is the same biome as its native ecosystem, it is probably more likely to become invasive.

3. As described in the case studies of the Indian Mongoose in Hawaii and the cane toad in Australia, introducing a nonnative species to control another species does not always work. Even when it does work, other native species could be adversely affected. If the population of the introduced species increases too much, it can cause competition for food and space with native species. The nonnative species may also introduce diseases that might harm or kill native species.

SCIENCE & GLOBAL ISSUES/BIOLOGY • ECOLOGY

REPORT SUMMARY

Chesapeake Bay Oysters

ONE HUNDRED YEARS ago Chesapeake Bay was the world's largest oyster-producing region, with fishermen harvesting more oysters than all other countries combined. Slowly but surely the oyster catch has declined and is now only 1% of what it was at the start of the 20th century. Among the factors causing this huge drop are destruction of habitat, reduction in water quality, disease, and overharvesting. The decrease in oysters has had a devastating effect on both the environment and the local economy. Without large numbers of oysters, the water in the bay is not filtered sufficiently. This, along with increased runoff rich in nitrogen and phosphorous, has allowed more algae to grow in the waters of the bay. As a result the oxygen levels in the bay are lower. "Dead zones" sometimes form as a result of eutrophication, with lethal consequences for many organisms, including the oysters. More and more families that have traditionally made a living from the oyster and fishing industries are leaving the area every year or having to find a different form of employment.

78

4. (LITERACY) (ET ASSESSMENT) Students' answers will vary. A complete and correct response will include a description of the data and any trends, and an interpretation of why the trends occurred.

Sample Level-3 Response

There is a lot of discussion about the issue of introducing nonnative oysters to Chesapeake Bay. My decision is that the nonnative oysters should be introduced to the bay. My decision is based on the following evidence:

First, it will increase the number of oysters in the bay. The nonnative oysters breed and grow quickly and can grow in the poor water conditions that presently exist in the bay.

Second, having more oysters will mean more jobs and more income for families and businesses that depend on the oyster catch.

Third, the presence of more oysters will lead to more filtering of the water in the bay. This will help to improve the water quality of the bay and will help increase the native oyster population.

Some trade-offs of my decision are that we do not know all of the effects of introducing the nonnative oyster into the bay, especially how it will affect other organisms and whether it will stay in the bay or spread into other areas.

REVISIT THE CHALLENGE

The challenge question asked what characteristics would increase the likelihood that a nonnative species would become an invasive species. The activity provided much of the answer to this question but a more complete answer will involve extending the final discussion a little further. As part of the summary discussion with the class, make sure that you include the following points:

- The characteristics common to many invasive species include rapid reproduction (for example, short gestation period, high number of offspring, ability to breed from a young age, ability to reproduce sexually and asexually), fast growth, nonspecific food needs, tolerance of a wide range of conditions, and ability to disperse to new areas.

- The environment plays a role in whether an organism can become established, in terms of whether there are sufficient resources and if there are predators or other mechanisms by which the growth of a population might be controlled. Essentially if the organism is able to exploit a habitat in the new environment, it can become established.

- If this habitat is occupied at the expense of other organisms in the environment, the species is regarded as invasive.

- If the organism damages resources that support the local economy, it is classed as invasive (for example, reducing fishing, farming, and hunting). Finally, if an introduced organism brings disease to the local people, it is considered invasive (for example, the Asian tiger mosquito spreading yellow fever or the Indian Mongoose being a vector for *Leptospirosis)*.

Nonnative oysters, Crassostrea ariakensis *(left), are much larger than the native oysters,* Crassostrea virginica *(right).*

Numerous efforts have been made to improve the Chesapeake Bay ecosystem and to restore the oyster resources of the bay. One proposal made in the early years of this century involved the potential introduction of a species of oyster that is native to the coasts of Asia, *Crassostrea ariakensis.* The hope was that this species would thrive, and filter the polluting algae from the bay's waters, improving conditions sufficiently for native oyster populations to begin to recover.

Crassostrea ariakensis is larger and tends to reproduce more quickly than the native oysters *(Crassostrea virginica).* It also grows much more rapidly than native oysters during the winter months. It can be harvested and sold and would provide a much-needed economic boost to the oyster fishing industry.

Crassostrea ariakensis can survive in a wide range of conditions, including those currently encountered in Chesapeake Bay. However, recent research has indicated that the nonnative species does not reproduce or grow as well when space is limited, for example when it has to compete with other species. *Crassostrea ariakensis* has been shown to have some resistance to the diseases that killed many of the native oysters, but they are susceptible to, and may carry, other diseases and parasites. These diseases, however, are not currently common in the Chesapeake Bay. The nonnative Asian oysters that would be introduced to the bay through the proposal would come from oyster farms in Oregon. ■

79

Invasive Species Information

Name of organism	Round Goby
Effects on economy	decreases types and numbers of certain fish reduces opportunities for fishermen to fish for trout and salmon, thereby reducing the income of the area
Effects on environment	competes with native fish seems to decrease biodiversity eats lots of food eats zebra mussels
Effects on human health	none mentioned
Information about breeding, reproduction, and lifecycle	rapid population growth (5,000 eggs per spawn) aggressive during and after spawning reproduces several times during the summer
Information about food sources and eating habits	consumes large quantities of food eats a wide variety of food can hunt in the dark
Information about habitat and methods of spreading	found in fresh water lives throughout the Great Lakes spreads through rivers and canals
Other information	accidentally introduced in ships' ballast water food for walleye

Invasive Species Information

Name of organism	Indian Mongoose
Effects on economy	eats crops that otherwise might be sold
Effects on environment	eats many native species decreases diversity some native birds have become extinct
Effects on human health	carries disease (Leptospirosis, rabies)
Information about breeding, reproduction, and lifecycle	breeds rapidly at 4 months old males can father pups females can have 2 to 5 pups per year
Information about food sources and eating habits	eats a variety of foods
Information about habitat and methods of spreading	can live in a variety of habitats generally lives alone but can live in groups can live near humans
Other information	intentionally introduced to reduce rat populations in sugar cane fields in Hawaii didn't protect sugar cane as intended generally lives up to 4 years in the wild

Invasive Species Information

Name of organism	Zebra Mussel
Effects on economy	blocks water pipes decreases some fish stocks, increases others
Effects on environment	clears water decreases food for some native fish can harm organisms, such as native mussels, clams, crayfish, and turtles
Effects on human health	none mentioned
Information about breeding, reproduction, and lifecycle	females reproduce at 2 years up to 1 million eggs per year
Information about food sources and eating habits	are filter feeders that eat algae and small animals filter 1 liter of water a day
Information about habitat and methods of spreading	can attach to boat hulls and other solid objects spreads in water currents can survive out of water for a few days
Other information	introduced accidentally in ships' ballast water

Invasive Species Information

Name of organism	Giant Salvinia
Effects on economy	threatens some crops clogs irrigation and water lines clogs waterways—interferes with transportation
Effects on environment	blocks sunlight and prevents oxygen moving through the water surface reduces microorganisms and the organisms that feed on them
Effects on human health	can be a breeding ground for mosquitoes, which can carry disease
Information about breeding, reproduction, and lifecycle	can clone (asexual reproduction) biomass can double in 1 week 1 plant can cover 40 square miles within 3 months
Information about food sources and eating habits	photosynthesis buds can withstand dry conditions can tolerate freezing air temperatures
Information about habitat and methods of spreading	slow-moving or still water spreads by water movement or by boats
Other information	forms large, thick mats very quickly can increase mosquito breeding

5 The Tragedy of the Commons

MODELING • 2 CLASS SESSIONS

OVERVIEW

Students will model "The Tragedy of the Commons" in a simulated fishing lake, showing how human use of resources in an ecosystem alters the sustainability of those resources.

KEY CONTENT

1. Ecosystem services are the natural resources and processes that humans rely on for survival.

2. There are many types of ecosystem services, some of which provide direct benefits and some of which provide indirect benefits.

3. Societies can prevent diminishment of common resources with appropriate regulations and enforcement.

4. Limits, such as fishing limits, must be monitored to ensure they are set at appropriate levels.

5. Scientists create models to compare a theoretical situation to an actual situation.

KEY PROCESS SKILLS

1. Students collect and record data.

2. Students identify and describe trade-offs.

MATERIALS AND ADVANCE PREPARATION

For the teacher
set of 10 Incident Cards
Scoring Guide: EVIDENCE AND TRADE-OFFS (ET)
Scoring Guide: GROUP INTERACTION (GI)

For each group of four students
tray or dish*
bag of 100 orange fish crackers*
bag of 30 yellow fish crackers*
set of 12 Character Cards
timer with beeper*

For each student
Student Sheet 5.1, "The Tragedy of the Commons"
Literacy Student Sheet 2a, "Writing Frame—Evidence and Trade-offs" (optional)
pair of chopsticks or a plastic spoon* (see note below)
cup*
paper towel*
Scoring Guide: EVIDENCE AND TRADE-OFFS (ET) (optional)
Scoring Guide: GROUP INTERACTION (GI) (optional)

Not supplied in kit

Masters for Literacy Skills Sheets are in Teacher Resources III: Literacy. Masters for Scoring Guides are in Teacher Resources IV: Assessment.

Purchase fish crackers in yellow and orange (if not available, substitute similar objects in different colors), and count out into plastic bags for each group. Be sure to alert students if you are using something other than yellow and orange fish crackers.

Students may have some difficulty picking up the fish crackers using the chopsticks, but should be able to pick up enough to stay "alive" during the rounds after a bit of practice. You may want to have students practice with chopsticks before beginning the activity. If you have students who find the chopsticks extremely difficult to use, or who are not able to participate in the activity because they cannot handle chopsticks, you may wish to have them use a plastic spoon instead.

SAFETY NOTE

Be sure that students do not eat the fish crackers that have been used. Make sure that you are aware of any students with severe food allergies, such as a nut allergy, and follow appropriate guidelines from your district and/or state in handling allergies in your classroom.

TEACHING SUMMARY

Getting Started

- Discuss with students the concept of a common as opposed to private property rights.

Doing the Activity

- (GI ASSESSMENT) Students work through the procedure for the Tragedy of the Commons model, discussing the results between each of the four games.

- (LITERACY) (ET ASSESSMENT) Students use the EVIDENCE AND TRADE-OFFS (ET) Scoring Guide to score each other's responses.

Follow-up

- As a class, discuss the results of the activity, and compare the scenarios the students modeled in the fourth game.

BACKGROUND INFORMATION

Aristotle, in the 4th century B.C., was perhaps the first political philosopher to express the theory of the Tragedy of the Commons when he wrote, "That which is common to the greatest number has the least care bestowed upon it." Oxford political economist William Forster Lloyd was the first to develop the theory behind the Tragedy of the Commons in his 1833 book on population control. However, the concept received minimal attention until 1968, when Garrett Hardin published an article in *Science,* titled "The Tragedy of the Commons: The population problem has no technical solution; it requires a fundamental extension in morality."

The premise of the Tragedy of the Commons is that the more people there are who have unrestricted access to a common resource, the more they will exploit it—without considering the consequences for others who have access to the resource or the long-term implications.

This has been demonstrated many times in Earth's history. Some of the most visible examples include the various fishery collapses of the past century (e.g., cod fisheries off the East Coast of the United States, anchovy and sardine fisheries out of Monterey Bay in California), freshwater depletion of lakes and rivers (e.g., Mono Lake in California, Lake Chad in Africa), and pollution of common resources (e.g., Love Canal in New York, worldwide problems with acid rain and air pollution).

Many argue that examples such as these demonstrate the need for some type of regulation of common resources, be it community policing, state or federal policies, or other types of regulation and enforcement. This can take many forms, from international fishing limits to local restrictions on park use. We can look to various indicators to measure the conditions of a common resource. For example, the condition of a fishery might be measured by regular species population counts or mean fish weights. Levels of particulate matter are an indicator of air quality. Ideally indicators and acceptable measures are set in conjunction with the scientific community and other appropriate experts. Indicators have been and are currently being applied successfully to improve the use of community resources. For the Great Lakes region, particularly in Lake Erie, a combination of indicator monitoring, guidelines for and restrictions on emissions, and punitive actions have brought hope that the devastation caused by industrial wastes might eventually be reversed.

Fisheries in Crisis

Many of the world's largest fisheries, such as the Atlantic cod, the Pacific sardine, and the Atlantic halibut, have collapsed and are no longer commercially viable; some have little hope of recovery. Of other fisheries around the world, biologists are in disagreement whether some are in decline or on the brink of collapse. In most imminent danger are the species that reproduce and mature slowly, such as sharks and large tuna, because they are being fished faster than the population can be replenished. Programs such as the Monterey Bay Aquarium's Seafood Watch (see the *Science and Global Issues* page of the SEPUP website *sepuplhs.org/sgi* for more information) have compiled a great deal of research on fisheries and are working to educate consumers on the sustainability of various fisheries. While trying to discourage people from buying and eating certain fish and promoting global sustainability-management practices, these projects could help fisheries recover. The tragedy of the ocean commons, however, may prevail due to economic and political pressure to continue the current practices.

References

Hardin, Garrett (1968). The Tragedy of the Commons: The population problem has no technical solution; it requires a fundamental extension in morality. *Science, 162,* 1243–1248.

GETTING STARTED

1 After students read the introduction, discuss with them what *common* means. In this context, a common is a resource that the community has access to and that may or may not be regulated. You may want to give them an example, such as a local park as opposed to a fenced backyard that only one family has access to, or a public lake compared to one on private property. If there is an example from the community around your school, you may want to use that as well (e.g., a local public golf course vs. a "members only" golf course).

5 The Tragedy of the Commons

ONE MAJOR CAUSE of ecosystem disruption is human activity. One of the things you will study in this unit is how people make decisions about the resources we use and rely on for our survival. Ecologists refer to these resources as **ecosystem services**. Ecosystem services include air, water, and food, which we benefit from directly, but also climate regulation and the cycling of nutrients, which are more indirectly beneficial.

In this activity, you will explore a theory known as the "Tragedy of the Commons." According to the **Tragedy of the Commons**, if people are allowed to use a common resource however they want, they will overuse the resource and eventually cause its destruction. Preventing the resource from being overused is not always easy, and can involve many trade-offs.

In the second half of this activity, you will decide which indicators to use to measure the health of a particular community common, Blue Lake. An **indicator** is an observation or calculation that shows the presence or state of a condition or trend. In this game-type model, the lake will be considered successful if the ecosystem services are maintained—namely, if it has the same or more fish than it started with by the end of the game.

Humans rely on many ecosystem services, such as fish or other food, for our survival.

80

DOING THE ACTIVITY

2 Discuss what a model is and the different ways models are used by scientists. Begin by bringing up familiar examples of models. Ask the students, *What do you think of when you hear the word model?*

Answers may include fashion models, model cars or trains, and the make and model of a vehicle. Ask the students, *How are toy models different than the real thing?*

Answers may include that they are smaller, or they look like the real thing but are not real, or that they are used to play with but do not function as the real object does. Explain to the students that in science, a model is used to represent something that scientists are studying. It might demonstrate how or why something works the way it does, or it might simulate an activity or a process. Tell the students that in this activity they will use a game model that simulates what happens in a lake where people fish.

Challenge

▶ How can the overuse of an ecosystem service be prevented?

MATERIALS

FOR EACH GROUP OF FOUR STUDENTS
100   fish crackers (orange)
 30   fish crackers (yellow or color other than orange)
      tray or dish
      set of 12 Character Cards
      timer that beeps

FOR EACH STUDENT
      Student Sheet 5.1, "Tragedy of the Commons"
      pair of chopsticks
      cup
      paper towel

> **Safety** ⚠
> Don't eat the crackers; many people have handled them. If you have any severe food allergies, such as a nut allergy, alert your teacher before handling the materials to ensure the materials will not harm you.

Procedure

2   **Part A**

1. Place 25 orange fish and 5 yellow fish in the tray in the center of your table. This represents Blue Lake and the fish in it. Each person will use a set of chopsticks to fish in the lake.

2. Read the following rules of the game:

   a. Each person is assigned a fishing limit by picking a Character Card from the cards labeled Game A. These are the instructions for you for this round. Tell your group what is on your card, so that everyone knows the others' fishing limits.

   b. You have 15 seconds for each round, and you will play four rounds per game. Each of you can take as many fish as your fishing limit allows within the 15-second round, but you must use the chopsticks to pick them up, and you must put them in your cup. You may pick up just one fish at a time.

   c. You need to catch at least two fish to continue fishing in the next round. If you catch more than two, score for yourself one dollar per extra orange fish and two dollars per extra yellow fish.

   d. Every fish left on the tray at the end of the round will reproduce one more fish of the same color. And so, add an equal number of fish to the existing population.

   e. During any round of any game, your teacher may hand your group an Incident Card. Follow the instructions on that card for the next full round.

(GI ASSESSMENT) As the students begin, assist groups as needed. The procedure for this activity provides another opportunity to assess the students with the GROUP INTERACTION (GI) Scoring Guide. As you pass by each group as they play the game, place an Incident Card at least once on their table, and tell the students that they have to incorporate whatever is on the card in their next round. If they are at the end of a game, have them incorporate it in the first round of the next game. You may wish to adjust the number of rounds, or allow students to use plastic spoons instead of chopsticks, depending on the results they are getting (e.g., one student is continuously unable to continue to the next round because he or she cannot use chopsticks). If you have a student who is still continuously unable to proceed to the next round, you may want to assign them a role, such as monitoring the timer or being responsible for maintaining the fish population between rounds. Be sure to remind them not to eat the crackers. You should expect approximately the results shown below, depending on students' dexterity with chopsticks:

SCIENCE & GLOBAL ISSUES/BIOLOGY • ECOLOGY

3. Begin playing. At the end of each round record your data for Game A on Student Sheet 5.1, "Tragedy of the Commons," and then empty your cup onto your paper towel. After four rounds, stop, and finish recording the data for Game A on your student sheet.

4. After the fourth round, discuss, as a group, what happened in Game A. Record your responses in your science notebook. Be sure to answer the following questions:

How did your fishing limit affect your behavior?

How did it affect what happened to Blue Lake?

How did each person do (did they catch enough to survive, did they earn extra money)?

What is the condition of the fishing community (did everyone catch enough to survive, did everyone earn some extra money)?

What is the condition of Blue Lake (are there fish left, will there be enough for the next generation)? Is this fishing practice sustainable?

Part B

5. Return all your fish from the previous game to the fish bag. Reset the game by adding or subtracting fish from the tray so that the lake again contains 30 fish (25 orange, 5 yellow).

6. Follow the same rules as for Game A. Repeat Steps 3 and 4, using Character Cards for Game B.

82

Approximate Student Results

Round	Results
A	decrease or complete disappearance of yellow and orange fish
B	trawler captains initially make more money; decrease or complete disappearance of yellow and orange fish
C	all catch enough fish to survive and make a small profit; both fish populations increase
D	varies, depending on limits set by students

4 Discuss with the class the results of the successive games and the effects that the fishing limits had on the fish populations at the end of the game. Students should conclude that having no limits or poorly planned limits are not a successful practice because individuals will make decisions for their own good and not necessarily for the good of the group. Be sure to discuss what each group tried in the fourth game and the results they saw. Sample answers to Student Sheet 5.1, "Tragedy of the Commons," appear in this Teacher's Edition at the end of this activity.

Based on students' results, bring out the idea that the limits must be carefully set, and someone must monitor what is working. Have the students discuss what happened in each round, so that they will explore the different types of limits and their effects on the fish populations. Make sure students also discuss the social and economic implications for each scenario. Discuss the concept of long-term versus short-term goals, how they differ, and what the results might be of each.

Part C

7. Play the game again, following the same rules as before. Repeat Steps 3 and 4, using Character Cards for Game C.

Part D

8. As a group, create a plan for a revised game that you think will continue to keep a population of fish in Blue Lake. Decide what each fisherman's catch limit will be. What will be your indicators that the Blue Lake fishery is continuing to survive? Are there any trade-offs you need to make to keep Blue Lake's fishery going? Record your plan in your science notebook.

9. Play four rounds according to your plan, but keep all of the rules the same as for Game A, and start with the same number of fish. Continue to record your data on Student Sheet 5.1, "Tragedy of the Commons," after each round.

10. As a group, discuss what happened in your game. Record your responses in your science notebook. Be sure to include the following questions:

    Did your new fishing limits change the results of the game as compared to Games A, B, and C?

    How did each person do (did they catch enough to survive, did they earn extra money)?

    What is the condition of the fishing community (did everyone catch enough to continue fishing, did everyone earn some extra money)?

    What is the condition of Blue Lake (are there fish left, will there be enough for the next generation)? Is this fishing practice sustainable?

Analysis

1. What differences did you notice in your results from games A, B, C, and D?

2. What might the results of each game mean in terms of the sustainability of Blue Lake?

3. Were both the orange and yellow fish populations successful? Why or why not?

4. Who was making decisions about the success of Blue Lake each round? What impact did those decisions have on the lake and on the other fishermen?

5. How did each individual affect the success of Blue Lake in the different games? Did this differ from how the group as a whole affected the success of Blue Lake?

 6. How does this game model the idea of the Tragedy of the Commons?

7. How do you think this model compares to a real situation? Explain your reasoning.

FOLLOW-UP

5 (LITERACY) (ET ASSESSMENT) Use Analysis Question 11b to review how the scoring guides work. Remind the students that you discussed in the previous activity how you use the Scoring Guides to provide feedback on the quality of their work. Let them know that this question will give them another opportunity to get used to the Scoring Guides. Remind them that the Scoring Guide does not include the specific content that they should address in their question, but it explains the expectations for a Level-3 and a Level-4 response. A sample Level-3 response appears at the end of this activity under Sample Responses item 11b. Analysis Question 11b is particularly helpful for assessing each student's ability to support a position. This Analysis Question can be scored using the EVIDENCE AND TRADE-OFFS scoring variable. For more information on this assessment, refer to Teacher Resources IV: Assessment. To help students evaluate the trade-offs of their management plan you may wish to pass out Literacy Student Sheet 2a, "Writing Frame—Evidence and Trade-offs." This sheet provides a literacy strategy known as a writing frame, which gives students a structure for communicating their ideas. More information about the use of the writing frame literacy strategy is in Teacher Resources III: Literacy. A sample student response to the Analysis Question, following the writing frame format, is shown in the pages that follow.

After students have written their responses, but before you score them, have students participate in a peer writing review. See Teacher Resources III: Literacy for more information on the peer review and writing frame strategies.

---

8. What factors other than fishing might affect the success of Blue Lake?

9. What role can each of the following play in preventing overuse of common resources?
   a. scientists
   b. individuals
   c. society

10. The air we breathe is considered a global commons because the entire planet shares it. Many places have severe air pollution. Who should determine how the air is managed in those places and if it is being managed successfully? Why should they be the one(s) to decide?

11. Think about the community you live in.
    a. What are some commons there?
    b. Imagine you are asked to be in charge of a committee that manages your community's commons. What management plan would you suggest to the committee? What indicators would you use to measure how well you were managing the commons? What evidence would you look for to show that you were successful? What trade-offs would you have to make to accomplish this?

KEY VOCABULARY	
ecosystem services	population
evidence	trade-off
indicator	**Tragedy of the Commons**

EXTENSION 1

Have students research successful examples of sustainably managed commons and analyze why they think the management programs were successful. Based on the information they find, they can try to determine why certain management programs are successful where others might not be. They can compare their findings with other group members' findings. Some examples include the Pacific halibut fishery (which will be covered later in this unit), private land reserves in Costa Rica, conservancies in Namibia, and watershed management in Darewadi, a village in Maharashtra, India.

EXTENSION 2

Have students read the original 1968 Tragedy of the Commons article in *Science* (see references), then discuss with their groups how the ideas from this article apply to this activity, their own communities, and the world.

EXTENSION 3

Have students try other modifications with the Tragedy of the Commons game, such as introducing an invasive species of fish (candy fish would work). The invasive fish would be inedible to humans and would outcompete the existing fish of a native population if it dropped below a certain level.

SAMPLE RESPONSES

1. Results for Games A, B, and C should be approximately the same for all groups, depending on students' familiarity with chopsticks. In Games A and B, this fish populations decreased dramatically or disappeared. In Game C the populations were sustained and likely increased. Results for Game D will vary according to the limits the students set.

2. Based on our results, we know that the highest the limits can be set is three fish per person each round in order for the fish populations to survive.

3. The results were not the same for the orange and yellow fish. The yellow fish went extinct in the lake much faster than the orange because they have a smaller population.

4. Each fisherman made their own decisions, depending on the card they got. If someone took lots of fish, the others did not get as many. When everyone took fewer fish everyone had enough.

5. In the first game, when everyone was allowed to take as many fish as they wanted, we ran out of fish very quickly because everyone took lots of fish. The only person who wasn't taking a lot of fish was Jane, who doesn't know how to use chopsticks, and she barely survived. In the second game, the fish disappeared because, even though two people were fishing in a way that could have kept the population going, the other two people had fishing limits high enough to wipe out the population. The

third game worked the best because everyone had low limits that they had to stick to. There were enough fish for everyone and even more fish at the end than when we started. We also saw that in the last game, when each person took just one more fish per round, the population dropped to zero, showing that if the whole group takes just a little bit more each time it is not sustainable.

6. This model shows that everyone has to work together if they are using a common resource. When we all were thinking only from our own perspective in the first round, we showed that this leads to the fishing in the lake being destroyed. When we all had lower limits, we prevented the tragedy of the commons, and our fish did very well. But we also showed in Game D that people sharing a common resource have to be very careful: we thought that if we each took just one more fish each round, we would still have enough fish, but we didn't. We saw how if we abuse our natural resources, such as food, we will not have enough resources to last a long time.

7. This model compares fairly well to real life. If you think of the lake representing the ocean, you can see that everyone is fishing out of the same resource. It is harder for people to see this because the ocean is so big. It seems like there would always be enough fish, but even the ocean has limits.

8. Blue Lake might be affected by pollution, which could kill the fish, or there could be a disease that could kill the fish. There also might be an increase in the population of predators eating the fish.

9. a. Scientists can help to keep track of how many fish there are and if the fish are healthy.

    b. People would not eat fish if they knew that too many fish were being caught or they were being caught in a harmful way.

    c. Society could get the government to set limits on fishing.

10. Students' answers will vary. A complete and correct answer would include a suggestion for whom should make decisions about how the air is managed and the student's reasoning behind his or her choice.

11. (ET ASSESSMENT) Students' answers will vary. A complete and correct response would include an example of a common in their community, viable suggestions for managing that common, the indicators they would monitor, evidence of success, and trade-offs.

Sample Level-3 Response

a. In my community there is a vacant lot near my house.

b. There is a lot of discussion about the issue of the vacant lot near my house. My decision, if I were in charge of a committee to manage it, would be to ask the city to set a large fine for littering there, and then to set up a "community watch" system, and monthly work days to help clean up the lot. One indicator that would show success would be the amount of garbage, and the evidence would be if there is less garbage, our plan is working. Another indicator would be how many kids are playing in the lot. If more kids are playing in the lot, our plan is successful. Overall, the less garbage and the more kids playing, the more successful our plan is. Some trade-offs of my decision are that people would have to be willing to give up their time to clean up the lot, and to be part of the community watch, but everyone would benefit from the cleaner lot.

REVISIT THE CHALLENGE

Encourage students to be creative in their answers, and to think about different types of ecosystem services, not just the lake used in the scenario. Based on the activity students might suggest more government regulation of commons, or more community-based decision-making around the use of commons.

Sample Student Response: Tragedy of the Commons

Game A
Fishing limit: unlimited orange, unlimited yellow fish per round

Round number	Starting number of fish in lake		Number of fish you caught		$ you earned ($1 per extra orange fish caught, $2 per yellow fish)
	Orange	Yellow	Orange	Yellow	
1	25	5	3	3	$7
2	10	0	6	0	$4
3	12	0	5	0	$3
4	0	0	0	0	$0
Total			14	3	$14

End Result (what's going on in your lake):

No fish left after Round 3.

Game B
Fishing limit: 3 orange, 3 yellow fish per round (6 total)

Round number	Starting number of fish in lake		Number of fish you caught		$ you earned ($1 per extra orange fish caught, $2 per yellow fish)
	Orange	Yellow	Orange	Yellow	
1	25	5	3	2	$5
2	10	0	2	0	$0
3	2	0	0	0	$0
4	0	0	0	0	$0
Total			5	2	$5

End Result (what's going on in your lake):

No fish left after Round 3.

Game C
Fishing limit: 3 orange, 0 yellow fish per round

Round number	Starting number of fish in lake		Number of fish you caught		$ you earned ($1 per extra orange fish caught, $2 per yellow fish)
	Orange	Yellow	Orange	Yellow	
1	25	5	3	1	$3
2	26	2	3	1	$3
3	28	0	3	0	$1
4	32	0	3	0	$1
Total			12	2	$8

End Result (what's going on in your lake):

We have way more fish of both colors than when we started.

Game D
Fishing limit: 3 orange, 1 yellow fish per round

Round number	Starting number of fish in lake		Number of fish you caught		$ you earned ($1 per extra orange fish caught, $2 per yellow fish)
	Orange	Yellow	Orange	Yellow	
1	25	5	3	0	$1
2	30	6	3	0	$1
3	40	8	3	0	$1
4	60	12	3	0	$1
Total			12	0	$4

End Result (what's going on in your lake):

We have more of each fish but not as much as in Game C.

6 Producers and Consumers

INVESTIGATION • 1–2 CLASS SESSIONS

OVERVIEW

In this activity, students observe plankton and investigate the link between plankton productivity and sustainable fisheries.

KEY CONTENT

1. Ecological biodiversity is the number of species found in a given ecosystem or area.

2. Biodiversity allows for a variety of habitats to be filled within an ecosystem.

3. Microscopic organisms, such as some plankton, form the basis for large food webs.

4. Fishery productivity can be linked to plankton productivity.

KEY PROCESS SKILLS

1. Students use microscopes to make and record observations.

2. Students analyze data.

MATERIALS AND ADVANCE PREPARATION

For the teacher

Transparency 6.1, "Marine Food Web"
Transparency 6.2, "Fish Tank Problem" (optional)
Scoring Guide: ANALYZING DATA (AD)
a supply of local pond water (optional)*

For each group of four students

8 prepared slides of preserved plankton (closterium, copepods, diatoms, euglena, rotifers, oscillatria, stentor, volvox)
dropper*
15-mL dropper bottle of methyl cellulose*
graduated cup with water containing live plankton

For each pair of students

microscope slide with a well*
coverslip*
microscope*

For each student

Student Sheet 6.1, "Plankton Dichotomous Key" (optional)
Science Skills Student Sheet 6, "Parts of a Microscope" (optional)
Science Skills Student Sheet 7, "Microscope Magnification" (optional)
calculator (optional)*

Not supplied in kit

Pond water is provided with your live specimen order. Order your specimens according to the instructions provided in the kit. Check the plankton under a microscope prior to class to determine if they are too active for close observation. If so, students will need to add methyl cellulose to their plankton samples to slow the planktons' movements. If not, direct your students to eliminate the methyl cellulose step. To tie this activity to your locale, try to obtain a local source of pond water for students to view as well. Check it in advance under a microscope to be sure it contains plankton.

Review the calculations students will perform in Part C, and decide if you will provide calculators for them to use.

SAFETY NOTE

Be sure that students are careful when carrying the microscopes and that they carry them properly, using two hands (one hand underneath and one hand holding the microscope arm). Make sure that students wash their hands thoroughly after the laboratory.

TEACHING SUMMARY

Getting Started

- The class explores the role of phytoplankton in marine ecosystems.

Doing the Activity

- Students observe plankton.
- Students examine the connection between plankton and the Atlantic herring fishery.

Follow-up

- The class discusses the connection between plankton and sustainable fishing.

BACKGROUND INFORMATION

There are eight types of plankton used in this lab. The four phytoplankton are oscillatoria, diatoms, closterium, and volvox. The four zooplankton are rotifers, copepods (commonly called cyclops), euglena, and stentor. These plankton are all fairly common and widespread, but plankton as a group are much more diverse. The term plankton refers to any drifting organism that lives, at least during the planktonic stage of its life, in open waters of the ocean or other body of water. Plankton are not associated with the bottom of the ocean (or lakes), and their movements are at the mercy of the currents. Many plankton are microscopic, but some plankton, such as jellies, can be very large. The lion's mane jelly *(Cyanea capillata)*, the largest known jelly in the world, can reach a diameter of 2.3 m with tentacles up to 36.5 m. There are also many aquatic species that have a planktonic stage, but then become non-planktonic. For example, many crabs, fish, cephalopods, and other organisms have a planktonic larval stage.

In both marine and freshwater systems plankton are generally the basis of the food web. Phytoplankton are the major source of primary production in most aquatic ecosystems, supporting organisms that are much larger. Zooplankton also form a major portion of the ocean biomass (the mass of all living organisms in a given ecosystem). A third group of plankton, bacterioplankton, break down organic material and play an important role in recycling nutrients in the ecosystem. The biomass of plankton has a direct impact on both fisheries and the general state of the ecosystem. Without the support of these primary producers and consumers, fisheries and entire ecosystems can collapse. Phytoplankton also play a key role in carbon sequestration, and are responsible for a large percentage of the oxygen production on Earth.

GETTING STARTED

1 ⓘ Show the class Transparency 6.1, "Marine Food Web." Ask them to write in their science notebooks a response to: *What role do the phytoplankton and zooplankton play in the sustainability of the ecosystem shown in this food web?*

Students will likely say that several organisms feed on the plankton, and because of this they support many other populations in the ecosystem.

DOING THE ACTIVITY

2 After students have read the introduction, write the following statements in a visible place: "Phytoplankton are producers." "Zooplankton are consumers." It is likely that your students will remember from middle school that producers are able to transfer light energy into chemical energy stored in sugars, whereas consumers must obtain the energy by eating other organisms. Review these concepts as necessary. Students will explore these concepts in greater depth in Activity 7, "Energy Flow Through an Ecosystem." As students examine the plankton in the illustration at the end of Part B in their Student Books, ask, *Based on the figure, which organisms do you think are phytoplankton, and which are zooplankton? What evidence do you have to support your claim?*

Allow student pairs to discuss this question, and ask for volunteers to share their thoughts with the class. Students are likely to suggest that those that look like they have structures that aid in motility are zooplankton. Students may also suggest that being able to see chloroplasts, a key organelle in photosynthesis, would be one type of evidence to support the identification of the producers. The image in the Student Book does not show chloroplasts in any of the organisms that are phytoplankton, but students will use the microscope to explore these organisms in more detail.

---

6 Producers and Consumers

1 IN KELP FORESTS or coral reefs near the shore of the ocean it is easy for us to see the various parts of an ecosystem, especially because the near-shore ecosystems tend to be particularly productive and have a high level of biodiversity. The level of biodiversity in an ecosystem, however, is not always obvious. For example, consider the open ocean: huge and deep bodies of waters away from coasts and continental shelves. The open ocean is an ecosystem that supports populations of fish, whales, and other animals. Think about a tuna or a whale in the middle of the ocean, far from any land, reef, or kelp forest. What does it eat? Where does its oxygen come from?

Much of the life in the open ocean consists of free-floating organisms called plankton. **Plankton** are drifting organisms that live for at least part of their life in the open ocean or other body of water. The majority of plankton are minuscule; in fact, one drop of ocean water can contain thousands of plankton. Most plankton inhabit the top 20 m (about 66 feet) of the water. Those are concentrated in this narrow layer of the ocean because that is as deep as sunlight penetrates water fairly easily. This light allows plankton that are capable of photosynthesis—phytoplankton—to survive. Phytoplankton are responsible for nearly half of the oxygen production on Earth! Other plankton, called zooplankton, are consumers that feed on phytoplankton or other zooplankton. Plankton are the sole food source for most larval fish and many open-ocean consumers. The blue whale is the largest living organism in the world. It's a consumer, and its diet consists entirely of plankton, which it strains from the water with the baleen plates in its mouth.

2

One blue whale (Balaenoptera musculus) consumes up to 4,100 kg of plankton, consisting of more than 300 different species every day.

3 Review your expectations for handling and using a microscope. If needed, review basic microscope technique and guidelines for drawing microscopic images. See Teacher Resources II: Diverse Learners for more information. Pass out the prepared plankton slides. Assist students as necessary as they sketch each organism and record the magnification level. For Part B, if the live plankton are active enough that they need to be slowed down for ease of viewing, demonstrate for students how to prepare a slide of live plankton using methyl cellulose.

Challenge

▶ How do plankton populations affect the sustainability of a fishery?

MATERIALS

FOR EACH GROUP OF FOUR STUDENTS

8   prepared sides of plankton
(closterium, copepods, diatoms, euglena, rotifers, oscillatria, stentor, volvox)
dropper
15-mL dropper bottle of methyl cellulose
graduated cup of water containing live plankton

FOR EACH PAIR OF STUDENTS

microscope
microscope slide with a well
coverslip

Procedure

Part A: Observing Prepared Slides

1. You and your partner will observe eight prepared slides of plankton. Choose one slide, and place it on your microscope stage.

   Hint: Most of the plankton you will see are multicellular creatures similar to the ones shown in the image at the end of Part B. You might also see some single-celled plankton on your slide.

2. Use the information on the next page, "Focusing a Microscope," as guidelines for how to use your microscope.

3. Begin by observing the specimen at the lowest level of magnification, and draw what you see.

4. Observe the specimen at each of the higher levels of magnification, and draw what you see at each level. **Note:** Use only the fine-focus knob for a middle- or high-magnification setting to avoid breaking the slide.

5. In your science notebook, sketch what you observe on the slides, as directed by your teacher. Label your sketch with the name of the plankton on the slide. Make notes on any features you see that help you to decide whether it is a phytoplankton or a zooplankton.

6. Repeat Steps 3–5 with each prepared slide.

Safety ⚠️

3

Always carry a microscope properly with both hands—one hand underneath and one holding the microscope arm. Because you are working with live organisms, wash your hands thoroughly after you are finished.

4 When students have completed Parts A and B, ask them to construct a table in their science notebooks as shown below. Conduct a class discussion to identify each of the organisms observed as phytoplankton or zooplankton, listing their evidence in support of their claim. If you are using the optional Student Sheet 6.1, "Plankton Dichotomous Key," introduce dichotomous keys here. You may want to conceal the names of the plankton on the slides using masking tape or a sticky note.

Organism	Phytoplankton or zooplankton?	Producer or consumer?
Closterium	phytoplankton	producer
Copepod	zooplankton	consumer
Diatoms	phytoplankton	producer
Euglena	zooplankton	consumer
Oscillatoria	phytoplankton	producer
Rotifer	zooplankton	consumer
Stentor	zooplankton	consumer
Volvox	phytoplankton	producer

5 Read the introduction to Part C with the class. Explain that plankton (zooplankton and phytoplankton) are fundamental organisms in most aquatic ecosystems. Their population sizes directly influence the sustainability of many ecosystems and fish populations. For example Atlantic herring are a small fish found along the East Coast of the United States that are commonly known as sardines or herring. The Atlantic herring were heavily fished in the 1960s. Plentiful populations supported a thriving fishery that caught, canned, and exported herring worldwide. When the population crashed due to overfishing, measures were taken to restore the population, which is now considered to be recovered.

Focusing a Microscope

Be sure that your microscope is set on the lowest power before placing your slide onto the microscope stage. Place the slide on the microscope stage. Center the slide so that the sample is directly over the light opening, and adjust the microscope settings as necessary. If the microscope has stage clips, secure the slide in position so that it does not move.

Observe the sample. Focus first with the coarse-focus knob, and then adjust the fine-focus knob.

After switching to a higher power magnification, be careful to adjust the focus with the fine-focus knob only.

Return to low power before removing the slide from the microscope stage.

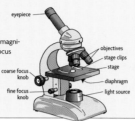

Part B: Searching for Plankton

7. Use the dropper to place a drop of water containing live plankton into the well of a microscope slide.

8. If your teacher directs you to, add one drop of methyl cellulose to the drop on the slide.

9. Carefully touch one edge of the coverslip to the water, at an angle. Slowly allow the coverslip to fall into place. This should prevent trapping of air bubbles under the coverslip.

10. Center the slide so that the well is directly over the light opening, and adjust the microscope settings as necessary.

Placing the coverslip.

11. Begin by observing the sample on the lowest objective lens. You may need to search the slide to find specimens, and they may move across your field of view.

4 12. Draw at least two different organisms that you observe. For each drawing be sure to record the level of magnification. Refer to the drawings on the next page to help you identify the organisms in your drawings.

87

---

6 Explain that biomass means the mass of all living organisms in a given ecosystem. The biomass of the Atlantic herring population cited in Procedure Step 13 is the estimated mass of all of the Atlantic herring in the fishery. Point out that the unit "t" stands for "metric tons." It may help students to visualize the amounts in this problem if you tell them that a one-dollar bill has a mass of approximately 1 gram. This means that a stack of 10 one-dollar bills would have a mass of about 10 g. You may also want to have something on hand that has a mass of approximately 10 g, such as 10 g of duckweed, or two nickels. The mass for one Atlantic herring is on average 0.125 kg. Using the dollar bill visualization, this would weigh about the same as $125 in one-dollar bills. Assist students as necessary in performing the calculations. If necessary, use Transparency 6.2, "Fish Tank Problem," to model the calculations for your students. Sample student calculations are shown below.

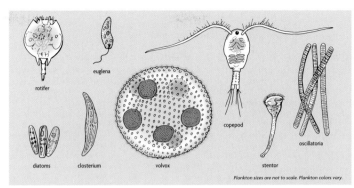

SCIENCE & GLOBAL ISSUES/BIOLOGY • ECOLOGY

euglena

rotifer

diatoms   closterium   volvox   copepod

oscillatoria

stentor

Plankton sizes are not to scale. Plankton colors vary.

Some of these microscopic plankton are phytoplankton and are able to perform photosynthesis. Others are zooplankton that consume the phytoplankton.

5 **Part C: Calculating Plankton Biomass**

The plankton you have been examining are only a few examples of the thousands of species of plankton found in the oceans and freshwater bodies around the world. The Atlantic herring *(Clupea harengus)* fishery is one of the largest commercial fisheries on the east coast of the United States. A **fishery** is an industry that catches or raises a specific type of fish or shellfish to be processed or sold. To better understand the link between plankton and this fishery, complete the calculations below in your science notebook.

6 **13.** It is estimated that the mature Atlantic herring population today has a biomass (total weight of the population) of approximately 2 million metric tonnes (2 billion kg). If an average adult Atlantic herring weighs 0.125 kg, how many adult Atlantic herring are there in the entire population?

Hint: $\dfrac{kg}{0.125 \text{ kg per fish}} = \underline{\hspace{2cm}}$ fish

14. An adult Atlantic herring consumes, on average, 10 g of plankton per day. How much plankton would the adult Atlantic herring population consume in a day?

15. In some places, human impacts on the marine environment, such as coastal erosion, global warming, and pollution, have caused up to a 70% decrease in the biomass of plankton. If there were a severe reduction of plankton available to the Atlantic herring population, and therefore a 55% decrease in the herring, how many mature Atlantic herring would be supported by the ecosystem? How many kilograms?

88

Procedure Step 13

$\dfrac{2,000,000,000 \text{ kg}}{0.125 \text{ kg per fish}} = 16,000,000,000 \text{ fish}$

Procedure Step 14

$\dfrac{16,000,000,000 \text{ fish} \times 10 \text{ g plankton}}{1 \text{ fish}} = 160,000,000,000 \text{ g plankton}$

Procedure Step 15

Calculate 45% of the fish population calculated in Procedure Step 13. Note: You could also calculate 55% of the population and subtract that from the original population.

$16,000,000,000 \text{ fish} \times 0.45 = 720,000,000 \text{ fish}$

$720,000,000 \text{ fish} \times 0.125 \text{ kg per fish} = 90,000,000 \text{ kg}$

$90,000,000 \text{ kg} \times \dfrac{1 \text{ mt}}{1,000 \text{ kg}} = 90,000 \text{ t}$

FOLLOW-UP

7 ✓ Use students' answers to Analysis Questions 4–5 to discuss the connection between plankton and the sustainability of fisheries. This is an opportunity to make sure students understand that these microscopic organisms play a large role in the sustainability of fisheries. Human actions that affect plankton are likely to have far-reaching affects on aquatic ecosystems since plankton are producers that capture light energy and serve as a food source for many organisms higher in the food web. Analysis Question 5 is also an opportunity for a Quick Check of students' skills at analyzing data. The inferences and conclusions they make are components of the ANALYZING DATA Scoring Guide. Students should be able to relate that if the plankton biomass decreased significantly, the herring population would also decrease, which would make the current levels of herring fishing unsustainable.

Analysis

1. Identify at least two similarities and two differences between phytoplankton and zooplankton.

2. What is the role of phytoplankton in an aquatic ecosystem?

3. Did you observe evidence of the roles of phytoplankton or zooplankton in your sample of live plankton? Explain.

4. How might changes in the amount of plankton in the ocean affect the ocean's ability to provide a sustainable source of food for the world's human population? Explain.

7

5. Strict fishing limits were set on the Atlantic herring fishery in the 1970s and 1980s because the population had dropped to about 75,000 metric tons. There was alarm that the population was so small that it was not sustainable if unlimited fishing continued. By the early 1990s the population returned to historically normal levels, and the yearly catch limit now ranges from 80,000 to 124,000 metric tons to keep the fishery sustainable.

   a. If the scenario in Procedure Step 15 were to occur, would the Atlantic herring fishery still be sustainable? Explain what indicator(s) you would use to monitor this.

   Hint: The biomass of the Atlantic Herring can be found in Procedure Step 13.

   b. What do you think would happen to the sustainability of the plankton population if this scenario occurred? Explain.

KEY VOCABULARY	
biodiversity	phytoplankton
consumers	**plankton**
fishery	producers
organism	zooplankton

SAMPLE RESPONSES

1. Two similarities are that all of the plankton are microscopic and live in aquatic environments. Differences include that the zooplankton have structures that help them move, but the phytoplankton do not. The phytoplankton are green because they contain chloroplasts, like plants, but the zooplankton do not.

2. Phytoplankton are producers and thus capture energy from the sun and use it to produce stored chemical energy. Other organisms eat the producers and use that energy.

3. The phytoplankton were green, like leaves in a plant, and probably have the same materials or structures for photosynthesis. The zooplankton's structures that allow them to move would let them get to the phytoplankton or other plankton so they could eat them because they are consumers.

4. If the plankton population is healthy, it can feed a lot of fish. Healthy, sustainable fish populations provide a source of food for humans in certain cultures. As long as fishing is kept at a sustainable level, the plankton can support the fish and there will be fish for food.

5. ✓ a. No, it would not be sustainable because there would only be about 90,000 metric tons of fish, and the fishing limits are higher than the population total. Even if they used the lower fishing limit, 80,000 t, that would be most of the population. Population levels would be your indicators.

    b. If this scenario occurred, the plankton population would probably get much larger because there would be fewer predators. But eventually they might run out of food, which would cause the population to be unsustainable.

REVISIT THE CHALLENGE

Make sure students understand that plankton are key to the fishery in the activity because they are the basis of the ecosystem. Students will explore the roles of producers and consumers in more detail in the next activity.

Plankton Dichotomous Key

Use the following key to determine what genus of plankton you are examining under the microscope. Look at each slide on low, medium, and high power on the microscope. In the table below, record all of the steps you follow to identify each plankton species.

1a. Most plankton are symmetrical in two planes . . . . *go to 2*

1b. Plankton are asymmetrical or symmetrical in only one plane . . . . *go to 6*

2a. Most plankton are spherical, with smaller, dark circles inside . . . . Volvox

2b. Most plankton are not spherical . . . . *go to 3*

3a. Most plankton are rectangular . . . . *go to 4*

3b. Most plankton are not rectangular . . . . *go to 5*

4a. Most plankton are stacked in multiples . . . . Diatoms

4b. Most plankton are not stacked, but are long and thin . . . . Oscillatoria

5a. Plankton is two to four times as long as it is wide . . . . Euglena

5b. Plankton is more than five times long as it is wide .Closterium

6a. Plankton has clear appendages . . . . .Copepods

6b. Plankton does not have clear appendages . . . . *go to 7*

7a. Most plankton are clearly defined, with a tail-like end . . . . .Rotifers

7b. Most plankton are not clearly defined, with an irregular, blob-like shape . . . . Stentor

Plankton Name	Steps to Identification
Closterium	1a, 2b, 3b, 5b
Copepods	1b, 6a
Diatoms	1a, 2b, 3a, 4a
Euglena	1a, 2b, 3b, 5a
Oscillatoria	1a, 2b, 3a, 4b
Rotifers	1b, 6b, 7a
Stentor	1b, 6b, 7b
Volvox	1a, 2a

7 Energy Flow Through an Ecosystem

INVESTIGATION • 2 CLASS SESSIONS

OVERVIEW

Students create a food web of a kelp forest ecosystem with which they explore the flow of energy between ecosystem organisms. They predict the effect of different events on the food web and the ecosystem. Students then construct an energy pyramid to examine how much energy is stored at each level of a food web.

KEY CONTENT

1. Producers form the bases of food webs, and when consumed, provide energy for consumers.

2. Food is as an energy source.

3. There are many varieties of consumers. Some are herbivores and eat only producers; some are carnivores and eat only other consumers; some are omnivores and eat both; and some are decomposers and eat only dead and decaying organic matter.

4. A food web is a diagram that shows energy flow through an ecosystem.

5. An energy pyramid is a diagram that shows how much energy is available for each level of organism (producers, consumers, etc.).

6. Consumers are placed at certain levels according to what they consume. Primary consumers eat producers, secondary consumers eat primary consumers, and tertiary consumers eat secondary consumers.

7. Ecosystems depend on a diversity of organisms to function.

8. Removal of one or more species from a food web can cause an ecosystem to collapse.

9. Some events that disturb an ecosystem have only a short-term effect, while others are long lasting.

KEY PROCESS SKILLS

1. Students make predictions.

2. Students identify and describe trade-offs.

MATERIALS AND ADVANCE PREPARATION

For the teacher

Transparency 7.1, "Organisms in an Ecosystem"

Transparency 7.2, "Food Web for an Ecosystem"

Student Sheet 7.1, "Kelp Forest Energy Pyramid"

Scoring Guide: UNDERSTANDING CONCEPTS (UC)

Literacy Student Sheet 5, "KWL," partially filled out in Activity 1, "Ecosystems and Change," and Activity 3, "Biomes"

For each group of students

sheet of chart paper*

set of colored pencils

For each pair of students

set of 12 Kelp Forest Organism cards

set of 4 Ecosystem Event cards

For each student

Student Sheet 7.1, "Kelp Forest Energy Pyramid"

Scoring Guide: UNDERSTANDING CONCEPTS (UC) (optional)

Not supplied in kit

Masters for Scoring Guides are in Teacher Resources IV: Assessment.

TEACHING SUMMARY

Getting Started

- Explore students' understanding of food chains and food webs.

Doing the Activity

- Students build a food web for the kelp forest ecosystem.

- Students use the food web to predict the short- and long-term effects of several events on the kelp forest ecosystem.

Follow-up

- ✓(UC ASSESSMENT) Students construct an energy pyramid for the kelp forest ecosystem and use the pyramid to evaluate proposals for a fishery's conservation.

BACKGROUND INFORMATION

Food webs are a visual tool for representing the links between organisms in an ecosystem. They show how energy flows among organisms, and the interconnectedness of species. Energy pyramids support this structure by showing the amount of energy that passes from one organism to another and from one consumer level to another. A pyramid shape represents the energy present at each trophic level in a food web. Because in an ecosystem energy moves from the producers to the various levels of consumers, there is less biomass and available energy at each subsequent level. Each organism takes in a finite amount of energy through the food it consumes, or, for producers, the light energy it takes in. The energy sustains life and is used to build and repair cells; and some is lost as heat. When an organism consumes another organism, a portion of the stored energy in the consumed organism is available for the new organism. The energy available to the consumer varies, depending on the ecosystem and the organisms, and can range from 5–25%.

If you assume that 10% is available at each new level in a meadow ecosystem, for example, a field mouse that eats grass obtains approximately 10% of the energy stored in the grass. If a snake eats the field mouse, the snake would only get 10% of the field mouse's energy. If you consider the amount of energy in the grass (producer) to be 100 units, the field mouse (primary consumer) gets 10 units of energy, and the snake (secondary consumer) gets 1 unit of energy. Understanding this concept allows students not only to see the amount of energy flow but also to see that there generally are no consumers above the tertiary level because there would not be enough energy available to sustain them. Decomposers will normally consume dead organisms at different levels of the energy pyramid, overall acquiring enough energy for themselves.

GETTING STARTED

1 Project Transparency 7.1, "Organisms in an Ecosystem." Ask students what the diagram shows about the relationships between organisms. Students should conclude that, because the images of the organisms are simply in a line, the diagram does not tell anything of their interrelationships or of the energy that flows from one to the next. Guide students, as needed, to these conclusions. Next, display Transparency 7.2, "Food Web for an Ecosystem." Ask the class, *What does this diagram show about the relationships between these organisms? What does this diagram show about the flow of energy between these organisms?*

Provide time for students to discuss their ideas with a partner, and then ask for volunteers to present their ideas to the class. Students should understand that the arrows indicate the flow of energy between organisms.

---

7 Energy Flow Through an Ecosystem

This harbor seal (Phoca vitulina) *is swimming in a forest of giant kelp.*

NOW THAT YOU are familiar with producers and consumers, you are going to learn about how these organisms interact within an ecosystem. Picture a seal swimming in the Pacific Ocean just off the coast of California. Chances are this seal is among a forest of seaweed including a species called giant kelp. Giant kelp *(Macrocystis pyrifera)* is a type of algae that grows up to two-thirds of a meter a day, and over 45 m (about 148 feet) in height. At its base is a woven knot of rootlike branches called a holdfast that attaches to rocks on the ocean floor. The kelp grows in clusters with each plant shooting upward to the surface, then spreading out and sheltering thousands of organisms in a complex ecosystem.

The kelp forest ecosystem is often compared to an underwater tropical rainforest, in part because of its high levels of biodiversity. The kelp are tall, with long leaf-like structures that create a canopy that blocks the light at lower ocean depths, providing habitat and nourishment for organisms that thrive in limited light conditions. Many species of aquatic organisms, such as sea urchins and anchovies, live and reproduce on and among the long strands.

When organisms in the kelp ecosystem die, other organisms, including specialized bacteria, consume their remains, keeping the nutrients flowing through the ecosystem. These essential organisms are called **decomposers.**

1 One way to show these interrelationships between the organisms in an ecosystem is by creating a **food web,** mapping what each organism eats and how the energy flows through an ecosystem. In the last activity the food web included plankton, herring, and whales. In this activity you will construct a food web for a kelp forest ecosystem and from it predict what will happen to the ecosystem in various circumstances.

Challenge

▶ How can we use food webs to predict the short- and long-term effects of particular events on an ecosystem?

90

DOING THE ACTIVITY

2 Each Kelp Ecosystem Organism Card that contains a producer has a dotted line across the middle, separating two metabolic processes performed by these organisms— photosynthesis and respiration. Note that the images for each organism are not to scale. You may find it helpful to suggest that students focus on one of the many pieces of information on the cards, such as "takes in oxygen," or "uses energy from the sun." In sorting the cards, students most likely will break the cards into two piles, one for organisms that use energy from the sun and one for those that do not. Encourage students to attempt additional ways to group the organisms. For example, they might further break down the card pile of organisms that do not use energy from the sun into subgroups based on what they consume.

3 Sample student work for Procedure Step 6 is shown below.

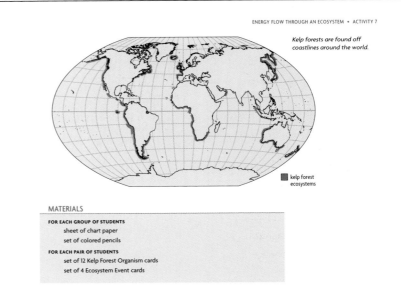

Kelp forests are found off coastlines around the world.

■ kelp forest ecosystems

MATERIALS

FOR EACH GROUP OF STUDENTS
sheet of chart paper
set of colored pencils

FOR EACH PAIR OF STUDENTS
set of 12 Kelp Forest Organism cards
set of 4 Ecosystem Event cards

Procedure

Part A: Construct a Food Web

2 1. With your group, read each Kelp Forest Organism card, noting the similarities and the differences in what substances are going into and coming out of each organism.

2. Sort the organism cards into at least two sets of cards based on similarities in the information about the organisms.

3. As a group, develop a system for further sorting the organisms within each set of cards. When your group comes to agreement, record in your science notebook the organisms in each set of cards and the feature(s) they have in common.

4. Construct an ecosystem food web to show the direction of energy transfer from one organism to another. Begin by laying the giant kelp card on the table in front of your group.

91

Sample Student Responses for Procedure Step 6

Producers	Consumers	Decomposers
acid kelp	bat star	bacteria
cyanobacteria	california	sea urchin
phytoplankton	sheephead fish	bat star
giant kelp	harbor seal	
	pacific herring	
	rockfish	
	sea otter	
	sea urchin	
	zooplankton	

4 Sample student Food Web for Procedure Step 7 is shown at right.

5 Remind students that arrows in a food web point in the direction of the organism that is doing the eating. This is because the arrow represents the pathway of energy as it is transferred from one organism to the next and flows through the ecosystem.

Sample Student Responses for Procedure Step 7

6 Discuss with students the consumer subsets of trophic levels, which are the positions organisms play in a food web. These levels are primary, secondary, and tertiary consumers. Explain that primary consumers eat producers directly, secondary consumers eat primary consumers, and tertiary consumers eat secondary consumers. Direct students to go through the list of consumers and, using the food web, identify the primary and secondary consumers. Students should conclude that some organisms fill more than one trophic level. For example, the rockfish is a primary consumer because it eats phytoplankton, and at the same time a secondary consumer because it eats sea urchins. Sample answers are provided below.

Sample Student Responses for Procedure Step 9

Primary consumers	Secondary consumers	Tertiary consumers
bat star	harbor seal	harbor seal
pacific herring	pacific herring	sea otter
rockfish	rockfish	
sea urchin	sea otter	
zooplankton	sheephead fish	

5. Look through the cards and identify all of the organisms that feed on giant kelp. Place these above the giant kelp card.

3 6. Continue placing cards on the table based on the organisms they feed on, forming a food web. When you have placed all of the cards, show your teacher your work.

4 7. With your group, record the food web on a piece of chart paper.

5 8. Draw arrows from one organism to the next to show how energy passes from one organism to another.

   Hint: Remember that arrows in a food web point in the direction of energy flow—*toward* the organism that is doing the "eating," as shown in the food web below.

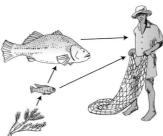

6 9. One way scientists classify organisms in an ecosystem is by describing how the organisms obtain energy. This is known as the organism's trophic role in the food web. Read about these trophic roles in the table below.

Trophic Roles of Organisms in an Ecosystem	
TYPE OF ORGANISM	**HOW ORGANISM GETS ENERGY TO SUSTAIN LIFE**
Producer	Transforms light energy or other energy sources into chemical energy
	The chemical energy is stored in carbon-containing molecules, such as simple sugars or starch.
Consumer	Feeds on other organisms to obtain energy
Decomposer	Feeds on other organisms and dead and decaying biological material and wastes to obtain energy

10. Select a colored pencil to represent each of the trophic roles shown in the table above. Make a key on the side of your chart paper to indicate which color indicates which role.

7 Decide if you will review students' work either in pairs or as a class. Pass out the Ecosystem Event Cards to each group. Suggest ways that students may think of short-term and long-term effects, such as short-term decrease of harbor seals and increase of rockfish and sea urchins in Event 3, and long-term collapse of the ecosystem because the increasing numbers of sea urchins eat all of the kelp that other organisms rely on.

8 When students have completed Procedure Step 14, have the class conduct an Informal Meeting of the Minds. Direct students to find a partner from a different group and compare their analyses. Ask pairs to share their discussions with the class. Make this an opportunity to empha-size the importance of linking cause and effect when predicting the effect of events on food webs. See the sample student response below.

---

11. With your group, color-code each of the organisms in the food web to indi-cate its role in the ecosystem.

7 Part B: Use a Food Web to Predict the Impact of Actions and Events on an Ecosystem

12. Obtain a set of Ecosystem Event Cards from your teacher. With a partner, select and read one of the cards.

13. Using the information provided by your kelp forest food web, discuss how the event described on the card affects the ecosystem.

   Hint: Choose one organism or factor in the web that is affected, and think of the chain of events that will then occur throughout the ecosystem. Scientists call this type of chain of events a trophic cascade.

8 14. Record the following for each event card in your science notebook:

   a. summary of the event
   b. what effect the event will have on the ecosystem in the
      i. short term
      ii. long term
   c. what effect the event will have on the flow of energy through the kelp forest ecosystem

9 Part C: Construct an Energy Pyramid

An energy pyramid is a diagram of the amount of the sun's energy that is stored in each level of organisms in a food web. The organisms use part of this energy, part of it is lost as heat, and part of it is stored and therefore available to other organisms.

15. With your group use the information from the kelp forest food web to place the name of each organism on the energy pyramid on Student Sheet 7.1, "Kelp Forest Energy Pyramid."

10 16. With the class discuss what the energy pyramid shows.

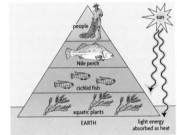

This energy pyramid shows how much energy is stored at each level of the food web.

Sample Student Responses for Procedure Step 14

Summary of event	Short-term effect	Long-term effect
Pesticide used to kill brown moths gets into ground water in California.	Phytoplankton and zooplankton die.	Sea urchins, herring, rockfish, and bat stars have less food and the populations decrease. Sea urchins eat more giant kelp because there is less phytoplankton. Might help sea urchin population stay stable.
New housing development built along the Pacific Coast.	Small plants die, sea urchins die.	Organisms (sea urchins, bat stars) that eat the algae die. Organisms that feed on sea urchins and bat stars (rockfish, sheephead fish, sea otters) have less food as well.
Harbor seals die off.	Most of harbor seals die. Rockfish and sea urchin populations grow.	More sea urchins and rockfish eat more of the giant kelp because the urchins and rockfish are not being eaten by harbor seals. Less kelp means that the numbers of other organisms that depend on kelp decrease.
Nitrogen runoff causes algal blooms.	Cyanobacteria and phyto-plankton popula-tions grow rapidly.	Kelp populations decrease because of the decrease in the amount of sunlight that reaches them due to the algal bloom. Populations that feed on phytoplankton and cyanobacteria (zooplankton and bat stars) increase, given the increase in available food.

9 Pass out Student Sheet 7.1, "Kelp Forest Energy Pyramid." Explain that a pyramid can be used to model the amount of energy that is passed from one set of organisms to the next in a food web. Direct students to fill in the pyramid by placing each organism from the kelp forest ecosystem on the appropriate level(s) of the energy pyramid, based on the trophic role it was assigned in Procedure Step 11. A sample student response to Student Sheet 7.1, "Kelp Forest Energy Pyramid" is shown below.

FOLLOW-UP

10 To evaluate their understanding of the energy pyramid ask students, *Which level contains the most energy?*

The producer level contains the most energy. Then ask, *Which level contains the least amount of energy?*

The tertiary consumers level contains the least energy. Then ask, *Why is there a different amount of energy available to the producers than to the tertiary consumers? What happened to the energy?*

The energy keeps the organisms alive. Some of this energy becomes stored in the organism, and some is lost to the environment as heat.

11 ✓(UC ASSESSMENT) Apply the UNDERSTANDING CONCEPTS (UC) Scoring Guide to students' answers to Analysis Questions 2–4. Analysis Question 7b is an ET QUICK CHECK opportunity to assess students' identification and comparison of trade-offs in the two proposals.

SCIENCE & GLOBAL ISSUES/BIOLOGY • ECOLOGY

Analysis

1. Name one organism from the kelp forest ecosystem that is:

   a producer
   a consumer
   a decomposer

11 2. What is the difference between the role of an organism that is a producer and one that is a consumer? How is a decomposer different from other consumers?

3. Explain the role of the sun in the kelp forest ecosystem.

4. Describe the flow of energy in the kelp forest ecosystem.

5. From the lake food web at right:

   a. predict what would happen if all of the walleye were fished out of the lake

   b. choose an organism other than the walleye, and predict what would happen if it disappeared from the lake

6. Explain why a pyramid is helpful for describing the amount of energy available in a food web.

7. Imagine you are an ecologist who studies kelp forest ecosystems. You have been asked by the federal government to evaluate two plans for managing the California sheephead fishery, which relies on kelp forests. A summary of two proposals follows. Read the proposals and determine:

   a. how the two proposals differ

   b. which proposal you think the government should implement

   In your recommendation include a discussion of the trade-offs you considered.

LAKE FOOD WEB

Proposals for Managing the California Sheephead Fishery

PROPOSAL A

Take population counts of California sheepheads once every three months.

If the fish population is below sustainable levels, decrease the size of the allowed sheephead catch. If the sheephead population is at or above sustainable levels, keep the catch limit at current levels.

Cost to implement this proposal: $750,000

94

Sample Student Response to Student Sheet 7.1

TERTIARY CONSUMERS
sea otters, harbor seals, bacteria

SECONDARY CONSUMERS
Pacific herring
California sheephead
rockfish

PRIMARY CONSUMERS
plankton
bat stars
sea urchins

PRODUCERS
cyanobacteria   acid kelp
phytoplankton   giant kelp

EARTH

sun

EXTENSION

Many of the species in the kelp forest ecosystem are fished commercially. Have students choose one species from the following: sea urchins, California sheephead, Pacific herring, and giant kelp. Provide resources and support as necessary as students research whether the fishery for their selected species is managed sustainably or unsustainably. Encourage them to focus on identifying competing fishery-management plans.

REVISIT THE CHALLENGE

Considering a change to one part of a food web and then thinking through the cascade of changes that follows allow students to understand the interdependence of organisms within an ecosystem. Emphasize that the alteration of any part of the food web can result in short- or long-term effects, sometimes drastic. Remind students that organisms rely on their food for energy and nutrients, both of which are necessary for survival and reproduction.

Return to the KWL chart the class began in Activity 1 and continued in Activity 3. Have students suggest items for the "What I Learned" column, based on what they have learned since Activity 3, "Biomes." A completed sample KWL is shown at right.

PROPOSAL B

Take population counts of California sheepheads and sea urchins once every three months. Measure the density of the giant kelp population once every three months.

If the size of any population is below sustainable levels, decrease the size of the sheephead catch allowed. If the size of each population is at or above sustainable levels, keep the sheephead catch limit at current levels.

Cost to implement this proposal: $1,250,000

KEY VOCABULARY	
biodiversity	energy pyramid
consumers	**food web**
decomposers	producers

Ecological Change KWL

Know	Want to know	Learned
• Humans have changed the environment (cut down rain forests, built buildings, paved roads). • Natural phenomena have changed the environment (volcanoes, earthquakes, tsunamis). • Habitat restoration projects can help restore the environment.	• How much of the environment have people changed? • What can be done to restore the environment? • What happens if we don't restore the environment? • How much does the burning of fossil fuels change the environment?	• Invasive species can change ecosystems dramatically. • Some ecosystems have been changed so much that they cannot support the species that were there originally (dead zones). • Some ecosystems that have changed can be repaired. • Some species that are introduced to ecosystems do not become invasive. • Common resources can be overused and often need to be managed. • Organisms in ecosystems depend on each other for energy. • Producers capture energy from the sun, then it can be used by other organisms in the ecosystem. • If organisms are removed from the ecosystem, it can have long- and short-term effects on the whole ecosystem or just part of the ecosystem.

SAMPLE RESPONSES

1. Students' answers should include at least one organism from each column in the table that follows.

Tropic Roles of Kelp Forest Organisms

Producers	Consumers	Decomposers
acid kelp	bat star	bacteria
cyanobacteria	california	sea urchin
phytoplankton	sheephead fish	bat star
giant kelp	harbor seal	
	pacific herring	
	rockfish	
	sea otter	
	sea urchin	
	zooplankton	

2. (UC ASSESSMENT) A complete answer would include correct definitions for producers, consumers, and decomposers. Students' answers will vary.

Sample Level-3 Response

A producer is an organism that captures energy from the sun that it can use to sustain itself. A consumer cannot, so it must feed on something else for its energy. A decomposer is different from other consumers because it eats dead or decaying things.

3. (UC ASSESSMENT) A correct and complete answer would state that the sun provides light and energy to the producers, which then support the consumers and decomposers. Students' answers will vary.

Sample Level-3 Response

The sun provides energy that producers use in making food for other organisms. Without the sun there would be no source of energy for producers, and this would result in no organisms to support the consumers and decomposers in the food web.

4. (UC ASSESSMENT) A correct and complete answer would include that the energy flows from the sun to producers, then consumers. It would also state that decomposers consume dead and decaying organisms at different levels of the food web. Students' answers will vary.

Sample Level-3 Response

The energy begins with the sun and is transferred to the producers. The producers use the sun energy to make carbon-containing compounds. Then consumers consume the producers, and in this process the energy is passed along to the consumers. This continues with higher-level consumers and the decomposers that feed on consumers and producers.

5. a. The zooplankton population would increase, leading to an increase in the phytoplankton population and the bass and freshwater drum populations. The northern pike would no longer have the walleye to consume, so they would rely on the crayfish, resulting in a decreased crayfish population.

    b. Students' answers will vary depending on the organism they select from the food web shown. A complete response would accurately describe which populations would increase and decrease as a result of removing the selected organism.

6. A pyramid has a large base and gets smaller as you move toward the top. This represents the energy available at each level in a food web. The most energy is contained in the producer population, which is shown at the base of the pyramid. As one moves up the pyramid, the other levels of consumers can be placed to show how the energy available is less at each level of consumer.

7. a. Proposal A costs less than Proposal B and would monitor only the California sheephead population. Proposal B costs more and would monitor the California sheephead population, the sea urchin population, and the giant kelp population.

    b. ✓ Student answers will vary. A correct and complete answer would state which proposal they recommend, why, and what trade-offs are involved. Students' answers will vary. One sample response might be:

    I think that the government should implement Proposal B. The trade-off is that Proposal B is more expensive than Proposal A. However, Proposal B monitors three populations instead of just one, so it will help to protect more of the ecosystem. With Proposal B we might see a problem in the ecosystem before the sheephead population numbers change.

8 Carbon Cycle

INVESTIGATION • 1–2 CLASS SESSIONS

OVERVIEW

Students explore a computer simulation that models the movement of carbon through the global carbon cycle, and they summarize the effect of human activities on the cycle.

KEY CONTENT

1. The carbon cycle is one of several biogeochemical cycles that move elements through multiple reservoirs, allowing the elements to be used repeatedly by living organisms.

2. Reservoirs in the carbon cycle include rocks and soils, the ocean and other bodies of water, producers, consumers, the atmosphere, and fossil fuels.

3. The total amount of carbon in the carbon cycle is fixed; it is neither created nor destroyed.

4. The amount of carbon in each reservoir fluctuates.

5. The carbon in different reservoirs is in different chemical forms, such as carbon dioxide or glucose.

6. Human activities, such as the burning of fossil fuels, have a major impact on the movement of carbon between reservoirs by releasing previously immobile forms of carbon.

KEY PROCESS SKILLS

1. Students make predictions.

MATERIALS AND ADVANCE PREPARATION

For the teacher
Scoring Guide: UNDERSTANDING CONCEPTS (UC)

For each pair of students
computer with Internet access*

For each student
Student Sheet 8.1, "Carbon Cycle" (available online only: see note below)

Scoring Guide: UNDERSTANDING CONCEPTS (UC) (optional)
Not supplied in kit

Masters for Scoring Guides are in Teacher Resources IV: Assessment.

Note: *Student Sheet 8.1, "Carbon Cycle" is found only on the* Science and Global Issues *website (sepuplhs.org/sgi). Sample student answers are also available on the website. Both are located in the teacher's section. Arrange for computers with Internet access for the day(s) students do this activity. Go to the* Science and Global Issues *page of the SEPUP website to access the simulation. You may want to bookmark this site for students. Make sure the browsers and supporting software are current and can properly run the simulation.*

TEACHING SUMMARY

Getting Started
- Review the movement of carbon-containing molecules between organisms in a kelp forest.

Doing the Activity
- The class models the movement of carbon between reservoirs in the carbon cycle.

Follow-up
- (UC ASSESSMENT) Students analyze the effect of human activities on the carbon cycle.

BACKGROUND INFORMATION

The carbon cycle is one of several biogeochemical cycles, which include the nitrogen, phosphorus, water, and rock cycles. Learning about the carbon cycle in an ecological context allows students to have a greater understanding of how carbon is passed between different reservoirs, particularly between organisms and the atmosphere, organisms and the ocean, and among organisms. The carbon can be stored and transferred in many forms (e.g., carbon dioxide, glucose and other sugars, methane, and calcium carbonate). In this unit, students focus on carbon dioxide and glucose transferred in the carbon cycle through photosynthesis and cellular respiration. The oceans play a major part in this exchange, particularly through phytoplankton and zooplankton.

A large and growing body of evidence supports the conclusion that human actions have significantly altered the carbon cycle and are continuing to do so. For example, the burning of fossil fuels and widespread deforestation have increased the amount of carbon-containing compounds found in the atmosphere. This has led to higher greenhouse-gas concentrations, which is causing average global temperatures to rise (the greenhouse effect). The ultimate results of this temperature rise are unknown, but depend in part on the magnitude of the temperature increase. The current and potential responses in the environment are subjects of much scientific research and modeling.

Scientific models predict that there will be a continued retreat of glaciers, permafrost, and sea ice, as well as a rise in sea levels and expansion of deserts. As a result, there will likely also be more extreme weather-related events and changes in precipitation patterns. In some areas deserts may become fertile, while other areas may suffer massive flooding. These changes may decrease regional biodiversity, as many species may not be able to adapt to rapid changes in the environment. Climate change may also disrupt agricultural regions in terms of location and yields, altering the sustainability of human populations in many countries.

GETTING STARTED

1 Have students refer to their food webs from Activity 7 and look at the flow of energy from giant kelp to sea urchins. Ask student pairs to discuss how they would describe the flow of carbon between these two organisms. Provide time for groups to talk, then ask for students to share their answers. Ask the class, *Where do the carbon-containing molecules in the giant kelp come from? Go to?*

Based on the information provided on the card, students are likely to say the carbon dioxide comes from the water, goes into the plant, and then is incorporated into a carbon-containing molecule. A more detailed answer would explain that the carbon comes from carbon dioxide dissolved in ocean water. The carbon dioxide is taken into the plant and incorporated into sugar molecules during photosynthesis. Then the carbon in the sugar molecule is either used in cellular respiration—and the carbon is released into the water as carbon dioxide—or is incorporated into the kelp itself. Do not expect that students will answer at this level of complexity until later in this unit when they learn about photosynthesis and cellular respiration.

---

8 Carbon Cycle

1 **E**SSENTIAL FOR LIFE on earth, carbon is an element that is found in many forms everywhere on earth. Coal, diamonds, limestone, and sugar, for example, all contain carbon. It is in organisms, the atmosphere, oceans and fresh water, soil on the earth's crust, and fossil fuels under the earth's surface. Each of these locations serves as a reservoir for carbon-containing molecules. As organisms interact in ecosystems and as geological changes occur, carbon flows from one reservoir to the next. A **carbon reservoir** is a natural feature, such as a rock, a pinch of soil, or an organism, that stores carbon-containing molecules and exchanges them with other carbon reservoirs. The movement of carbon between these reservoirs is known as the **carbon cycle.**

As you saw in Activity 7, "Energy Flow Through an Ecosystem," energy flows from one organism to another in a food web. This energy flow happens when one organism eats another and carbon-containing molecules pass from the eaten organism to the organism doing the eating. This flow of energy is just one of many paths carbon-containing molecules can follow in the carbon cycle.

In this activity you will model the pathways that carbon takes as it flows from one reservoir to another. You will consider how human activities alter the carbon cycle.

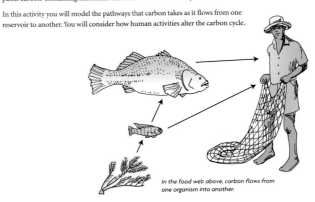

In the food web above, carbon flows from one organism into another.

Challenge

▶ How does human activity affect the movement of carbon through the carbon cycle?

MATERIALS

FOR EACH PAIR OF STUDENTS
computer with Internet access

FOR EACH STUDENT
Student Sheet 8.1, "Carbon Cycle"

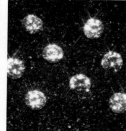

All of these materials contain carbon.

97

155

DOING THE ACTIVITY

2 Students should complete the carbon cycle simulation on the *Science and Global Issues* page of the SEPUP website *(sepuplhs.org/sgi)*. All directions for this simulation are on Student Sheet 8.1, "Carbon Cycle," which can be downloaded from the same website.

FOLLOW-UP

3 (UC ASSESSMENT) Discuss with the class how the pre- and post-industrial carbon cycles differ. See the *Science and Global Issues* website *(sepuplhs.org/sgi)* for more information on how to hold this class discussion. Analysis Question 3 is an opportunity for you to use the UNDERSTANDING CONCEPTS (UC) Scoring Guide to assess students' understanding of the carbon cycle.

EXTENSION

Slide presentations on other biochemical cycles are available on the *Science and Global Issues* page of the SEPUP website *(sepuplhs.org/sgi)*.

SAMPLE RESPONSES

1. The total amount of carbon atoms in the system stays the same even though carbon moves from reservoir to reservoir.

2. The carbon cycle shows how the carbon moves between carbon reservoirs on earth and in the earth's atmosphere. Humans can affect a part of the carbon cycle by doing such things as cutting down a forest. When the forest is removed, the trees will no longer remove carbon from the atmosphere. This means that more carbon dioxide may build up in the atmosphere reservoir if it is not removed in some other way. Thus, humans can create imbalances in the natural cycle of carbon on Earth.

Procedure

2 1. With your partner, visit the *Science and Global Issues* page of the SEPUP website at *sepuplhs.org/sgi* and go to the carbon cycle simulation. Use your student sheet to guide you through the simulation.

3 ### Analysis

1. What happens to the total amount of carbon as it moves through the carbon cycle?

2. In what ways does human activity affect the carbon cycle? Support your answer with evidence.

3. Explain one possible path a carbon molecule might take if it began in a small fish and ended up in a blade of grass.

This diagram of the carbon cycle shows how carbon is exchanged between carbon reservoirs by processes that involve geological changes and organism interactions.

98

---

3. (UC ASSESSMENT) A correct and complete answer would explain that the carbon would pass through reservoirs in the carbon cycle, eventually traveling from the small fish to a blade of grass. Students' answers will vary.

Sample Level-3 Response

Carbon is a part of molecules in the body of a fish. The fish respires and releases carbon dioxide into the water. The carbon dioxide is transferred from the water into the atmosphere. The grass takes in the carbon dioxide from the atmosphere and uses it during photosynthesis to create carbon-containing molecules. These carbon-containing molecules from photosynthesis are incorporated into the blade of grass.

4. By burning fossil fuels humans release a lot of carbon into the atmosphere. While there is already carbon cycling into and out of the atmosphere, humans are releasing carbon into the atmosphere at levels that are higher than natural levels. The natural system is not able to cycle the carbon out of the atmosphere at the same rate as it enters.

5. Algae are producers, which means that they take in carbon dioxide and create carbon-containing compounds from the carbon dioxide. As the algae populations increase, the dead algae cause an increase in bacteria, which consume the dead algae, and also the oxygen dissolved in the water. This means other organisms that normally depend on the oxygen have to move from the area or they will die. The only organisms left would be the algae and the bacteria.

REVISIT THE CHALLENGE

Discuss with students connections between the carbon cycle and food webs. They will be studying photosynthesis and cellular respiration in the next activity.

4. How has the burning of fossil fuels affected the global carbon cycle?

5. An algal bloom is an event in an aquatic ecosystem that occurs when the level of nutrients in an aquatic ecosystem rises. Higher nutrient levels increase the ecosystem's carrying capacity for algae, and the algae population multiplies dramatically. Describe how an algal bloom might alter the local carbon cycle in that ecosystem.

KEY VOCABULARY	
carbon cycle	organisms
carbon reservoir	photosynthesis
cellular respiration	

In comparison with the diagram on the previous page, this diagram shows how human population growth, use of technology, and burning of fossil fuels have altered the carbon cycle.

99

157

9 The Photosynthesis and Cellular Respiration Shuffle

INVESTIGATION • 1–2 CLASS SESSIONS

OVERVIEW

In this activity, students investigate photosynthesis and cellular respiration by organizing a series of images and statements and connecting this information to the carbon cycle. The activity includes an optional demonstration on making ginger ale to demonstrate fermentation, which will be referred to over the course of several activities.

KEY CONTENT

1. Photosynthesis is a cellular process through which organisms capture light energy from the sun and use it to generate and store energy.

2. Cellular respiration releases stored energy in glucose, allowing the organism to function.

3. Light is required for photosynthesis to occur, although parts of photosynthesis can happen in the absence of light.

4. Photosynthesis happens in the chloroplasts, which contain chlorophyll.

5. Only producers can perform photosynthesis.

6. Cellular respiration happens in the mitochondria and cytoplasm of cells.

7. Many organisms, including plants and plankton, perform oxygen-dependent cellular respiration.

8. Photosynthesis takes in light energy, carbon dioxide, and water, producing glucose and oxygen.

9. Cellular respiration takes in oxygen and glucose and produces carbon dioxide and water. Adenosine triphosphate (ATP) is also produced from cellular respiration.

10. The substances produced and consumed in photosynthesis and cellular respiration are complementary.

KEY PROCESS SKILLS

1. Students develop conclusions based on evidence.

2. Students make accurate interpretations, inferences, and conclusions from text.

MATERIALS AND ADVANCE PREPARATION

For the teacher

Transparency 9.1, "Kelp Forest Food Web"

Transparency 9.2, "Carbon Cycle"

Scoring Guide: UNDERSTANDING CONCEPTS (UC)

overhead markers*

2-liter plastic soda bottle with cap (optional)*

funnel, for food use only (optional)*

grater, for food use only (optional)*

1-cup measuring cup, for food use only (optional)*

¼-tsp measuring spoon, for food use only (optional)*

1-tbs measuring spoon, for food use only (optional)*

1 cup sugar (optional)*

1–2 tbs fresh ginger root (optional)*

1 lemon (optional)*

¼ tsp fresh granular baker's yeast (optional)*

cold water (optional)*

For each group of four students

set of 12 Photosynthesis & Cellular Respiration Shuffle paper strips

For each pair of students

computer with Internet access*

For each student

Student Sheet 9.1, "Photosynthesis and Cellular Respiration Diagram"

Group Interaction Student Sheet 2, "Developing Communication Skills" (optional)

Scoring Guide: UNDERSTANDING CONCEPTS (UC) (optional)

Not supplied in kit

If you plan to demonstrate making ginger ale, prepare the ingredients.

Masters for Scoring Guides are in Teacher Resources IV: Assessment.

Note: *Arrange for computers with Internet access for the day(s) students do this activity. Go to the* Science and Global Issues *page of the SEPUP website to access the simulation. You may want to bookmark this site for students. Make sure the browsers and supporting software are current and can properly run the simulation. If internet access is not available,* Photosynthesis and Cellular Respiration *cards are provided in the kit. Provide appropriate instructions for students, based on the simulation.*

TEACHING SUMMARY

Getting Started

- The class makes predictions about cellular respiration and photosynthesis.

Doing the Activity

- (UC ASSESSMENT) Students investigate and compare cellular respiration and photosynthesis

Follow-up

- (UC ASSESSMENT) Review the connections between the carbon cycle, photosynthesis, and cellular respiration.

BACKGROUND INFORMATION

In this unit, students learn about the most familiar type of cellular respiration, which is oxygen-dependent (aerobic) and occurs in many organisms such as macroscopic organisms, as well as microscopic plankton and other microbes. In general, cellular respiration is the metabolic process that releases stored chemical energy to make it available for cells to use. All organisms conduct some form of cellular respiration, but not all organisms require oxygen to do so. Many bacteria and archaea are lithotrophs, as opposed to organotrophs, meaning they rely on such inorganic materials as metal ions and sulfur as electron receptors for cellular respiration, instead of oxygen. Other organisms do not need the electron-transport chain; for example, yeast can obtain ATP strictly through fermentation without the electron-transport chain. Additionally, it is important to note that many organisms obtain oxygen without breathing. For example, many insects rely on diffusion to obtain intracellular oxygen.

Cellular respiration and photosynthesis have a direct link to ecosystem sustainability. Ecosystem collapse often begins with the removal of one or more species, which ultimately disturbs the balance between the carbon-containing compounds needed for cellular respiration and photosynthesis. As those two processes depend on each other, if the balance is disturbed long-term or permanently, the ecosystem is no longer sustainable. It is possible that another organism could fill the role of the species that was removed, but this often comes with a cascade of adverse side effects, such as happens with the invasive species that were studied in Activity 4, "Invasive Species."

GETTING STARTED

1 **Note:** Cellular respiration and photosynthesis are treated in more detail in the "Cell Biology: World Health" unit of this course.

Project Transparency 9.1, "Kelp Forest Food Web." Explain to students that this is a sample answer for the food webs they created in Activity 7, "Energy Flow Through an Ecosystem." Point out that this is one way to portray the food web, but not the only correct way. There are many possible versions, as they saw in Activity 7. Project Transparency 9.2, "Carbon Cycle." Have students identify where in the carbon cycle producers and consumers play a role.

2 After students read the introduction, ask them to predict where photosynthesis would occur in the kelp forest ecosystem, shown in Transparency 9.1, "Kelp Forest Food Web." As students offer answers, use an overhead marker to mark the organisms that perform photosynthesis (phytoplankton, giant kelp, acid kelp, and cyanobacteria). At this point students may not name all of these organisms. Because the class will revisit this diagram at the end of the activity, it is not necessary that they mark each organism or that you correct any incomplete or inaccurate answers. Then have students predict where in the kelp forest ecosystem cellular respiration would occur. Mark these organisms using a marker of another color.

Show students the video clip "Energy Flow in the Coral Reef Ecosystem," the link to which is on the *Science and Global Issues* page of the SEPUP website *(sepuplhs.org/sgi)*. Discuss how the energy flow in this ecosystem parallels that in the kelp forest ecosystem.

---

9 The Photosynthesis and Cellular Respiration Shuffle

1 **I**N THE PREVIOUS activity, "Moving Through the Carbon Cycle," you examined how carbon travels between reservoirs on earth. In this activity you will look more closely at how carbon and oxygen are continuously cycled by organisms and how these elements sustain both the organisms and ecosystems. You will examine what happens to carbon and oxygen at the cellular level.

Two fundamental cellular processes are cellular respiration and photosynthesis. **Cellular respiration** is the process by which cells release stored energy from sugars. **Photosynthesis** is the process in which producer cells use carbon dioxide, water, and nutrients to produce glucose and oxygen. Together these two processes make the carbon cycle possible, and move essential molecules through ecosystems.

All organisms in this community perform cellular respiration and some photosynthesize.

Challenge

2 ▶ How do carbon and oxygen cycle through the environment?

MATERIALS

FOR EACH GROUP OF FOUR STUDENTS
set of 12 Photosynthesis and Cellular Respiration Shuffle paper strips

FOR EACH PAIR OF STUDENTS
computer with Internet access

FOR EACH STUDENT
Student Sheet 9.1, "Photosynthesis and Cellular Respiration Diagram"

---

3 ◈ Have students work on Student Sheet 9.1, "Photosynthesis and Cellular Respiration Diagram," in pencil, as they will be changing the diagram over the next few activities. Tell them to label the paths they think oxygen, glucose, carbon dioxide, and water take through the ecosystem. Students should make their best guess if they are unsure. Their diagrams will vary, and may not be accurate at this point. The purpose of the diagram is to allow them to revisit their ideas, learning, and misconceptions about photosynthesis and cellular respiration throughout this sequence of activities. This is a formative assessment opportunity for you to determine your students' current understanding of photosynthesis and cellular respiration. There will be opportunities to address errors and misconceptions later on in this unit.

If you intend to demonstrate fermentation (an optional component of this activity), set up a ginger ale mixture to ferment over the next several days. See the link on SEPUP's *Science and Global Issues* website (*sepuplhs.org/sgi*) for detailed instructions.

DOING THE ACTIVITY

4 The simulation is on the *Science and Global Issues* website (*sepuplhs.org/sgi*). As students work through the simulation, encourage them to look closely at the diagrams. In particular, they should note the directions of arrows, indicating if materials are entering or leaving an organism. In the photosynthesis diagrams, for example, water will be shown as entering an organism, while in cellular respiration it will be leaving the organism. This is a good opportunity for students to work on their communication skills by discussing with their partners the details of the diagrams and what they mean. You may wish to use Group Interaction Student Sheet 2, "Developing Communication Skills," which gives students suggestions for communicating well when in a group. Once they have completed the simulation students might print a screen shot so that they have a record for their student notebooks of the information from the simulation.

5 (UC ASSESSMENT) If students need assistance in ordering the paper strips, encourage them to look for clues within the statements. For example, any statement that contains the word "producers" would go in the photosynthesis stack. You also may want to tell the students that some of the steps essentially happen simultaneously, so their order is interchangeable. For example, "Sunlight hits the green parts..." and "Producer takes in carbon dioxide..." could be in reverse order and still be correct.

Procedure

3

1. Complete Student Sheet 9.1, "Photosynthesis and Cellular Respiration Diagram," as directed by your teacher.

4

2. Find the "Photosynthesis and Cellular Respiration Shuffle" animation on the *Science and Global Issues* page of the SEPUP website at *sepuplhs.org/sgi*. Sort the images based on what you already know about photosynthesis and cellular respiration, and on what you can see in the images.

3. When you have completed the animation, follow your teacher's instructions to record the results in your science notebook.

5

4. Obtain the Photosynthesis and Cellular Respiration Shuffle paper strips from your teacher.

5. With your group, lay all of the strips out on the table, and read each one aloud.

6. Sort the strips into two piles, one for cellular respiration and one for photosynthesis. If you are unsure about where any of the strips belong, lay them out next to where you will be working so that you can see them as you work.

7. Choose a stack to start with. Put the strips in the order in which you think the processes are happening.

8. Repeat Step 7 for the stack you have not ordered yet.

9. If you had any strips that you did not place, try to decide where they belong now that you have ordered the other strips.

10. Once you have all of the strips in order, compare your strips to the results from the animation, and make any adjustments in the order of the strips that you need to.

   Note: There are more strips than animation images, and so more than one strip may fit with a single image.

6

11. Based on what you see in the animation and on the strips, write in your science notebook a short paragraph describing cellular respiration and one describing photosynthesis. Be sure you write in your own words, and do not just copy the strips.

The correct orders for the strips are as follows:

Photosynthesis: K, G, J, D, B, I
(steps K and G can be reversed)

Cellular Respiration: E, A, F, C, L, H
(steps C, L, and H are interchangeable)

6 Students' written summaries should be brief—a short paragraph for each process. Encourage students to put the process into their own words as much as possible. Procedure Steps 5–11 are an opportunity for a UC ASSESSMENT using the UNDERSTANDING CONCEPTS Scoring Guide.

FOLLOW-UP

7 Using transparencies 9.1, "The Kelp Forest Food Web," and 9.2, "Carbon Cycle," review students' predictions from the beginning of the activity and correct or add to them as appropriate. Emphasize to the students that cellular respiration happens in the cells of many organisms in the presence of oxygen, including plants, phytoplankton, and bacteria, as well as animals. You may want to foreshadow the next activity by asking the students why they think organisms respire, and review the difference between breathing (taking oxygen into the body) and cellular respiration (the metabolic process for accessing energy for cells). Also, emphasize photosynthesis and cellular respiration's dependency on each other. If only cellular respiration occurred, all of earth's oxygen would eventually be used up.

8 (UC ASSESSMENT) Note that in Analysis Question 4 students revise their Photosynthesis and Cellular Respiration Diagrams. Ask students to volunteer to describe what kinds of changes they made on their diagrams, and what new information led them to correct any misconceptions they had at the beginning of the activity. Be sure to remind students that they will revisit these diagrams over the next several activities, and will add to them and further correct them as they work. Analysis Questions 3 and 6 are UC ASSESSMENT opportunities, asking students to connect cellular processes to overall ecosystem health.

---

7 *Analysis*

1. What does a producer need for performing photosynthesis, and what does photosynthesis produce?

2. What does an organism need to perform cellular respiration, and what does cellular respiration produce?

3. What roles do photosynthesis and cellular respiration have in an ecosystem?

8

4. Go back to your diagram on Student Sheet 9.1, "Photosynthesis and Cellular Respiration Diagram," and revise it, or sketch a new one based on what you have learned in this activity. Be sure to show where enzymes are involved, as well as carbon dioxide, water, oxygen, and glucose.

5. If someone says, "Only organisms that breathe can perform cellular respiration," are they correct? Explain.

9

6. If the mitochondria of half the organisms in the ecosystem stopped functioning, what indicators in the ecosystem would change? Explain.

7. There are specialized producers that live in warm-water vents deep in the ocean. These producers do not perform photosynthesis, but instead perform a similar process with iron and other chemicals. Why do you think these producers use this process instead of photosynthesis?

KEY VOCABULARY	
cellular respiration	organisms
enzymes	**photosynthesis**

102

---

9 After students have completed the Analysis Questions, have a class discussion about Analysis Question 6. Depending on your students' responses, you may want to further clarify the connection between cellular processes and ecosystem health. Encourage students to discuss the same concept in terms of photosynthesis.

SAMPLE RESPONSES

1. Answers should contain the following information:

   A producer needs sunlight, carbon dioxide, and water. It also has to have chloroplasts with enzymes and chlorophyll. It produces oxygen and glucose.

   Students may also mention that producers need minerals or soil. It is important for students to understand that while plants and other producers may need minerals or soil to survive, these are not reactants in photosynthesis. **Note:** Phosphate is necessary for the formation of ATP from ADP (adenosine diphosphate), but this is not covered in detail in this activity.

2. An organism needs oxygen, glucose, and enzymes. They produce carbon dioxide, water, ATP, and heat.

3. (UC ASSESSMENT) Students' answers will vary. A correct and complete answer would include that photosynthesis and cellular respiration cycle oxygen, carbon dioxide, glucose, and water through the ecosystem. Photosynthesis and cellular respiration are also essential for the flow of energy in ecosystems.

   Sample Level-3 Response
   Photosynthesis and cellular respiration allow the carbon and oxygen that organisms consume and produce to be cycled through the ecosystem. They work together so that what is made from one process is used in the other. Without them the ecosystem would run out of carbon dioxide and oxygen, and everything would die.

4. Answers will vary. Their diagrams do not have to be entirely accurate at this point. Students will revise their diagrams as they complete additional activities in this unit.

5. The statement, "only organisms that breathe perform cellular respiration," is not correct. Oxygen has to get to the cells for cellular respiration to happen, but the oxygen can get there in many ways. Plants do not breathe, but they take in oxygen and perform cellular respiration.

6. (UC ASSESSMENT) Students' answers will vary. Students' choices of indicators will vary but may include a number of organisms in the ecosystem and the levels of oxygen and carbon dioxide. A correct and complete answer would explain that there would be a cascade of effects from the lack of cellular respiration. Students might suggest those organisms whose mitochondria stopped functioning would die due to the lack of cellular respiration.

   Sample Level-3 Response
   The mitochondria are where cellular respiration happens, so the organisms whose mitochondria stopped functioning would die right away. This would mean that the carbon dioxide levels would decrease, unless it was coming from another source. Eventually this would mean that there would only be half of the carbon dioxide needed for photosynthesis. Also, other organisms would die without the balance between cellular respiration and photosynthesis, unless they were able to get what they needed from neighboring ecosystems.

7. These producers would have to use something besides photosynthesis because there is no sunlight in the deep ocean.

REVISIT THE CHALLENGE

Students should understand that cellular respiration and photosynthesis cycle carbon through ecosystems. They should also know that the inputs and outputs of the two processes complement each other. The next several activities examine aspects of these processes, and the details of both are addressed in more depth in the "Cell Biology: World Health" unit of this course.

GETTING STARTED

1 Depending on your students' background knowledge, you may wish to discuss what rate means and its significance for cellular respiration. In particular, emphasize the difference between the rate of cellular respiration in an individual organism (e.g., one germinated bean) compared to the overall rate of cellular respiration in an ecosystem undergoing a changing number of organisms (e.g., increase in bacteria in a dead zone). Review the process of experimental design. As needed, emphasize the role of a control in an experimental design and how to chose an appropriate experimental variable. Discuss the need to keep all variables but one constant to isolate cause and effect. There are two Science Skills Sheets that you may wish to use with your students, Science Skills Transparency 2, "Using a Dropper Bottle," and Science Skills Student Sheet 4, "Elements of Good Experimental Design." Also, discuss the importance of writing clear, reproducible procedure steps. Explain to students how they will share class data upon completion of the lab. Groups can share data and information on variables they tested in a variety of ways. They might record their experimental variable, data, and group conclusions on butcher paper or white boards for students to observe in a "gallery walk," or a group might record its experimental variables, data, and group conclusion in a slide presentation or on an overhead transparency.

2 Introduce phenol red, an acid–base indicator, to test for the presence of carbonic acid. If your students are unfamiliar with acid–base indicators, you may want to quickly review them or demonstrate phenol red. To demonstrate, fill a clear plastic cup halfway with water and swirl in 5 to 10 drops of phenol red. The solution will be red. Have students observe the color change as you blow into the solution through a drinking straw. Point out to students

---

10 Respiring Beans

1 **A**s **YOU LEARNED** in the previous activity, photosynthesis is the chemical process that produces sugar molecules from carbon dioxide and water. Photosynthesis requires light and takes place in cells of green plants and other producer organisms. You have also learned that cellular respiration is a chemical process by which living cells, including plant cells, use oxygen to release energy from sugar molecules. During cellular respiration, sugars released in the breakdown of food react with oxygen to produce water and carbon dioxide and release energy. These are the two main reactions that cycle the carbon and oxygen needed to sustain an ecosystem and convert energy into usable forms. Without photosynthesis and cellular respiration ecosystems are not sustainable, as you saw in the case study about crabs in the Chesapeake Bay in Activity 1, "Ecosystems and Change."

In this activity you will use beans to investigate rates of cellular respiration. The beans have been germinated, which means they have sprouted and are starting to grow.

seed coat

embryo

food store

Germinated bean seeds have sprouted and started to grow.

In beans sugars are stored as starch, similar to starch stored in other plant structures, such as tree trunks. This stored starch provides the sugars that the new sprouting bean uses in cellular respiration. You will investigate the rate of cellular respiration with a chemical indicator called phenol red. Phenol red is red when a solution is basic and turns orange and then yellow if the solution becomes increasingly acidic. Because carbon dioxide makes water acidic, phenol red allows us to infer that cellular respiration is taking place. You will design your own experiment to test how one variable affects the rate of cellular respiration of sprouted beans.

Challenge

▶ How do various factors affect the rate of cellular respiration?

103

---

that you are being careful not to inhale any of the solution. The solution will turn orange, then yellow, as you exhale more carbon dioxide into the water. Depending on the setup of your classroom, you may want to do this demonstration with the cup set on an overhead projector, so that students can see the color change occurring on the screen at the front of the classroom. Explain to students that the color change to orange and then yellow indicates an increasing amount of acid. This demonstration can also be done with the bromothymol blue provided in the kit. Discuss with students that phenol red exhibits a color transition from yellow (pH of approximately 6.5) to red (pH of approximately 8.0). Above a pH of 8.1, phenol red will turn bright pink in color. Ask students how the indicator will help determine respiration rates. Be sure to emphasize that when carbon dioxide is added to water it dissolves readily and produces carbonic acid, making a solution more acidic with a lower pH. Students should look for color changes from red to yellow. Review with students the safety concerns in using chemical indicators, and be sure they are aware of the location of necessary safety equipment, such as an emergency eyewash station.

DOING THE ACTIVITY

3 Students begin by selecting a variable to test, such as temperature, light, or number of beans. Have at least one group of students test the number of beans. The rate of respiration will change depending on the number of beans, with more beans causing a faster change in the indicator as more respiration occurs. This will link to the increase in organisms and oxygen use, which is integral to the formation of dead zones as discussed in Activity 1, "Ecosystems and Change," and Activity 12, "Too Much Life." Notify students of any available equipment they may use (e.g., a refrigerator or hot water bath). You may wish to have students check with you before they begin writing their procedures and after they complete them. A sample procedure and data table are shown on Student Sheet 10.1, "Sample Procedure for Respiring Beans," should some groups need more structure.

In this investigation students keep informal notes in their science notebooks during the investigation, and then may refer to their notes to write a formal investigation report if assigned. Distribute a copy of Literacy Transparency 7 "Writing a Formal Investigation Report." You may wish to project Literacy Transparency 7, "Writing a Formal Investigation Report," to review with students the elements of an investigation. If appropriate, remind them that the

---

MATERIALS

FOR EACH GROUP OF STUDENTS

2

- 4 transparent, sealable cups
- 4 plastic disc inserts
- 250-mL Erlenmeyer flask
- timer
- 30-mL dropper bottle of phenol red indicator solution
- germinated beans
- dried beans
- masking tape
- permanent marker
- source of water

FOR EACH STUDENT

Student Sheet 9.1, "Photosynthesis and Cellular Respiration Diagram" from Activity 9

Procedure

3

1. As a group, you will design an experiment that demonstrates how one variable affects the rate of cellular respiration in beans. Your teacher will explain to you the materials that are available, in addition to those listed above, and explain any other conditions your experiment must meet. As a group, brainstorm a list of variables you can test. Decide with your group which variable on your list you will test.

2. Use the guidelines below to determine the procedure you will follow:

   a. The cups should be set up so that the beans are not in the liquid. Place the plastic disc insert into the cup to keep the beans out of the liquid, as shown below.

> **Safety** ⚠
> The indicator used in this activity, phenol red, will stain skin and clothing. If you get it on your skin or clothing, immediately flush the area with water.

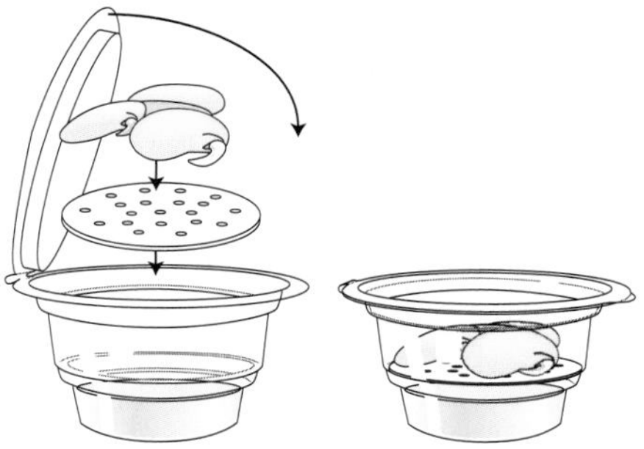

104

---

notes they take during the investigation help them to record their ideas and observations and to write a complete formal report at the end of the activity. As students complete their procedures, make sure they have also completed a data table to record all data collected. Facilitate students' writing of procedures as needed. Be sure to check procedures for clear, reproducible steps, and any safety issues. Make sure students have clearly identified their controls, constants, and variables. As needed, discuss with students how they will use the indicator to track respiration. **Note:** If you have CO_2 probes or other equipment available to measure the amount of CO_2 in the solution, you may want to offer those for the students' experiments.

4 As students set up their experiments, remind them that the beans should not be in the indicator solution, but supported on the plastic disc insert, with the indicator just reaching the bottom of the disc. You may want to prepare an example setup of this. Show students where to store their experiments, if they will not complete them within the class period. With well-germinated beans the indicator should change color within approximately 15 minutes. Larger beans may give a much faster change. Smaller beans may need to be left overnight. A completed sample data table appears below. This data indicates that beans respired less when cold, as shown by the longer time for the indicator to change color.

b. Use the indicator to track cellular respiration. Prepare your indicator solution by adding 25 drops of phenol red to 125 mL of water and swirling the solution to mix it.

c. Pour enough indicator solution into the bottom of each cup so that it is just below the plastic disc insert.

d. Set up a control. Determine with your group how you will set up your control and how you will set up your experimental variable. Use the masking tape to label each cup appropriately.

e. After your experiment is set up, you must fix the lids on the cups tightly to prevent any gas from escaping.

3. Write out your procedure in your science notebook. Have your teacher approve your procedure before you set up your experiment.

4. As a group, decide how you will collect your data. Set up an appropriate data table in your science notebook. In your science notebook predict what will happen, and explain why.

5. Set up your experiment. If your experiment will be left overnight, ask your teacher for further instructions.

4 **6.** Run your experiment, and collect and record your data.

7. Follow your teacher's instructions to clean up and dispose of your materials properly.

5 **8.** Follow your teacher's instructions on how you will share your results with the class.

6 **9.** Go back to your diagram on Student Sheet 9.1, "Photosynthesis and Cellular Respiration Diagram," and revise it or sketch a new one based on what you

7 have learned in this activity. Be sure you have indicated where enzymes are involved, as well as carbon dioxide, water, oxygen, and glucose.

8 *Analysis*

1. What variable did you test? Explain your choice.

2. What did your variable show about rates of cellular respiration? Identify the conclusions you can draw from your data.

Sample Student Data Table for Respiring Beans

Experimental variable being tested	no beans, room temperature	beans, room temperature	no beans, cold	beans, cold
Time to color change	did not change	10 min 38 sec	did not change	14 min 52 sec

105

5 As students complete their experiments, remind them of any cleanup procedures they may be unfamiliar with. Have students share their data in the way they discussed earlier.

6 After students have shared their data, have the class conduct an Informal Meeting of the Minds. Direct students to find a partner from a different group and compare experimental results and conclusions. Ask pairs to share their discussion with the class. Emphasize the value in comparing multiple data sets. As a class, discuss the relationship between the variables tested and cellular respiration rates. Be sure to have students consider experimental error as they discuss conclusions that they can draw. The discussion will vary depending on the variables students tested. Key points to bring out in a class discussion include:

- indicators are qualitative measurements subject to experimental error (e.g., color comparison is subjective).

- other potential sources of experimental error (e.g., inaccurate measurement, difference in bean sizes, or changing rate of respiration).

- ways to make the experiment more quantitative (e.g., use of probes to measure CO_2 levels).

7 ⓘ In Procedure Step 9, students return to their diagram on Student Sheet 9.1, "Photosynthesis and Cellular Respiration Diagram," to correct any errors or omissions. You may want to have students work in pairs or groups on their revisions. They will have a final opportunity to revise the diagram in the next activity.

FOLLOW-UP

8 (DI ASSESSMENT) (AD ASSESSMENT) (UC ASSESSMENT) There are several opportunities for assessment in this Activity. The DESIGNING INVESTIGATIONS (DI) Scoring Guide can be used to evaluate students' experimental designs, with Student Sheet 10.1, "Sample Procedure for 'Respiring Beans,'" serving as a sample Level-3 response. Areas of this scoring variable that can be assessed include the reasons for performing the investigation, the design of the investigation, and how the investigation was conducted and data collected. You may wish to assess this directly from the procedures in students' science notebooks, or by having them complete a formal lab report. Literacy Transparency 7, "Writing a Formal Investigation Report," can guide your students through how to write this. Apply the ANALYZING DATA (AD) Scoring Guide to evaluate students' responses to Analysis Question 4, particularly to assess their skills for making inferences and drawing conclusions. The UNDERSTANDING CONCEPTS (UC) Scoring Guide works well for Analysis Question 6. Continue the class discussion as prompted by the Analysis Questions.

SAMPLE RESPONSES

1. Students' answers should explain their variable and summarize their hypotheses.

---

3. How did your experiment compare to those of the other groups? What variables did other groups test?

4. Summarize the conclusions that can be drawn based on the experiments performed by the class. Include all relevant data that supports your conclusions.

5. In Activity 1, "Ecosystems and Change," you read about dead zones and the crabs in Chesapeake Bay not having enough oxygen because of an increase in bacteria in the water. How could you use data from this experiment to explain what is happening in Chesapeake Bay?

6. In Activity 3, "Biomes," you read about the characteristics of the temperate deciduous forest. Some trees in this biome lose their leaves in the fall, and cannot perform photosynthesis without them. Explain, based on what you learned in this activity, why the trees do not die over the winter months.

KEY VOCABULARY	
cellular respiration	photosynthesis
chemical indicator	variable

106

---

2. Students' answers should summarize their results and provide conclusions they can draw from the data.

3. Students' answers should compare their results to those of the rest of the class and summarize what other variables were tested.

4. (AD ASSESSMENT) Answers will vary depending on the variables chosen by the class. A correct and complete answer would summarize the conclusions that can be drawn based on everyone's experiments, and should include all relevant data. It will also include any trends in the data, and an interpretation of why the trends occurred.

Sample Level-3 Response
In our class experiments, the cold beans took 1–2 minutes longer to change the indicator. The warm beans took approximately 30 seconds less to change the indicator. As the number of beans was increased, the indicator changed faster. Based on the results of the experiments performed by the class, we can conclude that temperature affects rate of cellular respiration (colder means less cellular respiration and warmer means more), and that if there are more beans more carbon dioxide will be produced. The beans in the dark changed the indicator in approximately the same amount of time as the beans in the light, so we can conclude that for beans light does not affect the plant's ability to perform cellular respiration.

5. In this experiment, when there were more beans the indicator changed color more quickly, showing that there was more cellular respiration. This is what is happening in Chesapeake Bay. The bacteria perform cellular respiration. The more bacteria, the more cellular respiration will occur, which will consume more oxygen, eventually creating a dead zone.

6. (UC ASSESSMENT) A correct and complete answer would state that plants can store sugar (or starch) to use when needed, and that plants can perform cellular respiration without leaves. Students' answers will vary.

Sample Level-3 Response
We know from the introduction that plants can store sugars, and from this activity we know that beans are able to perform cellular respiration without having leaves. We also know from this experiment that beans can perform cellular respiration in the dark. This indicates that plants are able to use the stored sugars they already have even when they are unable to perform photosynthesis.

REVISIT THE CHALLENGE

Be sure students understand that changing certain variables affects the rate of cellular respiration. Discuss the use of the indicator, emphasizing that in this case the phenol red only indicates when CO_2 is present. It does not indicate that oxygen is present or absent. In the next activity students will use indicators to investigate photosynthesis and cellular respiration.

11 Respiration and Photosynthesis in Plants

LABORATORY • 2–3 CLASS SESSIONS

OVERVIEW

In this activity, students observe aquatic plants in various environments to obtain evidence that plants respire and photosynthesize. Students modify an investigation to test a variable and measure its impact on photosynthesis and cellular respiration.

KEY CONTENT

1. The stages of photosynthesis that produce oxygen happen in the presence of light.

2. Plants and other producers perform cellular respiration and, therefore, produce carbon dioxide.

3. Different variables, such as temperature, and amount of light, affect the rate of photosynthesis and cellular respiration.

4. Chemical indicators show chemical changes in a substance, such as when water becomes more acidic due to the addition of carbon dioxide.

5. Chemical indicators allow us to infer that a cellular process, such as photosynthesis, is occurring.

KEY PROCESS SKILLS

1. Students make and record observations.

2. Students develop conclusions based on evidence.

MATERIALS AND ADVANCE PREPARATION

For the teacher

Scoring Guide: DESIGNING INVESTIGATIONS (DI)

Scoring Guide: UNDERSTANDING CONCEPTS (UC)

Science Skills Student Sheet 4, "Elements of Good Experimental Design"

Literacy Transparency 6, "Setting up a Laboratory Investigation" (optional)

Literacy Transparency 7, "Writing a Formal Investigation Report" (optional)

For each group of four students

6 transparent sealable cups

4 sprigs of aquatic plants (*Elodea* or *Nitella*) each approximately 4–6 cm long*

30-mL dropper bottle of bromothymol blue (BTB)*

drinking straw*

250-mL Erlenmeyer flask*

beaker or container with at least 1,000-mL capacity*

roll of masking tape*

permanent marker*

source of water*

For each student

Student Sheet 11.1, "Sample Procedure for Plant Respiration and Photosynthesis" (optional)

Literacy Transparency 6, "Setting up a Laboratory Investigation" (optional)

Literacy Transparency 7, "Writing a Formal Investigation Report" (optional)

Scoring Guide: DESIGNING INVESTIGATIONS (DI) (optional)

Scoring Guide: UNDERSTANDING CONCEPTS (UC) (optional)

* Not supplied in kit

Masters for Science Skills Student Sheets are in Teacher Resources II: Diverse Learners. Masters for Literacy Skills Sheets are in Teacher Resources III: Literacy. Masters for Scoring Guides are in Teacher Resources IV: Assessment.

Students choose a variable to test in this investigation. Decide how much leeway to give them and what supplies you may need to have available. Note that, as written, this activity is not consistent with strict experimental design standards. To save instructional time and to have variety in student experiments, the students test two variables at one time (light and the variable of their choosing). If time allows, the activity can be split into two portions, determining the effect of light on the processes first, then choosing a second variable to test.

Determine where you will leave the experimental setups overnight. For darkness a light-proof cabinet, or a heavy cardboard box that is easily sealed works best. For the light setup a sunny windowsill or a spot under direct lighting is best.

There are many varieties of freshwater plants that can be used in this experiment. The most reliable and widely accessible are Anacharis *(also referred to as* Elodea*) and* Nitella flexilis. *Be sure to keep the plants submerged in tap water between activities. They can also be kept in a freshwater aquarium if one is available, but a plastic bucket or container with regular water will suffice. For best results, particularly if there is a time lag between when you get the plants and when the classes will use them, treat the tap water with a dechlorinator or aquarium water treatment. Do NOT use treated water in the experiment, as it may interfere with the use of the chemical indicators.*

If you have access to a spectrometer or similar equipment, you may wish to have students quantitatively measure the intensity of the color of the liquid before the aquatic plants are introduced to the solution and after they have run their experiments.

SAFETY NOTE

All of these materials are for laboratory use only, and none of them should be swallowed. Make sure students wash their hands thoroughly after the laboratory activity.

Be sure that students are careful not to wash any plants or partial plants down the drain. Elodea *and other plants are considered invasive species in many areas worldwide. Check with your appropriate local, county, or state agency about proper disposal methods. In many areas, it is sufficient to allow the plants to dry out and then throw them in the garbage. You may wish to line a strainer with several layers of cheese-cloth or coffee filters for students to filter the materials from their experimental setups.*

TEACHING SUMMARY

Getting Started

- Review experimental setups and materials.

Doing the Activity

- ✓ Students investigate cellular respiration and photosynthesis in various environments.

Follow-up

- (DI ASSESSMENT) (UC ASSESSMENT) The class discusses variables tested in their investigations.

BACKGROUND INFORMATION

Light-dependent and light-independent reactions

In the past light-dependent and light-independent reactions were referred to as light and dark reactions. Research on plants and other producers has deemed that terminology inaccurate, and it has been replaced. Research has shown that the entire process of photosynthesis, including the Calvin cycle, can occur in the presence of light. However, the Calvin cycle is not light dependent and therefore can also occur in the absence of light. Students will read about these phenomena in detail in the "Cell Biology: World Health" unit.

Bromothymol blue indicator

Bromothymol blue can be used to show when a solution has just changed to basic (blue) or acidic (yellow). When it is mixed with an acidic solution with a pH of 6.2 or lower it produces a yellow color. As the pH changes from slightly acidic to slightly basic the solution turns blue. At a pH above 7.6 the color no longer changes but stays blue.

GETTING STARTED

1 Explain to students that in this activity they will investigate cellular respiration and photosynthesis with an aquatic plant, either *Elodea* or *Nitella,* which are commonly used in freshwater aquariums. Ask students, *How can you tell if an aquatic plant is performing photosynthesis or cellular respiration?*

Answers will vary, but should include testing for the presence of oxygen (for photosynthesis having occurred) and carbon dioxide (for cellular respiration having occurred) in the water; the reverse (absence of oxygen for cellular respiration having occurred and absence of carbon dioxide for photosynthesis having occurred); or absence of carbon dioxide because it has diffused out of the solution. Discuss any other ideas your students offer.

11 Respiration and Photosynthesis in Plants

As you have learned, plants and other producers perform cellular respiration as well as photosynthesis. Ecosystems need a balance between these two processes in order to be sustainable. If this balance is altered, for example in a bleached coral reef or a dead zone, the sustainability of the ecosystem may be threatened.

Simplified chemical equations for cellular respiration and photosynthesis are shown below. As you can see, these two equations have similar components: energy, oxygen, carbon dioxide, water, and sugar.

Chemical Equations for Cellular Respiration and Photosynthesis

CELLULAR RESPIRATION

$$C_6H_{12}O_6 + 6O_2 \rightarrow 6H_2O + 6CO_2 + energy$$

One molecule of glucose (a type of sugar) reacts with six molecules of oxygen to form six molecules of water, six molecules of carbon dioxide, and release energy.

PHOTOSYNTHESIS

$$6H_2O + 6CO_2 + light energy \rightarrow C_6H_{12}O_6 + 6O_2$$

In the presence of light energy, six molecules of water react with six molecules of carbon dioxide to form one molecule of glucose and six molecules of oxygen.

In this investigation you will further explore cellular respiration and photosynthesis in plants, and measure the production and consumption of carbon dioxide during respiration and photosynthesis. You will use the chemical indicator bromothymol blue (BTB), which is blue when a solution is basic and turns green and then yellow as the solution becomes more acidic. Because carbon dioxide makes water acidic, BTB allows us to infer when cellular respiration and photosynthesis are happening in a plant.

Challenge

1

▶ How does changing one variable affect photosynthesis and cellular respiration in plants?

107

2 Tell the students they will be using a bromothymol blue (BTB) solution to investigate cellular respiration and photosynthesis with *Elodea*. Ask students how they would know that the plant caused any color changes, as opposed to simply the passage of time. Accept students' answers, and if necessary, guide them to the concept of having a control to test along with their experimental setup. You may want to review the terms respiration and photosynthesis in the context of the previous activity. Ask the students to predict what they think will happen if the plant is placed in the BTB solution for one class period. Accept their predictions. You may want to write their predictions on the board to refer to after the laboratory is complete. Ask the students to suggest other ways they could investigate photosynthesis and cellular respiration, and accept students' answers. Explain to students that they will investigate these processes under varying conditions, and that they will choose one of their own variables to test. Review investigation design as appropriate.

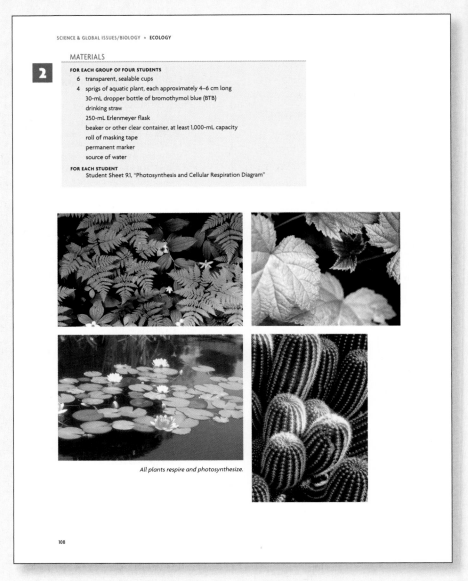

MATERIALS

2

FOR EACH GROUP OF FOUR STUDENTS
6   transparent, sealable cups
4   sprigs of aquatic plant, each approximately 4–6 cm long
    30-mL dropper bottle of bromothymol blue (BTB)
    drinking straw
    250-mL Erlenmeyer flask
    beaker or other clear container, at least 1,000-mL capacity
    roll of masking tape
    permanent marker
    source of water
FOR EACH STUDENT
    Student Sheet 9.1, "Photosynthesis and Cellular Respiration Diagram"

All plants respire and photosynthesize.

108

DOING THE ACTIVITY

3 Have the class brainstorm a list of variables they could test in addition to light. Accept all suggestions, which are likely to include temperature, amount of plant material, and amount of dissolved carbon dioxide in the starting solution. Depending on the materials available, tell students which variables they can test for this experiment. Caution students to pay careful attention to Procedure Step 4, which instructs them to blow through the straw only until the solution turns green. By exhaling into the solution, they are adding carbon dioxide to the solution. The carbon dioxide dissolves and reacts with the water to produce carbonic acid. This reacts with the BTB, and a color change occurs (from blue to green to yellow, depending on the amount of acid present.) If students accidentally exhale too much and turn the solution yellow, the experiment may not work; the solution will be too acidic, and they will not be able to detect additional acid in it. Also, if students do not fill the cups completely, there may be enough air for gas exchange to occur, leading to experimental error.

4 ✓ (DI ASSESSMENT) The validity of BTB as an indicator relies on two inferences. If the solution is green and becomes blue, the indicator is showing that acid levels have decreased. The first inference is that the acid-level decrease is caused by a corresponding decrease in carbon dioxide levels. The second inference is that the decrease in carbon dioxide is due to the plant performing photosynthesis and taking in the carbon dioxide. You may want to review this with your students and discuss other ways they could verify BTB as an indicator (e.g., using a carbon dioxide sensor to test carbon dioxide levels). You may want to have students get your approval of their experimental variables before they start Procedure Step 7. Students may chose variables similar to those tested in Activity 10, "Respiring Beans," or they may have other ideas. Provide guidance as needed. Remind students that BTB tests for the presence of CO_2 but does not indicate that oxygen is produced. If BTB that was green turns blue, it indicates a reduction in the amount of CO_2, which is not an indication of the presence of oxygen. The data tables students create for this investigation allows you a Quick Check assessment of their skills at setting up appropriate columns and labeling them correctly, which are components of the ORGANIZING DATA scoring variable. Students also practice keeping informal notes in their science notebooks during the investigation. If you have them write a formal or informal report, they may refer to these notes for the report. You may wish to project Literacy Transparency 6, "Setting up a Laboratory Investigation," to remind students of the elements of an investigation. Remind them that the notes they take during the investigation help them to record their ideas and observations. This is also an opportunity for you to use the DESIGNING INVESTIGATIONS (DI) Scoring Guide to assess students' procedures. A sample procedure is shown in Student Sheet 11.1, "Sample Procedure for Plant Respiration and Photosynthesis," which may also serve as a sample Level-3 response for scoring.

Procedure

3

1. As a group, brainstorm a list of variables you might test. Consult with your teacher to determine one variable that you can test in this activity. Follow your teacher's directions for setting up your experiment to test the variable. Remember that if it is to survive, the plant must be kept in water.

2. With your group determine your procedure to test your variable, record the procedure in your science notebook, and set up your data table for the investigation.

3. Fill the beaker with 600 mL of water. Add 60 drops of BTB to the water, and swirl the beaker until it is thoroughly mixed.

4. Have one person from your group slowly exhale through a straw into the beaker until the solution turns green. Be careful not to blow so much air through the straw that the solution turns yellow. Do not drink the solution!

5. Label your cups 1–6, and add one sprig of aquatic plant to cups 1 and 3.

6. Completely fill cups 1–4 with the green solution. With these cups you will test the effect of light on photosynthesis and cellular respiration.

4

7. Set up cups 5 and 6 to test the variable you chose in Step 1. They should be completely filled with solution.

8. Cap all six cups tightly so that no gas can escape. On your data table record the colors of the solutions in the six cups.

9. Place cups 1 and 2 in the sun or under fluorescent lights, according to your teacher's instructions. Place cups 3 and 4 in a dark location. Place cups 5 and 6 according to the experimental setup you designed.

10. In your science notebook, answer the following question: What was the purpose of preparing the solution of BTB, water, and a small amount of carbon dioxide? Predict if any of the vials will show a color change over the next few minutes or hours. Record and explain your prediction(s).

11. Check the cups every 15 minutes until the class period ends. Record your observations in your data table.

5 12. Make a final observation of the cups when you next return to class. **6**

7 13. Go back to your diagram on Student Sheet 9.1, "Photosynthesis and Cellular Respiration Diagram," and revise it, or sketch a new one based on what you have learned in this activity. Be sure you have indicated where enzymes are involved, as well as carbon dioxide, water, oxygen, and glucose.

Safety

Use caution when preparing the BTB solution. While using the straw, exhale only. Wash your hands thoroughly after the activity.

Because certain aquatic plants are considered invasive species in many areas, be careful not to pour any down the drain. Your teacher will provide disposal instructions at the end of the experiment.

5 Students should not complete the Analysis Questions until they have observed their results 18–24 hours after setting up the experiment. It will not harm the plants to stay in the BTB solution for longer periods of time, if necessary. There will likely be little or no color change during the initial class period. The next day (after a minimum of 18 hours) the solution kept in the light should have returned to blue, indicating it has become neutral or basic and demonstrating that photosynthesis has occurred. The solution put in the dark should still be green or yellow; it has had no access to light and therefore cannot perform photosynthesis long term. However, cellular respiration does occur, which will produce more carbon dioxide and maintain the green color or intensify the color change in the BTB (i.e., the green may become yellow). A completed sample data table is shown below.

FOLLOW-UP

6 Have the groups share their results with the class, and emphasize the value in comparing multiple data sets. Discuss the variables students tested and what results they observed. Discuss further variables or experiments they could investigate. You may also wish to discuss more sophisticated equipment and how that might assist them in their experiments.

7 ◆ (UC ASSESSMENT) In Procedure Step 13, students complete their diagrams on Student Sheet 9.1 by correcting any errors or omissions. Evaluate students' knowledge growth by applying the UNDERSTANDING CONCEPTS (UC) Scoring Guide to their diagrams, and their responses to Analysis Questions 5 and 6. Students' understanding of both of these questions should have improved over the last few activities. Discuss their responses by reviewing the evidence they examined and what it means. You may need to review acid–base indicators to clear up any misconceptions. Also, ensure that your students understand that they were testing for the presence of an acid, not the actual presence of carbon dioxide or oxygen. Analysis Question 8 requires some background knowledge. Depending upon your students' level of understanding, you may want to discuss this question as a class prior to their answering the Analysis Question on their own. The DESIGNING INVESTIGATIONS (DI) Scoring Guide can be used to evaluate students' experimental designs. Because you have already approved the students' experimental designs, this as an opportunity for students to peer evaluate each other's work. There are several areas of this scoring variable to assess, including the reasons for performing the investigation, their choice of variables, and how they conducted the investigation. You may wish to have students write a lab report after they complete the peer assessment. Literacy Student Sheet 7, "Writing a Formal Investigation Report," or Literacy Student Sheet 2b, "Designing Investigations," can guide your students in this.

Sample Student Data Table.

Plant respiration and photosynthesis. Variable #1: Light; Variable #2: Temperature

	With plant: room temperature, light	Control, without plant: room temperature, light	With plant: room temperature, dark	Control, without plant: room temperature, dark	With plant: cold, dark	Control, without plant: cold, dark
Starting color	green	green	green	green	green	green
Ending color	bright blue	green	green	green	greenish blue	green

SAMPLE RESPONSES

1. The solution in cup 1 turns from green to blue, and in cup 3 from green to yellow. The solutions in cups 2 and 4 do not change color. Students' answers for cups 5 and 6 will depend on the variable the students tested.

2. The change from green to yellow in cup 3 indicates that CO_2 has been added. The change from green to blue in cup 1 indicates that CO_2 has been removed. The observation that the color in cups 2 and 4 did not change indicates that there was no net loss or gain of CO_2 to the solutions in those cups. We can infer that the plants were performing cellular respiration in cup 3 where the CO_2 levels increased, and photosynthesis in cup 1 where CO_2 lessened.

3. Cups 2 and 4 are control samples, showing that light alone cannot cause a color change in BTB. They also show that color changes are not due to changes in how much carbon dioxide is dissolved in the water.

4. Students' answers will depend on the variable they decided to test, and are likely to include such variables as temperature and amount of light available.

5. (UC ASSESSMENT) Answers will vary depending on the variables chosen by the class. A correct and complete answer would summarize the conclusions that can be drawn based on the class's experiments.

Sample Level-3 Response

During photosynthesis, plants take in CO_2 and release oxygen, using the energy provided by light. The solution in cup 1, which contained plants, CO_2, and water, changed from green to blue when exposed to light. The color change indicates a decrease in the CO_2 concentration in solution. Cup 2, which contained no *Elodea* but was also exposed to light showed no color change, indicating no change in the CO_2 concentration. Cup 2 showed no color change, indicating that the plant was involved in causing the decrease in CO_2 seen in cup 1. The solution in cup 3 , which contained plants, CO_2, and water, changed from green to yellow when kept in the dark. The color change indicates an increase in the CO_2 in solution. This evidence indicates that in cup 1, the light was also involved in the decrease of CO_2.

SCIENCE & GLOBAL ISSUES/BIOLOGY • ECOLOGY

Analysis

1. Did you observe any color changes? Describe them.

2. Based on the color change(s) you observed, what can you infer about what gas was present in each tube at the start and at the end of the experiment?

3. What was the purpose of cups 2 and 4?

4. Describe the variable that you decided to test in cups 5 and 6. Describe your results, and explain what you concluded from them.

5. What evidence do you have from this activity that plants photosynthesize? Explain.

6. What evidence do you have from this activity that plants perform cellular respiration? Explain.

7. Did the color changes you observed occur at the same rate? What explanation can you provide for any similarities or differences in the rates?

8. You and your friend Danielle are talking about what you learned in class today. Danielle says, "I think plants photosynthesize during the day and respire at night." Do you agree with Danielle? What kind of experiment could you design to test her hypothesis?

9. How could the rate of plants' photosynthesis be an indicator for the overall health of an aquatic ecosystem?

   Hint: Think back to the case studies from Activity 1, "Ecosystems and Change."

KEY VOCABULARY	
cellular respiration	photosynthesis
chemical indicator	

110

6. (UC ASSESSMENT) Answers will vary depending on the variables the groups chose. A correct and complete answer would summarize the conclusions that can be drawn from everyone's experiments.

Sample Level-3 Response
During respiration, plants take in oxygen and release CO_2. The solution in cup 4, which contained plants, CO_2, and water, changed from green to yellow when kept in the dark. The color change indicates an increase in the CO_2 concentration in the solution. Cup 4, which contained no *Elodea* but was also kept in the dark, showed no color change, indicating that the plant was involved in causing the increase in CO_2, seen in cup 3.

7. Students should state that the change from green to yellow in cup 4 happened much more slowly than the change from green to blue in cup 1. One logical explanation is that photosynthesis in cup 1 was happening at a faster rate than in cup 4.

8. (UC ASSESSMENT) Answers will vary. A correct and complete answer would explain the student's hypothesis and how he or she would test it.

Sample Level-3 Response
I do not agree with Danielle, because plants can do both processes during the day. Our experiment showed that plants need light to perform photosynthesis, as shown by cup 3, which did not perform photosynthesis and therefore did not turn blue. We do not have proof that the plant does cellular respiration during the day, and we would have to do additional tests to prove that. If we had an instrument that could measure the levels of oxygen and carbon dioxide in the water, we might be able to see the levels changing throughout the day.

9. If an aquatic ecosystem is healthy, you would expect the rate of photosynthesis to stay fairly constant. Stress on the ecosystem could cause the rate to increase if there were an event that increased producers, such as an algal bloom, or decrease if the producers were removed, such as by a chemical spill.

REVISIT THE CHALLENGE

Make sure students understand that plants perform both cellular respiration and photosynthesis. In the next activity students will explore what happens in an ecosystem if there is an imbalance between these two reactions.

12 Too Much Life

INVESTIGATION • 1–2 CLASS SESSIONS

OVERVIEW

In this activity students explore what happens to the oxygen levels in an aquatic ecosystem as its number of organisms increases.

KEY CONTENT

1. Greater nutrient availability in aquatic environments can cause an increase in phytoplankton.

2. A large increase in nutrient availability that stimulates plant growth is called eutrophication.

3. Dramatic increases in phytoplankton make more organic matter available for decomposer bacteria, thus increasing the amount of bacteria.

4. Increases in bacteria deplete surrounding waters of oxygen, causing other organisms in the ecosystem to migrate or die.

5. Dead zones are created where there is a lack of organisms as a result of eutrophication.

6. Aquatic environments depend on a balance of photosynthesis and cellular respiration to prevent dead zones.

7. Dead zones have a significant impact on surrounding ecosystems and ecosystem services.

8. Experiments require a control and experimental setup.

9. Scientific models are created to represent actual phenomena.

KEY PROCESS SKILLS

1. Students make predictions.

2. Students take measurements, and collect and record data.

MATERIALS AND ADVANCE PREPARATION

For the teacher
Scoring Guide: GROUP INTERACTION (GI)
Scoring Guide: UNDERSTANDING CONCEPTS (UC)
Group Interaction Student Sheet 2, "Developing Communication Skills" (optional)
Science Skills Transparency 1, "Reading a Graduated Cylinder" (optional)

For each pair of students
SEPUP tray
stir stick
10-mL graduated cylinder*
graduated dropper*
timer*
piece of white paper*
30-mL dropper bottle of 0.01% methylene blue*
25 mL skim milk*
14 mL yeast solution*
paper towels*

For each student
3 sticky notes*
Scoring Guide: GROUP INTERACTION (GI) (optional)
Scoring Guide: UNDERSTANDING CONCEPTS (UC) (optional)

Not supplied in kit

Masters for Group Interaction Student Sheets and Science Skills Transparencies are in Teacher Resources II: Diverse Learners. Masters for Literacy Skills Sheets are in Teacher Resources III: Literacy. Masters for Scoring Guides are in Teacher Resources IV: Assessment.

The yeast solution needs to be prepared at least 15 minutes before students will use it. It is best to make a fresh batch for each class. The longer the yeast sits the less active it will be and experiments may fail. The mixture ratio is one tablespoon yeast to 100 mL lukewarm water. If you are unfamiliar with yeast, you may want to try making a test batch the day before. The water should be warm enough to activate the yeast, but not too hot (if it is too hot it will kill the yeast). Testing the water on your wrist as you would for a baby's bottle is a good method: the water should feel about the same temperature as your wrist. As the yeast activates it will begin to foam in the warm water.

SAFETY NOTE

All of these materials are for laboratory use only. None of them should be swallowed. Make sure students wash their hands thoroughly after the laboratory. Check your local regulations for guidelines on disposing of the methylene blue; it contains ethyl alcohol, is a body-tissue irritant, and is somewhat toxic by ingestion.

TEACHING SUMMARY

Getting Started

- Review the concept of dead zones and how they occur.

Doing the Activity

- Review controls and indicators in experimental design.

- (GI ASSESSMENT) Students explore what happens in a model aquatic ecosystem as the numbers of organisms increase.

- Students analyze how the model compares to an actual ecosystem.

Follow-up

- ✓(UC ASSESSMENT) The class discusses the implications of dead zones for commercial fisheries and aquatic ecosystems.

BACKGROUND INFORMATION

Eutrophication

Eutrophication, a dramatic increase in available nutrients that stimulates plant growth, occurs in aquatic environments around the world. Recent surveys have shown up to 54% of lakes in Asia to be eutrophic, 53% in Europe, 48% in North America, 41% in South America, and 28% in Africa. While eutrophication occurs naturally—for example, in seasonal floodplains—today it is generally a result of human activities, such as the runoff of fertilizers from agricultural areas and releases of untreated sewage. Eutrophication often involves the overabundance of one nutrient that becomes a limiting factor in the ecosystem. A limiting factor is a resource that controls a process. In freshwater ecosystems phosphorus is usually the limiting factor for plant growth, while nitrogen is most often the limiting factor in marine environments.

As it develops, eutrophication first affects primary productivity, causing an increase in the biomass of phytoplankton, often referred to as an algal bloom. Sometimes the phytoplankton are toxic or inedible, either killing off their consumers directly or passing on their toxins through consumers, making, for example, oysters or certain fish poisonous to humans (e.g., red tides, ciguatera, paralytic shellfish poisoning). In other cases the growing biomass of phytoplankton provides more dead organisms—increased nutrients for many kinds of bacteria, which severely deplete the dissolved oxygen in the ecosystem. These effects ultimately create dead zones where species other than algae and bacteria are unable to survive. Eutrophication also sets the stage for an invasive species to take over an area if the area begins to recover but does not yet have the biodiversity to outcompete the invaders for specific resources within the dead zone.

Reversal of eutrophication and the subsequent problems it brings is not always possible. Cleanup of the excess nutrients and prevention of nutrient and pollution input have restored ecosystems in some areas such as Malaren Lake in Sweden, but others, such as Hjalmaren Lake, also in Sweden, have not recovered. Many factors can block, hinder, or help the recovery, including the extent of the eutrophication, how long it has been occurring, the location, and how easily organisms can migrate back into the area from surrounding ecosystems.

Methylene blue indicator

Methylene blue indicates the presence or absence of oxygen in a solution. If oxygen is present in a container of water, for example, the addition of methylene blue turns the water blue. If there is no oxygen, the water becomes colorless.

One explanation for the color change is the presence of respiring microbes in a liquid. At one time, methylene blue was added to samples of pasteurized milk to test if the milk was free of bacteria. When added to active yeast solution, the solution turns from blue to colorless because the yeast organisms are respiring and therefore using up oxygen. For best results the methylene blue–yeast mixture should be carefully stirred.

GETTING STARTED

1 Review the concept of dead zones first introduced in Activity 1, "Ecosystems and Change." Next, show students the short video on dead zones, "In the Zone." The link is found on the *Science and Global Issues* page of the SEPUP website (*sepuplhs.org/sgi*). Discuss with students the connection between fertilizer runoff and the algae population, and review the connection between algae and bacteria population levels. Elicit students' responses to measure their current understanding of what impacts an increase in algae might have on the rest of the ecosystem. Students should be able to identify that a change in one population will result in a change in the other populations in the ecosystem. Have students use the "Read, Think, and Take Note" literacy strategy while they read the introduction. Remind them that the guidelines for the strategy can be found in Activity 1 should they need them.

After students have read the introduction, be sure that they understand the following:

- Yeast is a living, oxygen-consuming organism and performs cellular respiration.

- Oxygen dissolved in water is consumed by aquatic organisms performing cellular respiration.

- Sugar from the milk (lactose) is a food source for the yeast.

---

12 Too Much Life

1 **MOST UNDISTURBED ECOSYSTEMS** have an approximate balance of producers and consumers, and energy and nutrients flow between them, primarily in the form of carbon-containing compounds. If that balance is disrupted, however, it can have a significant impact on the ecosystem and the organisms within it.

In this activity you will examine what happens to oxygen levels as the number of organisms in an environment increases. Modeling a marine ecosystem, you will work with yeast, a live organism, to represent the organisms in a marine environment. You will use methylene blue, a chemical indicator that shows the presence of oxygen. Methylene blue is blue but turns colorless when the oxygen in the solution is no longer present.

2

Challenge

▶ How does the rate of cellular respiration affect the oxygen levels available in an aquatic ecosystem?

MATERIALS

FOR EACH PAIR OF STUDENTS
- SEPUP tray
- stir stick
- 10-mL graduated cylinder
- graduated dropper
- timer
- piece of white paper
- 30-mL dropper bottle of 0.01% methylene blue
- 25 mL skim milk
- 14 mL yeast solution
- paper towels

FOR EACH STUDENT
- 3 sticky notes

Safety ⚠️
Methylene blue will stain clothing and skin. Flush thoroughly with water if it comes in contact with clothing or skin. Milk and yeast solution are for laboratory use only. Do not drink or eat these materials.

111

DOING THE ACTIVITY

2 Discuss methylene blue, the chemical indicator in this activity. It is blue in color when added to a solution that contains oxygen, and turns colorless as oxygen is depleted from a solution. Remind students that methylene blue will stain clothing and skin, and to notify the teacher immediately if it comes in contact with clothing or skin. Also remind students that the milk and yeast solutions are for lab use only and that they should not be consumed.

Background Information

In the 1970s, part of Chesapeake Bay, on the east coast of the United States, was identified as one of earth's first marine dead zones. A **dead zone** is an area in a body of water where the water at the bottom has little or no dissolved oxygen.

When a large amount of nutrient-rich water flows into an area, causing an increase in plant growth—an occurrence known as **eutrophication**—the conditions are prime for a dead zone to develop, as shown in the diagram below. Phytoplankton populations increase quickly in the nutrient-rich water. When the phytoplankton die and sink, they increase the amount of organic matter available for bacteria to feed on at the bottom of the ocean. As their population grows, the bacteria's combined cellular respiration increases, depleting the surrounding water of oxygen. Very few organisms can survive this lack of oxygen, and so they migrate or die.

You learned in Activity 1, "Ecosystems and Change," about the crab jubilees that happen as a result of these dead zones in Chesapeake Bay.

Eutrophication can be caused by natural systems where nutrients are high, but increasingly it results from human-related activity, such as fertilizer run-off from agricultural areas or farms, sewage spills, vehicle exhaust, and storm water run-off that picks up sources of nitrogen, phosphorus, and other nutrients.

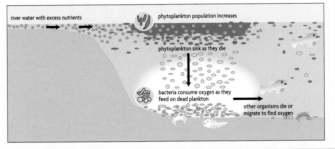

Since the 1960s, the number of dead zones in the world has doubled approximately every 10 years, and currently involves more than 245,000 sq km in more than 400 systems.

Many of these systems, including Chesapeake Bay, were once homes to important commercial and recreational fisheries. However, eutrophication combined with overfishing and other types of pollution has caused many of these fisheries to collapse or shrink considerably. Plans for healing these ecosystems seek to prevent eutrophication, while at the same time working to curb overfishing and pollution. ▪

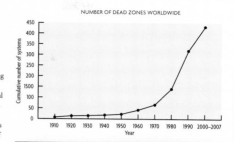

NUMBER OF DEAD ZONES WORLDWIDE

The brown plume is where water from rivers upstream flows into the Gulf of Mexico where large dead zones have been documented. This water contains high concentrations of fertilizer runoff (right).

The image at left, below, shows winter conditions in the Gulf of Mexico. The image to its right shows summer conditions. Red and orange represent the highest concentrations of phytoplankton and sediment in the water.

3 Review the Procedure with students after they have read it. Ask students why Cup A does not receive any yeast (it is the control). As needed, remind students of the control they used in the previous activities, "Respiring Beans," and "Respiration and Photosynthesis in Plants." You may wish to point out that Procedure Step 4 explains the best way to observe the results for the lab. You may also wish to review why it is necessary to wipe off the stir stick after each time they use it, and how to properly read a graduated cylinder (projecting Science Skills Transparency 1, "Reading a Graduated Cylinder," may be helpful here).

4 (GI ASSESSMENT) This is an opportunity to use the GROUP INTERACTION (GI) Scoring Guide to assess how well students work in pairs. You may need to remind them to stir the yeast solution before they remove it from the class container, as the yeast organisms tend to float to the top of the solution. Check to see that the pairs of students are wiping off their stir sticks between uses and that they are timing trials appropriately. Tell students that they may see a thin layer of blue at the top of the solution that does not change. As long as the rest of the solution has gone back to white (i.e., meythlene blue has turned colorless) they should consider this a stop point. Their stop point should be approximately the same color for each trial. **Note:** If your students find simultaneous trials challenging, they can run the trials independently but should start with E and work toward A.

---

3 ## Procedure

1. Make a data table in your science notebook, like the one below.

Eutrophication Data

	Cup A 0 mL yeast	Cup B 2 mL yeast	Cup C 3 mL yeast	Cup D 4 mL yeast	Cup E 5 mL yeast
Start time					
Stop time					
Total time					

4

2. With your partner, predict the order in which the experimental setups will lose their blue color. Explain your reasoning in your science notebook.

   Hint: Methylene blue turns colorless when oxygen is no longer present in a solution.

3. Using the amounts specified in the table below, add the milk, methylene blue, and water to each large cup in your SEPUP tray (Cups A–E). Mix well with the stir stick.

Cup Contents

	CUP A	CUP B	CUP C	CUP D	CUP E
Milk (mL)	5	5	5	5	5
Methylene blue (mL)	1	1	1	1	1
Water (mL)	5	3	2	1	0
Yeast solution (mL)	0	2	3	4	5

4. Place the tray on top of the white paper so you can compare the colors of the solutions. You may want to observe from the back side of the tray to see the solutions, as shown on the next page.

5. Start the timer for Cup A, and record the start time on your data table.

6. Add the yeast solution to Cup B, record the start time, and stir the contents. Be sure to record the start time as soon as you add the yeast to the cup.

7. Repeat Step 6 for each of the remaining cups, adding the amount of yeast solution indicated on the table.

8. Stir the contents of each cup approximately every 30 seconds, wiping off the stir stick between cups to avoid contamination.

Sample Student Response: Eutrophication Data

	A: 0 mL yeast	B: 2 mL yeast	C: 3 mL yeast	D: 4 mL yeast	E: 5 mL yeast
Start time	0:00	1:00	1:19	1:46	2:14
Stop time	None	12:22	9:00	6:50	5:20
Total time	N/A	11:22	7:41	5:04	3:06

5 Have students check their results with several other pairs to rule out serious experimental error. Students' results should be close to the same, but not exactly so. Students using different yeast solutions may have different results depending on how active the yeast are. After students have shared their data, have the class conduct an Informal Meeting of the Minds. Direct students to find a partner from a different group and compare experimental results and conclusions. Ask pairs to share their discussions with the class. Take this opportunity to emphasize the value of comparing multiple data sets.

FOLLOW-UP

6 Discuss as a class which solution turned white first. Have students explain their results, making sure they understand that the greater concentration of yeast meant more organisms, which in turn meant that the milk sugar was consumed faster because of more cellular respiration occurring. Students should conclude, therefore, that the oxygen was depleted faster in the cups with more yeast (i.e., more organisms).

7 ✓ (UC ASSESSMENT) Analysis Question 3 can be used as a Quick Check to assess students' interpretation of the data, a component of the ANALYZING DATA Scoring Guide, and the UNDERSTANDING CONCEPTS (UC) Scoring Guide can be used to evaluate students' understanding of eutrophication in Analysis Question 7.

---

9. Observe the large cups from the back side of the tray while continuing to stir the contents every 30 seconds. Record the times when the contents of each cup turn white.

5 10. Subtract the start time from the stop time to determine the total time it took the solution to turn white in each of your experimental setups.

view

6 *Analysis*

1. In what order did the solutions lose their color? Did this match your predictions? Explain.

2. **a.** What do the different parts of the model (that is, yeast and milk) represent?
   b. If Cup B and Cup E represent different ecosystems, how are they different?

7 3. **a.** How does the concentration of organisms in a body of water affect the rate of oxygen consumption?
   b. How does your answer to 3a relate to eutrophication?

4. What effect would an increase in phytoplankton have on the food webs in the surrounding ecosystem? Explain, using evidence from your investigation.

5. How does eutrophication cause a dead zone to occur, and how does that differ from an area where there is no eutrophication?

6. What effects might eutrophication and dead zones have on nearby fisheries?

7. Using the evidence you gathered in your experiment, how could you explain the eutrophication and dead zones in Chesapeake Bay?

KEY VOCABULARY	
cellular respiration	organism
dead zone	population
eutrophication	

115

SAMPLE RESPONSES

1. Student answers will vary depending on their predictions, but should show the order E, D, C, B, A.

2. a. The yeast represents the bacteria, the milk is their source of food, like the plankton in the ocean.

   b. Cup B is like an ecosystem where there is no eutrophication. Cup E is like an ecosystem where there is eutrophication. Because there is more yeast, there is more cellular respiration, and the oxygen gets used up quickly.

3. ✓ Answers will vary. A correct and complete answer would state

   a. that more organisms performing cellular respiration in a body of water will increase the rate of oxygen consumption, and

   b. that the greater the eutrophication the higher the phytoplankton population that provides food for bacteria, which then increase the rate of oxygen consumption.

4. Eventually the increased population of algae will die, which provides more food for the bacteria, which rapidly increase in number. As the bacteria population increases there will be more cellular respiration and less dissolved oxygen. As the oxygen levels decrease some organisms will die or have to leave the food web, and it could eventually result in a dead zone. Our investigation showed that more yeast (representing bacteria) in the milk (representing ocean water with oxygen) meant more cellular respiration was occurring to use up the oxygen so that the cups with more yeast ran out of oxygen faster.

5. In a dead zone there are a lot of bacteria that consume the oxygen in the water so that other organisms cannot live there. In an ecosystem where this is not happening it is more balanced, and the oxygen is replaced through photosynthesis. Eventually there is only bacteria and phytoplankton living in a dead zone because all of the other organisms have died or left because there is not enough oxygen.

6. If eutrophication occurs, there will not be enough oxygen for the fish to survive and reproduce, and so they would either leave the area or die. If there are no fish, the local fisheries will collapse. If this happened where the fish breed or in a large area, it might collapse the whole fishery and not just local fisheries.

7. (UC ASSESSMENT) Answers will vary. A correct and complete answer would relate the high levels of organisms and high oxygen consumption rates to the increase in bacteria in Chesapeake Bay depleting the available oxygen.

Sample Level-3 Response

In Chesapeake Bay there were lots of nutrients running off into the Bay, which provided more food for the algae. The algae population increased, which meant the bacteria population increased. This is the same as what happened in Cups D and E in our activity, where the increase in yeast meant that more oxygen was consumed. This means that the oxygen-consuming organisms have to either migrate or die, forming a dead zone.

REVISIT THE CHALLENGE

Students should be able to explain how their experiments modeled eutrophication and dead zones. They should also be able to explain that a dramatic increase in organisms due to nutrient increases will deplete the oxygen in an aquatic environment. Discuss with students how this ties into the sustainability of the ecosystem, particularly the dead zones' threat to fisheries.

13 Symbiotic Relationships

INVESTIGATION • 1–2 CLASS SESSIONS

OVERVIEW

In this activity, students use descriptions of interspecies interactions to determine their symbiotic relationships—parasitism, mutualism, commensalism, or amensalism.

KEY CONTENT

1. Organisms frequently have close ecological relationships, known as symbiotic relationships.

2. The four main categories of symbiotic relationships are: parasitism, commensalism, amensalism, and mutualism.

3. In parasitism one species benefits, and the other is harmed.

4. In commensalism one species benefits, and the other is not harmed and does not benefit.

5. In amensalism one species is harmed and the other species is not harmed and does not benefit.

6. In mutualism both species benefit.

KEY PROCESS SKILLS

1. Students make accurate interpretations, inferences, and conclusions from text.

MATERIALS AND ADVANCE PREPARATION

For the teacher
> Scoring Guide: UNDERSTANDING CONCEPTS (UC)

For each group of four students
> set of 16 Symbiotic Relationship Cards
> set of 4 Interaction Description Cards

For each student
> Scoring Guide: UNDERSTANDING CONCEPTS (UC) (optional)

Masters for Scoring Guides are in Teacher Resources IV: Assessment.

TEACHING SUMMARY

Getting Started

- Review students' current concepts about ecological relationships.

Doing the Activity

- Students classify symbiotic relationships.
- Students compare classification systems.

Follow-up

- (UC ASSESSMENT) Students compare symbiotic relationships to other ecological relationships.

BACKGROUND INFORMATION

Amensalism is a symbiotic relationship in which one species is harmed, while the other species neither benefits nor is it harmed. Amensalism appears to be rare, but frequently cited examples include organisms that excrete toxic chemicals. Bread mold is one example: the Penicillium produced by mold kills bacteria, but the mold does not benefit. Another example is algal blooms that give off toxic substances, such as the algae that cause paralytic shellfish poisoning; the shellfish are not harmed, but the people and other organisms that eat the shellfish might be.

Commensalism is a symbiotic relationship in which one species benefits, while the other species does not benefit nor is it harmed. An example of this is lichen that grow on trees.

Mutualism is a symbiotic relationship in which both species benefit. An example of this is bees and the flowers they pollinate. The bee obtains food from the flower, and the flower pollen is spread to other flowers for cross-pollination.

Parasitism is a symbiotic relationship in which one species benefits, while the other species is harmed, but not killed. One example is fleas living on dogs and other mammals: the fleas bite in order to obtain meals of blood and often cause swelling and itching at the bite mark, but not death.

GETTING STARTED

1 Ask the students, *How would you describe the relationship between a producer and a consumer?*

Students' answers should draw the conclusion that producers and consumers depend on each other. If necessary, remind students of the relationship between photosynthesis and cellular respiration, and the carbon and nitrogen cycles (if appropriate). Explain to the students that these cycles are interrelated within entire ecosystems on a large scale. Show students the video clip "Ancient Farmers of the Amazon." The link to this video is on the *Science and Global Issues* page of the SEPUP website *(sepuplhs.org/sgi)*. In your discussion, focus on the symbiotic relationship between the leaf cutter ant and the fungus, and which organism benefits. Do NOT give a name to this relationship, as students will be classifying different symbiotic relationships in the activity.

DOING THE ACTIVITY

2 Have students read the introduction and examine the photo of the crab covered in various organisms. Ask the students, *How do you think it affects the crab to have the other organisms growing on it?*

Answers will vary, but should include the idea that the crab is helped because the organisms provide camouflage to protect the crab from predators, and it is harmed because the organisms make the crab heavier and unable to move quickly. Explain to students that in this activity they will classify the relationships between several organisms. Ask the students how they would classify the relationship between the crab in the photograph and the organisms that are living on it. Accept students' responses. Distribute the Symbiotic Relationship cards to each group and have students conduct Procedure Steps 1 and 2.

---

13 Symbiotic Relationships **1**

2 **I**F YOU WERE asked to describe the interaction between two organisms in a marine ecosystem, you might think of a seal eating a fish, or a shore bird hunting for clams. As you have already learned, if an ecosystem and its food webs are examined closely, it turns out that many of the relationships between animals and plants are much more complex than "who eats whom." In this activity you will be examining the close relationships between many of the animals and plants that inhabit a kelp forest.

The close relationship of organisms in an ecosystem is known as **symbiosis.** As you learned in Activity 1, "Ecosystems and Change," coral polyps provide shelter for algae, and the algae perform photosynthesis, providing food for the coral. That symbiotic relationship is part of the balance required for an ecosystem to be sustainable. Ecologists study these relationships and their interactions within larger ecosystems in order to better understand how ecosystems function. In this activity you will categorize symbiotic relationships found in a kelp forest, and the advantages and disadvantages for the plants and animals involved.

Challenge

▶ How do organisms gain or lose from their interactions with each other?

This crab disguises itself by placing small anemones, algae, and other organisms on its carapace (shell) to make it blend in with the sea floor.

116

3 Have the groups share their classification systems with the class. Their classifications will likely closely mirror the scientific classifications of the relationships. This is another opportunity to emphasize the value in comparing and combining procedures and systems. There will likely be significant overlap but enough differences in how the groups have classified the cards. To give everyone the broadest picture, have one student volunteer from each group describe the group's classification system to the class. Then have the students raise their hands if they had similar systems. Choose a group with a different classification system to present their system to the class. Then highlight in the class discussion any systems that rely on relationships that are significantly different from those the students will see in the Interaction Description cards (parasitism, mutualism, commensalism, amensalism).

4 Pass out the Interaction Description cards, and have students complete Procedure Steps 5–8. Students' likely categorizations are shown on the next page.

When students have completed the Procedure have a class discussion about the differences and similarities between their original classification systems and those of the scientific community as described in the cards. Also discuss with students that it is often difficult to categorize the relationships as neatly as they are presented in this activity, because the relationships are on more of a continuum. For example, lichen and other plants that grow on a tree branch are considered commensal until they grow large enough to break the branch off the tree, at which point they are considered parasitic.

MATERIALS

FOR EACH GROUP OF FOUR STUDENTS
set of 16 Symbiotic Relationship Cards
set of 4 Interaction Description Cards

Procedure

1. With your group of four, read through the description on each of the Symbiotic Relationship Cards, noting the similarities and differences among the relationships.

2. Sort the cards into several sets according to the similarities in the symbiotic relationships.

3. In your science notebook, list the common features of each set of symbiotic relationships. Then write down the species pairs of each set.

3   4. According to your teacher's instructions, share with the class how your group classified the symbiotic relationships.

4   5. Get a set of Interaction Description Cards from your teacher. Each card represents a set of symbiotic relationships as classified by ecologists. Based on the information described on the Interaction Description Cards, place each Symbiotic Relationship Card under one of the Interaction Description categories.

6. In your science notebook, list the common features of each category of symbiotic relationships as described on the Interaction Description Cards. Then list the species pairs that belong to each set.

7. With your group, compare the two classification systems. Describe the similarities and differences of those systems.

8. Record your group's ideas in your science notebook.

Cleaner shrimp eat small parasites and dead skin from the mouth of a moray eel. The eel remains still while the shrimp works, and will not harm the shrimp.

117

FOLLOW-UP

5 (UC ASSESSMENT) The UNDER-STANDING CONCEPTS (UC) Scoring Guide can be used to evaluate students' understanding of symbiotic relationships in Analysis Question 3. You may want to have students score each other's answers and give them a chance to revise the answers prior to turning them in for your formal scoring. You may wish to have them incorporate specific terms, such as *host*, the organism that a parasite harms.

6 Discuss Analysis Questions 3 and 4 as a class. Students' answers will vary, but should generally follow the concepts in the sample responses at the end of the activity. Be sure that students discuss the possibility of the kelp forest ecosystem and the symbiotic relationships within it being damaged or collapsing due to overfishing of one species. Additionally, as needed, guide students into discussing the parallels between mutualism and the cycling of matter by the process of photosynthesis and cellular respiration. The class discussion should focus on the interdependencies found in symbiotic and other ecological relationships.

---

5 *Analysis*

1. Define each of the following, and cite an example:
   amensalism
   commensalism
   mutualism
   parasitism

2. Choose four of the symbiotic relationships you examined in this activity, one from each category. Describe the benefits and drawbacks within each relationship.

6

3. How would the food webs and the symbiotic relationships in the kelp forest be affected if the senorita fish were overfished and were no longer found in the kelp forest?

4. How are the mutualism examples you learned about in this activity similar to organisms in an ecosystem performing photosynthesis and cellular respiration?

KEY VOCABULARY	
amensalism	parasitism
commensalism	symbiosis
mutualism	

118

Sample Response to Procedure Steps 5–8

Interaction classification	Examples
Amensalism	diatoms and paralytic shellfish poisoning
Commensalism	decorator crab and small anemones, etc.
	bay pipefish and eelgrass
	bat stars and annelid worms
Mutualism	giant green anemones and algae
	acid seaweed and small fish and other organisms
	leopard, smoothhound, and dogfish sharks
	senorita fish and other fish
	greenling fish and fish-eating anemone
	fat innkeeper worm, arrow goby and pea crab
	black sea nettle and butterfish
	bay ghost shrimp and pea crabs, etc.
	red rock shrimp and California moray eels
Parasitism	ribbon worms and Dungeness crabs
	nematodes and sea urchins
	copepods and rubberlip surfperch

EXTENSION

Have students investigate additional examples of symbiotic relationships. Marine ecosystems in particular have a large number of examples, such as coral reefs. Terrestrial ecosystems, such as tropical rainforests and other forests or woodlands, provide many examples as well.

SAMPLE RESPONSES

1. Parasitism is a relationship in which one organism benefits while the other is harmed, for example, a dog and a flea. Mutualism is a relationship where both organisms benefit, for example, a clown fish and an anemone. Amensalism is a relationship where one organism is harmed but the other does not benefit, for example, algae that release a chemical that kills fish in the water around it, but the algae do not benefit. Commensalism is a relationship where one organism benefits and the other is not harmed but does not benefit, for example, a decorator crab and an anemone.

2. There are multiple examples in each category, but some examples are:

   Copedpods benefit from eating the gill tissue of the Rubberlip Surf Perch, but the drawback is that it harms the Surf Perch (parasitism).

   The decorator crab benefits from the camouflage of the small plants and animals. The drawback is that they make the crab heavier so it might not move as quickly to escape predators. It probably does not affect the small plants and animals (commensalism). The bat stars benefit from the worms eating the leftover food bits because it keeps them clean, and the worms benefit because they get nutrients. This relationship does not seem to have any drawbacks (mutualism).

3. (UC ASSESSMENT) Answers will vary. A correct and complete answer will explain the interdependency of organisms in a food web and point out that if the senorita fish is overfished, the entire food web, and symbiotic relationships, will be affected.

Sample Level-3 Response

The food web would be affected by the lack of senorita fish because some organisms in the ecosystem eat senorita fish, and the senorita fish eat other organisms in the kelp forest. The senorita fish also cleans parasites off of other fish, and if they were overfished, there would be a greater chance of other fish being harmed by parasites. If the senorita fish were gone and there was a large outbreak of parasites that infected a lot of other fish, it might cause a major problem in the kelp forest even though only one type of fish was overfished.

4. In mutualism organisms help each other. For example, painted greenlings gain protection from the stinging cells of the fish-eating anemone, and the anemones benefit because the greenlings attract prey for the anemone. The relationship between organisms performing photosynthesis and cellular respiration is similar because all of the organisms in the ecosystem help each other by making either oxygen and water or carbon dioxide and glucose, which are used by the other organisms. Without each other they would not survive. But it is also different because the relationship is not between individuals or specific species. It is between all the organisms in the ecosystem.

REVISIT THE CHALLENGE

Use the Analysis Questions to make sure that students are able to describe and give examples of the four types of symbiotic relationships: parasitism, commensalism, amensalism, and mutualism.

14 Investigating Population Growth Rates

INVESTIGATION • 1–2 CLASS SESSIONS

OVERVIEW

Students use an online simulation to investigate the effect of birth rates and carrying capacity on the growth rate of a population and explore how these rates are expressed in graphic form.

KEY CONTENT

1. Population growth rate is the rate of change in a population over specified intervals of time.

2. Population growth rate is affected by a number of factors, some of which constantly fluctuate.

3. Factors that affect population growth rate include birth rate, death rate, disease, predators, food availability, and human activities.

4. A positive growth rate indicates that the population is getting larger, while a negative growth rate indicates the population is getting smaller.

5. The trend of a growth rate can be altered if the factors influencing it change.

6. Sustained negative growth rates will eventually lead to population extinction.

7. Populations with a positive growth rate eventually reach a carrying capacity, at which point the ecosystem cannot support a larger population.

KEY PROCESS SKILLS

1. Students graph and analyze data.

2. Students identify and describe trends in data.

3. Students formulate explanations that account for data.

4. Students develop conclusions based on evidence.

MATERIALS AND ADVANCE PREPARATION

For the teacher

Student Sheet 14.1, "The Avril Seal Population"
Transparency 14.1, "Linear Growth Curve"
Transparency 14.2, "Exponential Growth: J-Curve"
Transparency 14.3, "Carrying Capacity: S-Curve"
Transparency 14.4, "Population Crash"

For each pair of students

computer with Internet access*

For each student

Student Sheet 14.1, "The Avril Seal Population"
Student Sheet 14.2, "Investigating Population Growth" (available online only: see note below)
sheet of graph paper*

Not supplied in kit

Note: *Student Sheet 14.2, "Investigating Population Growth" is found only on the* Science and Global Issues *website (sepuplhs.org/sgi). Sample student answers are also available on the website. Both are located in the teacher's section. Arrange for computers with Internet access for the day(s) students do this activity. Go to the* Science and Global Issues *page of the SEPUP website to access the simulation. You may want to bookmark this site for students. Make sure the browsers and supporting software are current and can properly run the simulation.*

Note that this activity covers population dynamics in detail, including density-dependent and -independent factors. If computers with Internet access are not available, an alternative lesson should be substituted.

TEACHING SUMMARY

Getting Started

• The class analyzes birth and death rates for the seal population near Avril Gulf.

Doing the Activity

• Students work with an online simulation to investigate the effect of birth rate and carrying capacity on population growth rates.

Follow-up

• ✓ The class discusses the links between population growth rates of Avril Gulf's salmon fishery and its sustainability.

BACKGROUND INFORMATION

Population growth rates reflect birth and death rates, and immigration to and emigration from the population. These numbers are rarely static, and are affected by both long-term factors (such as prolonged drought, recovery after a huge forest fire, or an increase in lifespan) and short-term stochastic events (such as massive storms or earthquakes). For organisms other than humans, human impact is almost always a factor when those organisms' population rates change, whether directly through such activities as hunting or fishing, or indirectly through such activities as encroachment on habitats, and burning fossil fuels that create pollution. Humans can also have a positive impact on other populations by, for example, instituting strict fishing limits on a threatened population, and setting up natural reserves.

Carrying Capacity

Carrying capacity is the size of a particular population that an ecosystem can support, and it is influenced by a variety of factors. For example, the carrying capacity of a forest for a population of blue jays would change if the forest were being intensely logged. Cessation or reduction of logging in that same forest might cause the forest's carrying capacity to return to its original level. There is debate over the earth's carrying capacity for the human population. Some argue that the human population has surpassed its carrying capacity, while others think that the population is still below (or near) it. Generally, a population of organisms does not reach a specific carrying capacity and then simply stop growing. Often the population surpasses the carrying capacity, at which point food availability or density-dependent factors cause the population to decline slightly. Then there are slight fluctuations in the population level that hovers around the carrying capacity.

The greater the population density, the more a density-dependent factor will influence population levels. For example, infectious disease is density-dependent because it relies on organisms being in close proximity to each other for transmission to occur. Density-independent factors, such as natural disasters, influence population levels regardless of the population density.

Discussions of sustainability often include information about population growth and carrying capacity. For example, a sustainably managed fishery would only permit levels of fish catch that maintain the population level for the species being caught or allow it to grow. Scientists and fishery managers examine population growth rates and estimate carrying capacities in order to set those limits accordingly. The same theory would apply for most situations where the goal was a "sustainable harvest." Other examples that could be managed in a similar way include logging and hunting.

GETTING STARTED

1 ⬥ Explain that this activity focuses on natural trends in population growth, as students are exploring with their ongoing duckweed population study, and on the ecological factors that affect these trends. Ask students if they can name any ecological conditions that promote or limit population growth. Students should propose such factors as available space, food, and climate.

2 Project the transparency of Student Sheet 14.1, "Avril Seal Population." Cover the data table so that only the graph is visible. Explain to the class that this is a population graph for the seals that hunt in areas where the salmon fishermen of the town of Avril Gulf do much of their fishing. Ask the class, *What does the graph show about the seal population?*

The population increased from 388 in 1980 to 430 in 1990, and then it decreased to 120 seals in 2005. Ask, *What factors and events might have caused the fluctuations in the population as shown in the graph?*

Make a list from students' suggestions. Factors that might affect the size of the population include the availability of food, the number of predators that prey on the seals, the number of seals that leave or join the population, and the impact of humans on the seal population, such as hunting or polluted waters.

3 Hand out Student Sheet 14.1, "The Avril Seal Population." Ask students, *What information does the table show?*

It shows the births and deaths for the seal population and resulting annual seal population number for the period 1980–2005. Ask students to examine the data provided in the table and to describe what has happened. Their responses should indicate that the population increased

from 1980 until 1990, and then decreased from 1990 until 2005. Explain that the graph shows only the final population at each five-year interval, while the table shows the initial and final populations, plus the births and deaths for each year. Discuss the advantages of representing this information in graphical and tabular form. The table conveys additional information about births and deaths and their contribution to the overall population numbers. The graph displays the final population at intervals of time, and is easier to interpret. Be sure to include the terms carrying capacity and population growth rate in your discussion, as they are defined in the introduction.

---

14 Investigating Population Growth Rates **1**

2 **T**HERE ARE LIMITS on the sizes of populations ecosystems can support. These limits—the **carrying capacities** for particular populations—are determined by the resources available and the other species present in the ecosystem. Carrying capacities of an ecosystem change as the resources in the ecosystem change. The graph below shows 25 years of population levels of zebra mussels in a lake.

This population of zebra mussels reached its carrying capacity around Year 14.

Initially the zebra mussel population grew to a point where the lake could not sustain it, but by Year 14 the population had decreased to a level at which the ecosystem was able to sustain it over an extended period of time. What factors do you think might change the carrying capacity for this population?

As you learned in the previous activity, many organisms have interdependent relationships. In predator–prey relationships, the size and health of one population is frequently closely tied to the size and health of the other, as you learned in Activity 7, "Energy Flow Through an Ecosystem."

A change in a population level is one indicator that can reflect the health of an ecosystem. A population of a successful invasive species, such as duckweed, will increase rapidly in a new habitat, possibly causing the populations of other, native species to shrink. This can change both population and biodiversity levels. You saw several examples of this in the first few activities of this unit. The **population growth rate** describes the change in a population over specified intervals of time. A positive growth rate indicates that the population is

Anchor covered with zebra mussels.

119

DOING THE ACTIVITY

4 Before students begin working with the online simulation, they should use graph paper to set up graph axes as shown below right. They will use this to record their work with the online simulation. Alternatively, you might have students print their work directly from the simulation, if you have the facilities to do so. Explain how you would like students to work with the online simulation. Direct students' attention to the graph on Student Sheet 14.1, "The Avril Seal Population." Ask, *During which period(s) did the seal population have a positive growth rate? What is your evidence?*

Answers should indicate that a positive growth rate occurred from 1980 until 1990, which is indicated by a line with a positive slope going up over the years. Ask the class to identify a period when there is a negative growth rate (1990–2005).

5 Students complete the population simulation on the *Science and Global Issues* page of the SEPUP website *(sepuplhs.org/sgi)*. All directions for this simulation are on Student Sheet 14.2, "Investigating Population Growth," which can be downloaded from the same website.

FOLLOW-UP

6 Use transparencies 14.1–14.4 to explain standard growth curves. Project Transparency 14.1, "Linear Growth Curve," and explain that when a population increases by the same amount at regular intervals, such as each month, year, or generation, this type of growth is called linear growth. An example would be a population that increases by two individuals every month. When plotted on a graph, this data set produces a straight line. A graph for any population undergoing linear growth or linear decline will be a straight line like the one shown

---

SCIENCE & GLOBAL ISSUES/BIOLOGY • ECOLOGY

growing, while a negative growth rate indicates the population is shrinking. A population that remains the same size has a zero-growth rate.

In this activity you will examine how different variables affect population growth rates of a fish population and the carrying capacity of the ecosystem the population lives in.

Challenge

3 ▶ How do changing variables alter population growth rates and ecosystem carrying capacities?

MATERIALS

FOR EACH PAIR OF STUDENTS
computer with Internet access
colored pencils

FOR EACH STUDENT
Student Sheet 14.1, "Avril Seal Population"
Student Sheet 14.2, "Investigating Population Growth"
sheet of graph paper

Procedure

1. With your partner, visit the *Science and Global Issues* page of the SEPUP website at *sepuplhs.org/sgi* and go to the population simulation. Use your student sheet to guide you through the simulation.

Analysis

1. Describe the shapes of the graphs you created when working with the online simulation. Explain what the shape of the curve indicates about the population.

2. Based on your work in this activity, describe the relationship between birth and death rates and the growth rate of a population.

3. Based on your work in this activity, describe the relationship between carrying capacity and the size of a population.

4. How do the sizes of populations of other species relate to the sustainability of the human population? Think of at least two examples, and describe the relationship of each to the human population.

120

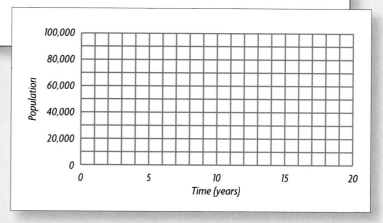

on Transparency 14.1, except that a decline will show a negative slope. Project Transparency 14.2, "Exponential Growth: J-Curve." Explain that when a population exhibits exponential growth, the rate of increase continually rises. When plotted on a graph, the curve for exponential population growth resembles the letter J and is often called a J-curve, as shown on Transparency 14.2. Exponential growth is more likely to occur during times of plentiful resources and in the absence of epidemics or massive deaths from external forces. Point out to students that exponential growth can happen over a short period of time (e.g., rapidly growing bacteria) or over a long period of time (e.g., human population), depending on the reproduction rate and lifespan of the organism.

Explain that no population can continue to grow forever. Eventually it will reach, or even temporarily exceed, the ecosystem's carrying capacity. Given the right conditions, the size of a population will reach the ecosystem's carrying capacity, and then remain relatively stable at that level.

Suppose a small population of a given species is introduced into an ecosystem for the first time. Typically, if there are ample resources and few predators, there will be an initial period of slow growth, followed by a period of exponential growth, which will then level off when the population reaches the carrying capacity. Data for this pattern of population growth—exponential, then stable at or near carrying capacity—produces a graph with a curved shape somewhat like the letter S. This is known as an S-curve. Show students Transparency 14.3, "Carrying Capacity: S-Curve," and direct them to compare this with the graphs they created in Procedure Part C. Explain that populations experiencing exponential growth often approach carrying capacity and resemble an S-curve. Emphasize that a population at or near its carrying capacity represents a population level that is in equilibrium with the other components of the ecosystem. Note that the population is not static: there is a constant interaction and exchange and slight fluctuations in the population.

Project Transparency 14.4, "Population Crash." Ask, *What is happening to the population shown by the graph?*

This population is experiencing a drastic decline in population size, also called a population crash. Ask, *What are some conditions that might cause this to happen?*

Population crashes can be caused by a variety of local events, including a shortage in the food supply, a disease among the population, or changes in the habitat of the species, such as the disappearance of the supply of uncontaminated water. You may want to point out that introduction of the smallpox virus by European explorers in the 15th and 16th centuries caused population crashes in many indigenous human populations, including those of North and South America.

Population decline is almost inevitable when a population exceeds the carrying capacity of its environment. This often occurs because humans alter the ecosystem in a way that reduces the resources available to organisms. Ask students to look at Student Sheet 14.1, "The Avril Seal Population," and describe the type(s) of growth the population graph represents. Students should use the words linear, exponential, and carrying capacity to describe their ideas.

7 ✓Analysis Questions 6, 7, and 8 are Quick Check questions that provide an opportunity to assess a number of components of the ANALYZING DATA scoring variable. With Analysis Question 6 check students' choices of indicators and how to analyze them. Analysis Question 7 assesses students' abilities to explain trends and relationships, and make inferences and conclusions from data. Analysis Question 8 focuses on trends and relationships in data and touches on one of the main arguments of human-population sustainability. Many experts believe that the human population long ago exceeded earth's carrying capacity and that we will experience a population crash if sustainable measures are not put in place.

EXTENSION

Go to the *Science and Global Issues* website *(sepuplhs.org/sgi)* for an activity demonstrating how scientists estimate population sizes for open-ocean organisms.

SAMPLE RESPONSES

1. Student answers will vary, but should include a description of the graph with accurate interpretation of what the graph indicates about population growth or decline.

2. If the birth rate is equal to the death rate, the population growth rate will be zero, because new individuals are born at the same rate as individuals die. If the birth rate is greater than the death rate, the population growth rate will be positive because new individuals are being added to the population. If the birth rate is less than the death rate, the population growth rate will be negative.

3. Carrying capacity is the population size that can be supported by an ecosystem. If the carrying capacity is met, the population size will no longer continue to increase. It may fluctuate a bit, but will remain relatively the same over a period of time, assuming the carrying capacity

stays the same and there are no drastic changes in the population or environment, like a disease killing half the population or the food source disappearing.

4. The human population is only sustainable if we have enough of the other species we rely on for food and other necessities. For example, if salmon were fished unsustainably, people would eventually have no salmon to eat. We could eat other fish, but if overfishing continued with other fish species, eventually we would have no fish to eat. The size of the bacteria populations in dead zones can also affect the human population. The larger the bacteria population is, the larger the dead zones. We cannot get fish or other food to eat from these dead zones. We can eat other organisms, but eventually there might not be enough food for the entire human population.

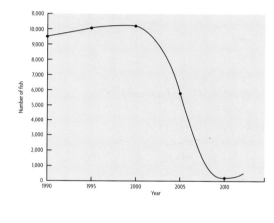

5. Some bacteria reproduce by doubling once every 20 minutes.

   a. If you started with one bacterium, how many would you have in three hours?

   b. Describe what would happen if the bacteria continued to reproduce for 24 hours (do not calculate an exact number).

   c. Suggest at least two limiting factors that will ultimately stop the increase of a bacteria population.

6. Scientists and policy makers often have to work together to set catch limits on fisheries. Imagine that a policy maker proposes to allow the fishing of a certain species to go on at current rates because, she says, "Fishing at current rates will not impact the ecosystem. We are removing fish at a rate lower than the birth rate of their population." Is this claim valid? What indicators would you look at to support or disprove this claim? Explain your reasoning.

7. Look at the population graph for the fish population shown below. How would you describe the growth rate? Is this population sustainable?

8. Examine the data in the Global Human Population graph provided below. Based on your work in this activity, how would you describe the global human population growth rate? Explain your reasoning.

121

197

5. a. 512

   b. There will be huge numbers of bacteria. (*Actual calculation:* $2^{72} = 4.72 \times 10^{21}$)

   c. Disease is one limiting factor that might keep the bacteria population from growing out of control. Another is lack of decaying and dead matter for them to feed on.

6. ✓The indicators you should look at to examine the validity of the claim is the size of the population of the fish, and what other factors influence the population size. If the fish population is small, any removal of fish at any rate will impact it severely. Also, if the death rate is high because of disease or high levels of predators, fishing could put too much pressure on the population and cause it to collapse. If either of these is true, the policy maker is incorrect and fishing will impact the ecosystem negatively.

7. ✓Answers will vary. A correct and complete answer would state that the growth rate was positive, then turned negative, and then crashed, indicating that fishing was no longer sustainable.

8. ✓Answers will vary. A correct and complete answer would state that the growth rate is positive and remains fairly steady. It should also state that the growth rate is exponential.

9. Answers will vary, but may include such examples as the amount of drinkable water, amount of oil, and food availability. A possible student response might be: I would look at the amount of pollution and amount of green space as environmental indicators, how much food is available for each person in the world and rates of disease in different countries for social indicators, and how many people are living below the poverty line and how money is distributed in different countries for economic indicators.

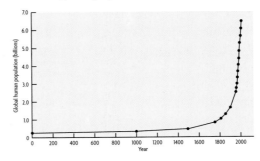

9. Some people claim that the human population has passed its carrying capacity. What kind of environmental, social, and economic indicators would you examine to support or argue against this claim?

KEY VOCABULARY

carrying capacity   population

density-dependent factors   population growth rate

density-independent factors

122

REVISIT THE CHALLENGE

Be sure students understand there are many factors that influence population growth rates. Have a discussion with students about what kinds of factors would influence population growth rates and whether the rate change would be negative or positive. Include in this discussion both natural and human-influenced factors.

15 Changes Due to Population Growth

MODELING • 1–2 CLASS SESSIONS

OVERVIEW

In this activity, students investigate how farmed salmon affects the surrounding environment. They also examine how decisions made at the fish farms alter population growth rates of wild salmon.

KEY CONTENT

1. Aquaculture is the practice of growing fish and other aquatic species for human consumption.
2. Some species are better suited to aquaculture than others.
3. Many types of aquaculture are employed around the world.
4. Aquaculture often harms the surrounding ecosystem.
5. The damage by aquaculture to the surrounding ecosystem can be mitigated in several ways.

KEY PROCESS SKILLS

1. Students formulate and revise scientific models using logic and evidence.
2. Students identify and describe trade-offs.
3. Students graph and analyze data.

MATERIALS AND ADVANCE PREPARATION

For the teacher
Scoring Guide: ORGANIZING DATA (OD)

For each group of four students
number cube*

For each student
sheet of graph paper*
Scoring Guide: ORGANIZING DATA (OD)
(optional)

Not supplied in kit

Masters for Scoring Guides are in Teacher Resources IV: Assessment.

TEACHING SUMMARY

Getting Started
- Introduce the practice of aquaculture.

Doing the Activity
- (OD ASSESSMENT) Students investigate how events affect two populations of salmon.

Follow-up
- The class discusses the benefits and trade-offs of aquaculture.

BACKGROUND INFORMATION

Some types of aquaculture are sustainable and provide much-needed nourishment and income for local communities. For example, farmed oysters, clams, and mussels are raised in the United States in ways that minimize environmental harm or even reverse it. Because these species rely on clean water, the farms' operators often support efforts to minimize pollution.

The farming of some seafood, however, has a higher environmental impact, and some farms of these species are considered unsustainable. For example, in many tropical nations shrimp farming has historically not been sustainable. Wild shrimp live in mangrove forest habitats, and the mangrove forests are additionally important in filtering pollutants from waters and protecting coastal areas from storms. However, in the past people removed mangrove forests so they could install shrimp farms. A farm operated for a few years and then moved elsewhere when too much waste built up at the site. Efforts are now being made to develop more sustainable methods of shrimp farming, but many of the destroyed mangrove forests may not recover.

Three major problems with aquaculture are:

· treating the farmed fish with antibiotics, which can lead to antibiotic-resistant bacteria making their way into the surrounding ecosystem.

· wild fish breeding with escaped farmed fish, introducing potentially detrimental genes into the wild population.

· feeding farmed fish fishmeal or fish oil, which requires a large amount of wild-caught fish.

Programs such as the Monterey Bay Aquarium's Seafood Watch rate the sustainability of different farmed fish based on a number of criteria including the type and location of enclosures used, the source of the fish raised, the content and source of the feed, and several other aquaculture practices.

See the *Science and Global Issues* page of the SEPUP website *(sepuplhs.org/sgi)* for links to more information on aquaculture in the United States and other countries.

GETTING STARTED

1 ◆ Poll students to find out how many of them have eaten some kind of fish or other seafood in the past week or month. Then ask, *Where do you think that fish or other seafood came from?*

Students should answer that it was likely caught in the ocean, a lake, or a river. Ask the students, *Do you think we could have fish farms to grow fish instead of catching wild fish? Would this help to prevent overfishing?*

Students' answers will vary. Some may know about forms of aquaculture, and some will speculate. Accept all students' answers. Next, take a second informal poll of the class to find out how many think the results of fish farming will be helpful, negative, or mixed. Tally their responses on the board to return to later in this activity. Brainstorm possible trade-offs of aquaculture with the students before they read the introduction, and list those on the board for later reference.

---

15 Changes Due to Population Growth

1 "I **DON'T UNDERSTAND WHY** *overfishing is such a big deal,"* you overhear someone say *in the grocery store. "Why don't they just grow fish on fish farms for us to eat and leave the wild ones alone? That way the wild ones can reproduce and increase their population. Besides, I thought that fish had lots of offspring, what are we worried about?"*

As the human population continues to grow, and the need for food grows with it, more and more fisheries are being overfished. Some fisheries, such as the salmon fishery along the west coast of the United States, have been temporarily closed due to shrinking populations.

Many people suggest that the solution to overfishing is aquaculture. **Aquaculture** is the growing of fish and other aquatic species for human consumption. There are species of fish that can be sustainably farmed. For example, tilapia farms in the United States are often viewed as sustainable and very successful. Native to Africa, tilapia grow and reproduce well in captivity and are raised in enclosed inland ponds where their wastewater is treated. Since more and more wild fish populations are declining, aquaculture is becoming an important food source.

It does not, however, work for all species. Some fish need specific habitats that cannot be recreated in captivity, some do not breed in captivity, and some have other limitations. On top of that, species such as salmon that can be farmed often cause major problems for the local, natural ecosystems.

Challenge

▶ How can the environmental harm from salmon farming be minimized?

MATERIALS

FOR EACH GROUP OF FOUR STUDENTS
number cube

FOR EACH STUDENT
sheet of graph paper

123

Aquaculture Systems

Aquaculture can be located on land, in oceans, or in bays, depending on the species raised. The most familiar aquaculture systems consist of inland ponds that hold a particular fresh or saltwater species, such as trout, tilapia, shrimp, or catfish. Some of these ponds are enclosed systems in which the water is treated and recirculated to prevent contamination of the environment. This is costly and requires electricity.

Raceways are another type of system. They divert water from a river or other source and guide it through long channels that house the fish being raised. The water is then treated before it rejoins the original source. In the United States raceways are used to raise rainbow trout, striped bass, and other species. Among ecologists there is concern that the farmed fish might escape and either interbreed with the wild fish or compete with them for food.

In this activity you will examine the aquaculture system of open-net pens. These are large net pens suspended in coastal waters or lakes and are frequently used for tuna and salmon farming. The water from the pens exchanges freely with the water in the surrounding habitat. This causes pollution and can spread disease from the farmed fish to the wild populations. There is also the chance that the farmed fish will escape, as with the raceway systems. You will explore some of the benefits and trade-offs involved in a widespread debate over farmed salmon. ■

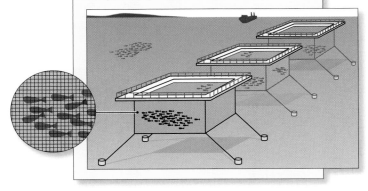

CHANGES DUE TO POPULATION GROWTH • ACTIVITY 15

Net pens are used to farm salmon.

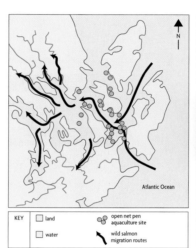

Atlantic Ocean

KEY			
	☐ land		open net pen aquaculture site
	☐ water		wild salmon migration routes

Most wild salmon hatch from their eggs in fresh water, and migrate down rivers or waterways to the ocean. Mature salmon migrate back to the same fresh water location to reproduce. The simplified map at left shows net pens located along wild salmon migration routes. Below, a wild salmon swims upstream during the fall.

DOING THE ACTIVITY

2 Have students read the Procedure carefully before they begin the investigation. Be sure students notice that at any point in the investigation, if they roll a 5 or 6 and their farmed population is not 1,400 or greater, they should roll again until they get a 1, 2, 3, or 4. Answer any questions about the Procedure before the students begin.

3 (OD ASSESSMENT) A sample student data table for Procedure Step 6 appears below and the corresponding sample graph on the following page. The ORGANIZING DATA (OD) Scoring Guide can be used to assess students' graphs. The sample graph is an example of a Level-3 response. A Level-3 graph would include correctly labeled axes, appropriate scales on each axis, and correctly plotted data, as shown in the sample graph. The students' data will vary depending on what numbers they roll for each generation.

---

2 *Procedure*

Your group will track two salmon populations, one wild and one farmed. The salmon farm is an open-net system set up in the coastal waters off of the East Coast of the United States, as shown in the illustration on the previous page. The wild salmon's migration routes, similar to those shown in the map of net pens and migration routes, bring them into close contact with the salmon farms.

1. Your group will collect data for 20 generations of salmon. In your science notebook set up a data table, similar to the one below, in which you enter your data on the salmon generations.

Comparing Wild and Farmed Salmon Populations

Generation	Wild population size	Wild population status	Farmed population size	Farmed population status
1	10,000		1,500	
2				
3				
4				
5				
6				

2. In Steps 3–6 you will follow the guidelines in the tables below to determine the status of your salmon population.

Wild Salmon Population				
NUMBER OF FISH	≤5,000	5,001–7,000	7,001–9,000	9,001–12,000
Population status	critically overfished	marginally overfished	stable	at carrying capacity

Farmed Salmon Population				
NUMBER OF FISH	≤5,000	5,001–7,000	7,001–9,000	9,001–12,000
Profit level	negative profit (loss)	no profit (break even)	moderate profit	substantial profit

---

Sample Student Response: Wild and Farmed Salmon Populations

Generation	Wild population size	Wild population status	Farmed population size	Farmed population status
1	10,000	at carrying capacity	1,500	substantial Profit
2	9,250	at carrying capacity	1,750	substantial Profit
3	8,750	stable	2,100	substantial Profit
4	7,250	stable	1850	substantial profit
5	6,500	marginally overfished	2,100	substantial profit
6	5,000	marginally overfished	1,850	substantial profit
7	4,000	critically overfished	2,200	substantial profit
8	4,500	critically overfished	1,850	substantial profit
9	5,000	marginally overfished	1,500	substantial profit
10	3,500	critically overfished	1,250	moderate profit
11	3,000	critically overfished	1,250	moderate profit
12	2,000	critically overfished	750	loss
13	500	critically overfished	500	loss
14	0	extinct	250	loss

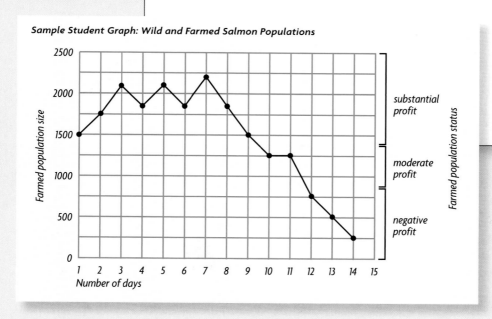

3. Begin your simulation by rolling the number cube to determine what happens to the first generation of salmon. The number cube key below tells you what the number you rolled means. Add to or subtract from the salmon populations as directed, and record the results in your data table. If you roll a 5 or 6 and your population is not 1,400 or greater, keep rolling until you get a 1, 2, 3, or 4.

Number Cube Key: Environmental Impacts

NUMBER ROLLED	SITUATION	ENVIRONMENTAL IMPACT	WILD POPULATION EFFECT	FARMED POPULATION EFFECT
1	Farmed salmon escape.	Escapees interbreed and compete for resources with wild population.	Loss of 500 salmon due to lack of resources and reduced fitness because of interbreeding	No change in population size
2	Disease at salmon farm	Disease spreads to wild population.	Loss of 1,500 salmon from disease	Loss of 250 salmon from disease
3	Antibiotics given to farmed salmon to prevent disease.	Kills "good" bacteria that the ecosystem needs to function	Ecosystem disrupted; causes loss of 750 salmon.	Disease decreases; population increases by 250 salmon
4	Decrease in density of salmon in pens	Milder environmental impact	Improved habitat causes increase of 500 salmon	Fewer salmon per pen, loss of 350 salmon
5	If farm has over 1,400 salmon, waste accumulates under pens.	Wastewater in local ecosystem causes habitat and food loss.	Reduction of available resources causes loss of 1,000 salmon.	Decrease in water quality causes loss of 500 salmon.
6	If farm has more than 1,400 salmon, new pen is built.	Takes up the space of wild salmon's habitat.	Decrease of resources causes loss of 500 salmon.	New pen houses more salmon; increase by 350 salmon

4. Record in your data table the status of each population, based on the information provided in Step 2.

5. Repeat Steps 3 and 4 until you have gone through 20 generations of salmon. If either population reaches 0 during the simulation, stop and move on to Step 6.

6. Construct a line graph that shows the population curves for the wild and farmed salmon populations.

Sample Student Graph: Wild and Farmed Salmon Populations

FOLLOW-UP

4 Have students discuss the kinds of events that affected their systems, and compare their graphs for both the wild and farmed populations. Be sure students discuss what happened to population levels in relation to the events that happened.

5 ✓ From the link on the *Science and Global Issues* page of the SEPUP website *(sepuplhs.org/sgi)* show students a video clip on sustainable fish farming. Discuss the benefits and trade-offs of the fish farm in the video. Have the students discuss how this compares to the salmon farm in the activity. Return to the poll of the class, and tell students you are going to ask the same questions you asked before the investigation. They are allowed to change their answers if their opinions have changed, or to keep their answers the same. Ask the students, *Do you think the results of fish farming will be helpful, negative, or mixed?*

Record these tallies of students' responses next to those already on the board. Discuss any changes with the class. If there were no changes, discuss why they think their opinions did not change. Have the class return to the list of the benefits and trade-offs of aquaculture and add or subtract from it as appropriate. As students offer suggestions, encourage them to think of the viewpoint from which they are making the observation. For example, if they point out that with more fish in pens, there is more environmental damage, they are looking at it in terms of the surrounding environment, not in terms of maximizing the number of fish in the farm. Analysis Question 4 is a Quick Check to ensure that students understand the term, and can identify trade-offs, which is a component of the EVIDENCE AND TRADE-OFFS scoring variable. This will be more formally assessed in the final activities of the unit.

---

4 *Analysis*

1. **a.** Define aquaculture.

   b. Describe at least two kinds of aquaculture systems.

2. Based on the graph you constructed in Procedure Step 6, explain the relationship between the population growth in the farmed salmon population and the wild population.

5

3. What are some of the possible environmental impacts of aquaculture? Which of these impacts are density-dependent factors and which are density-independent factors?

4. What are the benefits and trade-offs involved with aquaculture? Discuss at least two aquaculture systems.

5. Your model in this activity involved random events happening to the salmon populations. If you were to build and operate an open-net salmon farm, what are some steps you could take to minimize environmental harm and make the farm more sustainable?

KEY VOCABULARY	
aquaculture	population
density-dependent factors	population growth rate
density-independent factors	

128

SAMPLE RESPONSES

1. a. Aquaculture is raising fish or other aquatic species for human food.

    b. One aquaculture system is open-net pens, like the ones described in this activity. These are big pens in the ocean or lakes, and the water is shared with the environment around the pens. Another system is ponds, which do not have to share water with the surrounding environments because they can be built on land and have a filtering system.

2. Students' answers will vary depending on their graphs and what happened during their investigations. In this model, because the number cube determined that events happened randomly, it is possible for both populations to increase, both to decrease, or one to increase while one decreases. Students should discuss both populations, including what happened relative to each other. A possible response is shown below.

    Our graph showed that our farmed population of salmon grew and then decreased. At the beginning we were adding pens to our farm and treating the fish to prevent disease. But then a disease struck, and the population decreased. The wild population decreased and quickly went extinct. The events that happened on our farm caused our wild population to decrease, especially from diseases in the farmed salmon that spread to the wild salmon.

3. Aquaculture can have several impacts on the environment. Most of these are density-dependent because the impacts are bigger if the farmed salmon population is bigger and kept in a small area. For example, the wastewater from the salmon pens can accumulate and cause damage to the habitat near the pens. The higher the population density of the salmon, the more waste there will be and the more damage will result. This is also true for disease, and for more pens being built to house more salmon. The fish farmers probably use more antibiotics when there are more salmon, so this is also density-dependent. The salmon escaping is probably density-independent.

4. ✓ The benefit to using aquaculture for some fish is that you can raise them for human consumption and leave wild populations undisturbed. The system can be set up to have very little environmental impact, like an enclosed-pond system that treats the wastewater or raceways where water from a nearby river is diverted then returned. The trade-offs are that in many cases there are large environmental impacts that can damage the surrounding habitat and even the wild fish populations that the aquaculture should be protecting such as farmed fish escaping and using up resources.

5. Answers will vary depending on what numbers were rolled for each generation. A possible answer would be: In our investigation, there was a lot of disease in our salmon farm. To minimize the effect of this on the wild salmon population, the salmon farmer could monitor more carefully for disease and treat it right away. They could also move their pens away from where the wild salmon migrate, and so the wild salmon would be less likely to catch the disease.

REVISIT THE CHALLENGE

Discuss with the students their suggestions for minimizing the environmental impact of salmon farming. Discuss with them farming methods for other seafood.

16 Ecosystems Out of Balance

INVESTIGATION • 1–2 CLASS SESSIONS

OVERVIEW

In this activity, students interpret population graphs as they investigate four fisheries that are altering surrounding ecosystems. Students advise the fisheries on the consequences of their fishing and how to make their fishery more sustainable.

KEY CONTENT

1. Relationships between species in an ecosystem are interdependent.

2. Changes in the population of a species within an ecosystem affect other species in that ecosystem.

3. Removing a species from an ecosystem can have unintended consequences.

4. Some fisheries have significantly damaged associated ecosystems.

5. Changes in the population dynamics of an ecosystem can be a factor in an invasive species becoming established within that ecosystem.

6. Sustainable management of ecosystem services depends on continual input from scientists and other experts.

KEY PROCESS SKILLS

1. Students graph and analyze data.

2. Students interpret data.

3. Students identify and describe trends in data.

4. Students make accurate interpretations, inferences, and conclusions from text.

MATERIALS AND ADVANCE PREPARATION

For the teacher

Transparency 16.1, "Pacific Halibut Population"

Transparency 16.2, "Pacific Halibut Food Chain"

Transparency 16.3, "Pacific-Halibut-dominated Ecosystem Graph"

Scoring Guide: ANALYZING DATA (AD)

Scoring Guide: UNDERSTANDING CONCEPTS (UC)

For each student

Student Sheet 16.1, "Cod-dominated Ecosystem"

Student Sheet 16.2, "Tiger-shark-dominated Ecosystem"

Student Sheet 16.3, "Orca-dominated Ecosystem"

Student Sheet 16.4, "Caspian-seal-dominated Ecosystem"

Scoring Guide: ANALYZING DATA (AD) (optional)

Scoring Guide: UNDERSTANDING CONCEPTS (UC) (optional)

Not supplied in kit

Masters for Scoring Guides are in Teacher Resources IV: Assessment.

TEACHING SUMMARY

Getting Started

- Review the population graphs for an ecosystem with a sustainable fishery.

Doing the Activity

- Students formulate hypotheses on the impact of fishing on four ecosystems.

- (AD ASSESSMENT) Students analyze how sustainable fishery practices might alter the effects seen in the fisheries' ecosystems.

Follow-up

- (UC ASSESSMENT) (AD ASSESSMENT) The class discusses why sustainable practices are not currently implemented in all fisheries.

BACKGROUND INFORMATION

Scientists have documented many instances of the effect of ecosystem disruption due to species removal. Some ecosystems have a keystone species, which if removed, critically disrupts the balance for the ecosystem. One of the best-known examples of this is the sea otter and the kelp forests. Sea otters were hunted so much in the 18th and 19th centuries that by early in the 20th century they were near extinction. At this point scientists documented that the numbers of sea urchins, once prey for the otters, increased dramatically, consuming kelp forests and leaving rocky barrens devoid of the vast array of species that had resided there previously. This is referred to as a cascade effect, where the removal of one species causes a number of associated species to be affected as a result. The cascade effect is not limited to removal of a species, but can also occur with the introduction of an invasive species or as the result of an ecological disturbance. In the case of the sea otter, when they were no longer hunted, the populations eventually began to recover, and the kelp forests and associated ecosystems slowly returned as well. It should be noted, however, that in most instances the interactions are much more complex.

Initial theories approached the cascade effect as either "top down" (when the apex predator[s] of a food chain was removed) or "bottom up" (when the producers for an ecosystem were removed). As scientific understanding of ecosystem interactions has deepened, it has become clear that ecosystems can compensate to a degree if disrupted, but that too much disruption throws the ecosystem out of balance, causing a cascade effect. This can occur due to the loss of one species, or the reduction of several species.

Fisheries have been found to have a major impact on many ecosystems, although the effects are often not immediately apparent. For example, if an apex predator, such as a shark, were heavily fished, the species it had preyed on would increase due to lack of pressure from predation. As that species increases, its prey will decrease, and so on. In some instances the removal of a species (due to overfishing or other factors) has led to shifts in ecosystems whereby species are consuming less desirable prey. Stellar sea lions off Alaska, for example, have switched from eating herring to eating pollock, which have a lower nutritional value. In other cases overfishing has led to complete ecosystem collapse, such as off the coast of Namibia in Africa where overfishing of most fish in the ecosystem is believed to have led to massive jellyfish blooms due to the cascade effects of overfishing.

It is also important to note that ecosystems are in a constant state of flux. Scientists once believed that a "healthy" ecosystem exhibited only minor fluctuations unless there was some kind of disturbance. They have now found that many populations regularly undergo large fluctuations, and not necessarily in response to major disturbances such as volcanic eruptions or floods.

GETTING STARTED

1 Start by asking students, *What do you think population levels would look like if you graphed them for an ecosystem that had no pressure from fisheries?*

Students' answers should point out that while population levels of the species in the ecosystem might fluctuate a bit, they should remain fairly constant. Then ask students, based on what they have studied, *What do you expect to happen to the graph if an important species within the ecosystem were overfished?*

They should point out that the levels of all populations might change, either going up if they were a prey species, relative to the organism being fished, or down if they were a predator species. Ask the students, *If the fishery were sustainable, would you expect the same results?*

Students should answer that they would not expect to see as much of an impact, if any. If necessary, remind students that a fishery would be considered sustainable if it allows the ecosystem to remain in a relatively stable state.

---

16 Ecosystems Out of Balance

1 **O**RGANISMS WITHIN an ecosystem interact at all levels, depending on each other for their survival, either directly for food or shelter, or indirectly through the carbon cycle. As you saw in the previous activity, both native and introduced species have a significant effect on the ecosystem around them. The entire ecosystem is a complex network that can be drastically altered if the population of one (or more) species goes into a decline or a surge. In this activity you will take on the role of a fisheries biologist and determine how to make several fisheries more sustainable.

2 *You are a fisheries biologist who has, in the past, advised the Pacific halibut (Hippoglossus stenolepis) fishery, which is known for its successful sustainable practices. The Pacific halibut fishery is carefully monitored, and each year you and other fisheries biologists make a new set of recommendations on where and how many fish can be caught. The limits are adopted by the entire fishery. Several other fisheries have asked for your expert advice. These fisheries would like you to examine population data and other information for the species they fish and the species' ecosystems and, if they are not sustainable, to advise on how to make them more sustainable.*

A fisherman weighs the Pacific halibut he caught.

Challenge

3 ▶ How does information about relationships among organisms help to determine the sustainability of a species and an ecosystem?

129

Project Transparency 16.1, "Pacific Halibut Population." Discuss the graph, noting the labels on the axes and what is happening to population levels. Next, project Transparency 16.2, "Pacific Halibut Food Chain." Review the food chain with the students and have them suggest the roles of the organisms in the food chain. Now project Transparency 16.3, "Pacific-halibut-dominated Ecosystem." Have students identify which line correlates with each organism, and what the different axes of the graph show. Ask the students, *Do you think this is a stable, healthy ecosystem? What evidence supports your thinking?*

Students should answer yes because the population levels for all organisms stay fairly steady with slight fluctuations relative to each other. Be sure to clear up any misconceptions about the slight fluctuations in the population levels. Students should understand that population levels will normally not be a flat line, and some fluctuation is normal. Ask the students, *What do you notice about the population levels for the different organisms?*

Students should point out that the brittle stars and Pacific halibut follow the same pattern, and that the sablefish do the opposite. Then review the food chain with the students. Remind them that an upward arrow indicates that the organism above gets energy from (eats) the organism below. Have the students examine the graph at two specific points in time, one from the beginning of the graph and one from the end. Ask the students to describe what the data show at each point. If necessary, model a statement for them. For example: In 1975, the halibut and brittle star populations were about the same, and they were larger than the sablefish's. In 2000, the sablefish population was greater while the halibut and brittle star populations were lower, but still about the same as each other.

2 Ask the students, *Based on the information in the food chain we saw, what do you think is happening within the ecosystem?*

Guide the students, as necessary, to the conclusion that as the Pacific halibut population increases, they consume more sablefish, so the sablefish population decreases. Have the students take a top-down approach, and have them start with the apex predator, in this case the halibut, and work their way down the food chain. (This tactic will make the activity run more smoothly than if they started just anywhere in the chain.) Students should determine that as the sablefish population decreases, the brittle star population increases because fewer of them are being eaten by sablefish. Students should also notice that there comes a point when this relationship changes, likely due to an abundance of brittle stars (prey for sablefish) and relative scarcity of halibut to prey on the sablefish, and the pattern reverses. Over time, the pattern repeats itself, so that overall, all of the populations in the ecosystem remain fairly steady.

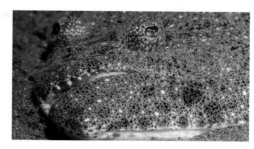

Pacific halibut are large flatfish that live on the ocean floor in coastal waters off the western United States and Canada.

MATERIALS

FOR EACH STUDENT

Student Sheet 16.1, "Cod-dominated Ecosystem"
Student Sheet 16.2, "Tiger-shark-dominated Ecosystem"
Student Sheet 16.3, "Orca-dominated Ecosystem"
Student Sheet 16.4, "Caspian-seal-dominated Ecosystem"

Procedure

Part A: Evaluating Fisheries' Sustainability

1. With your group, examine the food chain for the cod-dominated ecosystem, and the corresponding graph on Student Sheet 16.1, "Cod-dominated Ecosystem." This ecosystem is found in the North Atlantic Ocean.

2. Identify the role of each species in the food chain by determining what they eat and what they are eaten by.

3. With the key, label each line on the graph with the name of the organism.

4. Choose one time point on the graph, toward the beginning. Based on the information provided in the graph, explain in detail what is happening at this point with each species, relative to the other populations in the ecosystem. Write your description in your science notebook.

5. Choose a time point on the graph that is toward the end. Based on the information provided in the graph, explain in detail what is happening at this point with each species in the ecosystem. Include what this means about the food-chain relationships between the species. Write your description in your science notebook.

130

---

3 After students read the introduction, tell them that Pacific halibut comprise a large, commercial fishery off of the west coasts of the United States and Canada. Ask students, *Based on what you have seen, do you think this is a sustainable fishery? What indicators are you looking at to determine this?*

Students should answer that the fishery is sustainable, which is indicated by the continued relatively steady population levels for both the halibut and the other organisms within its ecosystem. Ask the students, *What would you expect to be different on a population graph for an ecosystem of a fishery that is not sustainable?*

Students should answer that they expect the population levels to change and not follow the same patterns. They should recognize that the population levels would not stay relatively steady.

DOING THE ACTIVITY

4 (AD ASSESSMENT) Procedure Step 7 is an opportunity for you to use the ANALYZING DATA Scoring Guide to asses students' ability to correctly identify and describe trends and relationships between variables. Sample Level-3 responses for each ecosystem are shown on the next page. Students may need varying levels of support, depending on their comfort level with analyzing graphs, particularly the orca-dominated ecosystem where the relationships are more complex. If students need assistance analyzing the graphs, you may want to suggest that they look first at what is happening with the population that is being fished and work up or down the food chain from there, or that they work their way through the graph asking themselves, "If species X is declining and it eats species Y, what is happening to species Y?" If students question the initial rise in the bay scallop population in the tiger-shark-dominated ecosystem, you might point them to the brief reading, which tells them that there was a bay scallop crash in the early 1960s, before the graph began, but the population began to recover in the early 1970s. Or ask them to speculate on what might be happening with the scallops, and discuss it with them after they have formed their own hypotheses. Depending on your students' abilities to analyze the graphs and food chains, you may opt to have them begin on Part B of the Procedure to help them interpret the graphs. The brief readings on the history of each fishery may help them in drawing their conclusions about the ecosystems.

---

6. Summarize the population growth rates for each population for the full time period shown on the graph. Write your summary in your science notebook.

4 7. Discuss with your group what the graph shows overall. Note any patterns or anything that seems out of the ordinary, as compared to the Pacific-halibut-dominated ecosystem you reviewed with your teacher. Write your observations in your science notebook.

5 8. Repeat Steps 1–7 for the tiger-shark-dominated ecosystem. This ecosystem is found in the Atlantic Ocean off the southern coast of the United States.

9. Repeat Steps 1–7 for the orca-dominated ecosystem. This ecosystem is found off the northwestern Pacific coast of North America.

6 10. Repeat Steps 1–7 for the Caspian-seal-dominated ecosystem. This ecosystem is found in the Caspian Sea, the world's largest enclosed body of water, located between the southern border of Russia and the northern border of Iran.

Part B: Fishery Histories

11. Read the brief history of the cod fishery below.

ATLANTIC COD

The Atlantic cod (*Gadus morhua*) fishery is one of the oldest fisheries in the world. There are records of explorers from Europe hunting for new cod fishing grounds as far back as 1000 A.D. Atlantic cod are found throughout the North Atlantic in waters up to 400 meters deep. While the Atlantic cod has been fished for more than 1,000 years, the invention of steamships and on-ship refrigeration in the early 1900s brought huge changes to the fishery. Overfishing of the cod intensified to the point that, in 1992, Canada declared a two-year moratorium on cod fishing off its shores. Soon other nations began to apply strict rules limiting the size and number of cod that were fished in an attempt to bring the cod population back to sustainable levels that would maintain a healthy ecosystem and support the fishery.

cod

12. With your group, compare this information with your observations of the cod-dominated-ecosystem graph. How does this information support or inform your conclusions about what the graph shows? Write down any additional observations or thoughts about what might be happening in the cod-dominated ecosystem.

---

5 If necessary, review with students that correlation does not necessarily mean causation. Reinforce this concept by reminding them that while fishing may be the cause of the population-level shifts on the graphs, there is no direct evidence of causation. You might want to give them an analogy to further illustrate this. For example, if 75% of students are wearing blue shirts on Friday, someone might infer that the students are wearing blue shirts because the school color is blue and there is a big football game after school. However, the true cause might be that the local pizza place is giving a special discount that day for everyone wearing a blue shirt.

6 Students should eventually reach the following conclusions:

Sample Level-3 Response
Cod-dominated Ecosystem

As the cod population decreased, there were more northern snow crabs because they were not being preyed on. As the northern snow crabs increased, they consumed more zooplankton, which in turn meant that fewer phytoplankton were eaten, and so their population increased.

Tiger-shark-dominated Ecosystem

As the tiger shark population decreased, the cownose rays were increasing. The bay scallops, which were increasing, started to decrease as the cownose rays increased and consumed more of them.

Orca-dominated Ecosystem

As the perch population decreased, the sea urchin population increased. This kept the sea otter and algae populations steady for a while, but the orcas did not have as much perch to eat. The orcas began preying on otters, and the otter population dropped, which meant the urchin population continued to rise. Eventually the orcas did not have enough perch or otters, and their population dropped. The algae population stayed steady because, while the perch population dropped, the urchin population rose, which meant that there was the same amount of pressure on the algae, but from different predators.

Caspian-seal-dominated Ecosystem

The seal population decreased as the kilka population decreased. In 1999, when these two populations were already far into decline, an invasive comb jelly was found, and it increased extremely rapidly. The zooplankton decreased, and the phytoplankton (not having its natural predators) rose rapidly. The plankton populations have leveled off somewhat, but the comb jelly population is still very high, and the kilka and seal populations are still declining.

SCIENCE & GLOBAL ISSUES/BIOLOGY • ECOLOGY

13. Repeat Steps 11 and 12 for the tiger shark fishery.

TIGER SHARK

The tiger shark *(Galeocerdo cuvier)* is one of the largest predatory sharks found in the world's oceans. Like many other shark species, the tiger shark is fished for its fins to make shark fin soup, a dish in Chinese cuisine that has become more popular around the world over the past few decades. The tiger shark is also fished for its liver, which is high in vitamin A. The shark is highly valued by sport fishers, particularly because it is known as a dangerous predator. Tiger sharks' gestation period is very long: 14–16 months between fertilization and birth. They give birth only once every three years, producing, on average, 40 pups. As shown in the food chain, tiger sharks feed on cow nose rays, which feed on bay scallops. The bay scallop population crashed in the early 1960s due to overfishing. Limits were set on scallop collection and the population started to recover in the 1970s.

tiger shark

14. Repeat Steps 11 and 12 for the perch fishery (part of the orca-dominated ecosystem).

PACIFIC OCEAN PERCH

Pacific ocean perch *(Sebastes alutus)* are caught primarily for human consumption. The population was heavily fished starting in the early 1960s. The fishery grew rapidly, but in 1990, the perch were declared overfished off the west coast of the United States. In 2003, a fishery management council put in place a plan that they hoped would allow the population to recover. Perch are slow growing, and only mature (are able to have offspring) after they are at least five years old. Some females do not mature until they are 15 years old.

perch

15. Repeat Steps 11 and 12 for the anchovy kilka fishery (part of the Caspian-seal-dominated ecosystem).

ANCHOVY KILKA

The anchovy kilka *(Clupeonella engrauliformis)* is one of the main commercially fished species in the Caspian Sea. Major fishing of the kilka began in the 1950s, and by the 1990s there were record catches as large as 400,000 tons annually. In 1999, an invasive comb jelly *(Mnemiopsis leidyi)* was found in the Caspian. It reproduced quickly, feeding on the same plankton the kilka relied on for food. Meanwhile, as the area around the sea became more developed, pollution in the sea began to take a toll, and by 2001, the kilka population plunged dramatically, resulting in catches of less than 60,000 tons annually.

kilka

132

213

7 Ask the students, *What other causes might there be for these population changes besides overfishing?*

Students' answers will vary, but may include disease, natural disaster, or another phenomenon that could harm the population being fished, which would then cause the cascade of effects seen in the graphs. You may want to have them discuss this in their groups and then as a whole class.

8 (AD ASSESSMENT) Parts a and b of Analysis Question 5 are opportunities for an ANALYZING DATA (AD) Assessment. Students will analyze one of the ecosystems they have investigated and explain their analyses to the people running the fishery. Students should use evidence from the graphs to support their analyses.

FOLLOW-UP

9 Discuss with students the difference in what they saw in the Pacific halibut fishery and the other fisheries. Ask, *Why do you think all fisheries do not follow the practices that the Pacific halibut fishery follows?*

Accept all answers. Then ask the students, *Would it change your answer if I told you that the Pacific halibut fishery operates near shore, and only in the United States and Canada?*

Students may speculate that this is a fairly small area and easier to monitor. They may also suggest that it is easier to work together when they are not working in the open ocean with many different countries. Remind students of the Tragedy of the Commons concept, introduced in Activity 5. They should think about the idea that the more parties involved and the bigger the common, the harder it may be to manage. They should also consider the fact that the more pressures there are on an ecosystem and a fishery, the more challenging it may be to fish the species sustainably. Students will re-examine this concept in the final activity of the unit.

---

7 *Analysis*

1. How does the size of the apex (top) predator population affect the other populations in the cod-dominated ecosystem? Is the effect similar or different in the orca-dominated ecosystem? Explain.

2. Choose one of the four ecosystems you examined in this activity, and draw a graph showing what you think the populations would look like if there were no fisheries present.

3. How is what is happening in the Caspian-seal-dominated ecosystem different from what is happening in the other ecosystems?

4. What impact might sustainable fisheries have on these four ecosystems?

8 5. Choose one of the four ecosystems, and in your role as a fisheries scientist, explain to the people who run the fishery what you think is happening in the ecosystem. Citing evidence from the graph and from the history of the fishery, write a summary that explains what is happening in the ecosystem. Include in the summary:

   a. your explanation of whether you think the fishery is sustainable

   b. what changes in the ecosystem indicate that the fishery is or is not sustainable

   c. how the overall biodiversity of the ecosystem has been affected

9 d. what advice you would provide about making the fishery sustainable, based on the other fisheries in this activity

KEY VOCABULARY	
fishery	population growth rate
invasive species	sustainability
population	

SAMPLE RESPONSES

1. (UC ASSESSMENT) Answers will vary. A correct and complete answer would state that if the apex predator population decreases, the population levels of the organisms below it on the food chain or within the food web will change because the ecosystem is no longer balanced. Students should point out that the orca-dominated ecosystem response is more complicated, but ultimately the effect is the same.

Sample Level-3 Response

The cod is the apex predator in the cod-dominated ecosystem. Instead of all the populations remaining fairly even, when the cod population decreased, the northern snow crab population increased because it had no predators. That meant that the zooplankton population decreased because it was being eaten by more crabs, which also caused the phytoplankton population to increase because they were no longer being eaten. By fishing out the cod, the fishery put the entire ecosystem out of balance. This is the same in the orca-dominated ecosystem, because eventually all the species in the ecosystem were affected when there were fewer perch. It just took longer because the orcas could eat sea otters or perch, and so they had another food when the perch first declined.

2. Students' graphs should roughly resemble the "Pacific-halibut-dominated Ecosystem Graph" they reviewed earlier. There will be some variety depending on the ecosystem they chose. All population levels should remain steady with minor fluctuations. Students may show in the Caspian-seal-dominated ecosystem that the introduction of the comb jelly still has an impact on the other populations in the ecosystem, particularly by shrinking the plankton population, which would cause a decrease in the anchovy kilka population. Some research indicates that invasive species might not have the same impact if there were no pressure from fishing, but other research indicates that invasive species would still have a strong impact.

The following graph is a sample response for the cod fishery.

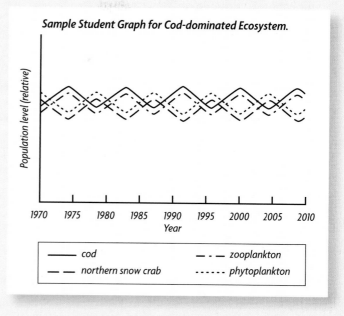

Sample Student Graph for Cod-dominated Ecosystem.

3. In the Caspian-seal-dominated ecosystem there was the added stress of the invasive comb jelly eating all the zooplankton, so the kilka had less food. In the other systems, the only stress that we knew of was fishing.

4. Students' answers will vary but should point out that if fishing is likely what is causing each ecosystem to become unbalanced, more sustainable fishing practices should improve the state of the ecosystems. Students may also note that this would take a long time in fisheries where the organisms are slow to mature and reproduce.

5. (AD ASSESSMENT) Answers will vary. A correct and complete answer would include evidence from the graph and the brief history of the ecosystem being described to explain why the fishery is unsustainable. Students should discuss population levels as indicators that the fishery is unsustainable, and may also include information about the balance in the ecosystem. Students' advice on how to make the fishery more sustainable will vary.

Sample Level-3 Response

a. I do not think the perch fishery is sustainable because the population has decreased dramatically.

b. In the orca-dominated ecosystem you can tell the perch were overfished because the population started a steep decline. When the perch were overfished, the otter population declined. You can see from the graph of the orca-dominated ecosystem that when the perch population started to decline it most likely led to other drastic population changes in the ecosystem.

c. The total number of species has stayed the same, but the population size of each species has changed. If the perch were being fished sustainably, the line would have stayed fairly steady or moved up and down around the same total amount of fish. The otters probably declined after the perch because the orcas needed them as a source of food when the perch became scarce. Since there were fewer otters and perch to eat the urchins, the sea urchin population got much bigger. The history tells us that the perch are starting to recover, and they will have plenty of urchins to eat, but for now several populations are lower than they were before the fishing started.

d. I would suggest that the perch fishery remain closed for several years, because perch take a long time to mature and reproduce. Once the perch levels go back up, it is important to keep the fishing limits low, and to monitor all of the population levels in the ecosystem carefully to make sure the ecosystem recovers and stays stable.

REVISIT THE CHALLENGE

Have a discussion with the class comparing the Pacific halibut fishery with the other fisheries they studied during the activity. Students should be able to explain how changes in one population will affect another population within the ecosystem. Ensure that students are able to articulate how the analysis of the data from each fishery in the activity could inform fisheries-management decision-making.

17 Ecosystem Change and Resiliency

READING • 1–2 CLASS SESSIONS

OVERVIEW

In this activity, students read about ecosystem disturbance, resiliency, resistance, and ecological succession. They will examine how biodiversity affects ecosystem resilience.

KEY CONTENT

1. Natural and human-caused events often disturb ecosystems.

2. Ecosystem disturbance varies in degree, from minor disruption to catastrophe.

3. If the disturbance is discrete, ecosystems can sometimes recover through ecological succession.

4. Primary succession occurs in areas devoid of input (e.g., soil and organisms).

5. Secondary succession occurs in disturbed areas where some input remains.

6. Ecosystem resilience refers to an ecosystem's ability to return to its previous state after a disturbance. It often depends on the biodiversity remaining within and living around a disturbed area.

7. Not all ecosystems are resilient enough to recover from a disturbance.

8. Some ecosystems are naturally resistant to certain invasive species. This can help prevent invasive species from becoming established in those ecosystems.

KEY PROCESS SKILLS

1. Students make accurate interpretations, inferences, and conclusions from text.

MATERIALS AND ADVANCE PREPARATION

For the teacher

"Read, Think, and Take Note" Guidelines

Scoring Guide: UNDERSTANDING CONCEPTS (UC)

For each student

3 sticky notes*

Scoring Guide: UNDERSTANDING CONCEPTS (UC) (optional)

Not supplied in kit

Masters for Scoring Guides are in Teacher Resources IV: Assessment.

TEACHING SUMMARY

Getting Started

- Introduce the concept of ecosystem disturbance.

Doing the Activity

- (LITERACY) Review the "Read, Think, and Take Note" strategy and guidelines.

- Students complete the reading, "Ecosystem Change and Resiliency," while using the "Read, Think, and Take Note" strategy.

- Students answer each other's questions from the reading.

Follow-up

- (UC ASSESSMENT) The class discusses ecosystem disturbance, resiliency, and succession.

BACKGROUND INFORMATION

Succession and Soil

Categories of ecological succession are primarily determined by the absence or presence of soil in the affected region. Primary succession refers to succession that occurs in an area devoid of soil where organisms establish new habitats. The most common examples of this occur on new lava flow or where glaciers have receded. Species such as lichen and algae are able to colonize this soilless habitat and set the stage for vascular plants to follow. These pioneer species provide organic material that breaks down into soil that less hardy vascular plants will eventually grow in. Secondary succession refers to succession occurring in a new habitat that already has soil, for example, where there has been a flood or fire, or in an area that had previously been cleared for agriculture or development and has been left fallow. In this instance the first species to colonize the habitat can be vascular or woody plants, as the soil is already available to them. In both instances the disturbance leaves the habitat more vulnerable to invasive species, because of the void left in the various habitats. If invasive species are present or introduced, they may be better suited to repopulating the new habitat quickly, thus outcompeting the native species. Often primary succession is followed by secondary succession, or there is a mix of the two due to the nature of the disturbance. Succession occurs in both terrestrial and aquatic ecosystems.

Climax Communities

In the past, ecologists referred to the concept of "climax communities" as a type of endpoint for succession. The idea centered on the theory that succession in a disturbed ecosystem would eventually reach a final, steady, typified state with certain organisms in a particular balance. Ecologists have since determined that the composition of species in a particular ecosystem is dynamic, and that there is no particular "climax community." Additionally, ecologists have found that there are multiple paths that an ecosystem can take while undergoing succession. Occasionally the term is still used to refer to mature, "old-growth" or "virgin" communities.

Resilience, Resistance, and Sustainability

The concept of resilience is often considered when examining a process or activity that threatens the sustainability of an ecosystem. Generally, if an ecosystem is affected by an event, but not past the point of resilience, the ecosystem is more sustainable. A random, one-time event such as an oil spill might harm organisms in the ecosystem, but not irreparably past the point of resilience. However, repeated disturbances or events that are drastic enough might affect an ecosystem so greatly that it will collapse. Various methods of ecosystem management allow us to avail ourselves of the ecosystem's services while maintaining the sustainability of the ecosystem. For example, if trees are logged at a rate at which the forest is still resilient and the general species composition and population dynamics are not altered or are able to recover, the forest ecosystem would still be sustainable. An ecosystem can also be resistant to disturbances, particularly to introduced species. This is often seen in the form of native predators in an ecosystem that are able to prey on an introduced species, thus preventing them from becoming invasive. Another example would be the effect of a disease found in a native population that an introduced species had no natural immunity to.

GETTING STARTED

1 ◆ Brainstorm with the class a list of factors they have seen in the unit thus far that endanger ecosystems (e.g., overfishing, introduced species). In particular, review the Yellowstone fires that were highlighted in the case study in Activity 1, "Ecosystems and Change." Have students read the introduction to this activity.

2 Show students the short video clip "Creating an Island Paradise." The link to this video is on the *Science and Global Issues* page of the SEPUP website (*sepuplhs.org/sgi*).

---

17 Ecosystem Change and Resiliency

1 THROUGHOUT THIS UNIT, you have mainly learned about human activities that cause ecosystems to change and some that allow them to resist change. These include overfishing, the introduction of invasive species, and runoff of chemicals, and more responsible interventions, such as sustainable fishery management and aquaculture.

However, a single event, whether natural, such as a volcanic eruption or forest fire, or human error, such as a large oil spill, can also bring long-lasting changes to ecosystems.

2

Challenge

▶ What determines if an ecosystem can recover from a major event?

Both natural phenomena such as volcanic eruptions (above) and human-caused phenomena such as oil spills (left) cause change in the ecosystems where they occur.

134

DOING THE ACTIVITY

3 After students complete the reading while following the "Read, Think, and Take Note" strategy, and have paired up to compare notes on the reading, assist them as necessary in answering each other's questions. Their questions may range from not knowing a vocabulary word to questions that make connections between the reading and other parts of the unit or their own experiences. Encourage all levels of relevant questions. Be sure students understand that they may not be able to answer all of the questions with their partners, but they should answer whichever they can. See Teacher Resources III: Literacy for more guidance if needed.

4 Hold a class discussion about the reading and the questions that arose. Encourage students to share their questions, especially those they were unable to answer. Solicit information from the class to assist in answering the questions. If the class cannot answer the questions, encourage the students to think about where they might find the information (e.g., from an ecologist, from a certain type of book at the library, or suggesting what search term to enter for an Internet search), rather than answering the questions for them. You may wish to discuss the definitions of the words *disturbance* and *resilience* in non-biology contexts. This would be particularly appropriate for students who are English Language Learners.

MATERIALS

FOR EACH STUDENT
5   sticky notes

Procedure

1. Use the "Read, Think, and Take Note" strategy as you complete the following reading.

3 2. When you have completed the reading, share your "Read, Think, and Take Note" responses with your partner. If possible, answer any questions your partner had about the reading. Note any similarities in your responses. Choose one response to share with the class.

4 3. Share your response to the reading in a class discussion, as directed by your teacher.

Reading

Ecosystem Change and Resiliency

In today's world there are few, if any, ecosystems left untouched by people in some way. In some cases this has resulted in major changes, and in others there have been very minor changes. Humans have influenced ecosystems for thousands of years, but current technology and large population size have intensified human impact. Yet while scientists previously thought that ecosystems would basically stay the same in the absence of human intervention, decades of research have shown that ecosystems are constantly changing and shifting.

Many things cause disturbances in an ecosystem. Ecologists use the term **disturbance** to refer to an abrupt event in an ecosystem that suddenly and significantly changes the resources available, the number or type of organisms, or the kinds of species present in an ecosystem. Natural disturbances include volcanic eruptions and fires. Two examples of disturbances caused by humans are oil spills and clear-cutting of forests. The response of an ecosystem to a disturbance depends in part on how major the disturbance is and the extent of the damage done.

An area like this Hawaiian coastline where there has been a recent lava flow has no soil and few, if any, living organisms present.

This area has undergone primary succession after a volcanic eruption.

In responding to a disturbance, an ecosystem undergoes what is referred to as ecological succession. **Ecological succession** is the natural process in which a disturbed area is gradually taken over by a species or groups of species that were not there before. For example, if a volcano erupted and the molten lava smothered a large area of land, eventually that area would undergo succession. In Hawaii and other volcanic locations, barren expanses of hard lava rock have turned into thick forest ecosystems in fewer than 150 years.

Primary succession is ecological succession that starts in an area where there are essentially no living organisms. In the lava-covered area, the first life you would see would be small organisms, such as spiders, that can live without soil. Eventually, dust and leaves from surrounding areas would collect in the cracks and crevices of the lava, and some of the more hardy plants, introduced by wind-blown seeds or birds, would begin to grow there. As the decades passed, more of the surface would become covered in plants, as leaves and other debris decayed and formed soil. The level of biodiversity would rise as more soil developed.

When an ecosystem undergoes a disturbance and the soil remains, **secondary succession** develops instead of primary succession. This might occur after a wildfire, or in a now-unused field where generations of ranchers had grazed cattle. Often there are still plants that survived the disturbance. If there are no further disturbances, those areas tend to return to their previous states. In Yellowstone Park after the huge wildfires in 1988, some of the first plants to grow back were grasses, small flowering bushes, and a bush called fireweed (named for its ability to grow well after fires). By 2000, small pine trees were beginning to replace the trees that had burned down, and today there are sections of burn areas in Yellowstone where it is difficult to tell that such a large fire ever occurred.

FOLLOW-UP

5 (UC ASSESSMENT) Continue the class discussion with a general review of primary and secondary succession, and ecosystem disturbance and resiliency. Be sure that students understand that succession can only occur if the disturbance is no longer a factor (e.g., an overfished fishery cannot recover if overfishing is still occurring). Encourage discussion of ecosystem disturbance and resilience in any local settings, such as a new suburban development, a park, a wetland, or other areas that students are familiar with. You can also encourage them to discuss these topics in terms of other case studies introduced in the unit (e.g., invasive species, salmon fisheries, and the Yellowstone fires). Analysis Questions 1 and 2 are opportunities for you to apply the UNDERSTANDING CONCEPTS (UC) Scoring Guide to assess students' understanding of the concepts of succession and resiliency.

SAMPLE RESPONSES

1. (UC ASSESSMENT) Answers will vary. A correct and complete answer should state that primary succession occurs where there is no input from before the disturbance, and secondary occurs when there is some input left, such as soil or some plants.

    ### Sample Level-3 Response
    Primary succession occurs after a disturbance where there is nothing left, such as after a volcanic eruption. Secondary succession occurs when there is still something left after the disturbance, including soil.

An ecosystem's ability to return to a stable state after a disturbance is a measure of its **resilience**. If an ecosystem has a high level of resilience, it will be much more likely to recover from a major disturbance. The level of resilience depends on several important factors, one of which is the native biodiversity within and surrounding the disturbed area. Because different species occupy different habitats and perform different roles within an ecosystem, the more species that survive the event the more likely those habitats and roles will be quickly filled again after a major disturbance. Another critical element for ecosystem resilience is the presence of species in nearby areas that might repopulate the disturbed area. For example, if a coral reef has been severely damaged by a large storm, fish and other organisms in nearby areas might help to repopulate the reef. Major disturbances, however, also increase the chances that an area will be occupied by invasive species, because there is so much available habitat. The resistance of an ecosystem is one factor that can help prevent this. The **resistance** of an ecosystem results from the natural factors within an ecosystem that help it to withstand external pressures and maintain normal functions. For example, if an invasive species of fish were released in a lake where there were native turtles that preferred to prey on those fish, the resistance of that lake to the invasive fish is high.

As ecologists learn more about ecosystem disturbance, resilience, and resistance, they have found that while ecosystems are often able to recover from major disturbances, they also have a point after which they cannot. One concern is that evidence suggests that many of the world's fisheries are at or beyond this point. Fisheries biologists and ecologists are working with many of the world's commercial fisheries to try to determine what, if anything, can be done to prevent our ocean ecosystems from being fished past the point of resilience. As you will see in the next activity, there are several possible solutions that may help to repair commercial fisheries around the world.

After wildfires in 1988, areas of Yellowstone National Park underwent secondary succession.

---

2. (UC ASSESSMENT) Answers will vary. A correct and complete answer would include that generally more biodiversity will lead to greater resilience. Students may also point out that an increase in invasive species would increase biodiversity but might decrease resilience.

Sample Level-3 Response

More native biodiversity in an area would indicate that it has more resilience. Less biodiversity would indicate less resilience. For example, if one fish in a kelp forest is overfished, but there are several other species that serve the same role in that ecosystem, the ecosystem is resilient. The level of resilience depends on the state of the area prior to the disturbance. If there were lots of invasive species in an ecosystem, the biodiversity is high, but that ecosystem would not have high resilience.

3. The resilience of an ecosystem refers to how well it can recover after a major disturbance. For example, if there is a forest fire and the plants are able to regrow quickly, the ecosystem is very resilient. The resistance of the ecosystem is how well the ecosystem can resist an external influence, like a disturbance. For example, if an ecosystem has a high level of native biodiversity and one population was decreased due to disease, another native species might take its role in the ecosystem, preventing an invasive species from becoming established.

4. You could use information about biodiversity and population levels to help them decide if an ecosystem is still resilient. These factors would indicate how stable an ecosystem is. A sudden change in biodiversity or population levels might indicate that the resilience is not as strong.

5 *Analysis*

1. What is the difference between primary and secondary successions?

2. How does the native biodiversity of an ecosystem affect its resilience?

3. How is the resilience of an ecosystem different from its resistance to disturbance?

4. What factors would you investigate to help you decide whether an ecosystem is nearing the point where it is no longer resilient and, therefore, unable to recover from a disturbance? Explain why you chose those factors.

KEY VOCABULARY	
disturbance	resilience
ecological succession	resistance
invasive species	secondary succession
primary succession	

138

REVISIT THE CHALLENGE

Revisit the examples from the unit that examined ecosystems that have had significant disturbances, including the Yellowstone fires and invasive species introductions in Activity 1, "Ecosystems and Change," and the fisheries in Activity 16, "Ecosystems Out of Balance."

18 Fishery Case Studies

TALK IT OVER • 1–2 CLASS SESSIONS

OVERVIEW

In this activity students analyze case studies that highlight two innovative fishery-management strategies. Students predict how each strategy might improve the sustainability of the fictional Avril Gulf tuna fishery.

KEY CONTENT

1. Historical case studies provide information that can be helpful in decision-making.

2. There are numerous approaches to fisheries management.

3. Aquaculture and marine reserves are two strategies for protecting fisheries in decline.

4. Successful fishery-management strategies must be tailored to each situation.

KEY PROCESS SKILLS

1. Students make accurate interpretations, inferences, and conclusions from text.

2. Students make predictions.

3. Students identify and describe trade-offs.

4. Students formulate explanations that account for data.

MATERIALS AND ADVANCE PREPARATION

For the teacher
> blank transparency*
> transparency markers*

For each student
> Student Sheet 18.1, "The Avril Gulf Tuna Fishery"
> > *Not supplied in kit*

TEACHING SUMMARY

Getting Started

- ✓ The class summarizes the current environmental, economic, and social state of communities surrounding Avril Gulf.

Doing the Activity

- ✓ Groups analyze a fishery-management strategy case study.

- Groups predict the impact of the management strategy on the communities near Avril Gulf and their tuna fishery.

Follow-up

- Groups share their predictions with the class.

- Discuss the use of case studies as a tool to investigate possible solutions.

BACKGROUND INFORMATION

Throughout history, fishery-management strategies have been the subject of much study and a great deal of controversy. The Atlantic cod fishery, discussed in Activity 16, "Ecosystems Out of Balance," is an example of a historical fishery that underwent a variety of management schemes by local, regional, and international governments. At various times fishing limits and quotas were imposed. The Atlantic cod fishery was instrumental in the development of international Exclusive Economic Zones (EEZs), zones in the sea over which a nation has rights to explore and control its marine resources. The general rule is that the EEZ extends 200 nautical miles from the coast of a country. Within these zones countries set limits and are supposed to be in control of who fishes (or drills for oil) in those waters. In the case of the Atlantic cod fishery, conflicts including the "Cod Wars" broke out over the exploitation of the fishery prior to the EEZs being set up (and in some cases after). Ultimately, the various strategies employed to save the Atlantic cod fishery were unsuccessful, as demonstrated by the fact that the fishery collapsed and has shown little sign of recovery. The two case studies in this activity are specific examples of successful management strategies that have been used in fisheries around the world.

REFERENCES

Babcock, R. C., Kelly, S., Shears, N. T., Walker, J. W., & Willis, T. J. (1999). Changes in community structure in temperate marine reserves. *Marine Ecology Progress Series, 198,* 125–134.

Taylor, R. B., Anderson, M. J., Egli, D., & Willis, T. J. (2003). *Cape Rodney to Oakakari Point Marine Reserve fish monitoring 2003: Final report.* Prepared for: The Auckland Conservancy Department of Conservation.

GETTING STARTED

1 ✓ Before students read the introduction, review the current environmental, economic, and social condition of the communities near Avril Gulf as shown in the information on Student Sheet 18.1, "The Avril Gulf Tuna Fishery." One way to summarize the current situation is to construct the table "Current Condition of Avril Gulf," shown below, on a transparency or chart paper. Fill in the table as a class, and then ask students, by a show of hands, if each factor is positive or negative. Mark this next to the description as shown. Encourage students to discuss the positive and negative nature of each factor and to support their reasoning with evidence from Student Sheet 18.1. The construction and analysis of this table parallels a table students will generate in the final activity. Determine the overall positive or negative state of the communities near Avril Gulf by looking at each column of the table. This is an opportunity for a Quick Check assessment, to ensure that students are able to distinguish between evidence and irrelevant information, a component of the EVIDENCE AND TRADE-OFFS scoring variable. Note that while the communities near Avril Gulf and the Avril Gulf tuna fishery are fictitious, they are based on actual fisheries and communities.

Use the table to discuss the current economic, environmental, and social status of the communities near Avril Gulf. Students' responses are likely to include the following statements: The economic situation is negative. There are fewer fish, which has led to smaller profits for those who fish.

Social and environmental conditions are also negative. People who fish are spending longer hours working to make a profit. Coastal erosion has led to a decrease in the fish population. Overall, the current state of Avril Gulf is in decline.

18 Fishery Case Studies

1 **Y**OU ARE A *fisheries biologist who has been asked to provide input on an upcoming decision on whether to reopen the tuna fishery in Avril Gulf (a fictitious fishery modeled after a combination of fisheries in the United States). The tuna near Avril Gulf spend most of their lives off the coast, or in the open ocean. The Avril Gulf tuna fishery was closed to fishing in 2000 after years of declining fish catches. The ecosystem reached such a state of depletion that federal and state officials decided to ban all commercial and sport fishing of this species.*

In this activity you will read about fishery management approaches that two fishery regions adopted when facing a fishery crisis. Your group will explore how the strategies might work with the Avril Gulf tuna fishery.

Challenge

▶ How can case studies guide what should be done with the Avril Gulf tuna fishery?

MATERIALS

FOR EACH STUDENT
3 sticky notes
Student Sheet 18.1, "The Avril Gulf Tuna Fishery"

Current Condition of Avril Gulf

Economic	Social	Environmental
• *The spotted flying fish is being sold for less profit than the Avril Gulf tuna. (–)* • *Decreases in fish numbers are leading to less income for fishermen. (–)*	• *The tradition of fishing is at risk because the ability to make a profit from fishing is decreasing. (–)* • *Fishermen are spending longer hours fishing to bring in profitable catches. (–)*	• *New housing developments lead to coastal erosion and increase of contaminants in costal waters. (–)* • *Avril Gulf's tuna population numbers led to the decision in 2000 to close the tuna fishery. Recently the tuna population has increased, but not to the levels of the early 1990s. (–)*

Ask the class to discuss and share their ideas about who is affected by the decline in the tuna fishery. Those immediately affected are the people who fish and work in the fishing industry, because they are making less money. This might spread to other areas near Avril Gulf, especially if the economy and social conditions continue to decline. Discuss with the class in what direction they think the communities near Avril Gulf will head. They should say that the future of

Avril Gulf depends on what actions are taken. Ask students, *What strategies can you think of that would help improve the economic, social, and environmental state of the communities around Avril Gulf?*

Students' ideas may include reopening the fishery, bringing new industries to Avril Gulf, and increasing tourism. Explain that in this activity students will analyze case studies that detail fishery-management strategies that communities have implemented to bolster their fisheries. They will then predict how these strategies might help or harm the sustainability of the Avril Gulf tuna fishery.

DOING THE ACTIVITY

2 ✓Assign each student group one of the two case studies. Remind students who are reading the "Open-Ocean Aquaculture in Hawaii" study that they may also refer to the information about salmon farming from the previous activity. As students read their case study, they will write a summary in their science notebooks. Encourage them to include detailed descriptions. Consider asking students to work on their summaries in pairs, and then have the group compare their summaries. The summaries from Procedure Step 3 can be used as a Quick Check to assess students' identification of trade-offs. Sample summaries for each case study are shown on the next page.

3 As they begin Procedure Step 4, refer students to Student Sheet 18.1, "The Avril Gulf Tuna Fishery," for information on which to base their predictions. Students' predictions should include an explanation of how the strategy might affect Avril Gulf in each of the three facets of sustainability: environmental, social, and economic. Tell students to be sure to explain the reasoning for their predictions. For example, students may predict that aquaculture in Avril Gulf will result in an increase

---

SCIENCE & GLOBAL ISSUES/BIOLOGY • ECOLOGY

Procedure

1. Due to the decline in the Avril Gulf tuna fishery, the governments of the areas near Avril Gulf are considering one of two strategies:

   a. creating a marine reserve to protect the Avril Gulf tuna, or

   b. opening aquaculture farms to farm tuna near Avril Gulf's shore

2. Your teacher will assign you one of these two strategies. Read the case study about your assigned strategy undertaken in a fishing region similar to Avril Gulf. Apply the "Read, Think, and Take Note" technique to your reading.

3. As you read describe the following in your science notebook:

   • the challenge the fishery was facing

   • the plan used to address the challenge

   • the impact the strategy had on the ecosystem's food web

   • the trade-offs associated with the strategy

   • how the strategy affected the community:

     a. economically

     b. environmentally

     c. socially

4. With your group, decide how the fishery management approach in your case study might affect the sustainability of the Avril Gulf tuna population and the community near Avril Gulf. Record your predicted outcomes.

Analysis

1. List the types of indicator data that could be used to monitor the environmental, economic, and social impacts of one plan on the community near Avril Gulf.

2. How can case studies help suggest solutions for communities facing sustainability challenges?

KEY VOCABULARY	
aquaculture	marine reserve
ecosystem	

140

---

of jobs because that is what occurred in the open-ocean aquaculture in the Hawaiian case study. Allow students to determine how to record their predictions.

FOLLOW-UP

4 Ask student groups to share with the class a description of the fishery-management strategy they analyzed and their prediction for how this strategy might help Avril Gulf. Write "Marine Reserve" and "Aquaculture" on the board. Ask students to identify the trade-offs associated with each. They might say that a marine reserve for Avril Gulf, while contributing to the growth of fish populations, will mean the end of fishing in the designated area. It may mean an increase in ecotourism, but this might have unforeseen

Sample Student Response: Procedure Step 3, Creation of the Goat Island Marine Reserve

Summarize the challenge the fishery was facing.	*Overfishing of lobsters and snapper fish led to population crashes in the late 1960s. The sea urchin population grew out of control and devastated the kelp forests.*
Describe the strategy used to address the challenge.	*Local communities convinced the New Zealand government to establish a marine reserve in the waters surrounding Goat Island. All fishing was banned in this area.*
Describe the impact the strategy had on the ecosystem's food web.	*Fish populations grew. Snapper density increased both within and outside the marine reserve.*
Explain the trade-offs associated with this strategy.	*More roads and infrastructure are created to support the research and education center, which has an effect on the environment.* *Fishing is no longer allowed in the area, but fish populations outside of the marine reserve increased and could be fished.*
Describe how the strategy affected the community.	*ECONOMICALLY—An education center was opened, which provides educational and diving tours. This brings in some income. Commercial and sport fishing outside of the marine reserve increased.* *SOCIALLY—Marine education increased. Ecotourism in the area brought new jobs.* *ENVIRONMENTALLY—Snapper and lobster density increased both on the marine reserve and in the surrounding waters. The percentage of mixed algae and kelp forest habitats increased while barren rock flats decreased. This meant an increase in the number of producers in the ecosystem. The kelp forest provides shelter for endangered populations of organisms. There is more road and beach traffic.*

Sample Student Response: Procedure Step 3 Open-Ocean Aquaculture in Hawaii

Summarize the challenge the fishery was facing.	*Most yellowtail are farmed, but the traditional farms were causing pollution and feeding lots of wild fish to the farmed fish. The farms were also catching juvenile fish from the wild, not raising them at the farm.*
Describe the strategy used to address the challenge.	*A farm in Hawaii started raising fish from birth at their farm, and they put the pens out in the open ocean to prevent pollution. They raised a native species of fish that are closely related to wild fish. They also used less wild fish in the food for the farmed fish.*
Describe the impact the strategy had on the ecosystem's food web.	*The farmed fish can transmit parasites to the wild fish if the farmed fish escape, but so far that has not been a problem.*
Explain the trade-offs associated with this strategy.	*This farm is more sustainable than the Japanese and Australian farms, because of where they have their pens, and what they feed their fish. This farm is successfully growing more fish for people to eat. But, the environment may be harmed if escaped farmed fish bring parasites to the wild populations.*
Describe how the strategy affected the community.	*ECONOMICALLY—The farmed fish brings money and jobs to the local community.* *SOCIALLY—Profits from farmed fish bring a degree of security. Farmed fish provided for jobs locally for both farm workers and scientists.* *ENVIRONMENTALLY—The open-ocean pens do not pollute the surrounding environment, but escaped fish can carry parasites into wild populations.*

adverse environmental consequences. The creation of aquaculture farms will fill an immediate need to increase the amount of Avril Gulf tuna available for sale. The trade-off is that aquaculture can harm native fish populations and may not work as well for other species of fish. This discussion foreshadows the next activity in which students analyze data to determine the impact of a fishery-management strategy over 5 to 10 years.

5 After students answer Analysis Question 2, discuss with the class the usefulness of case studies as a learning tool. Ask, *In what ways did the case studies help in your consideration of the fishery-management strategies?*

Students' responses may indicate that the case studies provided a way to see the decisions that other communities made in the past. The case studies highlighted the successes of each and the questions that arose. In this way, it helps the communities near Avril Gulf to make a decision based on the learning experiences of other communities.

EXTENSION

To further students' understanding of fishery sustainability problems and solutions, you might provide local case studies from newspaper articles, online sources, and magazines. Or, you may challenge students to locate them and bring them to class. Decide how you will hand them out to students and ask them to analyze them. Take this opportunity to highlight recent efforts to solve local sustainability challenges in your town, region, and state.

SAMPLE RESPONSES

1. Students' answers will vary based on the strategy they analyzed. Sample answers are listed below. **Note:** Several of the indicators fit in more than one category.

Creation of a Marine Reserve

Environmental indicators: animal and fish population numbers and densities, changes in habitats, rates of erosion of the beach and marine environment due to the new construction of roads and buildings

Social indicators: employment rates, number of tourists who come to the area, number of local residents who participate in commercial or sport fishing

Economic indicators: money generated from ecotourism, profits from fishing

Open-net Aquaculture

Environmental indicators: the rate at which escaped fish transmit parasites to wild fish, the amount of pollution from nets that gets into the surrounding environment

Social: the number of aquaculture jobs available, the size of fishing communities, general employment rates

Economic: profits made from the sale of farmed fish, the amount of money lost to fishermen due to the impact of the farmed fish on wild populations

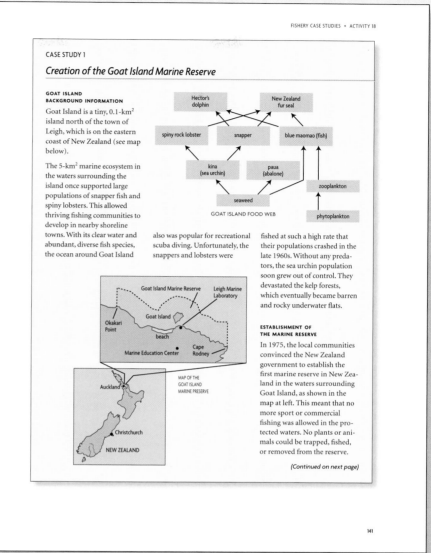

CASE STUDY 1

Creation of the Goat Island Marine Reserve

GOAT ISLAND BACKGROUND INFORMATION
Goat Island is a tiny, 0.1-km² island north of the town of Leigh, which is on the eastern coast of New Zealand (see map below).

The 5-km² marine ecosystem in the waters surrounding the island once supported large populations of snapper fish and spiny lobsters. This allowed thriving fishing communities to develop in nearby shoreline towns. With its clear water and abundant, diverse fish species, the ocean around Goat Island also was popular for recreational scuba diving. Unfortunately, the snappers and lobsters were fished at such a high rate that their populations crashed in the late 1960s. Without any predators, the sea urchin population soon grew out of control. They devastated the kelp forests, which eventually became barren and rocky underwater flats.

ESTABLISHMENT OF THE MARINE RESERVE
In 1975, the local communities convinced the New Zealand government to establish the first marine reserve in New Zealand in the waters surrounding Goat Island, as shown in the map at left. This meant that no more sport or commercial fishing was allowed in the protected waters. No plants or animals could be trapped, fished, or removed from the reserve.

(Continued on next page)

GOAT ISLAND FOOD WEB

MAP OF THE GOAT ISLAND MARINE PRESERVE

141

2. Case studies are valuable because they provide examples of actions taken in the past and detail the successes and failures that resulted. For example, the case studies from Activity 1, "Ecosystems and Change," provided information about what can happen if invasive species become established in an ecosystem. If a community had a problem with an invasive species, and they were considering introducing another nonnative species to try to control it, learning about the cane toad introduction in Australia might convince them not to introduce the nonnative predator. Case studies can help communities make informed decisions, and can show how interconnections within the ecosystems might help or harm the fisheries.

REVISIT THE CHALLENGE

Review the case studies briefly with the students so that they are prepared to reference them in the next activity.

(Continued from previous page)

When the marine reserve was established, fishing ceased and few boats roamed the Goat Island waters, allowing scientists the opportunity to study the ecosystems and changing populations of the reserve. In 1977, a marine education center opened to provide educational tours and guide diving expeditions in the waters of the reserve.

THE MARINE RESERVE BENEFITS THE WATERS OF GOAT ISLAND

The growth of the fish and lobster populations on the marine reserve was slow but steady. Within several years, fish and lobster populations grew at such a rate and density within the reserve that some spilled over into non-reserve waters. This "spillover effect" was a welcome surprise for sport and commercial fishermen who fished the waters beyond the boundaries of the marine reserve.

The vegetation on the marine floor gradually changed. Algae grew back in many of the rocky flats. The ecosystem became lush with mixed algae, including kelp—key producers in the marine ecosystem. As the algae returned, so did other organisms that depended on the algae for food and shelter.

QUESTIONS STILL REMAIN

While the marine reserve has provided valuable shelter to the endangered populations of fish and invertebrates of the Goat Island waters, questions remain about its long-term benefits. Since the creation of the marine education center, more roads and public facilities have been built near the mainland beach to accommodate growing numbers of visitors who snorkel in the waters. This has led to heavier road and beach traffic and erosion of the land. Tourism in the area has increased, providing jobs and raising awareness about the importance of protecting marine populations. But environmental protection agencies question how this increased use of the land might affect the long-term sustainability of the Goat Island Marine Reserve and the ecosystems it was built to protect. ■

Densities of Snapper (*Pagrus auratus*) Inside and Outside the Marine Reserve 2000–2003		
SURVEY DATE	RESERVE SNAPPER DENSITY (NUMBER OF FISH PER M²)	NON-RESERVE SNAPPER DENSITY (NUMBER OF FISH PER M²)
Late 2000	4.23	0.05
Early 2001	7.79	0.75
Late 2001	6.17	0.87
Early 2002	10.33	0.79
Early 2003	21.92	0.79

Habitat Type on the Goat Island Marine Reserve		
HABITAT TYPE	% OF RESERVE AREA, 1979	% OF RESERVE AREA, 1996
Shallow mixed algae	22	35
Large kelp forests	31	46
Rock flats	30	3
Other	17	16

CASE STUDY 2

Open-ocean Aquaculture in Hawaii

COMMERCIAL FARMING OF YELLOWTAIL

Since 1927, fish farmers have been growing yellowtail, a tasty fish and very popular sushi item. More than 75% of yellowtail that is sold worldwide comes from yellowtail farms, which are mainly in Japan, Australia, and Hawaii. The oldest farms are in Japan, and they provide a majority of the yellowtail to the world's markets.

Over the past several decades concerns over the sustainability of yellowtail farms have emerged. One of the biggest problems is that the yellowtail are farmed in nets kept in shallow, coastal areas, where the waste from the fish and leftover fish food pollutes the surrounding ecosystems. In Japan this has caused algal blooms. Also, at the Japanese farms the yellowtail are fed wild-caught sardines, which has caused a decline in the local sardine population. Another problem with the Japanese farms is that they catch wild, juvenile yellowtail and then raise them at the farms, which means the farms are depleting the wild population of yellowtail. Australian farms use a dried food, which causes less pollution, but still contains a high percentage of wild-caught fish.

KONA, HAWAII TO THE RESCUE

In 2005, as the consequences of the farming of yellowtail became more worrisome, an aquaculture farm in Kona, Hawaii, was built to be the world's first sustainable yellowtail fish farm. Open-ocean pens were anchored in ocean waters less than 1 km off the coast of the island of Hawaii, where deep water and fast currents could move clean water through the pens and help prevent pollution of the surrounding habitats.

The fish farmers chose to raise a species of yellowtail native to Hawaii, kahala (*Seriola rivoliana*), to minimize the risk of escaped farmed fish introducing genes that would be new to the wild fish populations. The farm went through a rigorous permitting process, and even set some of its fishery management policies to be stricter than required by the state and federal governments. The yellowtail farmers set up a system where a few adult fish are caught in the wild and kept as brood stock in tanks at the land-based hatchery to

(Continued on next page)

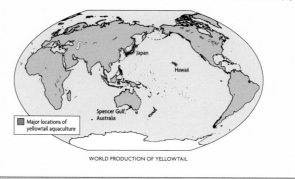

Major locations of yellowtail aquaculture

Japan

Hawaii

Spencer Gulf, Australia

WORLD PRODUCTION OF YELLOWTAIL

143

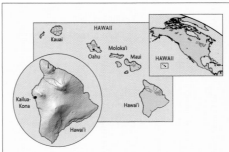

right into the mammal's jaws. This has prompted farmers to install detection devices to prevent escapes. Despite these efforts, escapes still occur. This presents two main problems: first, escaped fish may carry parasites and viruses that infect wild populations, and second, escaped farmed fish compete with wild fish for resources.

For the new Hawaiian farm, however, escapes are not as threatening as elsewhere. Farmed fish often have more parasites than wild fish because they live in such close conditions. The Hawaiian farm carefully controls the diet of their fish, which leads to fewer parasites. In fact, when the farm studied the parasites in wild fish from nearby waters they found that their farmed fish had fewer parasites. Because this species of fish has been heavily overfished in nearby waters, the addition of escaped fish to the wild population does not lead to increased competition for resources. Furthermore, the fear of new genes being introduced to the wild population is not a concern. The farm's yellowtail are so closely related to the wild fish that any escapees are considered part of the wild population. ∎

(Continued from previous page)

spawn offspring. The larval offspring are then fed a special type of zooplankton, which is also raised at the hatchery. Once the young fish have been weaned onto a commercial feed and are large enough, they are moved to the open-ocean pens to grow until they are big enough to be harvested and sold.

THE FOOD CHALLENGE

The yellowtail is carnivorous, and the adults feed exclusively on other fish. Initially the Hawaiian farm used a dried food that was approximately 80% fishmeal and oil from wild-caught fish. This did not meet the criteria the farm had set for being sustainable. Something had to change.

Through consultation with scientists and environmentalists, the Hawaiian farmers worked with their feed company to develop a food that contained only 30% fishmeal and oil, all of which they obtained from the sustainable Peruvian anchovy fishery or from canneries or other businesses that process caught fish for human consumption. The remaining 70% of protein in the food comes from agricultural protein and grains.

GREAT ESCAPES

A big problem with open-net pens everywhere is that they attract predators. Seals and dolphins have been known to rip open aquaculture net pens, freeing fish to escape—some

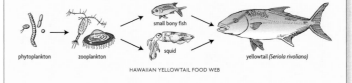

phytoplankton   zooplankton   small bony fish   squid   yellowtail *(Seriola rivoliana)*

HAWAIIAN YELLOWTAIL FOOD WEB

19 Making Sustainable Fishery Decisions

INVESTIGATION • 2 CLASS SESSIONS

OVERVIEW

In this activity, students analyze a set of indicator data cards to determine the effectiveness of a fishery-management strategy on the sustainability of the Avril Gulf tuna fishery.

KEY CONTENT

1. Marine reserves and aquaculture are two fishery-management strategies, each of which involves certain environmental, social, and economic consequences.

2. Analyses of indicators inform resource-management decisions.

3. Indicators from a variety of data types over extended periods of time provide more information than a limited set of indictors from a short period.

PROCESS SKILLS

1. Students make accurate interpretations, inferences, and conclusions from text.

2. Students make predictions.

3. Students identify and describe trade-offs.

4. Students formulate explanations that account for data.

5. Students make conclusions based on evidence.

MATERIALS AND ADVANCE PREPARATION

For the teacher

Card Set A—6 five-year aquaculture indicator cards

Card Set B—6 ten-year aquaculture indicator cards

Card Set C—6 five-year marine reserve indicator cards

Card Set D—6 ten-year marine reserve indicator cards

Scoring Guide: EVIDENCE AND TRADE-OFFS (ET)

Scoring Guide: UNDERSTANDING CONCEPTS (UC)

For each group of four students

set of 6 Fishery Indicator cards

For each student

Student Sheet 18.1, "The Avril Gulf Tuna Fishery," from Activity 18

Student Sheet 19.1, "Tracking Indicators"

Student Sheet 19.2, "Comparing Aquaculture and Marine Reserves in Avril Gulf"

Literacy Student Sheet 2a, "Writing Frame—Evidence and Trade-offs" (optional)

Literacy Student Sheet 3, "Writing Review" (optional)

Scoring Guide EVIDENCE AND TRADE-OFFS (ET) (optional)

Scoring Guide UNDERSTANDING CONCEPTS (UC) (optional)

Masters for Literary Skills Sheets are in Teacher Resources III: Library. Masters for Scoring Guides are in Teacher Resources IV: Assessment.

When preparing Student Sheet 19.1, make two copies for each student.

In Procedure Step 6 you will hand students only those indicator cards that they specify in their monitoring plan. Separate the cards ahead of time so that you have them available to hand out.

TEACHING SUMMARY

Getting Started

• Introduce the Fishery Indicator Cards.

Doing the Activity

• Student pairs develop a plan to monitor their strategy's implementation in Avril Gulf.

• Students analyze indicator data that their monitoring generated.

Follow-up

• The class compares fishery-management strategies.

• (ET ASSESSMENT) (UC ASSESSMENT) Students recommend a fishery-management strategy.

BACKGROUND INFORMATION

Indicators

Many indicators can be monitored to determine the level of success of a fishery-management plan. For example, fisheries biologists who monitor and advise the Pacific halibut fishery look at population levels of the halibut and their prey species, incidental catch of halibut by other fisheries, and the effects of recovery plans in place for other species within the ecosystem. In this activity the indicators presented are all based on actual indicators used in various fisheries management approaches. These indicators include fish-protein consumption (amount of fish that people eat), changes in local human-population size, fish population levels, critical habitat use, water transparency, and fishery-related employment.

The term *critical habitat* originated from the United States Endangered Species Act, referring to an area that contains features or resources essential for the conservation or survival of a species. Critical habitat use is an indicator that refers to specific habitat being used by the species under study. It includes areas needed for breeding and spawning, areas containing essential resources, such as a specific food source, and areas that are large enough for "normal behavior" to continue. In the context of a fishery, scientists can monitor how much of the critical habitat is being used by the fish population, which in turn indicates the potential success of the fish population.

Water transparency is another indicator emphasized in this activity. Water transparency refers to the turbidity and clarity of water and depends on the amount of suspended matter in a volume of water. This is often measured using a Secchi disk, a circular disk with a pattern on it. The disk is lowered into the water on a rope marked with depth readings. A depth measurement is taken when the pattern on the disk is no longer visible. While more transparent water indicates there is less suspended matter, it does not necessarily correlate to higher water quality for a fishery. For example, in the cold waters off of the coast of Peru where anchovy abound, there is a dense population of plankton. For the anchovy fishery in this region high water quality would be linked with less transparent water. In the tropics where the plankton is much less dense, one would expect to see much more transparent water.

19 Making Sustainable Fishery Decisions

YOUR GROUP HAS *been given $500,000 by the Avril Gulf Wildlife Protection Agency (AGWPA) to monitor a fishery management strategy for Avril Gulf. You will develop a monitoring plan and follow the results of implementing both of the strategies you analyzed in Activity 18, "Fishery Case Studies," and determine the effects of the strategies on the sustainability of the Avril Gulf tuna fishery.*

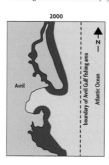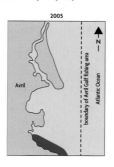

Challenge

▶ Which fishery management strategy is the best choice for the sustainability of the Avril Gulf tuna fishery?

MATERIALS

FOR EACH GROUP OF FOUR STUDENTS
   Set of 6 Fishery Indicator Cards

FOR EACH STUDENT
   Student Sheet 19.1, "Tracking Indicators"
   Student Sheet 19.2, "Comparing Aquaculture and Marine Reserves in Avril Gulf"

GETTING STARTED

1 After students have read the introduction, pass out a set of Fishery Indicator Cards to each student group. Encourage students to look at each set and summarize the trend indicated by the information on each. Remind students that the fishery was closed in the year 2010. Summarizing the data from 1995 to 2010, when the fishery was open, and then from 2010 to 2020, will allow students to interpret trends in the data. If students need assistance, review ways to think about trends in data over periods of time. One way to do this is to encourage students to describe the patterns that they see in the data. Check to see that students are using terms they have gained throughout the unit such as *population, growth rate,* and *indicator* and that they are able to apply content they have learned over the course of the *Science and Global Issues* Ecology Unit.

DOING THE ACTIVITY

2 Pass out Student Sheet 19.1, "Tracking Indicators." As students fill in the "Predicted Outcome" column, they should include explanations for their predictions. One pair will work with the aquaculture strategy, while the other will work with the marine reserve strategy. Encourage students to refer to Student Sheet 18.1, "The Avril Gulf Tuna Fishery," and the class chart, "Current Condition of Avril Gulf," they constructed at the start of Activity 18 for information on Avril Gulf. Sample answers are shown in the pages that follow. Check students' work to make sure they have explained the reasoning for their predictions.

3 Students will select the number of indicators and frequency at which each will be monitored. Note that students may choose any combination within the budget limit of $500,000. They may choose to monitor one indicator for 10 years and two indicators for five years at a total cost of $500,000, OR they may choose to monitor

four indicators for five years at a total cost of $500,000. Take this opportunity to discuss the trade-offs involved in formulating this plan, such as monitoring over a longer period of time provides a more complete picture of what is occurring in the fishery, but is more costly. Because of budget limits, not all indicators can be monitored. Students will need to first prioritize those indicators they wish to monitor, and decide how long they will monitor each.

4 Decide how you will hand out the indicator cards to each pair within a group. It is important that students have access to only the data they specified in their monitoring plan.

5 Recommend that students lay out each card next to the corresponding Fishery Indicator Card. This will allow them to see the progression in the data. Assist students

---

Procedure

1
1. Obtain a set of the Fishery Indicator Cards. With your group, lay out the cards on the table, and review the information they provide about the Avril Gulf tuna fishery.

2. Decide which pair of students in your group will investigate the aquaculture operation in Avril Gulf, and which pair will investigate the marine reserve.

2
3. With your partner, predict what each indicator might show if the strategy you chose in Step 2 were used in Avril Gulf. Record your thoughts in the "Predicted outcome" column on Student Sheet 19.1, "Tracking Indicators."

3
4. Develop a plan with your partner to monitor the fishery indicators. You have been allotted a budget of $500,000.

   Choose which of the six indicators on Student Sheet 19.1 you will monitor. The cost per indicator is
   - $125,000 for 5 years of monitoring, or
   - $250,000 for 10 years of monitoring

5. Record your plan in your science notebook.

4
6. Ask your teacher for the data collected as a part of your monitoring plan.

5
7. With your partner review the data.

8. On Student Sheet 19.1 record the "Actual outcome" for each indicator you monitored.

6
9. Share your results with the other pair in your group. Record evidence about the results of each strategy on Student Sheet 19.2, "Comparing Aquaculture and Marine Reserves in Avril Gulf."

10. With your group, discuss how each strategy affected the Avril Gulf fishery. Be sure to reference evidence from Student Sheet 19.2 in your discussion.

7
11. Obtain additional information on each strategy by comparing data with other groups in your class. Your teacher will explain how to do this.

8
12. Write a report to the Avril Gulf Wildlife Protection Agency (AGWPA) that recommends the continued use of either a marine reserve or aquaculture. In your report recommend one of the strategies, include a discussion of the trade-offs of your recommended strategy, and predict how well the strategy might reestablish the sustainability of the wild fish population. Be sure to include evidence from this activity, and Activity 18, "Fishery Case Studies," to support your recommendation.

as necessary in summarizing trends in the data. Strong summaries will include details and quantitative data as shown in the sample responses at the end of this activity. Students are asked to describe the trends in the information. Encourage them to discuss with their partners why the trends may have occurred. They are not provided with this information, but they can make inferences about the data and what they have learned about ecosystems, marine reserves, and aquaculture. For example, they might discuss why the percentage of fishery-related jobs dropped from 2013 to 2018, when aquaculture was used. Students will record their summaries in the right hand column, "Actual Outcome," on Student Sheet 19.1, "Tracking Indicators." Because students will not receive all of the indicator cards, their student sheets will only contain a summary of the indicators they chose to include in the monitoring plan.

6 Pass out Student Sheet 19.2, "Comparing Aquaculture and Marine Reserves in Avril Gulf." Ask pairs to share their results. Each should record the results from both strategies. Students then use this evidence to compare the success of each strategy at improving the economic, environmental, and social conditions of the Avril Gulf fishery and community.

7 At this point, student groups only have the evidence that they could afford to collect according to the monitoring plan they constructed in Procedure Step 4. This is an opportunity for you to point out that in real-life scientific research the amount of funding often determines the amount and nature of data collected. Pool the information from each group's monitoring report, recorded on Student sheet 19.2, into a class summary. This will allow a comparison of all information collected for both strategies and not just the limited data collected from one group's monitoring plan. Discuss the benefits of pooling data to summarize the impact of a strategy on an ecosystem. Prepare and post two charts like the ones on the next page. Samples of student information are shown in the light typeface.

Sample Class Summary: Effect of Aquaculture on Avril Gulf

Economic	Social	Environmental
• The price of fish decreases. (+)	• Fishery related employment increases. (+) • The percentage of fish that people eat locally increases. (+) (Note: These two indicators can be placed in either the social or economic column.) • The coastal population stays the same. (Neutral)	• The area of critical habitat used increases. (+) • The fish population increases. (+) • Water transparency increases at two data points. (+)

Sample Class Summary: Effect of a Marine Reserve on Avril Gulf

Economic	Social	Environmental
• The price of fish increases. (-)	• Fishery-related employment increases. (+) • The percentage of fish that people eat locally decreases. (-) (Note: These two indicators can be placed in either the social or economic column.) • The coastal population increases. (+)	• The area of critical habitat used increases. (+) • The fish population increases. (+) • Water transparency increases at three data points. (+)

When all groups have added information to the charts, discuss each piece of information with the class, asking students to decide if the result is negative or positive and write a − or + to indicate their ideas. As a class, assess the overall positive or negative state of each column for both charts, as students did in the Activity 18 chart, "Current Condition of Avril Gulf." Ask the class to discuss how each of the fishery-management strategies affected Avril Gulf. Take this opportunity to discuss the positive and negatives of each strategy and the trade-offs of using one versus the other. Discuss how each strategy affected or is likely to affect the sustainability of the Avril Gulf fishery.

8 (ET ASSESSMENT) Student reports can be scored using the Evidence and Trade-offs Scoring Guide. Students may use optional Literacy Student Sheet 2a, "Writing Frame: Evidence and Trade-offs," to help them write their recommendations. This sheet provides a literacy strategy known as a writing frame, which gives students a structure for communicating their ideas. More information about the use of the writing frame literacy strategy is in Teacher Resources III: Literacy. A sample student response is shown below. Procedure Step 12 is an opportunity for you to assess students' abilities to compare the two fishery-management techniques based on the information they have gathered on Student Sheet 19.2, "Comparing Aquaculture and Marine Reserves in Avril Gulf" and what they learned in Activity 18. A Level-3 report will

- recommend a strategy.

- incorporate evidence from Student Sheet 19.2 and Activity 18 to support the recommendation.

- include discussion of the trade-offs of the strategy.

- discuss the impact of the strategy on the sustainability of the fish population.

Trade-offs associated with the construction of a marine reserve include the elimination of all sport and commercial fishing in the designated area and an increase in ecotourism, which may have secondary unintended environmental consequences. Trade-offs associated with open-net-pen aquaculture might include fewer jobs than the marine reserve creates. There is also a reduction in water transparency in the area immediately surrounding the pens due to the spread of waste from pens into surrounding ecosystems. Refer to the sample Student Sheet 19.2, "Comparing Aquaculture and Marine Reserves in Avril Gulf," for evidence students may use. A sample Level-3 report appears below. Note that students' summaries will vary based on the data collected through their monitoring plan.

Analysis

 9

1. Which fishery strategy appears to be the most sustainable for the Avril Gulf tuna fishery? Explain why.

2. What other options might the communities near Avril Gulf consider implementing to meet the challenge of the declining fishery?

10

3. How do you think it would affect the ecosystem if the communities near Avril Gulf continued fishing spotted flying fish instead of Avril Gulf tuna?

4. What are two sustainability challenges your community is facing?

KEY VOCABULARY

ecosystem	population
fishery management	sustainability

147

Level-3 Response
Recommendation for the use of Aquaculture

There is a lot of discussion about the issue of which fishery strategy to use in the Avril Gulf fishery. I recommend that Avril Gulf and the Avril Gulf Wildlife Protection Agency continue to use aquaculture.

My recommendation is based on the following evidence:

From the data collected, it seems that the use of aquaculture has benefited the Avril Gulf tuna population and

Avril Gulf in several ways. Jobs increased for a while. The wild tunas' use of critical habitat increased in various regions, and its population seems to be recovering from overfishing. While these benefits are being seen, there are trade-offs associated with aquaculture. Mainly, water transparency is decreased in the areas immediately surrounding the pens, but not so much that it would harm the ecosystem. I think the use of aquaculture is sustainable in that it allows people to eat fish, and work for the aquaculture company, at least a few people. At the same time, it protects the native fish population so that it can increase and not be overfished.

Some trade-offs of my decision are that this creates fewer jobs than a marine reserve and that the water transparency around the pens is reduced.

After students have written their responses, but before you score them, have students participate in a peer writing review. A peer writing review presents a series of questions by which students evaluate each other's writing. It can be especially helpful in guiding them in how to write a complete and coherent response. Students can compare others' responses to the review questions to improve or revise their writing. Literacy Student Sheet 3, "Writing Review," lists questions and includes space for students to respond. See Teacher Resources III: Literacy for more information on the peer review and writing frame strategies.

FOLLOW-UP

9 Have the class discuss Analysis Question 1. Both strategies have benefits, but each also takes a toll on the ecosystem, which directly relates to the resources available to the people of Avril Gulf. Comparing the positives and negatives in each column on the charts the class constructed in Teaching Step 7 helps the class identify which strategy is more sustainable. After the discussion, have the class vote on which strategy they feel is the most sustainable.

10 (UC ASSESSMENT) Analysis Question 3 is an opportunity to assess student's understanding of ecosystems. Use the UNDERSTANDING CONCEPTS (UC) Scoring Guide to score students' work.

SAMPLE RESPONSES

1. Students' answers should indicate that either strategy will help the native population of fish increase. An increase in fish population will increase opportunities to fish in the Avril Gulf.

2. Some suggestions might include keeping the Avril Gulf tuna fishery closed, working to increase tourism in the area, or developing industries that would boost the economy in ways not dependent on the marine ecosystem.

3. (UC ASSESSMENT) A correct and complete answer would include that the organisms on the food web are interconnected and that fishing the spotted flying fish would likely cause a ripple effect throughout the food web.

Sample Level-3 Response
The spotted flying fish are lower on the food chain. This means that they eat the producers directly, whereas the Avril Gulf tuna do not. If communities near Avril Gulf started fishing the spotted flying fish, the zooplankton and phytoplankton levels might increase, since there would be fewer flying fish eating these particular organisms. Of course, if the blue-striped fish population remains large or increases, the increases in phytoplankton and zooplankton might not occur because the blue-striped fish might eat the growing zooplankton and phytoplankton populations.

Fishing the spotted flying fish also eliminates one of the Avril Gulf tuna's food sources, meaning that they will either compensate and eat blue striped fish, or will not have enough food and fewer will survive.

4. Answers should detail local or statewide challenges involving the use of resources in ways that are not sustainable.

REVISIT THE CHALLENGE

When students have completed the activity, return to the Challenge question with the class. Encourage students to discuss the difficulty in making the "correct" decision, and look at what might make the decision-making difficult. Revisit other instances from the unit where this was also the case, such as the invasive species case studies, and other fishery-related case studies and activities. Students should complete the unit with a basic understanding of the complexity of ecology and ecosystems management, particularly in terms of sustainable fisheries. They will return to the idea of conservation and biodiversity in the "Evolution: Maintaining Diversity" Unit.

Tracking Indicators

Strategy: _Marine Reserve /_ (Open-net Pen Aquaculture) (CIRCLE ONE)

Indicator	Predicted outcome	Actual outcome	
		5 years	**10 years**
Human consumption of tuna	The price of tuna might drop because aqua-culture will produce more tuna. The percentage of tuna people eat will increase because there are more tuna available.	The price of tuna dropped to the price of the tuna in 2000. The percentage of tuna that people ate increased.	The price of tuna dropped below $3.20/lb. The percent-age of tuna that people ate increased to the 1995 level of when the fishery was open.
Percentage change in Avril Gulf's coastal population	The population living on the coast will increase because there are more jobs available in the growing aquaculture farms. The fisheries will also have more fish from the aquaculture farms to clean, pack, and ship, so there will be more jobs compared to when the fishery was closed.	The coastal population stayed at the same level.	The coastal population stayed at the same level.
The Avril Gulf tuna population	The population will increase if aquaculture is used because this will decrease the need for fish-ing natural populations.	The fish population increased and reached a population size of approximately 5,700 fish.	The fish population increased rapidly from 2008 to 2013, and then more slowly from 2013 to 2018 to reach a population size of approximately 5,800 fish.
Avril Gulf tuna critical habitat use	The critical habitat area used by the fish will decrease because aquaculture has a negative impact on surrounding habitats. (Food scraps and waste are spread from the pens into surrounding waters.)	The critical habitat use increased along the coast.	The critical habitat use increased in the northern and southern regions along the coast.
Water transparency	The water transparency will decrease because food scraps and waste from the open-net pens will be released into the surrounding waters.	Water transparency increased at two of the three points moni-tored.	Water transparency increased at two of the three points monitored.
Fishery-related employment	Fishery-related employment might increase because new aquaculture farms will create more jobs.	Fishery-related employment increased.	Fishery-related employment increased.

Tracking Indicators

Strategy: (Marine Reserve) / Open-net Pen Aquaculture (CIRCLE ONE)

Indicator	Predicted outcome	Actual outcome	
		5 years	10 years
Human consumption of tuna	In the short-term people will eat less Avril Gulf tuna, and the price of Avril Gulf tuna will increase because fishing will no longer be allowed along part of Avril Gulf's coast. In the long-term, fish consumption will increase. The cost of the fish will decrease because of the seeding effect on the reserve that will increase fish populations in the coastal waters surrounding the reserve.	The price of tuna increased. The percentage of fish protein consumed decreased.	The price of tuna rose. The percentage of fish protein consumed decreased.
Percentage change in Avril Gulf's coastal population	Avril Gulf's coastal populations will increase because the reserve will add to the beauty of the coastline, making it an attractive place to live.	The coastal population grew.	The coastal population grew.
The Avril Gulf tuna population	The tuna population will increase because part of the fishes' breeding ground will be restored and the seeding effect will repopulate the waters surrounding the marine reserve.	The tuna population increased.	The tuna population increased.
Avril Gulf tuna critical habitat use	Because fishing along parts of Avril Gulf's coast will be banned, more tuna will use the critical habitats, which means they will have more offspring. (A second possible answer is that the fishes' use of critical habitat areas will decrease if the coastal human population continues to increase. Larger coastal populations can lead to more water pollution that damages the quality of the critical habitats.)	The critical habitat use increased.	The critical habitat use increased.
Water transparency	In the short-term the water transparency will increase because there will be no fishing boats in the area polluting the waters. In the long-term, water may become polluted if roads and an educational center bring more people to the area.	Water transparency increased at all three locations.	Water transparency increased at all three locations.
Fishery-related employment	In the short-term fishery-related employment will decrease because no more sport or commercial fishing will be allowed in the area of the reserve. In the long-term, if ecotourism increases there will be more jobs.	Fishery-related employment increased.	Fishery-related employment increased.

Comparing Aquaculture and Marine Reserves in Avril Gulf

	Evidence in support of	Evidence against
Aquaculture	Fishery related employment increases. (+) The price of fish decreases. (+) The percentage of fish that local people eat increases. (+) The area of critical habitat used increases. (+) The fish population increases. (+) Water transparency increases at two data points. (+)	The costal population stays the same. (Neutral)
Marine reserve	Fishery related employment increases. (+) The area of critical habitat used increases. (+) The fish population increases. (+) Water transparency increases at three data points. (+) The human costal population increases. (+)	The price of fish increases. (-) The percentage of fish people eat locally decreases. (-)

Unit Review: Ecology

Ecosystems

Ecosystems incorporate the interactions between communities of living organisms (biotic factors) and the involvement of the organisms with their nonliving environment (abiotic factors). Abiotic factors include light, temperature, precipitation, soil, rocks and minerals. Organisms, which live in habitats within ecosystems, play particular roles in their ecosystems. Some species are better suited to certain environmental conditions than others.

Natural and human-caused events often stress ecosystems in many ways. Ecosystem disturbances vary in degree, from minor disturbances to major events. When an ecosystem is able to recover from, or accommodate, stress it is demonstrating resiliency. Some events that disturb an ecosystem have only a short-term effect, while others cause long-lasting harm or change.

Ecosystem resilience is often related to the biodiversity within and around a disturbed area. Biodiversity refers to the variety of organisms in an ecosystem that fill multiple roles in the ecosystem. A heightened biodiversity does not necessarily increase the sustainability of an ecosystem, but constantly reducing biodiversity will make an ecosystem less sustainable.

An ecosystem responds to a disturbance through ecological succession, if the disturbance is not ongoing. Depending on the condition of the ecosystem once the disturbance ends, the ecosystem undergoes either primary or secondary succession.

Scientists group the ecosystems of the world into distinct types, or biomes. However, there is not perfect agreement on the number and types of biomes found on earth. Discussions of biomes in this unit and elsewhere in *Science and Global Issues* are based on the system that identifies biome groups as follows: tropical rain forest, desert, savanna, chaparral, temperate grassland, taiga, temperate deciduous forest, and tundra.

KEY VOCABULARY

abiotic	ecosystem
biodiversity	habitat
biome	organism
biotic	primary succession
community	resilience
disturbance	resistance
ecological succession	secondary succession
ecology	

Relationships within Ecosystems

Ecosystems rely on many organisms to make up the food webs that will maintain the flow of energy through the ecosystem and keep the ecosystem running. Producers are the organisms that form the basis of food webs, and, when consumed, provide energy for consumers. Often microscopic organisms, such as plankton, form the basis for large food webs. Within food webs there are different levels of consumers— primary, secondary and tertiary consumers—designated as such by what they consume. An energy pyramid picture shows how much energy is available for each level of organism. Changes in the population of a species within an ecosystem can affect other species within the ecosystem. Removal of an organism (or organisms) can cause a food web to collapse or have other unintended results because organisms frequently have close ecological relationships with each other, and these are known as symbiotic relationships. The four main categories of symbiotic relationships are: parasitism, commensalism, amensalism, and mutualism.

An adaptation is a trait (or traits) that helps an organism survive in a habitat. If the conditions in a habitat change sufficiently, or if the organism moves to an entirely different environment, the trait(s) may no longer be useful and the organism might not be as well adapted to the conditions.

Eutrophication is caused when a large increase in particular nutrients in aquatic environments causes an increase in phytoplankton. Dramatic increases in phytoplankton will increase the organic matter available for bacteria, thus increasing the amount of bacteria. Too much bacteria depletes surrounding waters of oxygen, causing other organisms in the ecosystem to migrate or die. The absence of organisms as a result of eutrophication creates areas referred to as dead zones.

KEY VOCABULARY

amensalism	mutualism
commensalism	parasitism
consumers	phytoplankton
dead zone	plankton
decomposers	producers
energy pyramid	symbiosis
eutrophication	zooplankton
food web	

Population Dynamics

Population growth rate is the change in a population over a given period of time. A positive growth rate indicates that the population is getting larger. A negative growth rate indicates that the population is getting smaller. Populations with a positive growth rate eventually reach a carrying capacity, at which point the ecosystem cannot support those populations. Continued negative growth rates eventually lead to population extinction.

Factors that affect population growth are birth rate, death rate, disease, predators, food availability, and human impact. The trend of a growth rate is likely to change if the factors influencing the growth rate change. Some conditions lead to exponential population growth for certain species.

KEY VOCABULARY

carrying capacity	limiting factor
density-dependent factors	population
density-independent	population growth rate

Invasive Species

Native species are those that are naturally found in an ecosystem. Because it is impossible for humans to know exactly which species are natural to an environment, it is generally considered that a species is native if it is thought to have existed in an environment for thousands of years. An introduced species is one that has been brought in to an environment in which it does not naturally occur. Such species are also referred to as nonnative, exotic, or nonindigenous. If a nonnative species causes harm to the environment, the economy, or human health, it is considered to be invasive.

No two species perform the same role in an environment. If a nonnative species displaces a native species from its role a decrease in biodiversity of the ecosystem might result, which may have an effect on other species in that ecosystem. In such a case, the nonnative species has had a negative effect on the environment, and that species is deemed invasive. Not all introduced species will succeed in a new environment. If an introduced species has traits that are well-suited to the new environment, it is more likely to become established. Changes in the population dynamics of an ecosystem are factors in the success of an invasive species becoming established within an ecosystem.

KEY VOCABULARY

invasive species	nonnative species

Photosynthesis and Respiration

Photosynthesis is a cellular process by which an organism captures light from the sun and uses it to store energy. In photosynthesis light energy, carbon dioxide, and water are taken in to produce glucose and oxygen. Only producers perform photosynthesis. Although sunlight is required for photosynthesis to occur, parts of photosynthesis can happen in the absence of light. The stages of photosynthesis that produce oxygen happen in the presence of sunlight. Photosynthesis happens in chloroplasts, which contain chlorophyll. Different variables, such as temperature and amount of light, affect the rate of photosynthesis and cellular respiration. Chemical indicators show chemical changes in a substance, such as the addition of oxygen or carbon dioxide. From changes in chemical indicators, therefore, it can be inferred that a cellular process, such as photosynthesis, is occurring.

Cellular respiration takes in oxygen and glucose and produces carbon dioxide, water and ATP. Most organisms perform cellular respiration, including plants and other producers. Cellular respiration happens in the mitochondria and the area just outside the mitochondria. Plants can perform cellular respiration independently of photosynthesis. Cellular respiration occurs at different rates under different conditions.

The substances produced and consumed in photosynthesis and cellular respiration are complementary. For example, aquatic environments depend on a balance of photosynthesis and cellular respiration to prevent dead zones.

The carbon cycle moves carbon between several major reservoirs. Reservoirs in the carbon cycle include rocks and soils, the ocean and other bodies of water, plants/producers, animals/consumers, the atmosphere, and fossil fuels. Although the amount of carbon in the different reservoirs fluctuates, the amount of carbon contained in the carbon cycle is a fixed amount. The carbon in different reservoirs is in different chemical forms, such as carbon dioxide and glucose. The carbon cycle is one of several biogeochemical cycles that move elements through different reservoirs and allow them to be used repeatedly by living organisms.

KEY VOCABULARY	
carbon cycle	chemical indicator
carbon reservoir	enzymes
cellular respiration	photosynthesis

Inquiry and the Nature of Science

Experimental design requires a clear, reproducible procedure and the choice of an experimental variable that will be manipulated independently of other variables. Many experiments include a control and an experimental setup.

Scientists develop models for representing actual phenomena and to compare theoretical situations to actual situations.

Historical case studies provide information that is helpful in decision-making.

KEY VOCABULARY	
evidence	variable
trade-off	

Fisheries Management

People around the world employ many types of aquaculture, some of which are detrimental to the surrounding ecosystem. Some species are better suited for aquaculture than others. The effects of aquaculture on the surrounding ecosystem can be mitigated in a variety of ways.

There are many types of ecosystem services, some of which provide direct benefits and some of which provide indirect benefits to people. Sustainable management of ecosystem services depends on continual input from scientists and other experts. One type of ecosystem service is fishing. Some fisheries have had a significant impact on the associated ecosystems. Over-fishing can be prevented with appropriate regulations and enforcement, and there are various approaches to fisheries management.

Limits, such as fishing limits, must be monitored to ensure they are set at appropriate levels. Analysis of indicators informs resource management decision-making. Indicators from a variety of fields should be examined, if possible.

KEY VOCABULARY	
aquaculture	indicator
ecosystem services	marine reserve
fisheries	sustainability
fishery	Tragedy of the Commons

Cell Biology: World Health

ALL ORGANISMS ARE susceptible to disease. The effects of diseases vary from mild to devastating and affect sustainability at the environmental, economic, and social level. For example, foot-and-mouth and mad cow diseases have periodically wiped out huge herds of cattle, causing economic hardship for those whose livelihoods depend on the cattle. Influenza pandemics have killed millions of people, and recent epidemics of H1N1 and SARS viruses have threatened entire cities.

Diseases are caused by infectious microbes, such as bacteria and viruses, genetic factors, and other events that cause breakdowns in the structure or function of cells. Understanding the mechanisms of a disease is essential to people's ability to prevent, eradicate, and cure it and to maintain the sustainability of populations and communities.

In this unit you will examine several diseases and their social, environmental, and economic consequences. You will learn about the mechanism of these diseases at the cellular level. You will also investigate the structures and functions of normal cells and some of the processes that occur inside these cells. At the end of the unit, you will make recommendations for how best to allocate limited funding to address world health problems.

156

1 World Health and Sustainability

TALK IT OVER • 2–3 CLASS SESSIONS

OVERVIEW

Students examine health data for several countries. They apply these data as indicators of the sustainability of the populations in those countries.

KEY CONTENT

1. Diseases are classified as infectious or noninfectious.

2. Infectious diseases are transmitted from person to person either directly or by vectors. Noninfectious diseases cannot be transmitted and are instead due to such factors as aging, the environment, behavior, or genetics.

3. Less-developed countries tend to have a greater proportion of deaths from infectious diseases than do more-developed countries.

4. The challenges of dealing with diseases affect progress toward sustainable development, by which existing communities improve their means of meeting their needs without endangering future generations' abilities to meet their needs. These needs include receiving appropriate medical care and living a full life span.

KEY PROCESS SKILLS

1. Students describe trends and relationships in data.

2. Students develop and support conclusions based on evidence.

MATERIALS AND ADVANCE PREPARATION

Because many activities in this unit require the teacher to use an overhead or data projector, make sure that one is always available.

For the teacher

Scoring Guide: GROUP INTERACTION (GI)

Transparency 1.1, "Disease and Income Level"

Transparency 1.2, "Top 10 Causes of Death by Income Level"

Group Interaction Student Sheet 2, "Developing Communication Skills" (optional)

For each group of four students

World Health Data Set 1

World Health Data Set 2

World Health Data Set 3

World Health Data Set 4

For each student

Scoring Guide: GROUP INTERACTION (GI) (optional)

Group Interaction Student Sheet 2, "Developing Communication Skills" (optional)

Masters for Group Interaction Student Sheets are in Teacher Resources II: Diverse Learners. Masters for Scoring Guides are in Teacher Resources IV: Assessment.

TEACHING SUMMARY

Getting Started

- (LITERACY) Conduct a Walking Debate and class discussion that focuses on world-health questions.

Doing the Activity

- (LITERACY) Introduce the use of a science notebook.

- Introduce the SEPUP 4–2–1 cooperative learning model.

- (LITERACY) Discuss the value of group communication skills.

- (GI ASSESSMENT) Introduce the GROUP INTERACTION (GI) Scoring Guide.

- Students examine four sets of health data for countries around the world.

- Students group the health indicators into social, economic, and environmental categories.

Follow-up

- Explain the purpose of SEPUP Analysis Questions.

- The class discusses the conclusions they develop from the health data and what they show about sustainability.

BACKGROUND INFORMATION

Infectious and Noninfectious diseases

Infectious diseases are caused by such pathogenic microbes as bacteria, viruses, parasites, and fungi. Infectious diseases are also referred to as communicable diseases. Strep throat and flu are examples of communicable diseases. Many infectious diseases are transmitted directly from one individual to another, and are called contagious. Others are transmitted by vectors, such as mosquitoes or ticks, and are noncontagious.

Noninfectious diseases, also referred to as noncommunicable diseases, cannot be transmitted from one person to another. Inherited genetic diseases, such as sickle cell disease and cystic fibrosis, are one group of noncommunicable diseases. Some noninfectious diseases are chronic degenerative conditions that progress slowly, and are usually of long duration. Heart disease and Type II diabetes are examples. Other diseases, such as some cancers and asthma, may have both genetic and environmental causes, and some cancers are caused by viruses. Noninfectious diseases are the leading cause of death worldwide, accounting for 60% of all deaths.

Purchasing-Power-Parity (PPP)

In this activity students examine financial information for various countries. The data are given in purchasing-power-parity (PPP) international dollars. The PPP between two countries is the conversion rate for the currency of one country compared to the other to determine the amount of money needed to purchase the same volume of goods and services in both countries.

Age-standardized Mortality Rate

The number of deaths per 100,000 people in a population is affected by the age distribution of the population. The age-standardized mortality rate adjusts for differences in the age distributions in order to remove age as a factor. The cancer mortality rate used in this activity is age-standardized.

Note: Loss of life index indicates the impacts of two broad categories of disease. It takes into account the number of deaths and the ages at which deaths occurred. It is generally expressed as a percentage of the total years of life lost to all causes of death, including communicable diseases, non-communicable diseases, and injuries.

GETTING STARTED

1 🔷 (LITERACY) This symbol represents an opportunity to elicit information from students about their experiences and ideas, which will help you direct your instruction. Sometimes you will be able to build on students' ideas and different perspectives, while at other times you will uncover ideas that are inconsistent with scientific explanations (but perhaps consistent with common reasoning). The Teaching Suggestions often provide strategies for uncovering and addressing these ideas. To get students thinking about world health and to find out the extent of their current knowledge, conduct a Walking Debate as described below. For more information about the Walking Debate see Teacher Resources III: Literacy.

This strategy works best when the question or issue has no single correct answer. Ask, *What most influences your health?*

Make four signs, labeled Genetics, Environment, Economic Status, and Lifestyle. Post the signs in four distinct areas of the room. Clarify with students that the word environment here is not referring to the outdoors or nature, but to environmental hazards people may encounter, such as cigarette smoke, pollution, and infectious agents in the air and water, as well as benign or beneficial environmental conditions, such as clean air and water. Have students stand near the sign representing what they think most influences their health. (If most of the students already agree on a particular option, you may want to assign some of them to the other options to foster the skills of debate and evidence analysis.) Have students, within the groups that formed, discuss the reasons for their choices, and have them appoint a spokesperson to report to the class. The spokesperson for each group will explain to the class the reasons that members of the group chose that option. Once each group has presented its rationales, allow students to change their minds and move to another area. Explain that

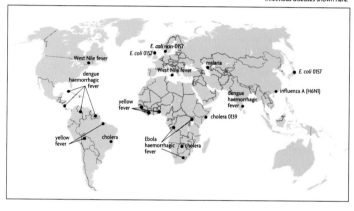

1 World Health and Sustainability

1 IVING ORGANISMS ARE vulnerable to disease. The effects of large-scale epidemics on human societies can be devastating. In the 14th century about one-third of the population of Europe died of the Black Death—bubonic plague. From 1918 to 1919 one-fifth of the world's population caught influenza during a pandemic that quickly killed as many as 40 million people—most of them between the ages of 20 and 40. The plague and influenza are examples of communicable—or infectious—diseases. **Infectious diseases** are transmitted from one person to another. **Noninfectious diseases** (also called noncommunicable diseases) are not transmitted from one person to another, and are caused by such factors as the environment, genetics, and aging. Noninfectious diseases also affect people everywhere in the world. The World Health Organization estimated that in 2005 more than 14 million people died of infectious diseases, while 35 million people died of noninfectious diseases.

Diseases affect human populations in many ways, including socially, economically, and environmentally. When people are sick or die from a disease, their suffering or death might touch a community on a social level or heighten a society's demand that a cure be found. There are negative economic effects related to the cost of

The World Health Organization is monitoring the emerging infectious diseases shown here.

157

students will get more information addressing the question of what most influences people's health over the course of this unit. To elicit more of students' ideas about diseases continue the discussion by asking, *What do you think is the leading cause of death worldwide?*

List the following possible answers on the chalkboard or a transparency: injuries, infectious diseases, noninfectious diseases, or accidents. On the board or overhead record the groups' responses for each category, and tell students that they will revisit them at the end of the activity. Explain to students that in this activity they will examine some health indicator data for various countries around the world to learn more about worldwide health.

DOING THE ACTIVITY

2 (GI ASSESSMENT) Activities in *Science and Global Issues* use a 4–2–1 cooperative learning model. Groups of four students share certain materials, pairs of students in the groups work together and discuss issues, and each student is responsible for recording ideas, observations, and thoughts. In this activity, students will work in groups of four and in pairs to examine world health data. Encourage students to work within their groups, with their partners, and with the other pair in their groups to solve problems and answer questions. Collaboration is essential for developing new ideas and gaining a better understanding of scientific concepts. If necessary, explain to students your expectations for successful group effort.

Give all students a copy of the GROUP INTERACTION (GI) Scoring Guide, and ask them to keep it with their science notebooks, as they will refer to it several times in this unit, and throughout *Science and Global Issues*. Let them know that you will use this throughout the unit at specific times to provide feedback on their work within their groups of four and with their partners. Take this opportunity to explain your expectations for group effort, and to discuss as a class what successful group work looks like. For more information on scoring how well students work together, see Teacher Resources IV: Assessment.

3 (LITERACY) Explain to your students that, as they conduct activities, they will record data, observations, hypotheses, conclusions, and thoughts in their notebooks. Keeping a science notebook helps them track data, note questions as they arise in investigations and discussion, and build science-writing skills. Decide how you would like students to record their work in each of the activities in this unit. For recommendations and more information, see Teacher Resources III: Literacy.

Students categorize the health-indicator data into the following three sustainability pillars: social, economic, and environmental. More information on these three pillars can be found on the *Science and Global Issues* page of the SEPUP website (*sepuplhs.org/sgi*). Sample groupings are shown on the next page, but other groupings are possible. Some of the indicators fit into more than one category or none of the three categories. Be sure to check students' reasoning for their groupings.

---

treatment and the loss of individuals' productivity, and a positive economic effect in terms of the numbers of people employed in the health-care industry. There is sometimes a link between the environment and disease, as is the case when polluted air or water or the presence of disease-carrying organisms makes people sick. With such social, economic, and environmental relationships disease is a major factor in the sustainability of populations and communities. **Sustainability** is the ability to meet a community's present needs without compromising the ability of future generations to meet their own needs.

In this unit, you will study life at the cellular level and see how research by cell biologists and medical professionals has advanced society's efforts to cure and prevent diseases. In this activity you will examine health indicators as you look at world health from a sustainability perspective.

Challenge

▶ What do health indicators show about world health and sustainability?

MATERIALS

FOR EACH GROUP OF FOUR STUDENTS
World Health Data Set 1
World Health Data Set 2
World Health Data Set 3
World Health Data Set 4

SOURCE: *The data in this activity come from two major public health organizations, the World Health Organization (WHO) and the U.S. Centers for Disease Control and Prevention (CDC).*

Procedure

2 1. With your team of four, decide which pair will examine World Health Data Set 1 and which will examine Data Set 2.

3 2. Work with your team to classify, and record in your science notebook, the indicators on the data sets into the following sustainability categories:

- Social
- Economic
- Environmental

Note: Some of the indicators may be placed in more than one category, or not in any of the three categories.

Follow your teacher's directions for sharing your classifications with the class.

4 3. With your partner, examine the data, and from that information sort the countries into two, three, or four groups. Record your groupings and the reasons for the way you sorted them in your science notebook.

Sample Groupings for Procedure Step 2

Social	Economic	Environmental
life expectancy at birth (female)	gross national income per capita	population with access to improved, sustainable sanitation
life expectancy at birth (male)	per capita government expenditure on health	
births attended by skilled health personnel	per capita total expenditure on health	percentage of male and female adults using tobacco
physicians	general government expenditure on health as % of total government expenditure	deaths among children under five years of age due to diarrheal diseases
pharmacists		
maternal mortality ratio		
under-five mortality rate	births attended by skilled health personnel	
adults who are obese	physicians	
percentage of male and female adults using tobacco	pharmacists	

Point out some of the connections between the economic and social indicators. For example, when a high number of employed adults die or are too sick to work, they are no longer contributing to the workforce, and the productivity of the community and country is affected. Also, the cost of treating chronic illnesses, such as heart disease and diabetes, in a large population over many years might be a burden on the economic resources of a country.

4 (LITERACY) As students review World Health Data Sets 1 and 2, emphasize that people can look at data in various ways and draw different conclusions, which is fine if they are able to explain their reasoning. Sample groupings are shown at right. Each sample is based on a single indicator, but some students may use a combination of indicators to group the countries. As students review more data, some are likely to notice that these health indicators are generally more positive for the United States, the United Kingdom, and Singapore and less positive for Ethiopia, Haiti, and Cambodia, with other countries tending to fall between these groups.

In general, based on all of the data, Ethiopia, Haiti, and Cambodia have relatively poor life-expectancy indicators, although fewer years of life lost to noninfectious diseases; Honduras

and Yemen have better life-expectancy indicators; and the United States, the United Kingdom, and Singapore have the best life-expectancy indicators. Students may put Argentina into either the middle or the best group.

5 (LITERACY) Throughout this unit, students will engage in small-group work and discussions. Good group communication skills will assist them in gaining a better understanding of content and having more meaningful discussions that support their learning. You may wish to use Group Interaction Student Sheet 2, "Developing Communication Skills," which gives students suggestions for communicating well when in a group. Consider applying the GROUP INTERACTION (GI) Scoring Guide throughout the course to provide students feedback about their interaction within groups. For more information about ways to support group interactions see Teacher Resources II: Diverse Learners.

After students complete Procedure Step 5, have a class discussion about the first two data sets. Ask for volunteers to explain how their groups sorted the countries based on the two data sets, and how the two data sets compare. Ask, *What are some possible reasons for the high under-five mortality rate in some countries?*

World Health Data Set 1

Life expectancy for females	Adult mortality per 100,000 people	Life expectancy at birth
50s: Ethiopia	30,001–40,000: Ethiopia	65 and younger: Cambodia, Haiti, Ethiopia, Yemen
60s: Cambodia, Haiti, Yemen	20,001–30,000: Yemen, Cambodia, Haiti	
70s: Argentina, Honduras	10,001–20,000: USA, Argentina, Honduras	70s: Argentina, Honduras
80s: UK, USA, Singapore	Fewer than 20,000: Singapore, UK	80 and older: USA, UK, Singapore
	Or:	
	20,001–40,000: Ethiopia, Yemen, Cambodia, Haiti	
	Fewer than 20,000: USA, UK, Argentina, Honduras, Singapore	

World Health Data Set 2

Loss of Life Index: noncommunicable diseases per 1,000 people	Loss of Life Index: communicable diseases per 1,000 people
0–20: Ethiopia, Haiti	61–80: Cambodia, Ethiopia, Haiti
21–40: Cambodia, Honduras	41–60: Honduras
61–80: Argentina, Singapore, UK, USA, Yemen	Fewer than 20: Argentina, Singapore, UK, USA, Yemen

Children have less mature immune systems, which makes them more vulnerable to and more severely affected by such illnesses as diarrheal diseases and pneumonia. Then ask, *Is there a relationship between life expectancy and the types of diseases people in a country are dying from?*

Countries with shorter life expectancy have a higher incidence of infectious disease. Young children are especially likely to die of these diseases. Countries with longer life expectancies have a lower incidence of infectious disease. As people live longer they are more likely to die from noninfectious diseases, such as heart disease, stroke, and cancer.

6 Sample student groupings for Data Sets 3 and 4 are shown on the next page.

After student groups have completed their discussions about placing countries in categories, hold another class discussion of students' observations about Data Sets 3 and 4.

Ask students if there is any financial information that can help explain the risk factors for a given country. The data suggest a direct relationship between the gross national income (GNI) and prevalence of adult obese females. Discuss students' ideas about possible reasons for this trend, which might include a high-fat, processed-food diet and sedentary lifestyle. They might note also that countries with higher GNI tend to spend more on health care and have better sanitation. Next, discuss students' predicted measurements for the missing indicators for some countries. For example, Cambodia has a fairly high cancer rate, similar to Gabon's. Students should predict that tobacco use in Gabon might be higher as well and similar to Cambodia's rate of tobacco use. For Argentina, there are a fairly low number of childhood deaths from diarrheal diseases and communicable diseases, and so access to improved sanitation is likely to be high.

4. In your science notebook, record the following for your groupings:
   - Trends in the data
   - Claims you can make about the data

5 5. Share your groupings with the other pair in your team. Explain the reasoning for your groupings.

6. In your science notebook, record the following for the groupings of the countries based on Data Sets 1 and 2:
   - Similarities and differences between the groupings of Data Sets 1 and 2
   - Claims you can make about the data
   - Questions you have about the data

7. In your science notebook list the countries that are missing certain indicator data, and note which they are. For each missing indicator, write what you predict the missing measurement might be, based on the other data given. Explain your reasoning.

6 8. Repeat Steps 1–7 for Data Sets 3 and 4.

7 9. Discuss with your team the similarities and differences in the groupings for Data Sets 1 and 2 and Data Sets 3 and 4. Record them in your science notebook.

159

---

7 Next ask students to discuss the links between World Health Data Sets 1 and 2 and World Health Data Sets 3 and 4. An example of a link would be that lower gross national income per capita is related to increased number of years of life lost to infectious diseases and vice versa. Another link is lower access to improved sanitation and greater number of years of life lost due to infectious diseases.

Then ask, *Are there any risk factors that are related to the incidence of disease and mortality?*

There is a direct relationship between poor sanitation and years of life lost to infectious diseases, and between poor sanitation and diarrheal diseases.

FOLLOW-UP

8 Point out to students that each activity in this book includes Analysis Questions to help guide them in their learning, provide ways for them to synthesize what they learned in the activity, and, in many cases, extend class discussion on the activity's connection to personal and global issues and sustainability.

All questions identified in this Teacher's Edition as assessment questions are to be completed individually.

9 ✓ To further emphasize the relationship between disease and income, project Transparency 1.1, "Disease and Income Level." Emphasize that countries all over the world have high incidences of disease, but the most problematic diseases differ, as shown by the graph of disease and income level. Next, revisit the question from the discussion at the beginning of the activity about what the leading cause of death is worldwide. Ask students to determine the answer based on the graph on Transparency 1.1. They should conclude that noninfectious diseases are the leading causes of death worldwide. Also point out that the data on Transparency 1.1 show that lower-income countries experience more deaths from all diseases compared to higher-income countries. Then project Transparency 1.2, "Top 10 Causes of Death by Income Level," and compare it to what students thought would be the leading causes of death at the beginning of this activity. Ask students if there is anything that surprises them about the data. They might be surprised that coronary heart disease is a major cause of death across the board. They may also be surprised to see that HIV/AIDS is not on the list for middle- or high-income countries, given the frequency of media attention about HIV/AIDS in the United States. Analysis Question 1 serves as a Quick Check assessment to ensure that students can accurately interpret

---

SCIENCE & GLOBAL ISSUES/BIOLOGY • CELL BIOLOGY

8
9
Analysis

1. What similarities and differences did you notice in the groupings for World Health Data Sets 1 and 2 and Sets 3 and 4?

2. Which indicator(s) in the data sets did not seem to show a trend? Suggest reasons why, using the data as evidence. **Evidence** is information used to support or refute a claim.

3. How is the sustainability of a community tied to disease? Give examples of social, environmental, and economic factors in your answer.

10

KEY VOCABULARY	
evidence	noninfectious disease
indicator	sustainability
infectious disease	

World Health Data Set 3

Gross national income	Per capita total expenditures on health
0–30,000 PPP international $: Cambodia, Ethiopia, Honduras, Haiti, Yemen, Argentina	Below 1,000 PPP international $: Honduras, Haiti, Cambodia, Yemen, Ethiopia
30,001–50,000 PPP international $: UK, Singapore, USA	30,001–50,000 PPP international $: USA, UK, Argentina, Singapore

World Health Data Set 4

Percentage of obese female adults	Access to improved sanitation
Less than 20%: Cambodia, Ethiopia, Yemen, Haiti, Singapore, Argentina, Honduras	36% and below: Haiti, Ethiopia, Cambodia
21%–40%: UK, USA	46%–66%: Yemen, Honduras
	91%–100%: UK, USA, Singapore

160

---

data from a table, and correctly identify and describe trends and relationships, which are components of the Analyzing Data scoring variable. Students' responses to Analysis Question 3 will be a good starting point for a deeper exploration of the effects of world health on sustainability.

10 This box lists the key vocabulary developed in this activity. When words are formally defined in an activity, they appear in bold type in the list. Encourage students to use these words when answering the Analysis Questions. Also, during informal and formal discussions listen for these words and see if students are applying them correctly. Decide how you will support students' understanding of the vocabulary—perhaps with a student glossary, or setting up a class word wall. For more suggestions on ways to develop students' understanding of and proficiency with scientific vocabulary, see Teacher Resources III: Literacy.

SAMPLE RESPONSES

1. ✓There is a direct relationship between income level and the incidence of infectious and noninfectious diseases. People in lower-income countries are more likely to die from infectious diseases, and people in higher-income countries are more likely to die from noninfectious diseases. The higher the life expectancy, the higher the proportion of deaths from noninfectious diseases, and vice versa. Poor sanitation is a risk factor for some infectious diseases, such as diarrheal diseases.
2. Cancer did not seem to show a trend. Possible reasons could be that there is a genetic component to cancer that is not dependent on economic conditions. There also might be environmental factors, such as pollution and viruses, which affect people no matter where they live.
3. It is difficult to sustain a community if the community is overwhelmed by a disease. An environmental factor such as lack of access to improved sanitation can cause people to get sick from infectious diseases. If many people are sick from diseases, there may not be enough doctors or hospital facilities to care for them, which are social factors. Also, people who are sick might not be able to work, which affects the productivity in the community, and therefore the economy.

REVISIT THE CHALLENGE

The health indicators show that countries all over the world have disease challenges, but the type, frequency, and severity of the problems differ. The types of diseases prevalent in a country are often influenced by the income level of the country. People in lower-income countries are more likely to die from infectious diseases, and people in higher-income countries are more likely to die from noninfectious diseases. In a given year, a larger fraction of the population in lower-income countries dies from all diseases than in higher-income countries. However, all countries experience problems with some diseases, such as cancer or heart disease. Tell students that they will be learning more about environmental factors involved in world health later in the unit.

2 Cells and Disease

LABORATORY • 1–2 CLASS SESSIONS

OVERVIEW

Students review the symptoms of two individuals, and compare their blood to normal blood in order to determine a diagnosis. Students are introduced to some of the causes of disease and the roles of abnormal human cells and foreign cells in noninfectious and infectious diseases. A case study describes the *Plasmodium* parasite, a foreign cell that causes malaria, and the sustainability issues associated with malaria.

KEY CONTENT

1. Some human diseases are caused by abnormalities that develop within the body's cells, while others are caused by microbes.

2. Some diseases, including sickle cell disease and malaria, are diagnosed by viewing blood samples from the affected individual through a light microscope.

KEY PROCESS SKILLS

1. Students use a microscope to make observations.

2. Students make conclusions based on evidence.

MATERIALS AND ADVANCE PREPARATION

For the teacher

Literacy Transparency 2, "Read, Think, and Take Note"
Scoring Guide: UNDERSTANDING CONCEPTS (UC)
Science Skills Transparency 3, "How to Use a Microscope" (optional)

For each group of four students

prepared slide, "Patient A Blood"
prepared slide, "Patient B Blood"

For each pair of students

microscope*
prepared slide, "Typical Human Blood"

For each student

6 Student Sheet 2.1, "Disease Information"
3 sticky notes*
Science Skills Student Sheet 6, "Parts of a Microscope" (optional)
Science Skills Student Sheet 7, "Microscope Magnification" (optional)
Scoring Guide: UNDERSTANDING CONCEPTS (UC) (optional)

Not supplied in kit

Each student will need 6 copies of Student Sheet 2.1, "Disease Information," over the course of the unit, one for each case study.

Masters for Science Skills Student Sheets are in Teacher Resources II: Diverse Learners. Masters for Literacy transparencies are in Teacher Resources III: Literacy. Masters for Scoring Guides are in Teacher Resources IV: Assessment.

TEACHING SUMMARY

Getting Started

- Discuss why the study of cells is important to understanding human health.

Doing the Activity

- Students complete the investigation.

- (LITERACY) Introduce the "Read, Think, and Take Note" reading strategy.

- (LITERACY) Students read a case study about malaria.

Follow-up

- Discuss the cellular bases of two diseases.

- Introduce the SEPUP Assessment System.

- (UC ASSESSMENT) Discuss how the structures of cells allow cells to perform their functions.

- Students learn about evidence and trade-offs.

BACKGROUND INFORMATION

Compound light microscopes and electron microscopes are two of the most important tools that have advanced scientists' work in the life sciences and cell biology. The size of an object that can be observed through a microscope depends on its magnification and resolution. Magnification is the ratio of the specimen's image to its actual size. Resolution is a measure of the microscope's ability to clearly distinguish two separate objects, and is inversely related to the wavelength of radiation passing through the specimen.

The Light Microscope

In a compound light microscope two lenses—the ocular lens in the eyepiece and one of the objective lenses—magnify an image when light passes through the specimen. The light is directed upward from below the microscope stage either by way of a mirror or from a built-in light bulb and is usually controlled by a condenser lens below the stage. A modern light microscope magnifies an image up to 1,000 times, a range in which scientists can study tissues, cells and some of their internal structures, and some living organisms. For a viewer to observe a particular level of detail, tissues or cells may have to be fixed and thin-sectioned. Sometimes staining a specimen with a dye allows a viewer to more easily view specific parts of the specimen. The resolution of a light microscope is approximately 200 nanometers, which is the size of a small bacterial cell; this limit is determined by the wavelengths of light that can be passed through the specimen.

The Electron Microscope

An electron microscope magnifies an image by focusing beams of electrons on the image. Electron microscopes can magnify specimens much smaller than a light microscope can, with the most powerful ones magnifying 1,000 times more than a light microscope. Because electron beams have much shorter wavelengths, the resolution is approximately 2 nanometers, which is 100 times higher than a light microscope. For an image to be viewed in an electron microscope, it must be preserved and dehydrated, which means living cells and organisms cannot be viewed with an electron microscope. There are two types of electron microscopes: transmission electron microscopes (TEMs), and scanning electron microscopes (SEMs). Transmission electron microscopes focus a beam of electrons through a thin slice of the specimen, making visible the details of the specimen. Scanning electron microscopes scan a beam of electrons back and forth across the specimen surface and produce a three-dimensional view of the specimen surface.

GETTING STARTED

1 ◆ Ask students where they think cells are involved in life processes. Students might know that cells make up skin and are part of what sloughs off when skin is dry. They might also say that cells (sperm and egg) are involved in the reproduction of organisms. Then ask why they think scientists and doctors study cells. Students are likely to say that doctors study cells to see if something is wrong or if someone is sick, and that scientists study cells to understand them and how they work. Some students may have had a medical professional take a throat culture or a blood sample from them. Throat cultures can detect the presence of disease-causing bacteria, such as the *Streptococcus* that causes strep throat. Blood samples are observed under a microscope to detect abnormal numbers or shapes of blood cells or infectious organisms.

2 Cells and Disease

1 I**N THE PREVIOUS** activity, you learned about some of the factors that influence world health and disease. A **disease** is any breakdown in the structure or function of an organism. Scientists who study a particular disease gather information about how that disease affects the organism. They look at all levels of the organism, from molecules and cells to organs and the whole organism. Some scientists, like cell biologists, use microscopes to study the structure and function of cells in the full array of organisms, from humans to plants to insects to microbes. A **microbe** is a microscopic cellular organism or a virus, and some microbes cause infectious diseases. One way to detect and study many diseases is to compare blood from healthy and sick individuals under a microscope. In this activity you will examine samples of blood from healthy and diseased people.

Challenge

▶ How do observations of cells help doctors and scientists diagnose and study diseases?

MATERIALS

FOR EACH GROUP OF FOUR STUDENTS
    prepared slide, "Patient A Blood"
    prepared slide, "Patient B Blood"

FOR EACH PAIR OF STUDENTS
    microscope
    prepared slide, "Typical Human Blood"

FOR EACH STUDENT
  6 Student Sheet 2.1, "Disease Information"
  3 sticky notes

161

DOING THE ACTIVITY

2 Project Science Skills Transparency 3, "How to Use a Microscope." Review the guidelines as necessary with your students. You may also choose to pass out copies of Science Skills Student Sheet 6, "Parts of a Microscope," to review with students. For more information and support for using microscopes, see Teacher Resources II: Diverse Learners.

3 Instruct students to read the patient histories and the table of possible diseases before you pass out the microscope slides. You may wish to have students discuss the disorders so that you make sure they understand that the diseases are difficult to distinguish based on symptoms alone. If necessary, pass out and review copies of Science Skills Student Sheet 7, "Microscope Magnification." Instruct students to refer to the guidelines in the Student Book as they observe the slide of typical human blood.

Focusing a Microscope

Be sure that your microscope is set on the lowest power before placing your slide onto the microscope stage. Place the slide on the microscope stage. Center the slide so that the sample is directly over the light opening, and adjust the microscope settings as necessary. If the microscope has stage clips, secure the slide in position so that it does not move.

Observe the sample. Focus first with the coarse-focus knob, and then adjust the fine-focus knob.

After switching to a higher power magnification, be careful to adjust the focus with the fine-focus knob only.

Return to low power before removing the slide from the microscope stage.

Safety ⚠️

Always carry a microscope properly with both hands—one hand underneath and one holding the microscope arm. Because you are working with live organisms, be sure to wash your hands thoroughly after you finish the laboratory.

Procedure

Part A: Using the Light Microscope

1. Your teacher will demonstrate the different parts of a microscope, as shown in the figure above.

2

2. In your group of four, review the rules for handling a microscope. Demonstrate your knowledge of the parts of a microscope, according to your teacher's instructions.

3. Review the guidelines for focusing a microscope shown above.

3 ### Part B: Observing Blood

You are a doctor who has recently seen two patients who reported similar symptoms. From your examination of each patient you have gathered more information, which is shown below.

HISTORY FROM PATIENT A:

- Patient reports periods of feeling sick, but feels well most of the time.
- Patient recently returned from working in Africa with the Peace Corps.
- Patient reports frequent fevers, chest pains, and lung infections throughout youth and adulthood.

162

---

4 You may wish to stop the class when they have completed Procedure Step 4, and have the class discuss what they observed. Ask students to describe the typical human red blood cells. They should notice that although the cells vary slightly, they are all round and red. Then ask students how the blood from Patient A compared to the typical human blood. Patient A's sample has fewer cells than the normal blood, and, while some of them are round, others are oblong or boomerang-shaped. Finally ask students how the blood from Patient B compared to the typical human blood. Students should notice that Patient B's red blood cells look normal, but purplish objects with black dots appear among the red blood cells.

- After a two-hour hike a few months ago, she became so tired and out of breath that physical movement was difficult. She experienced joint and muscle pain in her arms and legs.

SYMPTOMS SEEN ON EXAMINATION TODAY:

- Vision problems and yellowing of eyes and skin.
- Abdominal area is tender to the touch.

HISTORY FROM PATIENT B:

- Patient reports becoming sick shortly after returning from a trip to Africa in the past month.
- Patient reports severe headaches and fatigue for the past few weeks.
- Patient reports a fever and muscle and joint pain in the past week.

SYMPTOMS SEEN ON EXAMINATION TODAY:

- Yellowing of the eyes.
- Abdominal area is tender to the touch.

 4. Prepare a chart with four columns labeled as shown below.

Observations of Blood Samples

Slide	Shape of cells	Color of cells	Number of cells in field of view

With your partner, obtain a slide labeled "Typical Human Blood." This blood sample will serve as your reference. As you observe on medium or high power, record your observations in the chart.

A lab technician prepares a blood sample for viewing under the microscope.

5 Students should be able to eliminate polycythemia vera as a possible disease for either of the patients because each patient shows yellowing of the skin and eyes, and yellowing of the skin and eyes is not a symptom of polycythemia vera. Also, students might possibly preliminarily eliminate spherocytosis because it is diagnosed in childhood, and neither patient is a child.

6 (LITERACY) Tell students that they will read six case studies in this unit. The first case study, about malaria, appears in this activity. The literacy strategy "Read, Think, and Take Note" is an opportunity for students to record thoughts, reactions, or questions on sticky notes as they read. The notes serve to make concrete the thoughts arising in their minds and then serve as prompts to generate conversation or write explanations. Throughout this unit and the rest of *Science and Global Issues* you will see multiple opportunities for students to employ and become comfortable with this strategy. Explain to students that through these literacy strategies they are learning the ways in which proficient readers think while reading.

Display the guidelines shown on Literacy Transparency 2, "Read, Think, and Take Note," in your classroom for students to refer to. Look for additional occasions for students to apply this strategy when reading text. For more information on "Read, Think, and Take Note," see Teacher Resources III: Literacy.

Distribute six copies of Student Sheet 2.1, "Disease Information" to each student. Review with students the columns of the table on the sheet. Tell them that they will be completing one Student Sheet for each of the six diseases they will read about in the unit. The case studies will provide information about the mechanism of the disease and the various aspects of sustainability—social, economic, and environmental—that pertain to the disease. Tell students that they will need to use the information from the case studies in the last two activities of the unit. If necessary,

---

5 5. Based on the patient's report and the examination, the patient's symptoms suggest one of four possible diseases. Read the descriptions of those diseases below. For each disease, draw a sketch of what you predict you would observe in a blood sample under the microscope as compared to the typical human blood you just observed.

Possible Diseases

DISEASE	SYMPTOMS	DESCRIPTION
Polycythemia vera	weakness, disturbed vision, headache, dizziness, enlarged liver, abdominal pain due to an enlarged spleen	An abnormality in the bone marrow causes an overproduction of red blood cells, almost double in some cases. This increases blood volume and thickness, leading to life-threatening blood clots.
Sickle cell disease	joint and muscle pain, anemia, vision problems, abdominal pain, yellowish color of skin and eyes, and frequent infections	An inherited genetic mutation (error) changes the hemoglobin protein, causing the proteins to stack on one another within the red blood cells. This produces a sickle- or banana-shaped blood cell. Sometimes under the microscope the sickle cells appear flattened.
Spherocytosis	yellowish color of skin and eyes, abdominal pain from an enlarged spleen, pale skin, and weakness	A genetic disorder causes the red blood cells to become small, spherically shaped and fragile. These cells are destroyed by the spleen. It is often diagnosed in childhood.
Malaria	fever, headaches, extreme fatigue, mild yellowish color of skin and eyes, abdominal pain, and body aches	An infectious disease, malaria is caused by a single-celled parasite of the genus *Plasmodium* and is carried by mosquitoes. A *Plasmodium* appears as an irregular purple spot containing dark dots when a sample is stained and viewed under a microscope.

6. Decide with your group which pair will first observe Patient A's blood and which will first observe Patient B's.

7. Observe, and draw what you see on the slide sample at medium or high power.

8. Switch patients' slides with the other pair in your group. Repeat Step 7 for the other patient.

9. In your science notebook, write hypotheses for which disease is affecting each patient. Include the information from the slide samples you observed and the "Possible Diseases" table to support your hypotheses.

6 10. Follow your teacher's directions for reading the case study about malaria. As you read, follow the "Read, Think, and Take Note" strategy. To do this:

- Stop at least three times during the reading to mark on a sticky note your thoughts or questions about the reading. Use the list of guidelines below to start your thinking.

- After writing a thought or question on a sticky note, place it next to the passage in the reading that prompted your note.

- Discuss with your partner the thoughts and questions you had while reading.

---

establish a place for students to store the Student Sheet so they can refer to it throughout the unit. Sample responses for malaria on Student Sheet 2.1, "Disease Information," are at the end of Activity 2 in this guide.

FOLLOW-UP

7 Ask, *What diagnosis did you give to Patient A, and what was your evidence?*

Patient A has sickle cell disease, because some of Patient A's blood cells were the long, thin, banana-shape characteristic of this disease, and the patient's symptoms match those of sickle cell disease. Explain that sickle cell disease is an example of a genetic disease. It results from abnormal hemoglobin proteins caused by an inherited mutation in a gene. Hemoglobin is a protein inside the red blood cells that carries oxygen and is one of a group of proteins called transport proteins, which carry molecules and ions through the body. When blood oxygen levels are low, the abnormal hemoglobin proteins in individuals with sickle cell disease stack on one another into long rods, which causes the normally disc-shaped red blood cells to become irregularly shaped and rigid. These are sickle cells. The sickle cells can clump together in the blood vessels and clog them. Sickle cells have shorter life spans than normal red blood cells, which leads to anemia (a decrease in the number of red blood cells). Since red blood cells carry oxygen through the blood, anemia leads to lowered oxygen, which can damage cells, tissues, and organs. Next ask, *What diagnosis did you give Patient B, and why?*

Patient B has malaria because although her blood cells look normal, among them are irregularly shaped objects with dark dots inside. These objects are most likely malaria parasites. The patient's symptoms also match those for malaria. Explain that malaria is an example of an infectious disease caused by a microbe, or disease-causing microscopic organism.

Read, Think, and Take Note: Guidelines

As you read, from time to time, write one of the following on a sticky note:

- Explain a thought or reaction to something you read.
- Note something in the reading that is confusing or unfamiliar.
- List a word that you do not know.
- Describe a connection to something you learned or read previously.
- Make a statement about the reading.
- Pose a question about the reading.
- Draw a diagram or picture of an idea or connection.

11. Complete the information for malaria on Student Sheet 2.1, "Disease Information" after you read the case study.

Analysis

1. Compare each patient's blood sample to a normal blood sample. What abnormalities do you observe?

7 2. Based on your observations, which patient has an infectious disease? Explain how you know.

8 3. Observe the diagrams below. Which patient would you diagnose with sickle cell disease? Explain, using evidence from this activity.

Patient 1   *Patient 2*

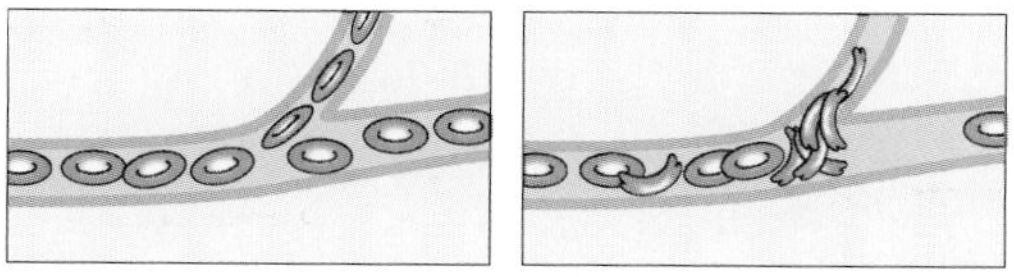

9 4. How do microscope observations of cells help doctors and scientists diagnose and study diseases? Give specific examples from this activity.

165

---

8 Ask, *Based on the diagram, how does the shape of normal red blood cells help them perform their function?*

The flexible disc shape allows them to flow through the blood vessels with the oxygen to carry it through the body. Then ask, *How does the shape of sickled red blood cells prevent them from performing their function?*

The sickled red blood cells are rigid and stack on one another. This causes them to clog the blood vessels, leading to weakness, pain, organ damage, and sometimes paralysis. This clogging is shown in the diagram in Analysis Question 3. Inform students that this is an example of how the structure of a cell helps it perform its function. If the structure is damaged in some way, the cell is no longer able to perform

its function as well or at all. Emphasize that people are made of cells and that when they become sick it is often because something has gone wrong at the cellular level.

9 (UC ASSESSMENT) Students' written work from Analysis Question 4 can be scored with the UNDERSTANDING CONCEPTS (UC) Scoring Guide. This is as an opportunity to introduce the SEPUP Assessment System. Provide all students with a UC Scoring Guide, and ask them to keep it with their science notebooks, as they will refer to it several times in this unit and throughout the *Science and Global Issues* course. Explain to the class that you will use the UC Scoring Guide to provide feedback on the quality of their work. Let them know that you will use their writing in Analysis Question 4 to model how the Scoring Guide works.

Begin by pointing out the scoring levels 0–4, and review the criteria for each score. Explain that the scores are based on the quality of their responses and do not correspond to letter grades. A Level-3 response is a complete and correct response. A Level-4 response signifies that the student has both achieved and exceeded the acceptable level of response. Let students know that you would like them to strive to improve by at least one level in later activities. At first, many students will write Level-2 responses, and they should strive to achieve Level-3 and Level-4 responses.

As a class, discuss what a Level-3 response would include. A complete and correct response for Analysis Question 4 will include specific examples from the activity about how scientists and doctors use the microscope to diagnose diseases. You may develop a Level-3 exemplar with the class or share with students the Level-3 response shown in the Sample Responses. Point out the elements that make the example a Level-3 response, and discuss how a Level 1 and a Level 2 are different. Ask students for ideas about how to improve the Level-3 response to make it a Level 4.

10 ✓ Analysis Question 5b is a Quick Check assessment to ensure that students understand the term, and can identify, trade-offs, which is a component of the EVIDENCE AND TRADE-OFFS scoring variable. One of the goals of *Science and Global Issues* is to teach students that:

1. decisions often involve trade-offs.

2. identifying trade-offs involves analyzing evidence.

10

5. From what you learned about malaria in the case study

   a. A **trade-off** is an exchange of one thing in return for another, giving up something that is a benefit or advantage, in exchange for something that may be more desirable. What are the trade-offs of using insecticides to kill the mosquitoes?

   b. What are the benefits of using insecticides to kill mosquitoes that might be carrying *Plasmodium*?

6. Based on the malaria case study, how does resistance develop in a population of disease-causing microbes?

KEY VOCABULARY	
cell	noninfectious disease
disease	protein
infectious disease	protist
malaria	sickle cell
microbe	**trade-off**
mutation	**vector**

166

Explain to students that in this unit they will make several decisions about world health and sustainability. In this activity students must decide what are the trade-offs of using insecticides to kill mosquitoes. In a decision involving trade-offs, something is given up to gain something else. Since many decisions involve trade-offs, it is important for students to understand that a perfect choice is often not possible. It is possible, however, to recognize and analyze the trade-offs associated with each decision. For example, when asked, "Paper or plastic?" at a store checkout counter, most shoppers make the choice quickly. But there are several trade-offs attached to choosing paper or plastic. A shopper who chooses paper may do so to avoid generating plastic waste or using up petroleum resources. In requesting the paper bag though, the shopper is contributing to other environmental problems, such as increased water and energy usage, and the higher amounts of solid waste and CO_2 emissions associated with making paper bags. Neither choice is particularly beneficial for the environment, and both choices have a downside. Identifying the trade-offs helps clarify the reasoning behind a decision, and the strength of the evidence relevant to making the most informed decision.

To further explore trade-offs, brainstorm with the class a list of decisions they make every day. Choose one, and talk through the associated trade-offs of deciding one way or another. This practice will familiarize students with ways of identifying and considering trade-offs for this and subsequent activities.

SAMPLE RESPONSES

1. Some cells in Patient A's blood are longer and thinner and curved. They are also not as red as the typical blood. There are purplish spots with dark dots among the red blood cells in Patient B.

2. Patient B probably has an infectious disease. The blood sample showed purplish spots with black dots that are probably the *Plasmodium* parasites that cause malaria. The patient has fever, abdominal pain, and yellowish eyes, which are symptoms of malaria.

3. Patient 2 (on the right) has sickle cell disease because the red blood cells are long, thin, and banana-shaped just like the cells from Patient A in the activity.

4. (UC ASSESSMENT) A complete and correct response will include the shape of the cells or the presence of microbes that can be seen under a microscope.

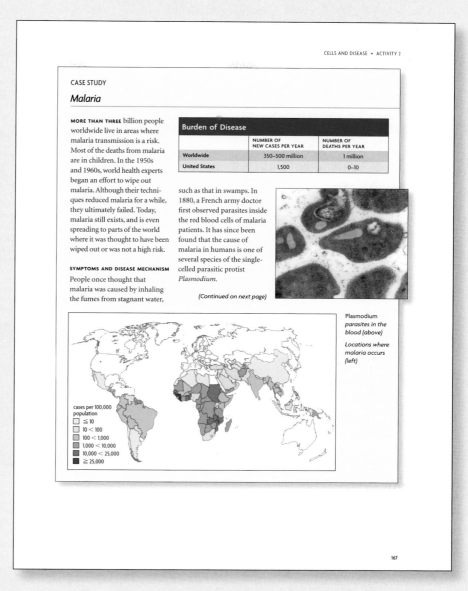

CASE STUDY

Malaria

MORE THAN THREE billion people worldwide live in areas where malaria transmission is a risk. Most of the deaths from malaria are in children. In the 1950s and 1960s, world health experts began an effort to wipe out malaria. Although their techniques reduced malaria for a while, they ultimately failed. Today, malaria still exists, and is even spreading to parts of the world where it was thought to have been wiped out or was not a high risk.

SYMPTOMS AND DISEASE MECHANISM
People once thought that malaria was caused by inhaling the fumes from stagnant water, such as that in swamps. In 1880, a French army doctor first observed parasites inside the red blood cells of malaria patients. It has since been found that the cause of malaria in humans is one of several species of the single-celled parasitic protist *Plasmodium*.

(Continued on next page)

Burden of Disease	NUMBER OF NEW CASES PER YEAR	NUMBER OF DEATHS PER YEAR
Worldwide	350–500 million	1 million
United States	1,500	0–10

Plasmodium parasites in the blood (above)

Locations where malaria occurs (left)

cases per 100,000 population
$\leq$ 10
10 < 100
100 < 1,000
1,000 < 10,000
10,000 < 25,000
$\geq$ 25,000

167

Sample Level-3 Response

Sometimes the cells of a person with a disease are abnormal, and the abnormality will be seen under a microscope. The banana-shaped cells in sickle cell disease are an example. Other times there are microbes causing an infection, and they can be seen in a sample under a microscope. An example is the purplish spots that are *Plasmodium* parasites that cause malaria. Doctors diagnose some diseases by observing such characteristics under a microscope.

5. a. The benefits are that the insecticide kills the mosquitoes and, therefore, the mosquitoes are no longer able to bite humans and infect them with the *Plasmodium* that they might be carrying.

    b. ✓ The trade-offs of using insecticides to kill mosquitoes that might be carrying *Plasmodium* are that the insecticides may harm wildlife (as was found with DDT), they may harm people, and mosquitoes will develop resistance.

6. Antibiotic resistance develops when a few microbes are genetically resistant to the antibiotic. When the antibiotic is used, the nonresistant microbes die off. Gradually, as the resistant microbes live and reproduce, they become a large part of the population, and the antibiotic no longer works.

REVISIT THE CHALLENGE

Discuss responses to Analysis Question 4 to make sure students understand the importance of observing cells in diagnosing and studying diseases.

(Continued from previous page)

Shortly after the discovery of *Plasmodium*, scientists determined that female mosquitoes, which breed in standing water, are the vectors for malaria. A **vector** is an organism that does not cause the disease itself, but spreads disease-causing microbes from one host to another.

The symptoms of malaria can be mild to deadly and include fever, chills, fatigue, an enlarged liver, an enlarged spleen, anemia (reduced number of red blood cells), seizures, coma, and kidney failure.

The following traces the steps of malaria infections:

1. A mosquito becomes infected with *Plasmodium* when it bites and sucks the blood of a human infected with *Plasmodium*.

2. When the infected mosquito bites a person it injects *Plasmodium* in its saliva into that person.

3. The *Plasmodium* travels from the point of the mosquito bite through the bloodstream to the liver and infects liver cells. The *Plasmodium* then begins to reproduce inside the liver cells. Sometimes *Plasmodium* remains in a person's liver and causes no symptoms. Other times the liver cells burst, releasing *Plasmodium*.

4. The *Plasmodium* travels back into the bloodstream from the liver, where it invades red blood cells and then reproduces. The infection is active at this point, and the person experiences symptoms.

5. The red blood cells eventually rupture, which releases the parasites back into the bloodstream where they might be picked up by another mosquito.

MALARIA PREVENTION AND TREATMENT

In the 1950s and 1960s, world health officials hoped to eradicate malaria worldwide with the chemical DDT (dichlorodiphenyltrichloroethane). DDT is a powerful insecticide that kills many insects, including mosquitoes. From 1947 to 1951, in areas where malaria was present in the United States, DDT was applied inside millions of households and over miles of swamps, fields, and forests. Through these DDT applications, malaria protists were effectively wiped out in this country. However, less concentrated efforts in other malaria-ridden parts of the world, and widespread spraying of DDT to kill all sorts of other insects, created *Plasmodium*-carrying mosquito populations that are now resistant to DDT.

Resistance develops if a few mosquitoes in a population are genetically able to withstand

The female Anopheles mosquito is a vector for malaria.

the toxic effects of DDT. When more DDT is applied, more mosquitoes that are sensitive to DDT die. The resistant mosquitoes, however, survive and reproduce greater numbers of resistant mosquitoes until they are a significant proportion of the population, making DDT ineffective.

Scientists also learned that DDT harms other organisms in the environment and is a threat to wildlife, especially birds. One effect of DDT on birds is eggshell thinning, causing the shells to break too soon and the embryo inside to die. Some evidence also suggests that DDT might cause cancer or neurological problems in humans. Today, DDT is banned for agricultural use worldwide, but it still is used in some places to control *Plasmodium*-carrying mosquitoes and prevent them from biting people.

DDT or alternative insecticides are typically sprayed on the inner walls of homes and on protective nets that are draped over sleeping areas, discouraging mosquitoes from coming near.

Studies have shown that insecticide-treated nets are an effective and low-cost tool to control mosquitoes. A large study in Tanzania, where there is a high rate of malarial transmission, investigated the effect of insecticide-treated and untreated nets on infection in children aged one month to four years. The results, summarized below, show that both reduce the risk of death from malarial infection, but that there is greater success with the insecticide-treated nets.

Treatment of malaria infections centers on several drugs that kill the *Plasmodium* parasites that cause malaria. Some drugs attack the parasites when they are present in the blood, while others kill them when they are in the liver. Currently, physicians prescribe combinations of drugs that act together to kill *Plasmodium*.

CHALLENGES TO PREVENTION AND TREATMENT

There are two problems health officials must overcome to make mosquito-net programs more successful in preventing malaria. First, nets that are manufactured and sold pretreated with insecticide must be retreated within

(Continued on next page)

Effectiveness of Mosquito Nets	
PREVENTION METHOD	PERCENT REDUCTION IN RISK OF DEATH
Insecticide-treated nets	27
Untreated nets	19

169

(Continued from previous page)

6 to 12 months for them to remain fully effective. Also, the nets, even though relatively low in cost, are still too expensive for some people living in countries with few economic resources. They must rely on programs that donate or reduce the price of the nets and retreatment kits.

There are also major challenges emerging with the drugs that treat malaria. In some areas, two types of *Plasmodium* that cause malaria have become resistant to the medication available for treatment, which means it no longer kills the parasite. The resistance of *Plasmodium* to drugs arises in the same way that mosquitoes acquire resistance to DDT. Since *Plasmodium* is less likely to develop resistance to several drugs at once, a combination of drugs is often given to patients. This approach often succeeds—as long as patients take all of the required doses of the medicine. But multidrug treatment is costly, and health care workers must monitor patients to make sure they complete their courses of treatment. In addition, it is often difficult to get all the right medicines to isolated communities.

Another potential challenge is the movement of malaria to areas with temperatures that were once too cold for the mosquitoes and *Plasmodium*. If the climate of an area changes in a way that favors the breeding and survival of mosquitoes and *Plasmodium*, the risk for malaria in that area increases. Scientists are working with models to predict how climate change could affect the risk of malaria around the world. The model below shows malaria returning to parts of the United States. The effect of climate change on malaria distribution continues to be a point of discussion in the scientific community. ■

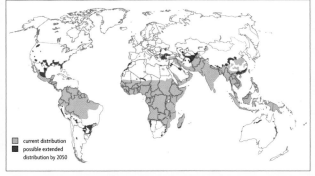

current distribution

possible extended distribution by 2050

A model prediction of the effect of climate change on malaria distribution worldwide

Disease Information

Disease	Malaria
Description of disease and symptoms	_Infectious disease caused by_ Plasmodium _parasites that are carried by mosquitoes; mild to severe fever, chills, fatigue, enlarged liver, spleen, seizure, coma, kidney failure, death._
Cellular mechanism of disease	Plasmodium _parasites enter through saliva of biting mosquito and travel through the blood to the liver where they infect liver cells. They begin to reproduce in liver cells. The parasites travel back to the bloodstream and infect red blood cells where they reproduce in an active infection. Red blood cells burst, releasing more parasites into blood._
Social factors	_Some don't take the full course of medication, which can lead to resistance._ _Sick people or people who die can't take care of their families._
Economic factors	_Some treatments are expensive._ _The community's economy suffers loss of productivity by workers._ _Nets are relatively inexpensive._
Environmental factors	Plasmodium _parasites are carried by mosquitoes._ _Climate change might enlarge the worldwide distribution of mosquito populations._ _Standing water where mosquitoes breed is often a product of weather._ _Insecticides may harm the environment._

3

What Is a Cell?

LABORATORY • 2–3 CLASS SESSIONS

OVERVIEW

Students begin by drawing and writing their initial ideas about cells. They then observe human, plant, protist, and bacterial cells under a microscope and sketch them. They compare the cells to determine similarities and differences between the cell types. A case study discusses tuberculosis, caused by the single-celled bacterium *Mycobacterium tuberculosis*, and the sustainability issues associated with this disease.

KEY CONTENT

1. Every organism is made of one or more cells.

2. Cells have particular structures that perform specific functions.

3. Every cell is surrounded by a membrane, which separates it from the outside environment.

4. Some plant cells contain chloroplasts.

5. A plant cell has a cell wall.

KEY PROCESS SKILLS

1. Students use a microscope to make observations.

2. Students make conclusions based on evidence.

MATERIALS AND ADVANCE PREPARATION

For the teacher

    Transparency 3.1, "Examples of Cells"

    Transparency 3.2, "Venn Diagram of Cells and Microbes"

    Science Skills Transparency 3: "How to Use a Microscope"

For each group of four students

    prepared slide of human cheek cells

    prepared slide of animal sperm cells

    prepared slide of typical *Bacillus* bacteria

    prepared slide of typical *Coccus* bacteria

    piece of onion*

    piece of *Elodea* plant*

    mixed protist culture

    dropper bottle of Lugol's solution*

    cup of water*

    dropper*

    pair of forceps*

For each pair of students

    microscope slide*

    microscope slide with a well*

    coverslip*

    microscope*

    paper towel*

    colored pencils*

For each student

    Student Sheet 2.1, "Disease Information"

    Science Skills Transparency 3, "How to Use a Microscope" (optional)

    Science Skills Transparency 4, "Microscope Drawing Made Easy" (optional)

  3 sticky notes*

*Not supplied in kit

SAFETY NOTE

Be sure that students are very careful not to grind the microscope lenses into the slides as the slides may crack.

Be sure that students do not wash any plants down the drain. Elodea is considered an invasive species in many areas worldwide. Check with your county or state agencies on proper disposal methods. In many places, it is sufficient to allow the plants to dry out and then throw them in the trash. You may wish to set up a strainer lined with several layers of cheesecloth or coffee filters, and ask students to filter the materials from their experiments.

Masters for Science Skills Transparencies are in Teacher Resources II: Diverse Learners.

The mixed protist culture contains Paramecium, Euglena, and Amoeba.

TEACHING SUMMARY

Getting Started

- Students discuss their ideas about what cells are and how they are involved in the functions of organisms.

Doing the Activity

- Students observe microscope slides of human, plant, bacterial, and protist cells.

Follow-up

- (LITERACY) The class discusses their groupings of cells on the Venn diagram.
- (LITERACY) Students read a case study about tuberculosis.

BACKGROUND INFORMATION

Protists

Protists are a large kingdom of organisms made up mostly of single-celled eukaryotes. A protist is a living organism that is not a plant, animal, fungus, or prokaryote. Some protists are plantlike because they contain chlorophyll and are able to photosynthesize. Examples of plantlike protists are euglena, diatoms, and red, brown, and green algae. Some protists are heterotrophs (they digest both plant and animal matter) and animal-like. Animal-like protists are classified into four groups based on their mode of movement: some don't move at all, and others have cilia, flagella, or cytoplasmic extensions for movement. Examples of animal-like protists are *Paramecium, Amoeba,* and the parasites in the genus *Plasmodium* that cause malaria. *Plasmodium* is considered a parasitic protist because it requires a host organism for it to reproduce and survive. At one time, animal-like protists were referred to as protozoans and were classified separately from the plantlike protists. Some protists are fungus-like heterotrophs that live in damp environments, and absorb nutrients from dead and decaying matter through their cell membranes. Examples of fungus-like protists are slime molds and water molds.

Bacteria

Bacteria are tiny single-celled prokaryotes with no nucleus or other membrane-bound structures. Instead, the genetic material is in the cytoplasm. The shape of a bacterium—sphere, rod, or spiral—depends on its type. Bacteria sometimes group in chains or clumps, but each cell is enclosed by a cell membrane and cell wall.

Plant Cells

Plant cells have a nucleus that encloses the genetic information. Plants rely on photosynthesis for their nutrition, and their cells have organelles called chloroplasts, containing the pigment chlorophyll, which is one of the pigments that make photosynthesis possible. Plant cells are enclosed by a cell membrane and a rigid cell wall that provides structure and support. Cytoplasmic streaming is often visible under a light microscope in plant cells, such as *Elodea.* Cytoplasmic streaming occurs when the chloroplasts and other organelles (not visible with a light microscope) move within the cell in what looks like streams. This allows nutrients and other materials to move throughout the cell, and allows for reorganization of the cell during cellular reproduction.

Animal Cells

Animal cells also have a nucleus that encloses the genetic information. They lack cell walls, but have membranes. The cells are often specialized, with unique shapes and structures that enable each cell to perform a specific function. The several types of organelles within the cell are enclosed by their own membranes.

With stains and an electron microscope or a good light microscope scientists can see the nuclei of animal, plant, and protist cells, and the absence of a nucleus in bacteria. The nucleus, found only in eukaryotes, houses the cell's genetic material, DNA, which is best viewed with an electron microscope. The nucleus is separated from the rest of the cell by a membrane, called the nuclear membrane. Mature red blood cells are an exception. The developing red blood cell ejects its nucleus, and since the mature red blood cell no longer has a nucleus, it does not carry any DNA.

GETTING STARTED

1 ◆ Write the following questions on the board or overhead. Use them as prompts for students to think about what they know or have heard about cells and for you to gauge their current knowledge of cells. Ask them to write and/or sketch their ideas in their science notebooks.

- What do cells look like?

- What are cells made of?

- What do cells do?

Ask students, with their groups, to write three analogies that describe cells in terms of common objects. An example is "a cell is like a room because it is separate from its environment." Ask for student volunteers to share their ideas with the class. Discuss the strengths and weaknesses of the everyday objects or ideas that students bring up. For example, one student might say that a cell is like a factory, while another says it is like a balloon. The strength of both analogies is that each is a structure with a boundary like the membrane that separates the inside and outside of a cell. The factory analogy is stronger, however, because it illustrates the structures that exist and the processes that go on within the cell, while the balloon is just filled with air.

Tell students that they will gain more detailed knowledge of cells in this unit.

---

3 What Is a Cell?

1 **A**LL LIVING THINGS are made of one or more cells. The **cell** is the basic unit of life and is where many life processes occur. Organisms made up of a single cell are called **single-celled organisms.** Bacteria and protists are examples of single-celled organisms. Other organisms, such as humans, dogs, and plants, are made up of trillions of cells, and therefore, are **multicellular organisms.** In this activity you will observe microscope slides of cells from various single-celled and multicellular organisms.

Challenge

▶ What are the similarities and differences in cells from various living organisms?

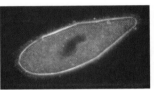

A Paramecium, shown above, is a single-celled organism. Grass, dogs, and people, shown at left, are multicellular organisms.

171

DOING THE ACTIVITY

2 After students have completed Procedure Step 1, project Transparency 3.1, "Examples of Cells," to prompt students' further thinking about cells and cell characteristics. Then review Science Skills Transparency 4, "Microscope Drawing Made Easy." Tell students that in this activity they will observe cells and microbes of various shapes and sizes. They will also observe some of the internal structures of these cells. If necessary, pass out copies of Science Skills Transparency 3, "How to Use a Microscope." Review with students the proper handling of a microscope before they begin the Procedure. Students will likely be able to focus on the slides without assistance. Finding and drawing the protists will be somewhat difficult because it is a live culture of moving organisms. Tell students that in this activity, they should concentrate on what they actually see in the microscope. Remind them that while the light microscope is a very useful tool, there are limits to the level of detail it can reveal. Explain to students that they will gain more detailed information about the internal structures of cells in later activities.

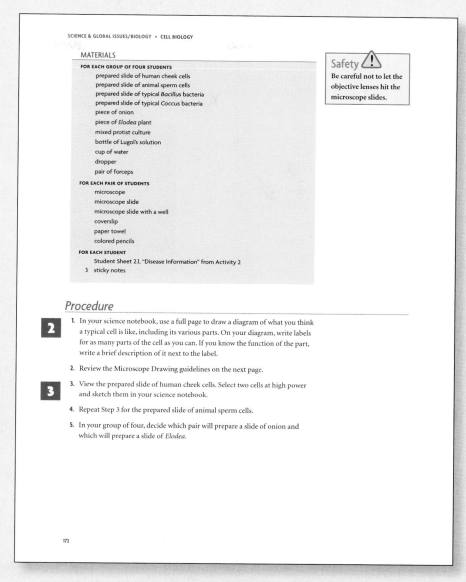

3 Encourage students to share the slides efficiently so that each student has a chance to observe and draw every slide provided.

Circulate around the room, assisting students as necessary. As you circulate, question students about what they are seeing in the field of view, and check that they are drawing and labeling accurately. Remind them to think about the similarities and differences they notice in the various types of cells. Some information about each of the cells as viewed in the microscope follows:

- The human cheek cells are irregular in shape and have a lightly stained cytoplasm and darker nuclei.

- The animal sperm cells are darkly stained round cells with long flagella (whiplike tails).

- The *Bacillus* cells are rod-shaped and have no nuclei.

- The *Coccus* cells are round and have no nuclei.

- The onion cells will be packed together and are fairly rectangular.

- The *Elodea* cells are packed together and are fairly rectangular. There are many round, green objects inside these cells, which are the chloroplasts. It will be difficult to distinguish the nucleus and other organelles among the chloroplasts. If your *Elodea* is healthy, students might see cytoplasmic streaming. If students do not notice this on their own, you may want to check some of the slides to see if it is occurring.

- The *Paramecia* are large, oblong, motile organisms. Their nuclei might be difficult to observe among all of the cell structures that are likely visible. By looking closely, students might observe cilia (hairlike projections) moving around the outside of the cell.

- The *Amoebae* may be difficult to find. They are more irregularly-shaped than any of the other cells students observe. The nucleus might be difficult to see among the cell structures that are likely to be visible.

- The *Euglena* are green, spindle-shaped, motile organisms that move with a flagellum.

Microscope Drawing Made Easy

Below is a picture taken through a microscope of the alga *Spirogyra*. The diagram to the right shows what a biologist or biological illustrator might draw and how he or she would label the drawing.

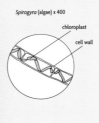

Spirogyra (algae) x 400

chloroplast

cell wall

SOME TIPS FOR BETTER DRAWINGS:

- Use a sharp pencil and have a good eraser available.

- Try to relax your eyes when looking through the eyepiece. You can cover one eye or learn to look with both eyes open. Try not to squint.

- Look through your microscope at the same time as you do your drawing. Look through the microscope more than you look at your paper.

- Don't draw every small thing on your slide. Just concentrate on one or two of the most common or interesting things.

- You can draw things larger than you actually see them. This helps you show all of the details you see.

- Keep written words outside the circle.

- Use a ruler to draw the lines for your labels. Keep lines parallel— do not cross one line over another.

- Remember to record the level of magnification next to your drawing.

173

6. With your partner, follow the instructions below to prepare your slide.

   IF YOU ARE PREPARING ONION:

   • Place one drop of water and one drop of Lugol's iodine solution on the slide.

   • Use forceps or your fingernail to peel off a piece of the very thin inner layer of the onion.

   • Place the piece of onion into the drops on the slide.

   IF YOU ARE PREPARING *ELODEA*:

   • Place 1–2 drops of water on the slide.

   • Select one small, thin, light-green leaf.

   • Place the leaf into the drops on the slide.

7. Carefully touch one edge of the coverslip to the water, at an angle. Slowly allow the coverslip to fall into place. This should prevent trapping of air bubbles under the coverslip.

Placing the coverslip

8. Observe the plant cells that you just prepared. Draw what you see at high magnification. Be sure to label your drawing with the name of your plant. When you have finished, do the same for the plant cell slide that was prepared by the other pair in your group.

Plant cells

4 Students will likely relabel structures and add cell structures, and should note what kinds of cells do or do not have certain structures.

9. With your partner, place 1–2 drops of the mixed protist culture on a clean microscope slide with a well. Observe and draw at high magnification two different types of protists.

10. View the prepared slide of typical *Bacillus* bacteria, focusing on one or two cells at high magnification. Draw one or two of the bacteria cells. Be sure to label your drawings with the name of the sample.

11. Repeat Step 11 for the prepared slide of typical *Coccus* bacteria.

12. Clean up according to your teacher's instructions.

4 13. Go back to the drawing of a cell that you made in Step 1. Add or change any information on that drawing based on your work in this activity.

14. Follow your teacher's directions for reading the case study about tuberculosis (TB). As you read, follow the "Read, Think, and Take Note" strategy.

15. Complete the information for tuberculosis on Student Sheet 2.1, "Disease Information," after you read the case study.

Analysis

1. Compare the four different types of cells (animal, plant, protist, bacteria) you observed. What structures do they have in common?

2. When you compare the *Plasmodium* protist you observed in Activity 2 and the two protists you observed in this activity, what similarities and differences do you notice?

3. When you compare the two types of bacteria you observed, what similarities and differences do you notice?

4. In your science notebook, create a larger version of the Venn diagram shown below. Use what you have learned about cells to record the unique features of the cells of each group of organisms in the appropriate space. Record any common features between groups in the spaces created by overlaps.

FOLLOW-UP

5 ✓(LITERACY) Quick check assessment to assess students' developing understanding of the unique and shared characteristics of cells of organisms.

6 After students have drawn their diagrams for Analysis Question 4, Project Transparency 3.2, "Venn Diagram of Cells and Microbes." Discuss the features that students used to classify the cells and microbes on the Venn diagram they created, and write their ideas on the projected Venn diagram. If students do not bring it up, tell them that some cells have a nucleus and others do not. Ask, *Based on your observations, can you conclude for certain which cells do and do not have a nucleus?*

Help students realize that for some cells they can be certain that a nucleus is present because it is clearly visible. But if they cannot see a nucleus, they cannot be certain there is no nucleus. For example, the nucleus may be hard to see if the classroom microscopes are not powerful enough or if it is obscured by other structures in the cell. Note also that, unlike the rectangular cell walls of plants, bacterial cell walls are not visible under a light microscope. Also, bring out the idea that some cells of plants, such as *Elodea* and other producers, contain a structure called a chloroplast, which is green due to the chlorophyll in it. Photosynthesis, the means by which a plant absorbs energy from the sun and produces sugars, takes place in the chloroplasts.

---

5   4. In your science notebook, create a larger version of the Venn diagram shown below. Use what you have learned about cells to record the unique features of the cells of each group of organisms in the appropriate space. Record any common features between groups in the spaces created by overlaps.

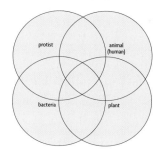

protist   animal (human)   bacteria   plant

6   5. Based on the Venn diagram you created, what features are common to all cells?

6. One focus of TB treatment is ensuring that people who are being treated are closely monitored by health care workers. Explain why this is important, citing evidence from the tuberculosis case study.

KEY VOCABULARY	
antibiotic	**multicellular organism**
bacteria	protist
cell	**single-celled organism**
latent	tuberculosis
macrophage	

7 (LITERACY) You may choose to assign the case study for homework. If you do, give students the sticky notes they will need to follow the "Read, Think, and Take Note" strategy at home. Begin class the next day by having pairs discuss what they wrote or drew on their sticky notes. Sample responses for tuberculosis on Student Sheet 2.1, "Disease Information" are at the end of Activity 3 in this guide.

SAMPLE RESPONSES

1. They all have a cell membrane. Students may also suggest that they all have cytoplasm and genetic material.

2. The cells are all single-celled organisms, but they have different sizes, shapes, and colors. They have different structures, such as the hairlike structures on the *Paramecium.*

3. All of them are single cells, but they vary in size and shape. Some are tiny and round, while others are elongated—thinner and longer than the round ones. There is no nucleus in either of the bacteria.

4. ✓See Venn diagram below.

7 CASE STUDY

Tuberculosis

TUBERCULOSIS IS A disease that has appeared in the human population for centuries. Evidence of TB infection has been found in the skulls of Egyptian mummies estimated to be at least 3,000 years old. TB is caused by the *Mycobacterium tuberculosis* bacterium and was common in Europe and North America in the 18th and 19th centuries. It declined in those regions as living conditions, nutrition, and treatment improved. Worldwide today, however, it is estimated that at least one-third of the human population is infected with TB bacteria.

Burden of Disease	TOTAL NUMBER INFECTED	ESTIMATED NUMBER OF DEATHS PER YEAR	ESTIMATED NUMBER OF NEW CASES PER YEAR
Worldwide	2 billion	1.7 million	9 million
United States	10–15 million	650	12,900

SYMPTOMS AND DISEASE MECHANISM

The physical symptoms of TB include appetite and weight loss, coughing, night sweats, fever, fatigue, and chills. TB usually infects tissue in the lungs, but can also infect other organs in the body, including the brain, kidneys, and spine. Since TB is an extremely infectious disease that can be passed through a cough, sneeze, or even talking with an infected person, people are at higher risk of infection if they live in densely packed urban areas or may be exposed to infected individuals in crowded, closed environments, such as hospitals, prisons, clinics, or airplanes.

(Continued on next page)

cases per 100,000 population
- 0–99
- 100–249
- 250–499
- 500 or more
- • data not available

Global distribution of tuberculosis cases

177

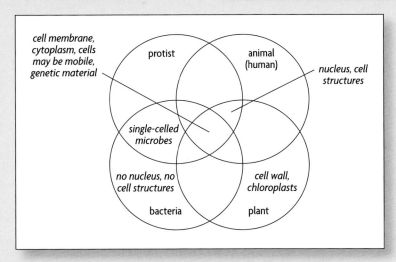

cell membrane, cytoplasm, cells may be mobile, genetic material

protist

animal (human)

nucleus, cell structures

single-celled microbes

no nucleus, no cell structures

cell wall, chloroplasts

bacteria

plant

5. Cell membrane, cytoplasm, and genetic material.

6. It is important for TB patients to be closely monitored during treatment because, if they do not take their antibiotics correctly and do not take the full course, there is a risk of antibiotic resistance developing. The patients who do not follow the treatment will not recover from TB and will pass resistant bacteria to other people.

REVISIT THE CHALLENGE

The Venn diagram is a good visual for reviewing the common and unique characteristics of cells.

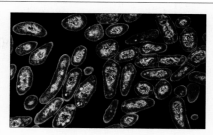

Mycobacterium tuberculosis *bacteria*

(Continued from previous page)

TB infection is latent or active. In a latent infection, the person has a positive skin or blood test for TB, but a normal chest X-ray. The bacteria are alive inside the body, but they are inactive. A person with a latent infection does not feel sick, has no symptoms, and cannot transmit the TB bacteria to others. Sometimes the latent form becomes active, and symptoms develop. Only 5–10% of people who are infected with TB bacteria, however, ever become sick or infectious. Antibiotic treatments after a person has tested positive for TB reduce the risk of latent TB becoming active, if the person takes the drugs for many months.

The following traces the steps that lead to a tuberculosis infection:

1. An uninfected person inhales TB bacteria in droplets that were released into the air by an infected person, whether minutes or hours earlier.

2. The bacteria enter the lungs, and if they are not immediately killed by the body's immune system, they are ingested by macrophages, a type of white blood cell. The macrophages do not destroy the bacteria.

3. Most of the time, the bacteria are held in check by the immune system. In this case, the infection is referred to as a latent infection.

4. If the infection becomes active, the TB bacteria multiply and travel to the blood. Possible reasons for a latent infection to become active include a weakened immune system, often due to HIV/AIDS infection, malnutrition, cancer, or aging. The bacteria might spread to other organs, but they can only be transmitted out of the body and to other people by the infected person's exhaling them from the lungs.

TUBERCULOSIS PREVENTIONS AND TREATMENTS

While there is a vaccine available to prevent TB, its effectiveness is limited. Worse, the vaccine has caused HIV-positive children to develop a TB infection. Health experts think that being able to accurately detect active TB infections is more beneficial than vaccination to prevent infections.

In 1943, a man critically sick with TB was the first to be given an antibiotic to treat TB. Impressively, the bacteria quickly disappeared, and the man recovered. Now there are a number of antibiotics to treat TB, and they are usually prescribed in combinations of two to four different drugs. Two of the most commonly prescribed today are isoniazid and rifampin. Isoniazid interferes with a bacterium's ability to make a compound needed in its cell walls. Rifampin prevents the bacterial cells from making proteins.

CHALLENGES TO PREVENTION AND TREATMENT

ANTIBIOTIC RESISTANCE

Like *Plasmodium*, TB bacteria have become resistant to many antibiotics. As with malaria, people who do not have access to timely and effective medical care or who don't complete a full course of treatment contribute to the resistance problem. In 2007, the World Health Organization (WHO) was notified of more than 400,000 cases of multidrug-resistant tuberculosis. Multidrug resistance in TB means that the bacteria are resistant specifically to the two main antibiotics, isoniazid and rifampin. Because WHO is not notified of all cases, experts think that there are many more cases. The cost of treating multi-drug-resistant TB infections can be 1,000 times more expensive than treating non-resistant TB infections.

HIV/AIDS AND TB CO-INFECTION

Another reason for the high numbers of TB infections is the relationship between TB and HIV/AIDS. These two diseases are so closely tied to one another that they are often referred to as a co-infection.

HIV weakens the immune system, which then allows latent TB to become active and infectious or makes the patient more vulnerable to TB droplets inhaled from the air. A person who is infected with HIV/AIDS is 50 times more likely to develop active TB in a given year than is an HIV-negative person. Also, the disease progresses more rapidly and deaths are higher in people infected with both HIV and TB than those who are infected only with TB. The primary cause of death in people infected with TB and HIV is the TB. Yet the vast majority of people with HIV worldwide have not been screened for TB. ■

HIV/AIDS co-infections as a percentage of the 9 million new TB cases per year

HIV co-infections (13%)

Disease Information

Disease	Tuberculosis
Description of disease and symptoms	This disease has been known for centuries. Symptoms include appetite and weight loss, coughing, night sweats, fever, fatigue, and chills. Usually infects lungs, but can infect any organ
Cellular mechanism of disease	Bacteria are inhaled through air from droplets from an infected person. Bacteria that aren't killed by the body are ingested by macrophages in lungs. A cluster of cells forms at the infection site (macrophages fuse and immune cells come to the area). The infection is latent because the immune system controls bacterial growth. Active infection: The bacteria are activated to reproduce and travel to blood and to other infection sites.
Social factors	TB is very infectious and usually acquired in crowded areas, such as clinics, airplanes, and crowded housing. Improper use of antibiotics has led to antibiotic resistance in the bacteria, making cure difficult A majority of people with both HIV and TB infection have not been screened for TB, even though TB often kills HIV-infected people.
Economic factors	People who cannot afford effective antibiotics may have access to cheaper, less effective antibiotics that contribute to the resistance problem. Community loses productivity of sick people who cannot work or who die. Treating and monitoring sick patients is expensive.
Environmental factors	Crowding in areas where air is not fresh.

4 What Do Cells Do?

INVESTIGATION • 1–2 CLASS SESSIONS

OVERVIEW

Students work with a computer simulation to match cellular functions to structures found in typical animal, plant, and bacterial cells.

KEY CONTENT

1. Cells have particular structures that underlie their functions, including a cell membrane and a cytoplasm that contain a mixture of thousands of different molecules.

2. All of the molecules in a cell form a variety of specialized structures and organelles, to perform such cell functions as energy production, transport of molecules, waste disposal, synthesis of new molecules, and storage of genetic material.

3. Plant cells contain chloroplasts, the site of photosynthesis.

4. The genetic information stored in DNA directs the synthesis of the thousands of proteins the cell needs.

5. Bacterial cells have neither a nucleus nor other membrane-bound organelles.

MATERIALS AND ADVANCE PREPARATION

For the teacher
Scoring Guide: UNDERSTANDING CONCEPTS (UC)

For each pair of students
computer with Internet access*

For each student
Student Sheet 4.1, "Structure and Function of Cells" (available online only: see note at right)

Scoring Guide: UNDERSTANDING CONCEPTS (UC) (optional)

Not supplied in kit

Masters for Scoring Guides are in Teacher Resources IV: Assessment.

Note: *Student Sheet 4.1, "Structure and Function of Cells," is found only on the* Science and Global Issues *website (sepuplhs.org/sgi). Sample student answers are also available on the website. Both are located in the teacher's section. Arrange for computers with Internet access for the day(s) students do this activity. Go to the* Science and Global Issues *page of the SEPUP website to access the simulation. You may want to bookmark this site for students. Make sure the browsers and supporting software are current and can properly run the simulation.*

TEACHING SUMMARY

Getting Started

- Discuss what all cells need in order to survive, and compare plant and animal cells.

Doing the Activity

- Students match various organelles to typical animal and plant cells according to the organelle's function.

- Students investigate the structures in prokaryotic cells.

Follow-up

- (UC ASSESSMENT) Review the relationship between cell structure and cell function.

GETTING STARTED

1 Ask students to look at the drawing of a cell that they did in Activity 3, "What Is a Cell?" Ask, *What structures must all cells have in order to function and grow?*

Compile a list on the board or overhead. Students are likely to say cell membrane, cytoplasm, and genetic material (DNA). Next ask, *What are some differences between plant and animal cells?*

Students are likely to say that plant cells have a cell wall and chloroplasts. Ask students to think about why plants have a cell wall. Give them time to discuss this briefly with their group. The cell wall provides structure and support for the cells and the plant. Use this example to emphasize the relationship between structure and function. Then, inform students that they will investigate the function of cell structures in more detail in this activity.

DOING THE ACTIVITY

2 All directions for the simulation are on Student Sheet 4.1, "Structure and Function of Cells," which can be downloaded from the *Science and Global Issues* website. A sample Venn diagram for Procedure Step 3 is shown at right.

---

4 What Do Cells Do?

1 **U**NDERSTANDING NORMAL CELL structures and their functions helps scientists understand what goes wrong to allow diseases, including the infectious diseases caused by microbes, to progress. Although there are many differences between cells of various organisms, such as plants, animals, and microbes, there are some key similarities in all cells.

One structure common to every cell is a cell membrane that separates it from the outside environment. Similarly, every cell has genetic material in the form of DNA, and a large number of proteins and other molecules that carry out the chemical reactions needed for a cell to live, grow, and reproduce. Some cells contain structures that are surrounded by a membrane, which creates a barrier between the inside of the structure and the rest of the cell. These membrane-bound structures are called **organelles.**

In this activity, you will learn about some common cell structures and their functions in the cell.

Challenge

▶ What are the functions of the structures in cells?

MATERIALS

FOR EACH PAIR OF STUDENTS
computer with Internet access

FOR EACH STUDENT
Student Sheet 4.1, "Structure and Function of Cells"

Procedure

Part A: Computer Simulation

2 1. Visit the *Science and Global Issues* page of the SEPUP website at *sepuplhs.org/sgi*. With your partner, go to "What Do Cells Do?" and follow the simulation.

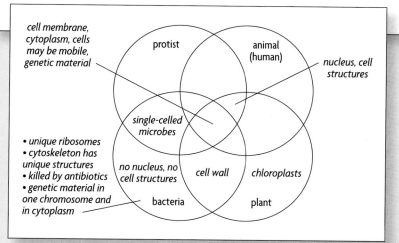

cell membrane, cytoplasm, cells may be mobile, genetic material

protist

animal (human)

nucleus, cell structures

single-celled microbes

• unique ribosomes
• cytoskeleton has unique structures
• killed by antibiotics
• genetic material in one chromosome and in cytoplasm

no nucleus, no cell structures

cell wall

chloroplasts

bacteria

plant

Part B: Comparing Cells

2. Read the following information about bacterial cells. This will prepare you to compare the cells of bacteria with those of animals and plants, which you investigated in Part A.

Reading

Bacterial Cell Structure

A bacterial cell does not have a nucleus or other membrane-bound structures. The genetic information of bacterial cells is stored in a large circular chromosome in the cytoplasm. The cell membrane of a bacterial cell performs the functions of many of the organelles of other organisms' cells. For example, to generate energy, a bacterial cell uses specific enzymes located in its cell membrane. Some bacterial cells can also perform photosynthesis at the cell membrane. The ribosomes in bacteria differ from ribosomes in eukaryotes in size and molecular composition, but like the ribosomes in eukaryotes, they carry out protein synthesis. In bacteria, as in eukaryotes, the cytoplasm also contains numerous enzymes that speed up reactions, such as the ones involved in digestion. Bacteria have an outer cell wall that makes them rigid and gives them shape. The cytoskeleton of prokaryotic cells serves some of the same functions as the eukaryotic cytoskeleton, but is made of different proteins. To move around, some bacteria use long tail-like structures called flagella, or short hair-like fibers called cilia. Although these flagella and cilia may appear similar to those of eukaryotes, they are made of different proteins and produce motion by a different mechanism than that of eukaryotic cilia and flagella.

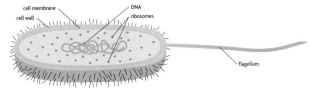

SCIENCE & GLOBAL ISSUES/BIOLOGY • CELL BIOLOGY

Antibiotics

There are a number of antibiotics that can treat bacterial infections. The chart below shows how some antibiotics kill bacterial cells or keep them from reproducing.

Four Classes of Antibiotics	
ANTIBIOTIC CLASS	MODE OF ACTION IN BACTERIAL CELL
ß-lactams	Interfere with cell wall structure
Tetracyclines	Interfere with protein synthesis
Quinolones	Interfere with the copying of bacterial DNA
Sulphonamides	Interfere with the production of an enzyme needed to copy the bacterial DNA

3. Use your understanding from the simulation and the reading above to make changes and additions to the Venn diagram you created in the simulation

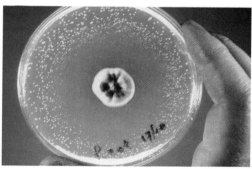

Penicillium *mold produces an antibiotic that has saved many lives.*

FOLLOW-UP

3 (UC ASSESSMENT) Analysis Question 2 asks students to demonstrate their understanding of the structures needed for a cell to produce a protein and perform its functions, and is an opportunity for you to apply the UNDERSTANDING CONCEPTS (UC) Scoring Guide to assess the progress of their understanding. Tell the class your expectations for satisfactory work.

To begin a review of the activity ask, *What functions do all cells—plant, animal, and bacterial cells—need to perform in order to survive?*

All cells must be able to obtain energy, produce proteins, and store, digest, and excrete materials. Ask, *What structures do all cells have in common in order to perform these functions?*

All cells have a cell membrane, cytoplasm, cytoskeleton, ribosomes, and a specialized area for converting energy to a usable form. Specialized cells are different from one another in the number and kinds of organelles they have. These allow them to perform their specialized functions. Be sure to emphasize that, while many diagrams show typical cells, not all cells are shaped the same, nor do they have the same numbers and kinds of organelles.

SAMPLE RESPONSES

1. Animal and plant cells are eukaryotic. Bacteria are prokaryotic.

2. (UC ASSESSMENT) A complete and correct response will include descriptions of the nucleus, the ribosomes, and how they work together to produce a protein.

Analysis

1. Label each of the following cell types as eukaryotic or prokaryotic:
    - Animal
    - Plant
    - Bacteria

3

2. **a.** Describe the structures an animal cell must have for it to produce a protein.

    b. Explain how these structures work together to produce a protein.

KEY VOCABULARY	
bacteria	Golgi apparatus
cell membrane	lysosome
cell wall	nucleus
cilium, cilia	**organelle**
cytoplasm	prokaryotic cell
cytoskeleton	ribosome
endoplasmic reticulum (ER)	vacuole
eukaryotic cell	vesicle
flagellum, flagella	

183

Sample Level-3 Response

a. To make a protein, an animal cell must have a nucleus, ribosomes, and endoplasmic reticulum. The nucleus encloses the genetic information in the cell, which is stored in codes in DNA molecules. Ribosomes are made of two subunits and are either freely floating in the cytoplasm or attached to the endoplasmic reticulum. The endoplasmic reticulum is a network of continuous sacs. The rough endoplasmic reticulum is covered with ribosomes.

b. The nucleus encloses the genetic information in an animal cell. The ribosomes assemble the proteins after receiving the genetic information from the nucleus. The proteins made on free ribosomes are part of the cytoplasm of the cell. The proteins made on the ribosomes of the rough endoplasmic reticulum become membrane proteins or leave the cell.

REVISIT THE CHALLENGE

Tell students to go back to their drawings of a typical cell from Activity 3, "What Is a Cell?" Instruct them to add more details to their drawings and to make any changes based on their learning from the computer simulation. Their drawings should include: cell membrane, cell wall (plant/bacteria), chlorophyll (plant), chloroplast (plant), cilia, cytoplasm, cytoskeleton, endoplasmic reticulum, flagellum, Golgi apparatus, lysosome, mitochondria, ribosome, vacuole, vesicle. Ask students to label those parts that are specific to only certain types of cells (plant, animal, protist, bacteria). Reiterate that bacterial cells do not have a nucleus or other membrane-bound structures.

What Do Specialized Cells Do?

OVERVIEW

Students engage in a computer simulation in which they match descriptions of specialized animal cells to animations of cells performing their functions. The simulation helps students understand the specific types, numbers, and organization of structures that specialized cells need for performing their functions.

KEY CONTENT

1. Cells have particular structures that enable their functions, including a cell membrane and a cytoplasm that contains a mixture of thousands of different molecules.

2. All of the molecules in a cell form a variety of specialized structures and organelles that perform such cell functions as energy production, transport of molecules, waste disposal, synthesis of new molecules, and storage of genetic material.

MATERIALS AND ADVANCE PREPARATION

For the Teacher

Scoring Guide: UNDERSTANDING CONCEPTS (UC)

For each pair of students

computer with Internet access*

For each student

Student Sheet 5.1, "Specialized Cells"

Scoring Guide: UNDERSTANDING CONCEPTS (UC) (optional)

Not supplied in kit

Note: *Student Sheet 5.1, "Specialized Cells," is found only on the* Science and Global Issues *website* (sepuplhs.org/sgi). *Sample student answers are also available on the website. Both are located in the teacher's section. Arrange for computers with Internet access for the day(s) students do this activity. Go to the* Science and Global Issues *page of the SEPUP website to access the simulation. You may want to bookmark this site for students. Make sure the browsers and supporting software are current and can properly run the simulation.*

Masters for Scoring Guides are in Teacher Resources IV: Assessment.

TEACHING SUMMARY

Getting Started

• Review the structures that are common to all living cells.

Doing the Activity

• Students complete the computer simulation to investigate the structures and functions of specialized human cells.

Follow-up

• (UC ASSESSMENT) The class discusses the specialized structures and functions of cells.

GETTING STARTED

1 Review the structures and functions of all living cells from the previous activity. All cells have a cell membrane, cytoplasm, cytoskeleton, ribosomes, and a specialized area for converting energy to a usable form. Next, to get students thinking about specialized cells, ask which type of structure they think a cell would have more of if it were specialized for movement. Since movement requires cytoskeletal fibers and energy, these cells would likely have more of these fibers and structures for energy conversion. Tell students that they will learn more about specialized cell structures and functions in the computer simulation in this activity.

5 What Do Specialized Cells Do?

1 **IN THE PREVIOUS** activity you examined some basic structures and organelles in cells. Many types of cells also have specialized structures that allow the cells to perform specific functions. For example, a muscle cell is specialized for movement, while a red blood cell is specialized for carrying oxygen throughout the body. In this activity you will examine the functions of some specialized cells.

Challenge

▶ What are the specialized structures and functions of cells?

MATERIALS

FOR EACH PAIR OF STUDENTS
    computer with Internet access

FOR EACH STUDENT
    Student Sheet 5.1, "Specialized Cells"

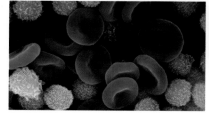

Some examples of specialized cells

184

DOING THE ACTIVITY

2 All directions for the simulation are on Student Sheet 5.1, "Specialized Cells," which can be downloaded from the same website as the simulation: *sepuplhs.org/sgi*.

FOLLOW-UP

3 (UC ASSESSMENT) Review with students some of the specialized structures and functions they learned about in the computer simulation. Analysis Question 1 asks students to demonstrate their understanding of specialized cell structures and functions, and is an opportunity for you to apply the UNDERSTANDING CONCEPTS (UC) Scoring Guide to assess the progress of their understanding. If necessary, review the UC Scoring Guide with students.

Procedure

2

1. Visit the *Science and Global Issues* page of the SEPUP website at *sepuplhs.org/sgi*. With your partner, go to "What Do Specialized Cells Do?" and follow the simulation.

Analysis

3

1. Pick two of the specialized cells that you observed in the computer simulation. For each cell:

   a. pick one specialized organelle or structure and explain its function.

   b. explain what would happen to the cell if the specialized organelle or structure were damaged or missing.

   c. explain what would happen to the organism if the specialized organelle or structure were damaged or missing.

KEY VOCABULARY	
cell	organelle
microbe	

185

SAMPLE RESPONSES

1. (UC ASSESSMENT) Students' answers will vary depending on the types of specialized cells they chose. A complete and correct response will address all three parts of the question.

Sample Level-3 Response

a. Neuron: The receptors on the membrane of a receiving neuron bind with neurotransmitters and open to allow ions to pass through. This excites the receiving cell.

   Absorptive intestinal cell: The microvilli on the cells increase the surface area of the cell so that the cell can absorb nutrients more efficiently.

b. Neuron: If the receptors were missing, the receiving cell would not be excited and could not receive the message.

   Absorptive intestinal cell: If the microvilli were missing, nutrients would not be absorbed at as high of a rate.

c. Neuron: Whatever signal is being passed through the neurons in the brain would not get past the receiving cell that is missing receptors, and whatever the signal should be triggering would not happen, which could lead to disease or death.

   Absorptive intestinal cell: The organism would not be able to absorb nutrients fast enough, and would eventually become malnourished or die.

REVISIT THE CHALLENGE

The Analysis Question provides a good summary of the structures and functions of some specialized cells. Be sure students understand that all cells contain the structures all cells need for the cellular processes, but that in specialized cells the number and organization of these structures contribute to its functions. Examples of these include the specialized arrangement of actin and myosin microfilaments in a muscle cell, the microtubule bundles in a sperm cell flagellum, the glucose transmembrane transporter in a β cell, the microvilli of an epithelial cell, and the receptors on the T cell, macrophage, and neuron. Of the structures that all cells have, they might be present in different amounts for the cells to perform their specialized functions. These include high numbers of mitochondria in muscle cells and the flagella of sperm cells, high numbers of vesicles in neurons and β cells, and high numbers of lysosomes in macrophages.

6 Cell Structure and Function

READING • 1 CLASS SESSION

OVERVIEW

Students read about the fundamental structures and functions of cells, including the cell membrane, cytoplasm, cytoskeleton, and genetic material, and about specialized cells. They also read a brief account of the development of the cell principle.

KEY CONTENT

1. Every cell is surrounded by a membrane that separates it from the outside environment.

2. All cells maintain homeostasis, a range of internal conditions that allows the cell to live and function.

3. All cells have cytoplasm. Within the cytoplasm of eukaryotic cells is a cytoskeleton that provides support and structure for the cell.

4. Nearly all cells contain genetic information. In eukaryotes, the genetic information is stored in the nucleus.

5. Multicellular organisms have specialized cells with an arrangement of structures that accomplishes a specialized function.

6. The cytoplasm of all cells (and the nucleus of eukaryotes) is the site of the reactions of metabolism.

KEY PROCESS SKILLS

1. Students make accurate interpretations, inferences, and conclusions from text.

MATERIALS AND ADVANCE PREPARATION

For the teacher

Literacy Transparency 3, "Read, Think, and Take Note"
Scoring Guide: UNDERSTANDING CONCEPTS (UC)

For each student

3 sticky notes*
Scoring Guide: UNDERSTANDING CONCEPTS (UC) (optional)

Masters for Literacy Transparencies are in Teacher Resources III: Literacy. Masters for Scoring Guides are in Teacher Resources IV: Assessment.

TEACHING SUMMARY

Getting Started

• Review what students learned about cells and disease in Activity 2, "Cells and Disease."

Doing the Activity

• (LITERACY) Students complete the Reading using the "Read, Think, and Take Note" strategy, and discuss what they wrote on their sticky notes.

Follow-up

• (UC ASSESSMENT) The class discusses the levels of organization that cell biologists study.

GETTING STARTED

1 (LITERACY) Review students' observations of normal and sickled red blood cells from Activity 2, "Cells and Disease." Stress the relationship between normal structure and function, and how the function of the red blood cell in carrying oxygen and circulating in the blood stream is disrupted when a structure in the red blood cells—in this case the hemoglobin protein—is abnormal. Explain that this is just one of many examples of how the function of a cell is related to its structure. Tell students that they will read more about cell structures and functions in this activity. If necessary, project Literacy Transparency 3, "Read, Think, and Take Note," to review with students.

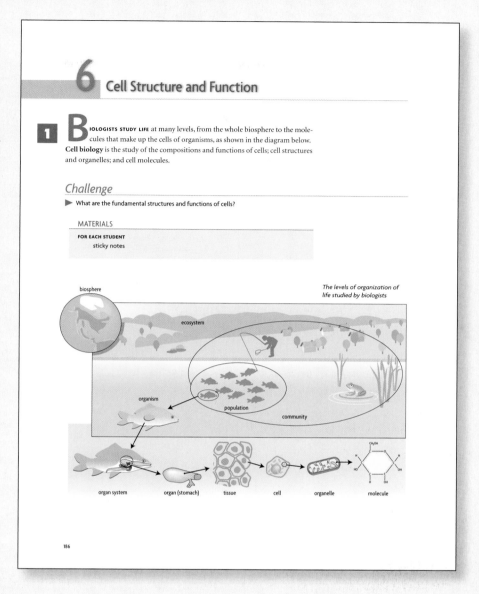

6 Cell Structure and Function

1 **B**IOLOGISTS **STUDY LIFE** at many levels, from the whole biosphere to the molecules that make up the cells of organisms, as shown in the diagram below. **Cell biology** is the study of the compositions and functions of cells; cell structures and organelles; and cell molecules.

Challenge

▶ What are the fundamental structures and functions of cells?

MATERIALS

FOR EACH STUDENT
sticky notes

The levels of organization of life studied by biologists

biosphere

ecosystem

organism

population

community

organ system   organ (stomach)   tissue   cell   organelle   molecule

186

Procedure

1. Follow the "Read, Think, and Take Note" strategy as you complete the Reading.

Reading

The Cell Principle

Englishman Robert Hooke was an influential scientist in the 17th century, who, while looking at thin slices of cork under a microscope, became the first scientist to observe and record cells. What he saw in the cork looked like a series of boxes that reminded him of the rooms, or cells, of a monastery. His observations led him to call these structures cells.

It was not until 1839, however, that German botanist Matthias Schleiden, from studies with a more powerful microscope, declared that entire plant organisms were made up of cells. This was a momentous discovery at the time, but within a year Schleiden's colleague, Theodor Schwann, a professor of animal studies, proposed that animals were also made up of cells. In 1855, physician Rudolf Virchow theorized that new cells could only come from existing cells.

The ideas of Schleiden, Schwann, and Virchow led to the development of the cell principle, which has been confirmed by many scientists. The **cell principle** states that

- all living organisms are made of cells.
- cells are the basic units of structure and function in living organisms.
- new cells are made from existing cells.

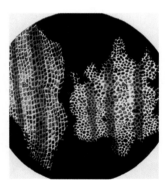

Robert Hooke's drawing of cork cells, 1659

187

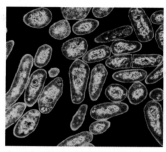 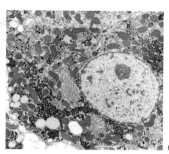

These prokaryotic cells (a) lack a nucleus. The single chromosome is located in the cytoplasm. In the enlarged human liver cell (b), the chromosomes are inside the nucleus.

All Cells Contain Genetic Information

All living cells contain hereditary information in the form of a molecule called deoxyribonucleic acid (DNA). From the information that is stored in DNA the cell makes the proteins and other molecules it needs to carry out all of its chemical processes and, for multicellular organisms, function within the larger organism.

Based on the location of the DNA in the cell, scientists classify living cells into two major categories—eukaryotes and prokaryotes. **Eukaryotes** are organisms with cells that contain a **nucleus,** a large organelle surrounded by a double membrane, where the DNA is stored. Of the organisms you have observed, animals, plants, and protists are eukaryotes. In most of the cells of multicellular eukaryotes, the nucleus contains the genetic instructions for the entire organism. **Protists** are single-celled microbes that have a nucleus. Examples of protists are the paramecium and amoeba, most algae, and some fungi. **Prokaryotes** are organisms with cells that do not have a nucleus, and their DNA is located in the cytoplasm. The **bacteria** you observed in Activity 3, "What Is a Cell?" were single-celled prokaryotes. Prokaryotes also lack many other cell structures found in eukaryotes.

All Cells Have a Cell Membrane and Cytoplasm

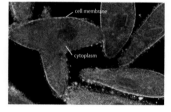

Every living cell has a **cell membrane** that serves as a barrier between the cell and its environment. The cell membrane lets some substances into and out of the cell, while preventing the movement of other substances. Within the boundary of the cell membrane of all cells, but outside the nucleus in eukaryotes, is a semi-fluid substance called the **cytoplasm.** All of the cell's internal structures and organelles are suspended in the cytoplasm. As you will see

DOING THE ACTIVITY

2 (LITERACY) Give students an opportunity to discuss their sticky notes from the "Read, Think, and Take Note" strategy. You may arrange this in a number of ways:

• Have each person in the group ask a question that came up in the reading, and have the group try to reach consensus on an answer.

• Have each person in the group discuss one, two, or three of his or her sticky notes with the group.

• Have each person in the group raise one point of confusion from the reading, and have the group discuss the point raised by each person.

FOLLOW-UP

3 (UC ASSESSMENT) Review with the class the levels of organization of life as shown in the diagram at the beginning of the activity. Cell biologists usually focus their work at the level of cells, cell structures and organelles, and the molecules that make them up. Cells have specific structures, such as a membrane, and molecules, such as DNA and proteins, that are necessary for them to survive, function, and reproduce. Analysis Question 4 asks students to demonstrate their understanding of the function of the cell membrane, and is an opportunity for you to apply the UNDERSTANDING CONCEPTS (UC) Scoring Guide to assess the depth of their understanding.

---

through the rest of this unit, many of the cell functions and reactions of metabolism occur in the nucleus and cytoplasm. **Metabolism** is the term for all of the chemical processes that maintain life and that occur within living cells.

All Cells Must Maintain Internal Balance

The external conditions in the environment surrounding cells can vary. To survive, however, cells must maintain constant internal conditions, such as water content and temperature—just as a whole organism, such as a human, must do. The process by which cells maintain constant internal conditions is called **homeostasis,** and it depends greatly on the membrane's regulation of what substances go into and out of the cell.

The Cytoskeleton

Inside the cytoplasm is a system called the **cytoskeleton.** As you might guess from its name, the cytoskeleton provides structure and organization to the cytoplasm and maintains the shape of the cell. But the cytoskeleton has other important functions. It plays a role in the transport of materials within cells, in the division of cells, and in the movements of cells when they crawl, swim, or contract. The cytoskeleton is made of three types of long, thin structures built of proteins. These are the actin microfilaments, intermediate filaments, and microtubules. These tubules and filaments are both able to assemble and disassemble in the cell when and where they are needed. Motor proteins cause microfilaments and microtubules to slide past each other as well, producing shortening or lengthening movements.

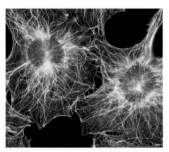

These cytoskeletons radiate from near the nuclei.

Cells in Multicellular Organisms Specialize

Multicellular organisms have anywhere from a few to many types of cells. In humans there are more than 220 types of cells, each with a specialized function and its own arrangement of cellular structures needed for the body to survive and reproduce.

Muscle cells, for example, are specialized to contract, whether as part of the skeletal muscles that interact with and move bones or the muscles surrounding digestive organs that contract to move food through your digestive system. These cells contain a highly developed system of microfilaments, which function to shorten the muscle cells when the muscle contracts. Muscle cells also contain many mitochondria, which supply the large amounts of energy needed for contraction.

Red blood cells, too, are specialized cells, but, unlike other human cells, they do not have nuclei, mitochondria, or other cell structures. Instead, red blood cells are packed with hemoglobin, a protein that carries oxygen.

189

SAMPLE RESPONSES

1. All cells have a membrane, cytoplasm, and genetic information in the form of DNA, and carry out metabolism.

2. Eukaryotes have a nucleus where genetic information is stored; prokaryotes do not have a nucleus and store genetic information in the cytoplasm.

3. The light microscope allowed scientists to observe living organisms on a more detailed level than with the unaided eye, and to observe organisms or structures too small to see with the naked eye.

4. (UC ASSESSMENT) A complete and correct response will discuss disrupted homeostasis and specific examples of the effect of disrupted homeostasis.

Sample Level-3 Response

If the cell membrane is damaged it cannot maintain balanced internal conditions by regulating what enters and leaves the cell. This results because materials the cell needs cannot enter the cell, and other materials cannot leave the cell. Also, harmful substances might get inside the cell.

SCIENCE & GLOBAL ISSUES/BIOLOGY • **CELL BIOLOGY**

A third example of specialized cells is the intestinal epithelial cells of the small intestine, which have microscopic structures called microvilli that function to increase the surface area of the cell. The increased surface area increases the rate of nutrient absorption.

2
3
Analysis

1. What are the similarities between all cells?

2. What is the major characteristic that classifies a cell as a prokaryote or eukaryote?

3. How did technology, namely the microscope, advance scientists' understanding of cells and microbes?

4. Some substances are damaging to cell membranes. What effects on the function of the membrane might the cell experience if the cell membrane is damaged?

KEY VOCABULARY	
bacteria	**eukaryote, eukaryotic**
cell	**homeostasis**
cell biology	**metabolism**
cell membrane, membrane	**nucleus**
cell principle	**prokaryote, prokaryotic**
cytoplasm	protein
cytoskeleton	**protist**
deoxyribonucleic acid, DNA	

190

REVIST THE CHALLENGE

The fundamental structures of cells are a membrane, cytoplasm, and genetic information in the form of DNA. The cell membrane helps to maintain balanced internal conditions (homeostasis) by serving as a barrier between the cell and the environment, and regulating what enters and leaves the cell. The cytoplasm contains molecules needed for cellular metabolism. The genetic information (DNA) is used to make proteins and other molecules that carry out cell processes. The cytoskeleton provides structure and support for the cell. The cytoskeleton also helps to transport materials within the cell and plays a role in the movement of cells. Multicellular organisms have specialized cells that contain an arrangement of structures needed for the cells to perform a specialized function.

7 A Model Membrane

MODELING • 1–2 CLASS SESSIONS

OVERVIEW

Students investigate a detergent bubble model of the cell membrane, which demonstrates the properties and functions of this essential cell organelle. The properties they investigate include: the fluid nature of the membrane; its ability to reseal small breaks; and the channels through which substances enter or exit the cell. A case study of diabetes introduces membrane proteins that function as receptors (for insulin) and transporters (of glucose).

KEY CONTENT

1. Every cell is surrounded by a membrane that serves as a barrier between the cell and its environment.

2. The cell membrane is made mainly of phospholipids and proteins.

3. The membrane is a fluid structure that gives the cell flexibility and strength.

4. Models help us understand cellular processes that are difficult to observe in living cells, but they have limitations.

KEY PROCESS SKILLS

1. Students make and record observations.

2. Students analyze data.

MATERIALS AND ADVANCE PREPARATION

For the teacher
Transparency 7.1, "The Phospholipid Bilayer"

Transparency 7.2, "Diabetes, Body Weight, and Income Data"

Literacy Transparency 3, "Read, Think, and Take Note" (optional)

0.5-L bottle of dishwashing detergent*

300-mL bottle of glycerin*

2 1-gallon (3.78 liter) plastic milk bottles*

large beaker (optional)*

10 L water*

For each group of four students
tray

500 mL of bubble solution*

8 straws*

ball of cotton string*

plastic tube

spool of cotton thread*

toothpick*

paper clip*

scissors*

supply of paper towels*

For each student
3 sticky notes*

Student Sheet 2.1, "Disease Information," from Activity 2

Not supplied in kit

Prepare the bubble solution. Rinsed 1-gallon (3.78-liter) plastic milk bottles are convenient containers for mixing and storing the solution. You may use the same bubble solution for all classes. For each group of four students you will need to mix: 500 mL water + 50 mL dishwashing detergent + 30 mL glycerin. If your largest class is 24 students, you will need to multiply this recipe by six. Add a shallow layer of bubble solution (about 500 mL) to each group's tray before they begin the activity. This solution can be reused throughout the day. A large beaker is helpful for collecting the bubble solution after the activity.

Masters for Literacy transparencies are in Teacher Resources III: Literacy.

TEACHING SUMMARY

Getting Started

- Introduce the bubble film model for the cell membrane.

Doing the Activity

- Students investigate the properties of a bubble film.

Follow-up

- ✓ Review the properties of the model bubble membrane and how they compare to those of a cell membrane.
- (LITERACY) Students follow the "Read, Think, and Take Note" literacy strategy while reading a case study of diabetes.
- The class discusses the relationships between a country's income level, its percentage of overweight people, and its incidence of diabetes.

BACKGROUND INFORMATION

The fluid nature of the cell membrane is due to the structure of the phospholipid bilayer. Lipids, which include fats, oils, and waxes, are composed primarily of carbon, hydrogen, and some oxygen atoms. The phospholipids that make up the cell membrane have two hydrocarbon chains, often referred to as the tails of the phospholipids, attached to a phosphate group, often referred to as the head of the phospholipid molecule. The phosphate head is hydrophilic (water-loving, or attracted to water), while the hydrocarbon tails are hydrophobic (water-hating). In the presence of water, these molecules spontaneously arrange themselves so that the hydrophilic heads face toward the water, and the hydrophobic tails of each layer line up with and across from each other.

Detergent and soap molecules also have hydrophobic hydrocarbon chains attached to a hydrophilic head. Detergent molecules line up side by side to form a bubble film similar to the cell membrane bilayer, but with a key difference. In the bubble membrane, the hydrophobic tails line up pointing toward the air inside and outside the bubble, while the hydrophilic heads face a thin layer of water in the middle of the bubble film.

Despite the differences in arrangement of the bubble membrane and the cell membrane, some of their properties, including their fluid nature, are similar. For example, the process of vesicles fusing to the cell surface has been compared to the process of detergent bubbles coalescing.

GETTING STARTED

1 After students read the introduction and Challenge, ask, *What do you think are the functions of the cell membrane? Why does every cell need one?*

Likely answers include keeping things inside of the cell in and harmful things out, and allowing substances to go in and out of the cell. Students should realize that without a cell membrane, the cell would either not exist, or it would essentially fall apart, its contents mixing into the surrounding environment. Explain to the class that the film of a detergent bubble has some properties in common with cell membranes, and that each student group will create detergent bubble models to investigate properties of the membrane that they cannot observe directly. Stress that this model, like many models, does not show all properties of the subject it represents.

7 A Model Membrane

DESPITE THEIR VARIETY, all cells have certain structures in common that perform essential functions. One such structure is the cell membrane. The cell membrane is the outermost membrane and the barrier between the cell and its external environment.

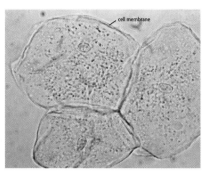
Human cheek cells

The cell membrane supports and protects the cell. If you compare a cell to a house, the membrane of a cell functions like the outside walls, roof, and doors of the house. It separates the cell from its environment, and helps maintain the homeostasis that lets the structures and molecules in the cell function. This includes regulating amounts of vital substances in the cell, such as salts and glucose, by controlling their movements into and out of the cell. Other key roles of the cell membrane are keeping out dangerous substances and organisms, such as disease-causing microbes, and sending and receiving signals from other cells.

Both infectious and noninfectious diseases may involve the cell membrane. When the membrane is unable to keep out disease-causing microbes, infection results. HIV and *Plasmodium* are examples of microbes that must first interact with and enter cells in order to infect humans. Noninfectious diseases can disrupt normal membrane function. Some forms of the genetic disease muscular dystrophy, for example, prevent damaged muscle cell membranes from healing by interfering with their normal ability to reseal small tears.

1 In this investigation you will explore a model that displays some of the features of a cell membrane.

Challenge

▶ What structures and characteristics help the cell membrane perform its functions?

191

DOING THE ACTIVITY

2 Remind students to be patient and to form new bubbles when they need to. Help students who are having problems with some of the Procedure steps.

MATERIALS

FOR EACH GROUP OF FOUR STUDENTS
    tray
    500 mL of bubble solution
  8 straws
    ball of cotton string
    plastic tube
    spool of cotton thread
    toothpick
    paper clip
    scissors
    supply of paper towels

FOR EACH STUDENT
    Student Sheet 2.1, "Disease Information" from Activity 2
  3 sticky notes

Procedure

1. To make the model, begin by filling the tray with a shallow layer of bubble solution.

2. Each person in your group should unwrap a clean straw, and use a piece of masking tape to label the straw with your initials. Keep track of your own straw throughout the activity.

3. Allow each of you, one by one, to make a single large bubble by gently blowing into the bubble solution. In your science notebook record your observations of the solution film—the membrane—that forms the bubble. If your bubble pops before you can finish your observations, make a fresh bubble. Let everyone in your group practice making a bubble. Take turns making the additional bubbles when they are needed in the rest of the Procedure.

4. Make a fresh bubble. Try dropping a toothpick through the film. In your science notebook record your observations. Remove the toothpick, and dry it with a paper towel.

5. Make a fresh bubble. Then insert the plastic tube into the bubble. In your science notebook, record your observations.

6. Now coat the plastic tube completely with the bubble solution in the tray. Make a fresh bubble. Insert the coated tube through the bubble. Record your observations. While the tube is inserted in the membrane, drop a toothpick through the plastic tube. In your science notebook, record your observations.

7. Move the plastic tube slowly and carefully from side to side, while it is in the bubble. Insert a second solution-coated object, such as a straw, into the bubble film, and move it around the bubble membrane also. In your science notebook, record your observations.

8. Carefully remove the tube and straw from the bubble. In your science notebook, record your observations.

9. Thread the cotton string through four of the straws to make a square about three-fourths the size of the tray. Knot the ends together. Then tie handles onto two opposite sides of the square, as shown below.

10. Submerge the square in the solution. Then, slowly pull it up, first from an angle, and then vertically as shown in the diagram below at left, until you have removed the square with the film from the tray. Then grasp both string handles and adjust the square to a horizontal position as shown below at right. Gently move it up and down, and observe the film. (If it pops, form a new one). In your science notebook, record your observations of the film.

11. Cut a piece of cotton thread 6–7 cm in length. Knot it to form a small circle.

3 (LITERACY) If necessary, project Literacy Transparency 3 to review with students the "Read, Think, and Take Note" guidelines. If you assign the diabetes case study for homework, be sure that students have sticky notes for following the strategy. Begin the next day by asking students to discuss with their partners or groups the main points of the case study and their comments on their sticky notes.

FOLLOW-UP

4 Project Transparency 7.1, "The Phospholipid Bilayer" to review membrane structure. Point out that a phospholipid molecule has a head and two tails. The heads are attracted to the watery environments inside and outside the cell, and so the heads of the molecules are lined up to face outward in the outside layer, and inward toward the cytoplasm in the inner layer. The lipid tails line up against each other within the bilayer. Explain that the phospholipids move laterally, giving the membrane a fluid behavior, like the bubble film. As in the bubble film, the cell membrane can reseal small breaks. Review students' answers to Analysis Questions 1–4, and expand on them to establish that the model demonstrates the following membrane properties:

- The phospholipid molecules flow laterally, as observed with the bubble film, which gives the membrane its fluid properties. Proteins also move laterally, as observed when students moved the straw or tube transport proteins laterally in the detergent film.

- Phospholipids or objects surrounded by phospholipid membranes are more likely to pass directly through the cell membrane than other objects, as demonstrated when only the tube coated with detergent solution could pass through the membrane.

- Some objects cannot get through the bubble membrane, which demonstrates the membrane's selective permeability.

- Transport proteins allow some proteins or objects into the cell, as modeled with the straw and tube "channels" through which the toothpick entered the cell.

Ask students what they think are some shortcomings of this model of the cell membrane. Students might suggest that the cell membrane would be more stable and last much longer than a detergent bubble. You can also let them know that the structure of a cell membrane is somewhat more complex than shown. Cell membranes contain a variety of proteins with additional functions, which they will learn about in later activities.

SCIENCE & GLOBAL ISSUES/BIOLOGY • CELL BIOLOGY

Cell Membrane Structure

The cell membrane is made mainly of proteins and phospholipids. The phospholipids form two layers—a bilayer—that gives the membrane both flexibility and strength. You saw this property with the detergent bubbles, which are also made of a type of lipid. The phospholipids in each layer of the cell membrane move from side to side in the cell membrane, trading places with each other and making the membrane a fluid structure.

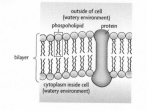

12. Float the circle of thread on the film made with the straws, and form an opening in the film by popping the inside of the circle with the end of a partially unfolded paper clip. In your science notebook, record your observations.

Note: Be patient and gentle during Steps 12 and 13. If your film breaks, place the square of straws back in the bubble solution to form another film.

13. Use the straight end of the paper clip to gently remove the circle of thread from the film. In your science notebook, record your observations.

14. Now that you have worked with a simple model of the cell membrane, read the box above about the actual structure of the cell membrane.

3 15. Follow your teacher's directions for reading the case study about diabetes. As you read, follow the "Read, Think, and Take Note" strategy.

16. Complete the information for diabetes on Student Sheet 2.1, "Disease Information" after you read the case study.

4 *Analysis*

1. Based on your observations of the bubble film in Procedure Steps 3 and 7, what do you think scientists mean when they say that the cell membrane is fluid?

2. a. What did you have to do to make objects pass through the bubble membrane without breaking the bubble?

   b. A cell membrane is mostly made of phospholipids. Which would be more likely to be able to move across a cell membrane: a structure made of proteins, or a structure made of proteins coated with phospholipids? Explain, based on the model.

   c. The cell membrane can be described as a selective barrier. What does that mean?

194

305

5 ✓Analysis Question 6 serves as a Quick Check assessment to ensure that students can accurately interpret data from a table, and correctly identify and describe trends and relationships, which are components of the ANALYZING DATA (AD) scoring variable. After students have individually responded to Analysis Question 6, begin a class discussion of this question 6 by projecting Transparency 7.2, "Diabetes, Body Weight, and Income Data." You may also want to have students reference the data in the case study, which matches the transparency. Ask students if they notice a trend between incidence of diabetes and income level. The higher-income countries tend to have a higher percentage of diabetes compared to lower-income countries. Then ask students what the relationship is between income and being overweight. The higher-income countries tend to have a higher percentage of overweight men and women compared to lower-income countries. Ask students why they think this is the case. People in higher-income countries tend to have a diet that is higher in calories, and a more sedentary lifestyle. These are risk factors for Type II diabetes. Bring out the idea that these data show that lifestyle can influence the type of disease that a country is dealing with.

3. A small break in a cell membrane sometimes closes back up. What properties of the model that you just explored showed how the membrane can reseal itself?

4. In addition to the phospholipid bilayer, cell membranes also include specialized proteins. These proteins are embedded in the membrane and, like the phospholipids, are able to move side to side in the membrane. Some of these proteins function as transporters, allowing other molecules into the cell. Explain how you modeled transport proteins in the Procedure.

5. From what you learned about diabetes in Case Study 3, explain the effect a destroyed transport protein has on the membrane and the cell.

5 6. Based on the diabetes case study, what conclusions can you make about the relationships between body weight, a country's income level, and diabetes?

KEY VOCABULARY	
cell membrane	membrane
diabetes	transport protein

SAMPLE RESPONSES

1. The phospholipids move from side to side and trade places with one another in the membrane, which makes it flexible and fluid.

2. a. To make an object pass through the bubble film without breaking the bubble, the object had to be coated in the bubble solution, or it could pass through the plastic tube.

    b. A structure made mostly of proteins coated in phospholipids would be more likely to move across a membrane made up mostly of phospholipids because the object coated in bubbles passed through the bubble film while a dry object broke the film instead.

    c. It means that a cell membrane only allows certain molecules to pass through, and prevents other substances from entering the cell.

3. The hole that was formed in the center of the thread circle simulated a hole in the membrane. The resealing of the membrane was simulated when the thread circle was pulled away and the hole closed up.

4. When a dry toothpick or a dry plastic tube was inserted into the bubble film, the film broke. When the plastic tube was coated in bubble solution it could be inserted into the film without breaking it, which simulated a protein channel. Then, the toothpick passed through the plastic tube that was inserted in the film, simulating a substance crossing the membrane through a transport protein.

5. If the transport protein that lets glucose into the cell isn't functioning, the membrane will no longer allow glucose into the cell and glucose will build up outside of the cell. This can disrupt the ability of the cell and the organism to maintain homeostasis.

6. ✓ There is a higher percentage of overweight men and women in higher-income countries and a higher percentage of diabetes compared to lower-income countries. This makes sense because being overweight is a risk factor for diabetes.

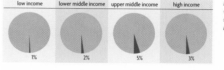

REVISIT THE CHALLENGE

The cell's phospholipid bilayer provides the membrane with fluid properties and the ability to separate the cell from its surroundings and reseal small breaks. The transport proteins allow substances to enter the cell that would otherwise not be able to cross the lipid bilayer. Taken together, these properties protect the cell and allow it to control what enters and leaves.

problems of metabolism that disrupt homeostasis and cause the complications that may lead to disability or death.

People with Type I diabetes must give themselves regular insulin injections and carefully monitor their blood sugar levels and intake of carbohydrates. Some people with Type II diabetes require insulin shots, while others take only an oral medication and follow a healthy diet.

The more carefully people maintain their blood glucose levels within the normal range, the lower the risk of serious health consequences from either type of diabetes.

DIABETES PREVENTION AND TREATMENT

Approximately 90% of the people around the world with diabetes have Type II diabetes. Excess body weight and lack of physical activity increase the risk

of developing Type II diabetes. Previously, Type II diabetes was observed mostly in adults, but today it is becoming common in children as well. Actions people can take to help prevent or control Type II diabetes include:

- maintaining a healthy body weight.
- exercising with moderate intensity on most days of the week.
- avoiding tobacco use.

Regular blood tests will detect elevated levels of blood sugar that predict Type II diabetes. This gives at-risk individuals an opportunity to take the actions described above, and reduce their chances of developing diabetes and the serious complications that may follow and reduce life expectancy. World health experts estimate that lifestyle changes by people at high risk could reduce Type II diabetes by 35 to 58%.

The causes of the immune reactions that lead to Type I diabetes are unknown, although there is evidence that genetic and environmental factors may increase the risk of developing Type I diabetes. There are currently no preventive measures.

CHALLENGES TO PREVENTION AND TREATMENT

Diabetes has serious social and economic impacts on afflicted individuals, their families, and the health care system. These include effects on people's ability to work and the costs of treatment. Body weight is an important indicator for the risk of Type II diabetes. Although losing weight and exercising reduce the risk of Type II diabetes—and sometimes reverse its course—making lifestyle changes is difficult. This is a key challenge to preventing Type II diabetes. ∎

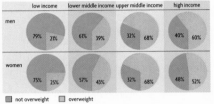

Overweight and nonoverweight men and women in countries at four average income levels.

Disease Information

Disease	Diabetes
Description of disease and symptoms	*Noninfectious disease that affects all ages of people around the world.* *Symptoms include excessive urination, thirst, hunger, weight loss, fatigue, and changes in vision. Eventual complications include blindness, kidney failure, coronary heart disease, stroke, and amputation from infections.*
Cellular mechanism of disease	*Two types: Type I and Type II* *Both result in high levels of glucose in the blood.* *In Type I the pancreas does not produce enough insulin because immune cells destroy cells that make it.* *In Type II the body doesn't produce enough insulin or cells cannot respond to insulin. Both types disturb normal glucose balance and affect homeostasis.*
Social factors	*Lifestyle choices of being overweight, exercising too little, and using tobacco increase risk for Type II diabetes.*
Economic factors	*Economic impact on individuals, families, and health care system due to high numbers of cases*
Environmental factors	*None*

8 The Cell Membrane and Diffusion

LABORATORY • 2–3 CLASS SESSIONS

OVERVIEW

Students use plastic dialysis tubing to model the cell membrane and investigate the role of the cell membrane in regulating the passage of water and other substances into and out of the cell. They also investigate the properties of substances that can and cannot cross the model membrane. A case study introduces the function of receptor proteins and endocytosis in infection by HIV/AIDS, and the sustainability issues of HIV/AIDS.

KEY CONTENT

1. Diffusion is the movement of a substance from an area of higher concentration to an area of lower concentration.

2. Some substances can diffuse across cell membranes. The diffusion of a liquid, such as water, across a membrane is called osmosis.

3. The cell membrane is selectively permeable, meaning that only certain substances can move into or out of the cell.

4. In an experiment a control provides a standard of comparison for judging experimental effects.

5. Models help us understand cellular processes that are difficult to observe in living cells, but models have limitations.

KEY PROCESS SKILLS

1. Students make and record observations.

2. Students collect and record data.

3. Students identify and describe trade-offs.

MATERIALS AND ADVANCE PREPARATION

For the teacher
    Scoring Guide: ANALYZING DATA (AD)
2 balloons*
    vial of peppermint oil*
4 test tubes*
    thermometer*
    large beaker*
    hot plate*

For the class
    supply of 20% sucrose solution*
    supply of 40% sucrose solution*

For each group of four students
4 pieces of dialysis tubing (to model the cell membrane)*
3 9-oz clear plastic cups *
    180-mL bottle of distilled water*
    60-mL bottle of liquid glucose solution*
    60-mL dropper bottle of glucose indicator
    30-mL bottle of Lugol's iodine solution*
    60-mL bottle of liquid starch solution*
    250-mL beaker*
    50-mL graduated cylinder*
2 small test tubes*
    funnel*
    dropper*
    timer*
    permanent marking pen*
    colored pencils*
    ruler*
    access to running water*

For each student
    Student Sheet 2.1, "Disease Information" from Activity 2
3 sticky notes*
    Scoring Guide: ANALYZING DATA (AD) (optional)

                                      Not supplied in kit

Masters for Scoring Guides are in Teacher Resources IV: Assessment.

Each class will need 1,000 mL of 20% sucrose solution and 600 mL of 40% sucrose solution.

For the 20% sucrose solution, add 200 grams of sucrose to 800 mL of water. For the 40% sucrose solution, add 240 grams of sucrose to 360 mL of water. Mix both solutions thoroughly to ensure that the sucrose dissolves.

For the balloon demonstration

Fill a balloon with tap water to the size of a water balloon that fits in your hand, and tie the balloon tightly. Fill a second balloon with the same amount of water, add 5 drops of peppermint oil, and tie the balloon. Note that it is important to add the water first, as pure peppermint oil will damage the balloon.

SAFETY NOTE

Be sure that students are very careful not to get Lugol's iodine on their skin or clothing as it may stain. Be sure that they wash their hands when they have completed the laboratory.

TEACHING SUMMARY

Getting Started

- Use a balloon model to demonstrate diffusion and selective permeability.

- Introduce students to the dialysis tubing model of a cell membrane.

Doing the Activity

- Students complete Part A of the laboratory to investigate osmosis (the diffusion of water).

- Demonstrate the glucose indicator that will be used in Part B.

- Students complete Part B of the laboratory to investigate diffusion of solutes, modeling the selective permeability of the cell membrane.

- (LITERACY) Students follow the "Read, Think, and Take Note" literacy strategy to read a case study about HIV/AIDS.

Follow-up

- ✓(AD ASSESSMENT) Discuss the results of the investigation in Part B.

BACKGROUND INFORMATION

Diffusion is the spontaneous movement of molecules from an area of higher concentration to an area of lower concentration. This process leads to an increase in the entropy, or disorder, of a system, because the pre-diffusion state is more ordered than the post-diffusion state. Diffusion occurs any time molecules are able to travel freely between adjacent areas of different concentrations. Osmosis, the movement of water across the semipermeable cell membrane from higher to lower water concentration (down a concentration gradient), is a form of diffusion. Cells can move some substances from areas of lower concentration to areas of higher concentration, but this *active transport* requires the expenditure of energy.

The simulated cells prepared with the plastic dialysis membranes in Part A of this activity model the behavior of cells in solutions containing greater or lower concentrations of dissolved solutes. The simulated cells contain a sugar solution that models the cytoplasm.

Hypertonic solutions contain a higher concentration of solute than the cell contains. Hypotonic solutions contain a lower concentration of solute than the cell. Cells placed in hypertonic solutions shrink because water moves out of the cell to dilute the solute concentration in the surrounding liquid. Conversely, cells placed in hypotonic solutions swell and may even burst, as water moves into the cell to dilute the solute concentration inside the cell.

The plastic dialysis membranes in Part B of this activity simulate the permeability of cell membranes to glucose and iodine molecules, and their impermeability to starch molecules. These differences in permeability in the model are due to the size of the pores in the dialysis membrane compared to the size of the starch, glucose, and iodine molecules. Starch molecules are too large to pass through the pores of the dialysis membrane; glucose and iodine molecules are small enough to pass through. However, with a cell membrane, other factors, such as the charge and shape of the molecule, determine whether it can diffuse through the membrane.

The movement of glucose through the dialysis membrane occurs through simple diffusion from higher to lower concentration. However, in an actual cell membrane, the movement of glucose requires the presence of a transport protein and is called facilitated diffusion. In this activity, it is important to focus on the selective permeability of the cell membrane—in other words, its ability to allow only selected substances to move into and out of the cell.

GETTING STARTED

1 Begin with the balloon demonstration of selective permeability. Carry the two balloons as you walk around the room, and ask students to observe and smell the balloons. Ask them what they conclude about the permeability of the balloon, and to describe their evidence. They should conclude that a balloon does not allow water through, but it does allow peppermint through. Explain that the balloon is an example of a semipermeable membrane—it is only permeable to some substances.

Discuss the movement of the peppermint oil as an example of diffusion, in which molecules move spontaneously from an area of higher concentration (inside the balloon) to an area of lower concentration (the room), thereby equalizing the concentration throughout the system. Diffusion occurs until equilibrium is reached, at which point movement of the substance into and out of the balloon is equal. Remind students that the bubble film was one model of a cell membrane. Tell them that the balloon membrane is a second model of a cell membrane. Each model demonstrates specific aspects of the cell membrane's function. Explain that in this activity they will work with dialysis tubing, creating a third model of the cell membrane. Show students the dialysis tubing, and demonstrate how to fill and tie it. Emphasize that each student is responsible for observing and recording observations of each part of the activity.

---

8 The Cell Membrane and Diffusion

1 **A** **KEY FUNCTION OF** the cell membrane is regulating what substances enter or leave the cell. In many cases, substances move into or out of the cell through the process of diffusion. In **diffusion,** a substance moves from a solution with a high concentration of the substance to a solution with a low concentration of the substance. This is shown in the diagram at right.

In this activity, you will test a variety of substances to see if they will diffuse through a model cell membrane made of plastic, rather than the detergent film you used in Activity 7, "A Model Membrane."

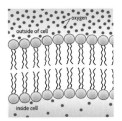

Challenge

▶ What factors determine whether a substance moves across a model of the cell membrane?

MATERIALS

FOR THE CLASS		
	supply of 20% sucrose solution	250-mL beaker
	supply of 40% sucrose solution	50-mL graduated cylinder
FOR EACH GROUP OF FOUR STUDENTS		2 small test tubes
4	pieces of dialysis tubing (to model the cell membrane)	funnel
3	9-oz clear plastic cups	dropper
	180-mL bottle of distilled water	timer
	60-mL bottle of liquid glucose solution	permanent marking pen
	60-mL dropper bottle of glucose indicator	colored pencils
		ruler
	30-mL bottle of Lugol's iodine solution	**FOR EACH STUDENT**
	60-mL bottle of liquid starch solution	Student Sheet 2.1, "Disease Information" from Activity 2
		3 sticky notes

Procedure

Part A: Investigating Water and Sucrose Solutions

1. Have someone in your group use the marking pen to label one cup "40% sucrose," one cup "20% sucrose," and one cup "0% sucrose." Fill each cup half-full with the appropriate sucrose solution.

2. Obtain three pieces of dialysis tubing, which represent cell membranes, and prepare them for use:

   a. Wet them by dipping them into a beaker of tap water.

   b. Squeeze one end of each membrane between your thumb and forefinger to make an opening.

   c. Use a clean dropper or faucet to run water through each membrane.

3. Fill each dialysis tube with 20% sucrose solution by following these directions:

   a. Tie a very tight knot in one end of the dialysis tube. Use the beaker and funnel to add enough 20% sucrose solution to the tube to fill approximately 3–4 cm of the tube, as shown at left below.

   b. Tie a knot in the top end of the tube, leaving a little space in the tube above the level of the liquid, as shown at right below. This "bag" is now a model of a cell enclosed by its cell membrane.

Safety ⚠️

Be careful not to get Lugol's iodine on your skin or clothing as it may stain. Wash your hands with soap and water when you complete the laboratory activity.

Fill (a) and close (b) the tube.

199

313

DOING THE ACTIVITY

2 Students should notice the dialysis-tube simulated cells are shrinking, swelling, or staying the same, depending on the concentrations of sucrose inside and outside the membrane. When students have completed Part A of the Procedure, ask them to describe and explain the changes they observed in the model cells in solutions of lower, equal, and higher sugar concentration. Refer to the Background section for information to support the discussion. Bring out the idea that, in both cases, water crossed the membrane from a region of higher water concentration (lower sugar concentration) to lower water concentration (higher sugar concentration). This process—the diffusion of water—is called osmosis. You may want to introduce this term, which will be defined in Activity 9. Explain that the water actually moves in both directions, but that more water moves from the side of the bag with a higher water concentration to the side with a lower concentration than moves in the opposite direction. You may wish to add that diffusion is a spontaneous process—it takes place whenever dissolved substances are able to move freely between areas of different concentration.

If you wish, allow one set of dialysis tubes from Part A to sit overnight. Begin the next day with observations of the tubes. The tube placed in a hypotonic environment should have swelled even more while the one in a hypertonic environment shrank even more.

---

4. Rinse the tied tubes in running water and dry them carefully on a paper towel. Set the filled tubes on a clean paper towel. Do not place them in a cup.

5. Rinse and dry the beaker.

6. In your science notebook, create a data table to record your results.

7. Place one tube in each of the cups of sucrose solution (40%, 20%, and 0%) at the same time. The solutions in the cups represent the environment outside each cell.

2 8. Allow the tubes to remain in the cups for 20 minutes. Every 5 minutes, observe the tubes, and record any changes in the model membrane or its contents.

   Note: Lift the tubes out of the cups to make observations and then place them back in the solutions.

Part B: Membranes and the Movement of Molecules

9. Add the following to two small test tubes:

   test tube 1: 2–3 drops water

   test tube 2: 2–3 drops starch

10. Add 1 drop of Lugol's solution to test tubes 1 and 2 to be sure the indicator solutions are working properly. In your science notebook, record your observations.

3 11. Your teacher will demonstrate the glucose indicator. In your science notebook, record your observations from the demonstration.

4 12. Based on the information in the table below, which molecules do you think will pass through the model membrane? In your science notebook

   a. record your hypothesis of which will pass through.

   b. explain your reasons for your hypothesis.

Molecular Formulas for Three Molecules	
MOLECULE	MOLECULAR FORMULA
Glucose	$C_6H_{12}O_6$
Iodine	I_2
Starch	polysaccharide made of thousands of glucose molecules linked together

200

---

3 Demonstrate the reaction of the glucose-indicator solution. Label and set up four test tubes, as shown in the table below.

Glucose Indicator Reactions	
Tube	Solution in tube
1	5 mL iodine + 10 drops glucose indicator
2	5 mL starch + 10 drops glucose indicator
3	5 mL glucose + 10 drops glucose indicator
4	5 mL water + 10 drops glucose indicator

Heat the four test tubes in a water bath set at 80°C. Leave them in the bath for approximately 30 seconds or until you see a color change in the test tube containing glucose.

The table below shows sample results. Tell students that the amber color of the iodine should disappear and leave the blue of the glucose indicator.

Results of Glucose Indicator Reactions

Tube	Solution in tube	Results after heating	What the results mean
1	5 mL iodine +10 drops glucose indicator	Amber color of iodine disappears, and solution stays blue	No glucose present
2	5 mL starch +10 drops glucose indicator	Blue	No glucose present
3	5 mL glucose +10 drops glucose indicator	Orange, brown, or green	Glucose present
4	5 mL water +10 drops glucose indicator	Blue	No glucose present

Note: When starch and iodine are mixed to give a dark purplish-black color, the purplish-black will also disappear when glucose indicator is added, leaving the blue of the indicator visible.

Set the test tubes in an area of the room for students to reference during the lab.

4 Instruct students to read Procedure Step 12 carefully. Depending on their science experience, you may wish to point out that the numbers of atoms in the formulas give a general idea of the size of the molecule. Likely hypotheses from students will be that because starch is made of thousands of linked glucose molecules, it might be too big to get through the membrane. Iodine is made of only two iodine atoms, so it might be able to get through. Students' hypotheses for glucose, which is an intermediate size, may vary.

---

13. Investigate your hypothesis.

   a. Fill the 50-mL graduated cylinder with 35 mL of water.

   b. Test a few drops of the water in your test tube to be sure it doesn't contain any glucose or starch. Then clean your tray.

   c. Wet a piece of dialysis tubing by dipping it into the beaker of water. Squeeze one end of the membrane between your thumb and forefinger to make an opening. Use a clean dropper or faucet to run water through the tube.

   d. Tie a tight knot in the bottom of the tube.

   e. Add about 5 mL of glucose and 5 mL of starch to the tube.

   f. Tie the tube shut, just above the level of the solution.

   g. **Rinse the outside of the tube thoroughly under running water. This is important: there must not be any glucose or starch on the outside of the tube!**

   h. Slowly place the filled membrane tube into the graduated cylinder so that it is surrounded by water, as shown at right.

14. In your science notebook, create a data table to record your observations.

15. After 5–10 minutes, remove a dropper full of liquid from the graduated cylinder.

   a. Test a few drops of the solution from the graduated cylinder with Lugol's solution in a small test tube.

   b. Test 5 mL of the solution from the graduated cylinder with 10 drops of glucose test solution in a small test tube.

   c. In your science notebook, record your results and what they tell you about the movement of glucose and starch across the membrane.

16. Add 3 drops of Lugol's solution to the liquid in the cylinder.

17. Observe for 5–10 minutes. Record your observations and what they tell you about the movement of iodine across the membrane.

5 18. Follow your teacher's directions for reading the case study about HIV/AIDS. As you read, follow the "Read, Think, and Take Note" strategy.

19. Complete the information for HIV/AIDS on Student Sheet 2.1, "Disease Information" after you read the case study.

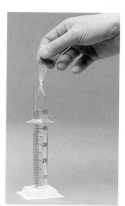

Placing the tube into the cylinder

5 (LITERACY) If you wish to assign the HIV/AIDS case study for homework, be sure to give students sticky notes for the "Read, Think, and Take Note" literacy strategy. Begin the next day by having students discuss with their partners or groups the main ideas of the reading and their comments on the sticky notes.

FOLLOW-UP

6 ✓ (AD ASSESSMENT) Analysis Questions 1 and 2 may be scored using the ANALYZING DATA (AD) Scoring Guide. Introduce the ANALYZING DATA (AD) Scoring Guide, and tell the class your expectations for satisfactory work. Analysis Question 6 is a Quick Check assessment to ensure that students understand the term, and can identify trade-offs, which is a component of the EVIDENCE AND TRADE-OFFS (ET) scoring variable.

7 Ask for students to volunteer to describe the evidence and their conclusions about which substances could cross the model membrane. Urge them to use the terms **diffuse** and **diffusion** as they describe the model. Students can detect that glucose and iodine could diffuse across the membrane, while starch could not. Glucose diffused because the solution on the side of the membrane opposite of where it was placed in the beginning tested positive for glucose with the glucose indicator. The glucose diffused from an area of high concentration to an area of low concentration. You could see that Lugol's iodine diffused because a dark purplish-black color appeared on the side containing starch, but not on the side containing the iodine. Since the solution on the side containing iodine did not turn purplish-black, the starch did not diffuse, even though it was in high concentration on one side compared to the other. Ask students to compare the results to their hypotheses and to explain why there was diffusion with iodine and glucose and not with the starch. If they do not think of the size of the molecules, tell them that the dialysis membrane contains pores or holes of a certain size, and only molecules of a certain size can pass through. The iodine and glucose were small enough to pass through the pores in the dialysis membrane; starch molecules were too big. This simulates the selective permeability of the cell membrane—only selected substances can move into or out of the cell. Stress that size is only one factor that determines whether a substance can cross a cell membrane. Others include the shape and charge of the substance. This is a shortcoming of the dialysis membrane model.

Tell students that while glucose moved by simple diffusion through the simulated cell membrane, the cell must have a membrane transport protein that forms a channel that allows glucose to cross an actual cell membrane. This type of diffusion is called facilitated diffusion and it occurs with molecules that can only move through the membrane with the help of a membrane transport protein. This is another way that the dialysis membrane model does not accurately simulate the functions of the cell membrane.

Analysis

6 1. In Part A, what changes did you observe in the model cell when the external environment surrounding the model cell contained each of the following:

    a. a less concentrated solution than the cell's contents. Explain.

    b. a more concentrated solution than the cell's contents. Explain.

    c. equally as concentrated as the cell's contents. Explain.

7 2. In Part B, which substances passed through the model membrane? Explain why. Support your explanation with evidence from the laboratory.

3. In Part B, did the results support your hypothesis? Explain.

4. Some substances, including glucose, cannot directly cross the lipid bilayer of a cell membrane. What structures do you think are in the membrane to allow for the transport of substances that cannot cross on their own?

    Hint: Think back to the bubble film model.

5. The diffusion of water across a membrane to equalize the concentrations of solutions on either side of the membrane is called osmosis. Explain:

    a which part of the model illustrated osmosis.

    b. what conditions are necessary for osmosis to take place.

6. Based on the HIV/AIDS case study, what are the advantages and trade-offs of working to develop an HIV/AIDS vaccine, as opposed to focusing on education?

KEY VOCABULARY	
cell membrane, membrane	hypothesis
control	osmosis
diffuse, diffusion	phospholipid (lipid) bilayer
HIV/AIDS	

SAMPLE RESPONSES

1. (AD ASSESSMENT) A complete and correct response will describe the observation of the tube, and where water moved in order to equalize the concentration.

Sample Level-3 Response:

a. The tubing swelled, and the model cell became fuller. The model cell placed in the less sugary environment swelled as water moved into the cell to equalize the concentration.

b. The tubing shrank, and the model cell became smaller. The model cell placed in the more sugary environment shrank as water diffused out of the cell through the membrane to dilute the more sugary environment and equalize the concentration.

c. The model cell did not shrink or swell. Since the concentration of sugar was equal on the inside and outside of the model, water movement in and out was equal, and the model cell remained the same size.

2. (AD ASSESSMENT) A complete and correct response will describe the evidence for whether each molecule could cross the model membrane, and why or why not.

Sample Level-3 Response

Glucose and iodine could cross because they were small enough to get through the pores of the dialysis tubing. The evidence that glucose crossed was that the solution outside of the membrane, which did not contain glucose solution at the beginning of the investigation, tested positive for glucose. The evidence that Lugol's iodine crossed was that a blue-black color appeared inside the tubing, where the starch solution was first added, but not on the side containing the iodine. This indicates that the iodine could cross the membrane to enter the bag, but the starch could not cross the membrane to leave the bag.

The starch did not cross because it was too big to get through the pores of the dialysis tubing.

3. Each student's answer will depend on his or her hypothesis. The answer should be consistent with what they concluded in Analysis Question 2.

4. Transport proteins of some type would help molecules cross that cannot cross on their own. We saw this in the bubble membrane model with the plastic tube. The plastic bead broke the membrane, but it could go through the plastic tube without breaking the bubble membrane.

CASE STUDY

HIV/AIDS

BEFORE 1981, HIV/AIDS was unknown to the medical community. Today 30 million people across the world are infected with HIV/AIDS.

The distribution of cases worldwide is shown in the map below. Of the 2.7 million new cases, 370,000 are in children age 14 and younger. More than 90% of these newly infected children are babies born to mothers who are HIV positive.

SYMPTOMS AND DISEASE MECHANISM

In the summer of 1981, doctors in the United States observed an unusual number of cases of a rare skin cancer and a rare pneumonia. All of the patients had one other disease characteristic in common: reduced immunity to certain diseases. It soon became clear that some populations, such as intravenous drug users and hemophiliacs, were more likely to be affected than the general U.S. population, indicating that at least one way it was acquired was from blood. The disease was named acquired immunodeficiency syndrome (AIDS).

Within three years after its discovery, scientists showed that an infectious blood-borne virus was the cause of AIDS. They named this virus human immunodeficiency virus (HIV) because it reduces the function of the immune system. At first, doctors and scientists hoped that the discovery of the virus would soon lead to effective vaccines for HIV/AIDS prevention. HIV, however, proved to be a rapidly mutating virus, and over a fairly short period of time, new variations of the virus emerged. Because the virus changes so rapidly, the

(Continued on next page)

Burden of Disease	TOTAL NUMBER INFECTED	NUMBER OF DEATHS PER YEAR	NUMBER OF NEW CASES PER YEAR
Worldwide	30 million	2 million	2.7 million
United States	1.1 million	14,110	44,000

Global distribution of HIV/AIDS cases

- <0.1%
- 0.1% – <0.5%
- 0.5% – <1.0%
- 1.0% – <5.0%
- 5.0% – <15.0%
- 15.0% – <34.0%
- data not included

5. a. Osmosis was illustrated by the movement of water into or out of the bag in Part A with the sucrose.

    b. For osmosis to take place there has to be a higher concentration of a substance that cannot cross the membrane on one side of the membrane than on the other side. To equalize the concentration of the substance, water diffuses from the area of higher concentration of water (lower concentration of the substance) to the lower concentration of water (higher concentration of the substance) and dilutes the substance.

6. ✓ The advantage of developing an HIV/AIDS vaccine is that vaccination would be more effective at stopping HIV/AIDS than educational programs about prevention because people have to follow through and act on what they learn in the education programs, whereas vaccination only requires that people get a shot. The trade-offs of developing a vaccine is that both the development and the cost of the vaccine itself are more expensive than education programs and it may take a long time to develop an effective vaccine. If this takes away resources from education, the number of HIV/AIDS cases is likely to increase faster. When education is effective, it can reduce HIV/AIDS cases immediately, while a vaccine might take many years to develop.

(Continued from previous page)

development of vaccines and treatments has been a much greater challenge than anticipated.

HIV is an infectious disease that destroys a specific type of white blood cell in the immune system. The virus membrane attaches to and fuses with the cell membrane of these white blood cells. The virus appears in blood, semen, vaginal fluids, and breast milk of infected individuals and is transmitted in one of four ways:

- transfusion of infected blood.
- sexual contact with an infected person.
- needle or syringe contaminated with the blood of an infected person.
- an infected mother to her child during pregnancy, birth, or breast-feeding.

While some people show symptoms shortly after infection with HIV, many do not develop symptoms for 10 years or more. Early symptoms include fatigue, fever, diarrhea, weight loss, and swollen lymph glands. The diagnosis of HIV infection is upgraded to AIDS when the patient develops at least one serious illness, such as pneumonia, TB, or hepatitis C, and that patient's number of specific white blood cells (lymphocytes) falls below a certain level. Because the immune system also protects against cancer,

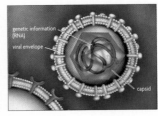

genetic information (RNA)
viral envelope
capsid

A model of an HIV virus approaching the cell membrane of a white blood cell

HIV/AIDS increases the risk of some cancers.

HIV/AIDS PREVENTION AND TREATMENT

There are a number of preventions and treatments for HIV/AIDS infection. An early intervention was rigorous screening of blood donors to prevent transmission of the disease from a blood transfusion. One primary area of prevention today focuses on educating teenagers and adults about risky sexual activities. For example, HIV/AIDS education that promotes using condoms or abstaining from sexual activity is an effective prevention measure. Programs that focus on drug users and convince them not to share needles have also been effective in prevention. A major medical advance was the creation of a drug that prevents mother-to-child transmission of the virus during pregnancy and labor.

Treatment of HIV/AIDS involves a combination of

several drugs, which do not cure HIV/AIDS, but greatly improve the length and quality of life. In the 1990s, combinations of drugs, which cost about $15,000 per patient per year, became available in developed countries. Then generic drugs were developed, which drove down the price of the drugs. This, along with support from organizations, made the combination drugs accessible to people in developing countries at $295 per year. Today, generic drugs are available in developing countries for $88 per year.

HIV/AIDS RESEARCH

For years, a major focus of HIV/AIDS research has been on a vaccine to prevent transmission of the virus. As yet, however, there is still no effective vaccine, in part because the virus evolves so rapidly. Most vaccines, such as the ones against polio and seasonal flu, cause a person's immune system to produce

---

REVIST THE CHALLENGE

Review the factors that determine whether a substance moves across a membrane model. These include the difference in concentration of the substance across the model and the selective permeability of the membrane. Stress that pore size determines what crosses the dialysis membrane. The situation is more complex with the cell membrane, where the shape and charge of a substance, and in some cases the presence of a transport protein, also determine whether it can cross the membrane.

proteins called antibodies. Antibodies disable or kill a disease-causing microbe, such as a virus. With this type of vaccine, the antibodies stop the infection before the person gets sick. The antibodies produced by vaccination against one variation of AIDS, however, will not protect against other variations. And once a person is infected, HIV "hides" inside cells of the immune system, where antibodies cannot reach the virus. Research for an effective HIV/AIDS vaccine continues to be the focus for scientists who study HIV/AIDS.

CHALLENGES TO HIV/AIDS PREVENTION AND TREATMENT

Despite significant progress in prevention and treatment, the global level of success in controlling HIV/AIDS infections worldwide has not been as high as hoped. In some places providing educational programs and other preventive measures are not effective in reaching and changing the behavior of enough people to make much of a difference. Data from 64 countries show that young people, a key audience for AIDS information, do not have accurate and complete knowledge about HIV/AIDS. This means they are less likely to take measures to prevent infection. To this date only about half of those countries have set goals for education and other prevention strategies. Additionally, many people already infected are not able to get the drugs they need because they cost too much or are not available. ■

Disease Information

Disease	HIV/AIDS
Description of disease and symptoms	Infectious disease that affects white blood cells Virus is found in semen, vaginal fluid, and breast milk. Symptoms include fatigue, fever, diarrhea, weight loss, and swollen lymph glands. Disease is diagnosed as AIDS when certain symptoms and infections occur and white blood cell counts fall below a certain level.
Cellular mechanism of disease	The blood-borne virus reduces the function of the immune system. It is transmitted by sexual activity, hypodermic needles used in or by an infected person, and from mother to child during pregnancy, birth, and breast-feeding.
Social factors	An effective prevention is education about sexual abstinence, using condoms, and not sharing needles. Screening is also effective. However, some people do not have access to education, prevention, or treatment.
Economic factors	In developing countries the cost of combined medication treatments has been reduced from $15,000 to less than $150 per year, but that is still too expensive for some. Research to develop a vaccine and new medications has been going on for decades.
Environmental factors	None

Cell Membrane Structure and Function

OVERVIEW

Students read more about the structure and function of the cell membrane. They also read about how viruses breach a cell membrane to invade a host cell.

KEY CONTENT

1. Every cell is surrounded by a membrane that separates it from its environment.

2. The cell membrane is made of a fluid mosaic of molecules, mainly phospholipids and proteins.

3. Diffusion is the movement of substances from higher to lower concentrations.

4. The cell membrane is selectively permeable, meaning that only certain substances move into or out of the cell.

5. Some substances diffuse freely across the cell membrane, while others enter through protein channels in a process called facilitated diffusion.

6. Some substances are transported into the cell against, or up, a concentration gradient by transport proteins. This process requires the cell to expend energy and is called active transport.

KEY PROCESS SKILLS

1. Students make accurate interpretations, inferences, and conclusions from text.

MATERIALS AND ADVANCE PREPARATION

For the teacher

Transparency 9.1, "The Cell Membrane"
Scoring Guide: UNDERSTANDING CONCEPTS (UC)

For each student

Scoring Guide: UNDERSTANDING CONCEPTS (UC) (optional)

If you do not have access to a computer with a projector, make transparencies of the presentation slides, and project them on the overhead.

Masters for Scoring Guides are in Teacher Resources IV: Assessment.

TEACHING SUMMARY

Getting Started

- Review the structure and properties of the phospholipid bilayer and the role of transport proteins in membrane function.

Doing the Activity

- (LITERACY) Students complete the reading, following the Stopping to Think literacy strategy.

Follow-up

- (UC ASSESSMENT) Discuss the structure and function of the cell membrane, and display a slide presentation that further explains the processes that occur across the cell membrane.

BACKGROUND INFORMATION

Cell Membrane Transport Proteins

Certain ions, such as sodium and potassium ions, and polar molecules, such as glucose, cross the cell membrane by passing through transport proteins that are embedded in the membrane. These membrane proteins are specific to the types of molecules they transport. For example, the glucose transport and sodium ion transport proteins differ in structure and function. One group of membrane transport proteins, called channel proteins, serve as channels or tunnels that allow molecules or ions to pass through. Another group of membrane transport proteins, called carrier proteins, bind to the molecules being transported and change shape in order to shuttle them from one side to the other. Channel proteins are involved in passive diffusion of some substances, such as glucose. Passive diffusion of other substances and all active transport processes require carrier proteins.

GETTING STARTED

1 Project Transparency 9.1, "The Cell Membrane." Ask for student volunteers to state what they learned about the basic characteristics of the cell membrane in the bubble model from Activity 7, "A Model Membrane." The membrane is made of phospholipids that are organized into two fluid and flexible layers. The structures of the phospholipids in the cell membrane determine the types of molecules that can freely cross the bilayer. Remind students that they also modeled the role of transport channels—proteins that let molecules enter the cell that would not otherwise be able to cross the membrane. In this activity, they will learn more about membrane structure and function.

DOING THE ACTIVITY

2 (LITERACY) The reading is supported with a strategy called Stopping to Think, which helps students process the information they read. In this activity, Stopping to Think questions focus students' attention on important ideas they encounter in the text. These questions do not require a written response and are different than the Analysis Questions found at the end of the activity. For more information on this strategy, see Teacher Resources III: Literacy. Sample responses for Stopping to Think sections 1–3 are shown on the next pages.

---

9 Cell Membrane Structure and Function

1 UNDERSTANDING THE CELL membrane is the key to understanding many diseases, and is of great value in developing treatments. Some diseases disable the ability of the cell membrane to reseal after it has been penetrated, and some destroy the function of the cell's transport channels. The immune system recognizes foreign cells through receptors on the membrane of both the foreign and immune cells. Many disease-causing pathogens, such as the HIV/AIDS virus and the polio virus, infect humans by recognizing and binding to the cell membrane, and then entering the cell. Preventing and treating such diseases as HIV/AIDS can improve the quality and length of people's lives and improve their social and economic well-being.

Challenge

▶ How do the structures of the cell membrane help it function?

Procedure

2 1. When reading, answer the Stopping to Think Questions in your mind.

Reading

Molecular Building Blocks of Cells and the Cell Membrane

Four types of large molecules, called **macromolecules,** are essential building blocks for all of the structures in a cell. These macromolecules are carbohydrates, lipids, proteins, and nucleic acids. Each type of macromolecule is made of one or more chains of simpler compounds, or subunits. The table below shows the kinds of subunits that make up each type of macromolecule.

Macromolecule Subunits	
MACROMOLECULE	SUBUNITS
Carbohydrates	sugars
Lipids	fatty acids
Proteins	amino acids
Nucleic acids	nucleotides

206

A phospholipid molecule

The cell membrane is made mostly of lipids and proteins. The lipids give the membrane its strength, yet allow it to remain flexible and fluid. The bubble film in Activity 7, "A Model Membrane," modeled the lipid layer that is the basis for the structure of the cell membrane. Most of the lipids in the cell membranes of animals, plants, protists, and bacteria are members of a special class of lipids, called phospholipids. A **phospholipid** is a lipid with a phosphate head attached to two long lipid tails.

The structure of the membrane results from the properties of the phospholipids. The heads of phospholipid molecules are attracted to water, so they face the watery environment inside and outside the cell. The tails line up and point toward the middle of the membrane. This results in a double-layered structure called a phospholipid (lipid) bilayer, as shown at right.

Proteins are embedded in the membrane's phospholipid bilayer, also shown at right. Some of these proteins are linked to carbohydrate chains. Membrane proteins are able to move sideways through the membrane, just as you were able to move tubes through the bubble membrane. The complex arrangement of proteins in the membrane reminded scientists of the tiles in a mosaic. This led scientists to refer to the structure of the cell membrane as a **fluid mosaic model,** shown below.

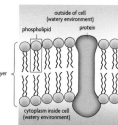

The phospholipid bilayer of the cell membrane with an embedded protein

There are many proteins in the membrane of a typical cell. One kind of protein acts as channels or pumps, controlling what enters and leaves the cell. You modeled these channels when you inserted straws and tubes through the bubble membrane. You also modeled the glucose channel with the dialysis membrane.

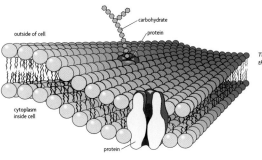

The fluid mosaic model for the cell membrane

3 The building blocks of a cell membrane are phospholipids and proteins. There are also carbohydrates.

The phospholipids form a bilayer that is fluid and lets certain substances pass but not others. There are various proteins embedded in the fluid membrane. Some of the proteins have carbohydrates attached. The arrangement reminded scientists of the tiles in a mosaic, but unlike a mosaic made of tiles, this membrane mosaic is fluid and has no fixed pattern.

The functions of the phospholipids are to give the membrane strength and flexibility. Some membrane proteins serve as channels to transport substances, while others send or receive signals to and from other cells. Other proteins interact with foreign cells or viruses.

Other membrane molecules made up of proteins or proteins linked to carbohydrates act as signaling or receptor proteins. These molecules are involved in cell-to-cell communication. An example of a receptor is the membrane protein that binds to insulin hormone. The body needs insulin to regulate blood glucose levels. When blood glucose levels are high, insulin attaches to receptors in the membranes of liver and muscle cells. This stimulates the cells to take up glucose from the blood and store it as glycogen or fat.

STOPPING TO THINK 1

3

What are the molecular building blocks that make up the cell membrane?
How are these molecules arranged in the cell membrane?
What are the functions of these molecules in the membrane?

The Cell Membrane Controls What Enters and Leaves the Cell

DIFFUSION AND OSMOSIS

The cell membrane is **semipermeable,** or **selectively permeable,** which means not all substances can cross it. This property helps the cell maintain homeostasis—stable internal conditions—by controlling what enters and leaves. You modeled this property of the membrane with the dialysis tubing in the last activity: small molecules, like water and glucose, could cross the dialysis membrane, while large molecules, like sucrose and starch, could not. Size is one factor that determines whether a molecule can cross the cell membrane. Other factors determining whether certain molecules can cross a cell membrane are the molecules' shape and electrical charge.

For the cell to function properly, it must allow desirable substances, such as nutrients, to enter, and allow wastes to leave. Many of these substances enter and leave the cell by diffusing from an area of high concentration to an area of low concentration. When a substance moves naturally from high to low concentration, the cell does not have to expend energy. For example, oxygen diffuses from a high concentration outside the cell across the membrane into the cell. As the oxygen is used up and the concentration in the cell drops, more oxygen enters the cell. Similarly, as carbon dioxide builds up inside the cells of the body it diffuses from high concentration across the cell membrane to lower concentration outside of the cell.

Water also diffuses naturally in both directions across the cell membrane. The overall direction of movement of water depends on the concentration of dissolved substances inside and outside the cell. Diffusion will continue until the two solutions have an equal concentration of the dissolved substance. When a cell is placed in a solution with a higher concentration of dissolved substances, water will move out of the cell, and the cell will shrink, as shown in the diagram at right. When a cell is placed in a solution with a lower concentration of dissolved substances, water will enter the cell and the cell will swell. This diffusion of liquid water across a semipermeable membrane is called **osmosis.**

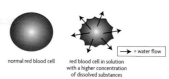

normal red blood cell

red blood cell in solution with a higher concentration of dissolved substances

→ = water flow

PASSIVE TRANSPORT

Not all substances used or produced by the cell can freely diffuse through its membrane, especially substances that are electrically charged or are very large in size. Proteins in the cell membrane must transport the substances in or out. When a membrane protein moves a substance from higher to lower concentration through a protein channel, the process is called **facilitated diffusion,** or **passive transport,** because it does not require energy. An example of facilitated diffusion is the movement of glucose from high concentrations outside the cell into the cell through a glucose transport protein.

ACTIVE TRANSPORT

In some cases, proteins transport substances into or out of a cell against the normal direction of diffusion. The molecules of the substance are moving from low to high concentration. This process is called **active transport** (shown below), and it requires the cell to expend energy. An example of active transport is the pumping of substances like calcium and sodium out of the cell.

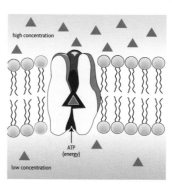

high concentration

ATP (energy)

low concentration

The active transport of a substance from low to high concentration requires energy.

209

TRANSPORT BY VESICLES

Sometimes materials are transported across the cell membrane by vesicles, which are small compartments surrounded by a membrane. To transport materials into the cell, the membrane forms a pocket that then pinches into the cell, forming a vesicle. This formation and movement of vesicles into the cell is called **endocytosis.** To transport materials out of the cell, a vesicle in the cytoplasm fuses with the cell membrane, and re-forms a smooth outer membrane, releasing its contents to the outside. This process of releasing material in vesicles to the outside of the cell is called **exocytosis.** Both of these processes are shown below. The fluid nature of the membrane is key to its ability to form and release vesicles. The movement of the vesicles within the cell involves the cytoskeleton and requires energy.

Endocytosis

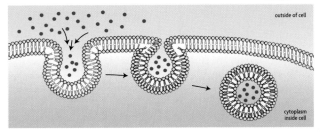

Exocytosis

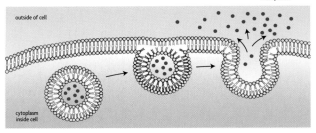

4 The types of movement that happen across the cell membrane are diffusion, facilitated diffusion (passive transport), and active transport. Endocytosis and exocytosis move materials in and out of the cell via compartments called vesicles, which are surrounded by a membrane.

Two types of movement that require energy are active transport and movement in vesicles. Active transport requires energy because it moves a substance from an area of lower concentration to an area of higher concentration, which is against the direction of diffusion. Movement in vesicles requires energy for the cell to move the vesicles to or from the cell membrane.

5 A virus is different from a bacterial or animal cell because it is not a cell and is not capable of reproducing independently. Viruses are made of genetic material and some proteins surrounded by a protein coat.

Viruses need host cells because they do not have the ability to reproduce on their own. They use the host cell's structures to produce new viruses.

4

STOPPING TO THINK 2

What types of movement happen across the cell membrane?
Which type of movement(s) across the cell membrane need(s) energy? Why?

Viruses and the Cell Membrane

The causes of many human infectious diseases are viruses that enter our cells. HIV/AIDS is a well-known example. Like all viruses, HIV/AIDS is not made of cells, and is not capable of producing offspring on its own. Instead, a virus must invade a cell in order to reproduce. Viruses can infect cells in plants and animals, and can even infect bacteria. A virus is mainly composed of its genetic material and a few proteins, surrounded by a protein coat, and sometimes a lipid membrane. To make copies of itself, the virus invades a cell and uses the cell's structures. Because of this, the invaded cell is called a host cell. Most viruses don't infect every type of cell in the body. Instead, each virus infects one or a few types of cells. HIV/AIDS, for example, only infects cells of the immune system. When the virus comes into contact with an immune system cell, it must first cross the cell membrane. If the virus does not cross that first barrier, it does not infect the cell, cannot produce more viruses, and will eventually be destroyed.

STOPPING TO THINK 3

What makes a virus different from a bacterial or animal cell?
Why do viruses need host cells?

Viruses can infect many sorts of organisms, including animals, plants, and bacteria. They attach to a cell by interacting with the lipids, proteins, or carbohydrates of the cell membrane. Some viruses, such as those that infect bacteria, invade a cell by making a hole in the membrane and injecting themselves into the cell through the hole. Other viruses, like HIV, have an external membrane similar to the cell's membrane. The virus membrane fuses with the cell membrane, allowing the virus to enter the cell. Still other viruses, such as flu viruses, get a "free ride" into the cell through the cell's endocytosis mechanism. In endocytosis the part of the cell membrane in contact with the virus surrounds the virus and pinches into the cell, in a process similar to the one shown on the previous page. Once the virus is inside the cell it will use others of the cell's structures to make more viruses. These new viruses then exit the cell in one of two ways: 1) by pinching off, or budding, from the host cell without destroying the host cell, as is the case with HIV/AIDS; or 2) by breaking the host cell open, killing it in the process, as is the case with polio virus.

FOLLOW-UP

6 (UC ASSESSMENT) Analysis Questions 3, 5, and 6 are an opportunity for you to use the UNDERSTANDING CONCEPTS (UC) Scoring Guide to assess students' understanding of the structure and function of the cell membrane. If necessary, pass out copies of the Scoring Guide, and review the standards for a Level-3 Response.

Analysis

1. What functions and properties of the cell membrane depend on each of the following?

   a. Phospholipids

   b. Proteins

   c. Carbohydrates

2. Explain why it is important for the cell membrane to be fluid.

 3 a. What are the functions of the cell membrane?

   b. Explain which parts of the cell membrane allow it to perform these functions.

4. What determines whether or not a substance can cross the cell membrane?

5. Explain how the cell membrane helps the cell maintain homeostasis—a stable internal environment. Name specific structures of the cell membrane and describe their functions in your explanation.

6. Imagine a single-celled organism living in a pond. What would happen to the organism if runoff from irrigation caused the pond to become significantly salty? Use evidence to support your explanation.

KEY VOCABULARY	
active transport	**macromolecule**
cell membrane, membrane	**osmosis**
diffusion	**passive transport**
endocytosis	**phospholipid**
exocytosis	phospholipid (lipid) bilayer
facilitated diffusion	protein
fluid mosaic model	**semi-permeable, selectively permeable**
lipid	vesicle
lipid bilayer	virus

212

SAMPLE RESPONSES

1. a. Phospholipids form the bilayer barrier between the inside and outside of the cell, and give the membrane its fluidity.

    b. Proteins transport substances that cannot freely cross the membrane. They are also involved in sending and receiving signals.

    c. Carbohydrate chains attached to proteins are involved in some signaling processes.

2. A fluid membrane allows the membrane to heal small breaks. It also allows vesicles to fuse with the membrane to release their contents, and allows some viruses to fuse with the membrane and enter the cell.

3. (UC ASSESSMENT) A complete and correct response will describe at least two functions of the cell membrane and the components that contribute to the function.

Sample Level-3 Response

    a. The cell membrane regulates the substances that move into and out of the cell and contains structures for cell-to-cell communication and signaling.

    b. The phospholipid bilayer, protein channels, and protein pumps move substances in and out, and maintain the cell's homeostasis. Protein receptors allow for signaling and communication between cells.

4. The size, shape, and electrical charge of a substance determine whether or not it can cross the membrane.

5. (UC ASSESSMENT) A complete and correct response will discuss at least two ways that the membrane maintains homeostasis by allowing substances in or out of the cell.

Sample Level-3 Response

The membrane allows certain substances in and out, which helps to maintain homeostasis. This is accomplished by the lipid bilayer itself and by protein channels that only allow certain substances to enter or leave the cell. The cell can also communicate with other cells through signaling or receptor proteins. These signals sometimes cause the cell to take up or release certain substances to maintain stable internal conditions (homeostasis).

6. (UC ASSESSMENT) A complete and correct response will include the parts of the osmosis model that explain why the cell would lose water in a salty environment, and the consequences for the cell.

Sample Level-3 Response

An organism that lives in fresh water would lose water if it were surrounded by a salty environment. This would happen just as it did with the model cell when it was placed in a sugar environment. Water diffuses out from high-water (low salt) to low-water (high salt) concentration to equalize the concentration on both sides. If too much water leaves the cell, homeostasis will be disrupted and the cell will die.

REVISIT THE CHALLENGE

Discuss the roles of both phospholipids and proteins in membrane function. Stress that the phospholipid bilayer creates a barrier between the watery environments inside and outside the cell, and gives the membrane its strength and fluidity. Membrane proteins facilitate diffusion and active transport of substances that could not otherwise cross the membrane, and enable cells to communicate and interact with each other. Finally, emphasize the theme of cell structure and function illustrated by Activities 7–9: structures in the membrane have specific properties that allow them to perform their specialized functions. This is a recurring theme in cell biology.

10 Functions of Proteins in Cells

RESEARCH PROJECT AND PRESENTATION • 2–3 CLASS SESSIONS

OVERVIEW

Students learn about the diverse roles of proteins in cells. Each pair of students researches one protein of a certain type, and groups present combined research on the protein type to the class.

KEY CONTENT

1. The genetic information stored in DNA directs the synthesis of the thousands of proteins the cell needs.

2. Proteins are often classified according to their functions. Enzymes are a large group of proteins that act as biological catalysts to speed up the chemical reactions in cells.

KEY PROCESS SKILLS

1. To communicate effectively students employ appropriate vocabulary to explain concepts and learn to speak clearly and logically.

MATERIALS AND ADVANCE PREPARATION

For the teacher

Scoring Guide: COMMUNICATION SKILLS (CS)
Scoring Guide: UNDERSTANDING CONCEPTS (UC)
Transparency 10.1, "Protein Folding" (optional)

For each student

Student Sheet 10.1, "Summary of Functions of Proteins" (optional)
Scoring Guide: COMMUNICATION SKILLS (CS) (optional)
Scoring Guide: UNDERSTANDING CONCEPTS (UC) (optional)

Masters for Scoring Guides are in Teacher Resources IV: Assessment.

TEACHING SUMMARY

Getting Started

• Introduce students to some of the functions of proteins.

Doing the Activity

• Students examine eight classes of proteins, and each pair of students researches an example from one of these classes.

• (LITERACY)(CS ASSESSMENT) Student groups present their research to the class.

Follow-up

• (UC ASSESSMENT) The class discusses why proteins are sometimes called the "workhorses" of the cell.

BACKGROUND INFORMATION

Cells require thousands of proteins if they are to live and function. Proteins are the "doers" or "workhorses" of most living processes and can be classified into eight groups. One major class of proteins is the enzymes. Enzymes catalyze reactions that synthesize large biological molecules, including DNA, RNA, proteins, fats, and complex carbohydrates, such as starch and cellulose. Enzymes also catalyze the metabolism of food to release energy. The other groups of proteins are transport proteins (such as hemoglobin), motor proteins, signaling proteins (including hormones, such as insulin), receptor proteins, proteins of the immune system (antibodies), storage proteins, and structural proteins (such as those involved in the structure of bone, muscle, and hair). For the purposes of this activity, proteins involved in the interactions of microbes with host cells have been included with antibodies in a category called immune system and disease proteins.

Proteins are polymers made of chains of amino acids. There are 20 amino acid building blocks, and they are arranged in varying sequences and numbers to make each kind of protein. The amino acids are linked together by a type of covalent bond called a peptide bond. A single linear chain of amino acids is a polypeptide. Some proteins are made of just one polypeptide chain, while others are made of two or more joined together. The sequence of amino acids is referred to as the primary structure of the protein.

As soon as it is synthesized, each protein folds into a specific three-dimensional shape that is essential for it to function properly. This folding takes place as a result of disulfide bonds and weak interactions, such as hydrogen bonds, that form spontaneously between amino acids at various points in the amino acid chain or between amino acids in other chains.

The complex shape of a protein forms binding sites that are essential to the protein's function. For example, hemoglobin has binding sites that fit oxygen molecules. If the shape of a hemoglobin protein is altered, it changes the shape of the binding site; an oxygen molecule would no longer fit, and that protein will not function properly, even if its amino acid sequence stays intact. Similarly, an enzyme has a binding site for its substrate(s). If the shape of the enzyme is altered in a way that affects this binding site, it can no longer act as a catalyst.

GETTING STARTED

1 ◆ Ask students to name the protein functions important to such living organisms as humans. Students might say that proteins are an important part of our diet and nutrition because they build muscle. This is a common, but incomplete and superficial impression of the roles that proteins play in all living cells. Describe for students the examples of collagen and keratin, which are two structural proteins. Collagen forms strong fibers outside of cells, and makes up almost half of the total protein of the human body. Without collagen, tissues in the body would lose strength and structure. Keratin is a tough, fibrous protein in hair and nails, as well as in the claws, hooves, feathers, and beaks of animals. Explain that protein in our food provides essential amino acids that our bodies do not synthesize on their own, as well as other molecular building blocks and energy. The protein we eat is not directly put to work; it is first broken down into amino acids and used by the ribosomes in cells throughout our bodies to synthesize human proteins.

After students read the introduction and Challenge, ask them to read the table that describes the various classes of proteins. Clarify any confusing vocabulary and the functions of each group of proteins as needed.

---

10 Functions of Proteins in Cells

1 **T**HERE ARE THOUSANDS of proteins at work in most cells. A **protein** is a macromolecule made up of one or more chains of amino acids folded together into a complex three-dimensional structure. Each protein performs a certain function, such as speeding up a chemical reaction, transporting a specific molecule into or out of the cell, or fighting disease. The information for producing all of the proteins a cell needs is stored in the cell's DNA. In eukaryotes the DNA is located in the nucleus, and in prokaryotes it is in the cytoplasm.

The genetic material of viruses is enclosed by a protein coat, or capsid. Viruses must have such proteins to be able to infect human cells, and they stimulate a body's immune-system response. In this activity you will research proteins to learn more about their functions in both human cells and viruses.

Challenge

▶ What are the functions of proteins in cells and viruses?

  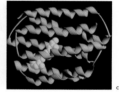

Models of three proteins: hemoglobin (a), insulin (b), and rhodopsin (c)

213

DOING THE ACTIVITY

2 Assign each group of four students one of the types of proteins that are presented in the Student Book: enzymes, transport, structural, motor, storage, signaling, receptor, and immune system/disease. Since storage and structural proteins might be less interesting to students, we suggest that you focus on the first six groups of proteins. If there are more types of proteins than groups in your class, decide which types best fit your classroom goals. If there are more groups than types of proteins, assign students to additional examples. Additional enzymes that might be included are catalase and reverse transcriptase. Other interesting options are growth hormone and erythropoietin (both signal proteins). Depending on the resources available to you, you may wish to have students research their proteins in the computer lab or in the library, or both. You might also have students begin the activity in class and then research on their own for homework, or structure research time over the next few days, while in class you move them to the next activity in the Student Book. Student Sheet 10.1, "Summary of Functions of Proteins," can be used to prepare for the presentation. A sample response to Student Sheet 10.1, shown at the end of this activity, may help you advise students of your expectation for the depth of their research.

3 (LITERACY)(CS ASSESSMENT) The presentation is an opportunity for you to use the COMMUNICATION SKILLS (CS) Scoring Guide to assess students' ability to effectively communicate information. Introduce the COMMUNICATION SKILLS (CS) Scoring Guide and tell the class your expectations for satisfactory work. Students might make brochures, posters, slide presentations, or devise another means to help communicate their group's research to the class. Before groups give their presentations, you may wish to review your expectations for speaking and listening; when their own group is not presenting, students are part of the listening audience. You also may wish to set up a system for students to record information from the presentations. This could be a classroom chart, a set of notes, or a set of questions that students have about what is being presented. Alternatively, distribute copies of Student Sheet 10.1, "Summary of Functions of Proteins," on which students may record information from the presentations.

Another approach is to have the class conduct an Informal Meeting of the Minds. Direct students to find a partner from another group and compare the information that they collected from the presentations, and answer the questions that they have. Ask pairs to share their discussions with the class. Be sure students secure answers to their questions.

SCIENCE & GLOBAL ISSUES/BIOLOGY • CELL BIOLOGY

Classes of Proteins

CLASS OF PROTEIN	FUNCTION	EXAMPLES
Enzymes	Catalyze (speed up) chemical reactions Thousands are present in most types of cells.	pepsin, DNA polymerase
Transport proteins	Carry small molecules and ions	hemoglobin, glucose transporter (GLUT 4)
Motor proteins	Enable movement in cells and tissues	myosin, dynein
Signaling proteins	Carry signals between cells	insulin, glucagon
Receptor proteins	Mediate a cell's response to a stimulus Many receptors interact with signaling proteins.	insulin receptor, rhodopsin
Immune system and disease proteins	Bind to and inactivate foreign substances and microbes, participate in infection and immune response	antibodies in the immune system, influenza virus, hemagglutinin protein
Storage proteins	Store such materials as amino acids and iron for later use	albumin, ferritin
Structural proteins	Provide protection and support	actin, keratin

Procedure

2
1. Your teacher will assign your group one of the eight classes of proteins to research and present to the rest of the class.

2. With your group, decide which example protein in your assigned class of proteins each pair will research. Examples are shown in the table above.

3. Work with your partner to research the following for your assigned protein:
   - Its function and location in specific cell types, cell structures, or viruses.
   - Other proteins or structures it interacts with, if relevant.
   - The effect on the cell or virus when this protein is damaged or missing.

3
4. With your group of four, create a presentation for your classmates about your assigned protein class. Your presentation must include the following:
   - A title that includes the name of the class of protein you were assigned and the general function that was provided in the chart, "Classes of Proteins."
   - All of the information each pair researched in Step 3.

214

FOLLOW-UP

4 (UC ASSESSMENT) Analysis Question 3 is an opportunity to assess students' understanding of the functions of proteins. Using the UNDERSTANDING CONCEPTS (UC) Scoring Guide, tell students your expectations for a complete and correct response. Ask, *How would you respond to someone who says that the reason people need to eat protein is to build muscle?*

Students should answer that proteins provided in food do help to build muscle, but building muscle is just one of many protein functions. Bring out the idea that proteins eaten in food are broken down into their subunit amino acids, which the cells of the organism need for producing proteins essential to cell function. For example, a person who eats a chicken egg cannot use the egg proteins directly. Instead, these proteins must be broken down into amino acids that the human cells then use to produce human proteins. Depending on your curriculum goals, you may wish to review the folding structures of proteins with Transparency 10.1, "Protein Folding."

Analysis

1. Why are proteins called "the workhorses" of the cell? Give at least three examples.

2. What are the similarities between all proteins?

4 3. What would happen to an organism if each of the following types of proteins is damaged or missing? Explain your answers.

   a. Antibody

   b. Myosin

   c. Glucagon

   d. Pepsin

KEY VOCABULARY	
enzyme	receptor protein
motor protein	signaling protein
protein	transport protein

215

SAMPLE RESPONSES

1. Proteins are workhorses because they perform thousands of functions in cells of living things. For example, enzymes speed up chemical reactions, transport proteins carry such substances as oxygen to the cells, and receptor proteins in cell membranes receive signals.

2. All proteins are three-dimensional structures made of chains of amino acid subunits.

3. (UC ASSESSMENT) A complete and correct response will give an evidence-based answer for each of the four damaged or missing proteins.

    Sample Level-3 Response

    a. The immune system would not destroy certain microbes because antibodies recognize foreign material.

    b. Muscle movement would be difficult because myosin is involved in the contraction of muscles.

    c. The cells would not release glucose into the blood when blood glucose levels are low because this is triggered by glucogen. This means that blood glucose levels would stay low and out of balance.

    d. Digestion would be disrupted because pepsin digests proteins.

REVIST THE CHALLENGE

Proteins are extremely important in thousands of ways for cells to function. Because of this, they are considered "workhorses" of cells. They are responsible for most cellular functions, including catalyzing reactions, providing shape and internal structure, transporting substances, sending and receiving signals, mediating the immune response, and enabling motility of cells and materials within cells. Within each class of proteins are numerous proteins, each with its own specialized role.

Summary of Functions of Proteins

Protein	Function and location	Effect on cell or organism if protein is damaged or missing
Pepsin	Pepsin is an enzyme produced by the stomach lining that begins breaking down proteins from food. It is one of three classes of digestive proteins. It works best in an acidic environment like the stomach.	The proteins in food will not be broken down. This will cause a buildup of unusable protein in the body, which can lead to kidney problems and a shortage of building blocks for protein synthesis.
DNA polymerase	DNA polymerase is an enzyme found in the nucleus of every cell that replicates new strands of DNA. It adds nucleotides to a growing strand of DNA that is made based on a template strand.	DNA would not be replicated, and cells would not divide properly to produce functional offspring cells.
Hemoglobin	Hemoglobin is an iron-containing protein that transports oxygen through the circulatory system. It is located inside red blood cells and gives blood its red color. One hemoglobin protein can bind as many as four molecules of oxygen.	Sickle cell disease can result if there is a mutation in the gene for hemoglobin protein. In sickle cell disease the mutated hemoglobin molecules stack on one another and cause the red blood cells to become sickle-shaped. These cells can clump and clog blood vessels.
Glucose transporter (GLUT 4)	GLUT 4 is activated by insulin to take up glucose in skeletal muscle cells, cardiac (heart) muscle cells, and fat cells. It transports glucose from high concentration to low via facilitated diffusion either into or out of the cell, but most often into the cell from the blood.	Glucose would not be transported, and it would either build up in the blood or in the cell. If it builds up in the blood, diabetic symptoms may result. At the same time, the cells do not get the glucose they need for energy.

(continued on next page)

Summary of Functions of Proteins (continued)

Protein	Function and location	Effect on cell or organism if protein is damaged or missing
Actin and myosin	These filament proteins work together in the cytoplasm of most cells, and are especially abundant in muscle cells. Actin forms microfilaments, which support the cells' shape and structure, and are involved in cell motility, including muscle contraction. Myosin has projections that allow it to "walk" along actin microfilaments in muscle cells and cause muscle contraction.	Muscles could not contract; cells would lose shape and structure; and cells such as macrophages and such single-celled organisms as amoebae would not be able to move.
Dynein	This motor protein is involved in the bending movements of cilia, such as those in cells that line the respiratory system, and flagella, such as those found in sperm cells.	Cilia and flagella could not move. Cells that rely on these structures, such as sperm cells, would not be able to move.
Insulin	Insulin is a protein hormone produced by the pancreas. It triggers the uptake of glucose from the blood by liver, muscle, and fat cells when the glucose levels rise.	It would disrupt normal glucose homeostasis. Diabetes (a disease stemming from elevated blood sugar) can result if there is no insulin or lowered insulin production.
Glucagon	Glucagon is a protein hormone produced by the pancreas that triggers the release of glucose to the blood in order to increase the glucose level in the blood.	It would disrupt normal homeostasis. Blood glucose levels would get too low if glucagon production is deficient.

(continued on next page)

Summary of Functions of Proteins (continued)

Protein	Function and location	Effect on cell or organism if protein is damaged or missing
Insulin receptor	This is a transmembrane protein—it spans across a cell membrane. When it binds to and is stimulated by insulin, it stimulates the GLUT 4 transporter to transport glucose into the cell from the blood.	A defective insulin receptor cannot signal the uptake of glucose from the blood. Glucose builds up in the blood and Type II diabetes may result.
Rhodopsin	Rhodopsin is a protein pigment of the rod photoreceptor cells in the retina. It allows vision in dim light conditions.	The rod cells would be damaged by bright light, and vision under dim light conditions would be impaired.
Antibodies	Antibodies are produced by bone marrow cells and are important proteins of the immune system. They lock onto and disable foreign pathogens in the body. They also trigger the production of memory cells that stimulate a strong and fast immune response if the pathogen is ever encountered again.	Pathogens would not be disabled, and memory cells would not be made. The immune system would not be as effective.
Influenza hemagglutinin	Influenza hemagglutinin is part of a protein on the surface of the flu virus. Hemagglutinin plays an important role in flu infection because it allows the virus to enter the cells of the body.	The flu virus would not enter cells of the body and, therefore, would not infect the cells.

11 Investigating Enzyme Function

LABORATORY • 2–3 CLASS SESSIONS

OVERVIEW

Students investigate the conditions needed for the proper functioning of enzymes. They design an experiment to test the effects of temperature and pH on the enzyme lactase.

KEY CONTENT

1. Enzymes are a large group of proteins that act as biological catalysts to speed up the chemical reactions in cells.

2. Enzymes' structures and functions are affected by such factors as temperature and pH.

KEY AND PROCESS SKILLS

1. Students design and conduct a controlled experiment.

2. Students formulate a testable hypothesis.

3. Students analyze data and draw conclusions based on the data.

MATERIALS AND ADVANCE PREPARATION

For the teacher

Transparency 11.1, "How Enzymes Work"

Scoring Guide: DESIGNING INVESTIGATIONS (DI)

Scoring Guide: GROUP INTERACTION (GI)

Science Skills Student Sheet 4, "Elements of Good Experimental Design"

Literacy Transparency 7, "Writing a Formal Investigation Report"

small test tube*

small balloon

150 g active dry yeast*

water*

For each group of four students

30-mL dropper bottle lactase solution*

100 mL lactose solution*

100 mL glucose solution

125 mL yeast suspension*

30-mL dropper bottle pH buffer 4*

30-mL dropper bottle pH buffer 6*

30-mL dropper bottle pH buffer 8*

30-mL dropper bottle pH buffer 10*

hot plate*

beaker of water*

For each pair of students

2 10-mL graduated cylinders (1 for yeast, 1 for lactose)*

2 beakers*

10 small test tubes*

large pipette*

9 small balloons

test tube rack*

thermometer*

marking pen*

water*

For each student

Scoring Guide: DESIGNING INVESTIGATIONS (DI) (optional)

Scoring Guide: GROUP INTERACTION (GI) (optional)

Scoring Guide: ANALYZING DATA (AD) (optional)

Group Interaction Student Sheet 2, "Developing Communication Skills" (optional)

Science Skills Student Sheet 4, "Elements of Good Experimental Design" (optional)

Literacy Transparency 7, "Writing a Formal Investigation Report" (optional)

Student Sheet 11.1a, "Sample Procedure: Temperature" (optional)

Student Sheet 11.1b, "Sample Procedure: pH" (optional)

safety goggles*

Not supplied in kit

Prepare the following solutions for each group of students:

- *Lactose solution: Mass 5 grams of lactose. Add 100 mL of water. Swirl to mix until all of the lactose is dissolved.*

- *Glucose solution: Mass 10 grams of glucose. Add 100 mL of water. Swirl to mix until all of the glucose is dissolved.*

- *Yeast suspension: Mass 3 grams of yeast. Add 125 mL of lukewarm water and swirl to mix. Note: The yeast suspension should be prepared fresh just before the start of the activity for each class.*

Masters for Group Interaction Student Sheets are in Teacher Resources II: Diverse Learners. Masters for Literacy Transparencies are in Teacher Resources III: Literacy. Masters for Scoring Guides are in Teacher Resources IV: Assessment.

TEACHING SUMMARY

Getting Started

- Review the role of enzyme proteins in cells, and introduce or review lactase.

- Explain the role of yeast in the laboratory experiment.

Doing the Activity

- (DI, GI, AD ASSESSMENT) Students design and complete the laboratory.

Follow-up

- The class discusses the mechanism of enzyme function.

BACKGROUND INFORMATION

When an enzyme catalyzes a reaction, it does so by binding to the reactant(s), which in enzymatic reactions are called substrates. The shape of the enzyme includes a binding site that fits its substrate(s). The analogy of a lock and key helps illustrate the close molecular fit of the binding site of an enzyme and its substrate, as shown on Transparency 11.1, "How Enzymes Work." A change in the shape of the enzyme is analogous to changing the lock so that the key—the substrate of an enzyme—no longer fits; thus the reaction does not occur.

In this activity, students investigate the effects of temperature and pH on the enzyme lactase, not on the rate of the chemical reaction. They do this by first treating the enzyme. Because the yeast that will indicate the presence of glucose produced from the reaction grow best at 30°C–40°C, the enzyme reactions occur when students have returned the enzyme to this temperature range. High temperatures and variations in pH and salinity disrupt the weak interactions that maintain a protein's normal shape, which in turn may alter the configuration of the enzyme's binding site for its substrate or for factors that regulate the level of enzyme activity. The effect of temperature on enzymes and other proteins is the reason that very few organisms can survive if their internal temperature rises above 45°C–50°C. Temperatures that are too low slow down most chemical reactions, but not by affecting the enzyme shape. Temperatures that are too low decrease the overall kinetic energy of the solution, and thus reduce the number of interactions between the enzyme and the reactants.

The lactase enzyme supplied for this laboratory comes from a fungus called *Aspergillus oryzae*, which functions best in basic (alkaline) conditions.

The breakdown of lactose catalyzed by lactase is an example of a hydrolysis reaction. In hydrolysis, a water molecule reacts with a larger molecule, which breaks into two smaller pieces. Many metabolic reactions, including ones involved in digestion of proteins and carbohydrates from our food, involve hydrolysis.

GETTING STARTED

1 Begin by reminding students that they heard a presentation about enzymes in the previous activity. An enzyme is a protein that speeds up, or catalyzes, a specific chemical reaction. Ask students what are some of the specific things that enzymes do in cells. Write students' answers on the board or overhead. Likely answers include digestion and DNA replication. Emphasize that these reactions would proceed slowly or not at all in the absence of the appropriate enzyme. Ask, *What is unique about each protein's structure that allows it to perform its function?*

Every protein is folded into a specific shape and has one or more regions called binding sites. Each binding site has a unique shape that matches the shape of the reactant or other molecule it interacts with. If you discussed Transparency 10.1, "Protein Folding," with students, you can use it to review the folding of the protein chain that results in its unique shape. Tell students that they will investigate two factors that affect the structures and functions of proteins—temperature and pH. Explain that pH is a measure of a solution's acidity.

Ask students if they have or know anyone with lactose intolerance. Likely at least one student will say yes. Explain that lactose is the sugar in milk, which when digested in the lining of the small intestine breaks into two sugars, glucose and galactose. Discuss with students that levels of lactase often begin to decrease during childhood, and lactose intolerance may develop as early as age six or at any time through old age. This is a good time to point out to students that the names of enzymes usually end in "-ase" or "-in."

---

11 Investigating Enzyme Function

1 **W**HEN HIV INFECTS a cell, enzymes aid in the virus's reproduction. On the other hand, when the body's immune system is activated, immune cells engulf the pathogen and use enzymes to digest it. Enzymes are required for the majority of reactions and activities that take place within cells. An **enzyme** is a type of protein that speeds up, or **catalyzes,** a specific chemical reaction. Each enzyme has a region called a binding site, which has a unique shape that matches the shape of the reactant it interacts with. Any factor that changes the binding site can reduce or prevent the action of the enzyme.

In this activity you will design, conduct, and report on an investigation to determine whether pH and temperature affect the function of the enzyme lactase. Lactase is a digestive enzyme found in the small intestine of humans. When people consume lactose, which is a sugar found in milk, lactase breaks down the lactose into two simple sugars, glucose and galactose. Both simple sugars are readily absorbed by your body.

$$\text{lactose + water} \xrightarrow{\text{lactase}} \text{glucose + galactose}$$

Some people's bodies no longer produce lactase, and so they can no longer break down the lactose in milk or foods that contain milk. Instead, bacteria that live naturally in the small intestine consume the lactose. A product of the digestion of lactose by bacteria is carbon dioxide gas, which can cause abdominal pain. When diarrhea also occurs, doctors may suspect that these are symptoms of lactose deficiency in a condition called lactose intolerance.

This milk has reduced lactose, allowing people who cannot break down lactose to drink it without unpleasant consequences.

Challenge

2 ▶ How do pH and temperature affect the function of the enzyme lactase?

216

---

2 Explain to the class that they will use yeast to measure the activity of the lactase enzyme on lactose under varying conditions. Explain that yeasts are a group of microorganisms (classified as fungi), and that the yeast for the activity is baker's yeast, which is what makes bread rise. Explain that yeast cannot digest lactose, but they can digest glucose. When yeast digest glucose, a by-product is carbon dioxide gas. In this laboratory, students use balloons to collect the carbon dioxide gas and to indicate the presence of glucose. The more glucose there is, the more CO_2 will be produced by the yeast as they digest it. A word equation for the digestion of lactose catalyzed by lactase is:

$$\text{lactose + water} \xrightarrow{\text{lactase}} \text{glucose + galactose}$$

The reactants are lactose and water, and the products are glucose and galactose. A word equation for the digestion of glucose by yeast is:

$$glucose \xrightarrow{yeast} carbon\ dioxide + water$$

The reactant is glucose; the products are carbon dioxide and water.

To demonstrate these processes, fill a small test tube with 4 mL each of glucose and yeast that has been activated in lukewarm water. You can use the solutions from one of the groups to do this. Fix a small balloon securely over the test tube opening, and place it in a beaker of water at 35°C–40°C. Explain that yeast grow best in this temperature range. Let the test tube sit for approximately 10 minutes, and then have students make observations. This demonstration shows students the materials that they may use in their experiments. Explain that pH is a measure of how acidic or basic a substance is. Pure water has a pH of 7, which is neutral. A solution with a pH less than 7 is acidic, and a solution with a pH greater than 7 is basic.

MATERIALS

FOR EACH GROUP OF FOUR STUDENTS	FOR EACH PAIR OF STUDENTS
30-mL dropper bottle lactase solution	2 beakers
100 mL lactose solution	2 10-mL graduated cylinders
100 mL glucose solution	10 small test tubes
125 mL yeast suspension	9 small balloons
30-mL dropper bottle pH buffer 4	large pipette
30-mL dropper bottle pH buffer 6	test tube rack
30-mL dropper bottle pH buffer 8	thermometer
30-mL dropper bottle pH buffer 10	permanent marking pen
hot plate	water
beaker of water	FOR EACH STUDENT
	safety goggles

Safety ⚠

Wear safety goggles at all times during this laboratory. Keep your hands away from the hot plate, and wear insulated gloves or use potholders to move the beaker as you finish. Know the safety procedures in case of a fire. Do not allow solutions to touch your skin or clothing. Clean up spills immediately. If accidental contact occurs, inform your teacher, and rinse exposed areas.

Procedure

3

1. With your group of four, decide which pair will investigate pH and which pair will investigate temperature.

4
2. With your partner, design in your science notebooks an experiment to test how your assigned variable affects the enzyme lactase. While designing your investigation, think about the following questions:
   - What is the purpose of the investigation?
   - What will you observe, and how will you measure it?
   - What controls will you need?
   - What materials will you need for your investigation?
     Note: You may not need all of the materials on the Materials list.
   - How will you record your observations?

5
3. Your teacher will provide a list of guidelines you must follow to complete the investigation. Ask your teacher to answer any questions you have and to approve your procedure before starting your investigation. If necessary, change your procedure.

4. In your science notebook, write or draw a hypothesis about what you think will happen in each of the test tubes you will observe.

5. Conduct the investigation you designed, and record your results in your science notebook.

6
6. Share your results with the other pair in your group. In your science notebook, record the results of the other pair.

DOING THE ACTIVITY

3 Review with students the safety guidelines to follow during the experiment.

4 (GI, DI ASSESSMENT) If students do not already have copies of the DESIGNING INVESTIGATIONS (DI) and GROUP INTERACTION (GI) Scoring Guides, pass them out. Tell students that this laboratory will give them an opportunity to design an investigation of two factors that determine enzyme function. It also allows them to demonstrate their ability to work together as they plan and conduct their investigations. Project or distribute copies of Literacy Transparency 6, "Setting up a Laboratory Investigation," and introduce or review the elements of an investigation. You may wish to distribute copies of Science Skills Student Sheet 4, "Elements of Good Experimental Design" and Group Interaction Student skills Sheet 2, "Devel-

oping Communication Skills." For more information, see the Facilitating Group Interaction section of Teacher Resources II: Diverse Learners. If necessary, review the guidelines for Level-3 responses according to the DESIGNING INVESTIGATIONS (DI) and GROUP INTERACTION (GI) Scoring Guides. Tell students that they must work within the following parameters:

- The lactose should not be mixed with the lactase until after the lactase has been heated. This is because lactose can break down into glucose when it is heated, and interfere with the results.

- Once the yeast is added to a test tube, fix a balloon over it as quickly as possible before placing the tube in a water bath. Because the water bath provides a temperature favorable to yeast growth, the yeast will quickly begin to digest any glucose that is present and release carbon dioxide into the balloon.

5 Check for any elements that students missed in designing their experiments. Refer to Student Sheet 11.1a, "Sample Procedure: Temperature," and Student Sheet 11.1b, "Sample Procedure: pH," for the guidelines of amounts of materials and controls to set up. Tell students about any additional materials or equipment available for their use, such as ice or a refrigerator. Explain that each group must share a hot plate. While one pair is heat-treating the lactase, the other is treating it with acid and base. When it is time to run the experiment with the yeast, students can discard the water used to heat the lactase and prepare the 37°C water bath. If students are struggling with the design, you may wish to have them brainstorm ideas as a class or pass out copies of Student Sheets 11.1a and 11.1b to provide some guidance. Sample data tables are shown at the end of the activity.

6 (LITERACY) After students have collected and recorded the data from their investigations, have the class conduct an Informal Meeting of the Minds. Direct students to find a partner from another group and compare the results of their investigations. Then tell students to go back to their groups, share the new information with their partner, and then share it with the other pair in the group. Make this an opportunity to point out how important it is for scientists to verify with each other the results of an investigation.

Assign students to write a formal investigation report. Project or distribute copies of Literacy Transparency 7, "Writing a Formal Investigation Report," and review its elements with students. Tell them that these formal reports are similar to those of practicing scientists, who publish the reports of their work in journals, on posters, or in oral presentations for their colleagues.

Analysis

1. What is the relationship between lactose and lactase?

2. What evidence from your experiment indicated whether lactase was functioning?

3. What were the controls in the experiment? What information did they provide?

4. **a.** Does temperature affect the function of lactase? If yes, what is the effect? Explain, using evidence from the investigation.

   b. Does pH affect the functioning of lactase? If yes, what is the effect? Explain, using evidence from the investigation.

5. Did the results support your hypothesis? Explain.

6. Most human cells function at a temperature of 37°C and a pH of around 7. From what you learned in this activity explain why it is important for humans to maintain temperature and pH homeostasis.

7. In areas with limited resources, the population may not have access to clean, treated water. Untreated water may contain pathogens, such as the bacteria that cause the disease cholera. In those places people must boil or treat the water they plan to drink or cook with. Apply evidence from this laboratory to explain why boiling destroys biological contaminants in drinking water.

KEY VOCABULARY	
binding site	lactose
catalyze	pH
enzyme	protein
lactase	

218

FOLLOW-UP

7 (AD ASSESSMENT) Analysis Question 4 may be scored with the ANALYZING DATA (AD) Scoring Guide. Distribute copies of the AD Scoring Guide if students do not already have copies. Review your expectations for a Level-3 response. Project Transparency 11.1, "How Enzymes Work," and point out on the transparency the binding site and its role in bringing together the reactants and speeding up the reaction. You may wish to point out that an enzyme is not used up by the reaction, but can continue to catalyze the breakdown of more substrates. Also point out the effect of heat on the shape of the binding site, which will no longer fit the substrate(s). The answer to Analysis Question 6 is an opportunity to emphasize to students why it is important for cells and organisms to maintain homeostasis.

EXTENSION

Have students research the enzyme in pineapples that digests proteins. Ask them to apply that information to conducting an investigation testing the effects of fresh and canned pineapples on the protein that causes gelatin desserts to gel. Depending on your curriculum goals, leave this investigation as open-ended as is appropriate. They will find that fresh pineapple prevents gelatin from setting, while canned pineapple does not. Eventually, students should realize, or be led to the idea, that the enzyme in pineapple is inactivated by the high temperatures involved in the canning process.

SAMPLE RESPONSES

1. Lactase is an enzyme that breaks down (digests) the reactant lactose into the products galactose and glucose.

2. The yeast grew and produced carbon dioxide when they digested the glucose, indicating the lactase was functioning to break down lactose and produce glucose.

3. Depending on the students' design, the controls may vary slightly. Controls could be any one of the following in similar amounts as in the experimental condition:

   glucose + yeast
   (demonstrates that the yeast digest glucose)

   lactose + yeast
   (demonstrates that the yeast do not digest lactose)

   lactase + yeast
   (demonstrates that the yeast are not affected by the lactase alone)

   yeast alone
   (demonstrates that the yeast are living)

   lactose + lactase + yeast
   (demonstrates that the lactase catalyzes the breakdown of lactose to produce glucose for the yeast to digest)

4. (AD ASSESSMENT) A complete and correct response will explain the effect of temperature or pH, using evidence from the experiment.

Sample Level-3 Response

a. Temperature did affect the functioning of lactase. When the enzyme was heated to 80°C or higher, and then mixed with the lactose and yeast, no carbon dioxide was produced. This indicated that glucose was not present, and that the lactase did not break down the lactose into glucose and galactose. This shows that high temperatures decrease or disable the activity of the lactase.

b. The pH did affect the function of lactase. At pH 4, there was no production of carbon dioxide, meaning there was no glucose present because the enzyme was not functioning to break down lactose. At pH 6, 8, and 10 there was production of carbon dioxide, indicating that the enzyme was functioning to break down lactose. However, there was more carbon dioxide produced, making the balloon puffier, as the pH went up from 6 to 8 to 10, with pH 10 producing the most carbon dioxide. This means that the more acidic, or lower, the pH the conditions are, the more disabled the lactase was.

5. Students' answers will vary depending on their hypotheses. A sample answer follows:

   The results matched my prediction. I hypothesized that both temperature and pH would affect the enzyme. When the temperature and acid levels got to a certain point, the yeast did not produce carbon dioxide, which meant that glucose was not present and the lactase was not functioning to break down lactose into glucose and galactose.

6. Enzymes function best at certain temperatures and pH. If humans function at 37°C and pH 7, then these will likely be the best conditions for the enzymes as well. If the temperature or pH is too far from these levels, the enzymes will no longer function.

7. When you boil water, it destroys enzymes in the bacteria that are in the water. Without these enzymes, the bacteria die and, therefore, cannot make you sick.

REVISIT THE CHALLENGE

Use Transparency 11.1, "How Enzymes Work," to review the normal function of the enzyme lactase and the effects of temperature and pH on the enzyme in altering the binding site of the lactase.

Sample Procedure: Temperature

Temperature Data Table

Balloon number	1 (yeast)	2 (glucose + yeast)	3 (lactose + yeast)	4 (lactase + yeast)	5 (40°C)	6 (60°C)	7 (80°C)	8 (100°C)	9 (lactose + untreated lactase + yeast)
Observation 1 (0 mins)	Balloon limp	Limp	Limp	Limp	Limp	Limp	Limp	Limp	Limp
Observation 2 (5 mins)	Limp	Limp	Limp	Limp	Limp	Slightly puffy	Slightly puffy	Limp	Slightly puffy
Observation 3 (10 mins)	Limp	Slightly puffy	Limp	Limp	Slightly puffy	Puffy	Slightly puffy	Limp	Puffy
Observation 4 (15 mins)	Slightly puffy	Puffy	Limp	Limp	Puffy	Puffy	Limp	Limp	Puffy
Observation 5 (20 mins)	Slightly puffy	Puffier	Limp	Limp	Puffy	Puffy	Limp	Limp	Puffy
Observation 6 (25 mins)	Slightly puffy	Puffy	Limp	Limp	Puffy	Puffy	Limp	Limp	Puffy
Observation 7 (30 mins)	Slightly puffy	Puffy	Limp	Limp	Puffy	Puffy	Limp	Limp	Puffy

Sample Procedure: pH

pH Data Table

Balloon number	1 (yeast)	2 (glucose + yeast)	3 (lactose + yeast)	4 (lactase + yeast)	5 (pH 4)	6 (pH 6)	7 (pH 8)	8 (pH 10)	9 (lactose + untreated lactase + yeast)
Observation 1 (0 mins)	Balloon Limp	Limp	Limp	Limp	Limp	Limp	Limp	Limp	Limp
Observation 2 (5 mins)	Limp	Limp	Limp	Limp	Limp	Limp	Limp	Limp	Slightly puffy
Observation 3 (10 mins)	Limp	Slightly puffy	Limp	Limp	Limp	Limp	Limp	Limp	Puffy
Observation 4 (15 mins)	Slightly puffy	Puffy	Limp	Limp	Limp	Tiny bit puffy	A little puffy	Slightly puffy	Puffy
Observation 5 (20 mins)	Slightly puffy	Puffier	Limp	Limp	Limp	Tiny bit puffy	A little puffy	Slightly puffy	Puffy
Observation 6 (25 mins)	Slightly puffy	Puffy	Limp	Limp	Limp	Tiny bit puffy	A little puffy	Puffy	Puffy
Observation 7 (30 mins)	Slightly puffy	Puffy	Limp	Limp	Limp	Tiny bit puffy	Puffier	Very puffy	Puffy

12 Photosynthesis and Cellular Respiration

READING • 1–2 CLASS SESSIONS

OVERVIEW

In this activity, students complete a computer simulation of photosynthesis and cellular respiration. Then, they read about the details of photosynthesis and cellular respiration, including the light-dependent and light-independent reactions of photosynthesis, and the three stages of respiration: glycolysis, the Krebs cycle, and the electron transport chain.

KEY CONTENT

1. The energy for life is derived primarily from the sun.

2. The structure and organization of cells and internal cell parts are essential for the cell to transform and release energy needed for cellular functions.

3. Plants capture energy by absorbing light and using it to form chemical bonds between the atoms of carbon-containing molecules.

4. The chemical bonds of food molecules store energy.

5. Energy is released when the bonds of food molecules are rearranged in the reactions of cellular respiration to form new compounds.

6. Cells temporarily store the energy released by cellular respiration in adenosine triphosphate (ATP) molecules.

KEY PROCESS SKILLS

1. Students make accurate interpretations, inferences, and conclusions from text.

MATERIALS AND ADVANCE PREPARATION

For the teacher
   Scoring Guide: UNDERSTANDING CONCEPTS (UC)

For each pair of students
   computer with Internet access*

For each student
   Student Sheet 12.1, "Anticipation Guide: Photosynthesis and Cellular Respiration"
   Scoring Guide: UNDERSTANDING CONCEPTS (UC) (optional)
                                    Not supplied in kit

Masters for Scoring Guides are in Teacher Resources IV: Assessment.

Arrange for computers with Internet access for the day(s) students do this activity. Go to the Science and Global Issues page of the SEPUP website to access the simulation. You may want to bookmark this site for students. Make sure the browsers and supporting software are current and can properly run the simulation.

TEACHING SUMMARY

Getting Started

- Review with students what they have already learned about photosynthesis and cellular respiration.

Doing the Activity

- Students complete the computer simulation.

- (LITERACY) Introduce Student Sheet 12.1, "Anticipation Guide: Photosynthesis and Cellular Respiration."

- (LITERACY) Students complete the Reading.

Follow-up

- ✓(LITERACY) (UC ASSESSMENT) The class reviews the statements on Student Sheet 12.1, "Anticipation Guide: Photosynthesis and Cellular Respiration."

GETTING STARTED

1 Ask students, *What have you already learned about photosynthesis?*

If students completed the "Ecology: Living on Earth" unit of *Science and Global Issues,* their answers should mention the reactants (carbon dioxide and water), the products (glucose and oxygen), where photosynthesis occurs (cells of green plants and other producer organisms), and the types of organisms that perform photosynthesis. Next ask, *What have you already learned about cellular respiration?*

If students completed the Ecology unit, they should say that it happens in all cells, takes place in mitochondria in eukaryotes, requires oxygen and glucose (or sugars), and produces carbon dioxide and water. If students have not mentioned energy, you might ask them the role of each process in providing energy for cells and the organism. Photosynthesis allows plants to harness energy from the sun, while cellular respiration allows all organisms to convert that energy into a readily usable form. Tell students that they will build on their understanding of photosynthesis and cellular respiration in this activity, and will examine the processes in more detail at the cellular and molecular levels.

DOING THE ACTIVITY

2 Download and copy instructions for the simulation from the *Science and Global Issues* page of the SEPUP website *(sepuplhs.org/sgi).*

3 ⬙ (LITERACY) After students have completed the computer simulation, distribute copies of Student Sheet 12.1, "Anticipation Guide: Photosynthesis and Cellular Respiration." If students are unfamiliar with this strategy, review it with them. Student Sheet 12.1 provides a preview of impor-

---

12 Photosynthesis and Cellular Respiration

1 **E**VERY LIVING CELL needs a source of energy. Without energy, metabolism—all of the chemical reactions that occur within cells—will not occur. In this activity, you will learn how the complex chemical reactions of photosynthesis and cellular respiration help meet the energy needs of living things. You will examine the organelles, molecules, and chemical reactions involved in these two processes. You will also learn how a microbe or chemical that disrupts one or more of the steps of photosynthesis or cellular respiration causes disease.

solar energy (sunlight)

photosynthesis in chloroplasts

$CO_2 + H_2O$

carbon-containing molecules + H_2O

cellular respiration in mitochondria

ATP — powers most cellular work

heat

Photosynthesis and cellular respiration meet the energy needs of organisms.

Challenge

▶ How do photosynthesis and cellular respiration meet the energy needs of all organisms?

MATERIALS

FOR EACH STUDENT
Student Sheet 12.1, "Anticipation Guide: Photosynthesis and Cellular Respiration"

Procedure

1. Fill in only the Before column of Student Sheet 12.1, "Anticipation Guide: Photosynthesis and Cellular Respiration."

2. Visit the *Science and Global Issues* page of the SEPUP website at *sepuplhs.org/sgi.* With your partner, go to "Photosynthesis and Cellular Respiration" and follow the simulation.

3. Complete the Reading.

4. Fill in the After column on Student Sheet 12.1, "Anticipation Guide: Photosynthesis and Cellular Respiration."

219

---

tant concepts in the Reading. It allows students to express what they think the two processes are all about, and correct any misconceptions when they have finished the Reading. You might read the statements aloud, and clarify any questions students might have about their meaning. Instruct each student to record whether they agree or disagree with each statement by placing a "+" or "−" in the "Before" column. You may also want to discuss with students their reasoning for their predictions. Explain that they will have a chance to revisit these statements after the activity to see whether their ideas have changed or remain the same. Instruct them to complete the Reading. Tell them to mark the "After" column for each statement on the "Anticipation Guide" after they finish the reading.

FOLLOW-UP

4 (LITERACY) Review with students the important ideas in the text by asking them to share their answers to the statements in the "After" column of Student Sheet 12.1, "Anticipation Guide: Photosynthesis and Cellular Respiration." Sample responses are shown at the end of this activity. Discuss with them any answers that are not accurate, and help them find the relevant information in the text.

Reading

Energy for Life

EVERY CELL NEEDS A SOURCE OF ENERGY

As you learned in the "Ecology: Living on Earth" unit of *Science and Global Issues,* all cells need energy if they are to function. **Cellular respiration** is the process by which cells break down complex molecules, such as sugars, to release energy. Some of the energy is released as heat while the rest is stored temporarily in other molecules, such as adenosine triphosphate (ATP). ATP is used when the cell needs energy. For example, whenever your muscles contract, ATP supplies the energy. As you also learned in the "Ecology" unit, **photosynthesis** is the process by which the cells of producers capture the sun's energy and store it in sugars. All producers and consumers ultimately depend on these sugars for their energy needs.

The following equations summarize the two processes.

Cellular respiration: sugars + oxygen $\rightarrow$ carbon dioxide + water + energy

Photosynthesis: carbon dioxide + water + light energy $\rightarrow$ sugars + oxygen

As you can see from the equations, the components of cellular respiration and photosynthesis are nearly identical. In fact, cellular respiration is often described as the opposite of photosynthesis. The two processes, however, are far more complex than the equations indicate.

PHOTOSYNTHESIS

Photosynthesis only occurs in certain pigment-containing cells of producers. This differs from cellular respiration, which occurs in all types of cells in all organisms. A **pigment** is a molecule that absorbs light energy. All producers contain pigments, which are essential for photosynthesis. The most common pigment in producers is chlorophyll. Chlorophyll is what makes the stems and leaves of producers green. In most producers the chlorophyll is contained in chloroplasts.

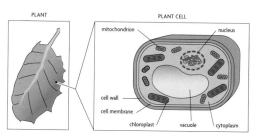

PLANT · PLANT CELL — mitochondrion, nucleus, cell wall, cell membrane, chloroplast, vacuole, cytoplasm

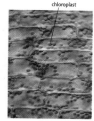

chloroplast

Light micrograph of Elodea cells

Chloroplasts are relatively large organelles surrounded by two membranes. Chloroplasts absorb energy from sunlight, as shown in the diagram below. Inside the chloroplast is a fluid-filled space called the **stroma** and stacks of connected membrane sacs called **thylakoids.** The thylakoid membranes contain the chlorophyll, and the stacked structure greatly increases the membrane surface area that can absorb light.

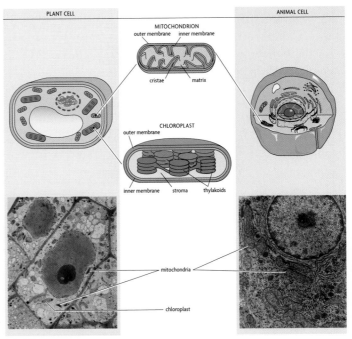

Mitochondria are present in both plants and animal cells, while chloroplasts are present only in plant cells.

THE REACTIONS OF PHOTOSYNTHESIS

The reactions occurring in photosynthesis are grouped into two stages, light-dependent and light-independent reactions. The **light-dependent reactions** rely on chlorophyll and other pigments in the thylakoid membranes to harness the energy of light. In a complex series of reactions, water breaks down into oxygen, hydrogen ions (protons), and electrons. Each reaction requires a unique enzyme. The oxygen is released to the atmosphere, some of the energy from the reactions goes into making ATP from ADP, and the protons and electrons combine with the carrier molecule, NADP$^+$, to form NADPH.

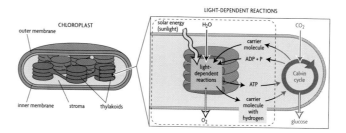

The NADPH and ATP are important to the light-independent **Calvin cycle,** which is a series of enzyme-catalyzed reactions that take place in the stroma of the chloroplast. During these reactions carbon dioxide combines with the hydrogen ions and electrons produced from water during the light-dependent reactions. This results in the production of the high-energy sugar glucose. The glucose is used in cellular respiration or is converted to another form, such as starch, and stored for later use. Starch is a type of carbohydrate. A starch macromolecule is made of many glucose molecules linked together.

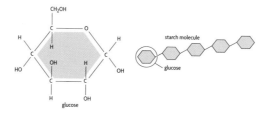

The reactions in the Calvin cycle occur in the presence or absence of light and are referred to as **light-independent reactions.** During the Calvin cycle ATP and NADPH are converted back into ADP and NADP+. These will be used again in the light-dependent reactions in the thylakoid membranes.

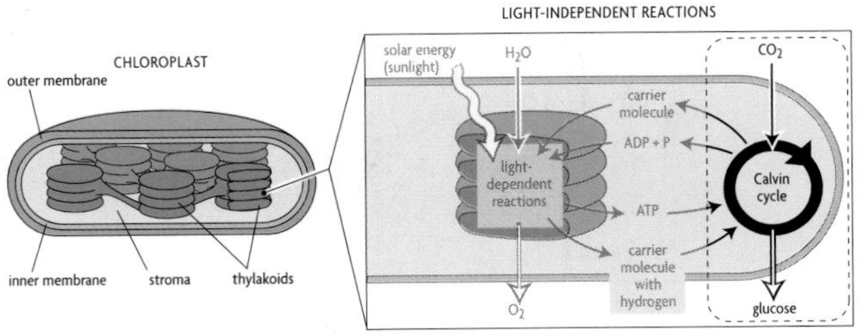

CHLOROPLAST

LIGHT-INDEPENDENT REACTIONS

The reactions of the Calvin cycle continue as long as carbon dioxide, ATP, NADPH, and enzymes are present. Certain plant diseases, such as the plum pox virus that attacks several kinds of fruit trees, inhibit enzymes involved in the Calvin cycle. This prevents the plant from making the sugar it needs to support cellular respiration. Trees infected with plum pox may eventually stop producing fruit. Organisms that feed off the fruit may need to find another food source, and communities that rely on fruit sales may suffer economically.

CELLULAR RESPIRATION

Each reaction in cellular respiration also requires a unique enzyme, and, as in photosynthesis, diseases or poisons may reduce the activity of these enzymes. This can have serious consequences for an organism, since cellular respiration is the process by which energy is released for cells to use. It is important not to confuse cellular respiration with breathing, which is often called respiration. Breathing gets oxygen into your lungs, but the oxygen has no purpose until it enters your cells and plays its part in cellular respiration.

In prokaryotes, such as bacteria, the reactions of cellular respiration that require oxygen occur on the cell membrane. In eukaryotes, these reactions take place in the cells' mitochondria. **Mitochondria** are organelles that have two membranes, an outer membrane and an inner membrane that is folded within the outer, which play central roles in the reactions of cellular respiration. The outer membrane contains specialized proteins that make the membrane very permeable to ions and small molecules. The inner membrane is less permeable, but it contains transport proteins to allow for the passage of some molecules. The inner membrane also contains enzymes needed for cellular respiration. The inner membrane is folded to form many **cristae,** finger-like projections that provide a large surface area for the reactions of cellular respiration. Inside a mitochondrion is a space called the **matrix.**

THE REACTIONS OF CELLULAR RESPIRATION

Cellular respiration begins with the process of glycolysis. **Glycolysis** means "the breaking of sugar." This first step takes place in the cytoplasm. In glycolysis, the energy from ATP breaks a glucose molecule, releasing hydrogen ions and creating two smaller molecules of pyruvic acid. The carrier molecule, NAD$^+$, combines with these hydrogen ions and with electrons to form NADH. Glycolysis also produces new ATP molecules, resulting in a net gain of 2 ATP molecules for each molecule of glucose that is broken down.

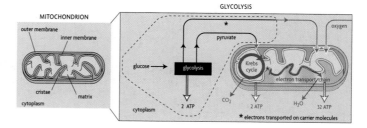

If oxygen is present, the pyruvic acid molecules produced during glycolysis are then further broken down, releasing large amounts of energy in a process called **aerobic respiration.** In eukaryotic cells, the pyruvic acid molecules first enter the mitochondrion where they are stripped of a carbon atom and are also temporarily combined with the enzyme helper, coenzyme A. This combination, called acetyl CoA, becomes part of the next stage of cellular respiration, the **Krebs cycle.** The Krebs cycle takes place in the matrix of the mitochondrion.

In the Krebs cycle the acetyl CoA breaks down and releases coenzyme A and pyruvic acid. The carbon atoms of the pyruvic acid end up in carbon dioxide, which is released as waste. Two molecules of ATP are produced and the carrier molecules NAD^+ and FAD^+ pick up electrons and hydrogen ions to form NADH and FADH, respectively. These are transferred by the carriers to the cristae of the mitochondria's inner membranes to take part in the final stage of cellular respiration, the **electron transport chain.**

During this stage, electrons and hydrogen ions are released when NADH and FADH, are converted back to NAD^+ and FAD^+. In a series of enzyme-catalyzed reactions, electrons combine with hydrogen ions and oxygen to make water, which then leaves the mitochondrion. The movement of electrons through the electron transport chain releases energy, which converts 32 more molecules of ADP into ATP. Aerobic respiration, therefore, produces a total of 36 ATP molecules for each glucose molecule.

Since the reactions of the electron transport chain need oxygen, they will stop if oxygen is not available, which prevents the Krebs cycle from operating.

Some organisms do not need oxygen for cellular respiration and instead use a process called **anaerobic respiration.** This process also occurs for short periods of time in muscle cells when insufficient oxygen is present to conduct aerobic respiration. Anaerobic respiration, also known as fermentation, takes place in the cytoplasm of a cell. There are two types of fermentation: lactate fermentation and alcoholic fermentation.

In lactate fermentation the pyruvic acid that is produced by glycolysis is changed into a form of lactic acid. This is the type of anaerobic respiration that occurs in muscle cells. However, anaerobic respiration does not sustain muscle cells for very long: as lactic acid builds up, fatigue and muscle cramps result. This same process in bacteria causes food to spoil, and with certain bacteria such fermentation allows us to make cheese and yogurt.

In alcoholic fermentation, shown in the figure below, pyruvic acid reacts with water to form acetaldehyde and release carbon dioxide. (When yeast is added to bread dough, alcoholic fermentation releases carbon dioxide, which helps the bread to rise.) In the presence of electrons and hydrogen ions that have been transported by NADH the acetaldehyde is then converted into ethanol. This is the same process that occurs, for example, when energy companies convert corn into the biofuel ethanol and when people make wine from grapes.

During fermentation there is a net gain of only two molecules of ATP. When compared to the net gain of 32 ATP molecules produced during the Krebs cycle and the electron transport chain stage, it is clear that aerobic respiration provides much more energy to cells than does anaerobic respiration.

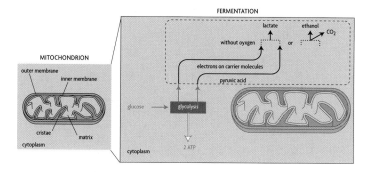

Some diseases and toxins disrupt cellular respiration in plants and animals. For example, powdery mildew fungus and cyanide both inhibit the electron transport chain. Powdery mildew causes premature death of infected plants, and cyanide is highly toxic to organisms that respire aerobically. Some genetic disorders involve mutations in certain enzymes of cellular respiration. In lactate dehydrogenase deficiency, for example, the enzyme that converts pyruvic acid to lactic acid is affected, which causes fatigue, and muscle damage if the afflicted person exercises intensely. Diabetes can also disrupt respiration. If insulin levels become too low, cells don't get enough glucose to meet their cellular respiration needs, and the body switches to fat as an energy source. As fat is broken down to be used for cellular respiration, a by-product of the process builds up and makes the blood acidic. This condition can lead to coma and death.

Analysis

1. Describe the roles of enzymes in photosynthesis and respiration.

2. **a.** What is chlorophyll?

   b. What is chlorophyll's role in photosynthesis?

3. Describe how a plant cell is specialized for photosynthesis at:

   a. the level of organelles and other cellular structures.

   b. the molecular level.

4. Compare aerobic and anaerobic respiration. What are the similarities? What are the differences?

5. In a chart like the one below, write the differences between photosynthesis and cellular respiration.

Photosynthesis and Cellular Respiration Comparison

	Photosynthesis	Cellular respiration
In what cells and cell structures does it happen?		
Reactants		
Products		
How does it contribute to the organism's energy needs?		

5 ✔ (UC ASSESSMENT) Analysis Question 7 is a Quick Check opportunity to check students' understanding of the process of photosynthesis. Analysis Question 8 is an opportunity for you to use the UNDERSTANDING CONCEPTS (UC) Scoring Guide to assess students' understanding of enzyme function. Review the Scoring Guide if necessary, and tell the class your expectations for satisfactory work. You may wish to set some criteria for satisfactory work as this question requires students to apply what they learned about enzymes in this activity and in Activity 10, "Functions of Proteins in Cells." For example, you might require students to explain both the general effect of and at least one specific effect of a dysfunctional or missing enzyme.

---

6. What are some of the similarities of photosynthesis and cellular respiration?

7. If you mixed carbon dioxide and water in a test tube, and placed the test tube in the sunlight, would photosynthesis take place? Explain.

5 8. How might reduced enzyme function lead to disease? Give at least two specific examples.

KEY VOCABULARY

adenosine triphosphate (ATP)	**light-dependent reactions**
aerobic respiration	**light-independent reactions**
anaerobic respiration	**matrix**
Calvin cycle	**mitochondria, mitochondrion**
cellular respiration	organelle
chloroplast	**photosynthesis**
cristae	**pigment**
electron transport chain	**stroma**
glycolysis	**thylakoids**
Krebs cycle	

228

SAMPLE RESPONSES

1. Enzymes catalyze the many reactions that are part of photosynthesis and respiration. They bind to reactants and speed up their reactions.

2. a. Chlorophyll is a pigment.

   b. Chlorophyll absorbs light energy.

3. a. A plant cell contains organelles called chloroplasts that are specialized for photosynthesis. The chloroplast has membrane sacs called thylakoids and an interior space called the stroma. The thylakoid membranes are structures specialized for the light-dependent reactions. The light-independent reactions take place in the stroma.

   b. At the molecular level, plants contain special pigments, enzymes, and electron carriers needed for photosynthesis.

4. The similarities are that both produce energy and both begin with glycolysis and produce ATP. Aerobic respiration differs from anaerobic respiration in that it uses oxygen to further break down the products of glycolysis, thereby producing additional ATP.

5.

Photosynthesis and Cellular Respiration Comparison

	Photosynthesis	Cellular respiration
In what cells and cell structures does it happen?	Plant cells, chloroplasts	All cells. Glycolysis takes place in the cytoplasm, and aerobic respiration takes place in mitochondria (in eukaryotes).
Reactants	Carbon dioxide and water	Oxygen and glucose
Products	Oxygen and glucose	Carbon dioxide and water
How does it contribute to the organism's energy needs?	Harnesses energy from the sun and stores it in glucose	Releases energy from glucose and stores it in ATP

6. The similarities are that both processes involve energy, take place in specialized structures, and require enzymes.

7. ✓ Photosynthesis would not occur because there must be enzymes and chlorophyll present for photosynthesis to happen.

8. (UC ASSESSMENT) A complete and correct response will explain the general effect of a dysfunctional or deficient enzyme and at least two specific examples.

Sample Level 3-Response

If an enzyme is dysfunctional or deficient, it cannot catalyze the reaction that it normally catalyzes. This can lead to build up of reactants (as in lactose intolerance), prevent the production of important products (such as DNA), or prevent a reaction, such as one of those involved in respiration or photosynthesis, in turn preventing the cell from getting or releasing energy.

REVISIT THE CHALLENGE

Review the big ideas of this Reading. Plants and other producers harness energy from the sun and convert it into chemical energy stored in glucose. Both producers and the consumers that eat producers must use cellular respiration to convert this energy into a more usable form—adenosine triphosphate (ATP). Photosynthesis and aerobic cellular respiration are complex series of reactions dependent on specialized cellular organelles that organize the enzymes and other molecules necessary for the reactions to take place.

Anticipation Guide: Photosynthesis and Cellular Respiration

Before starting the activity, mark whether you agree (+) or disagree (-) with each statement below.

After completing the activity, mark whether you agree (+) or disagree (-) with each statement below. Under each statement, explain how the activity gave evidence to support or change your ideas.

Before   After

_____   __+__   1. All living cells need energy to function.

Stated in the reading

_____   __−__   2. If no sunlight is available, the cells of producers immediately run out of energy.

This is incorrect because in both the presence and absence of sunlight the cells of producers can rely on glucose that they have previously stored as an energy source. If deprived of light for such a long period that they run out of glucose, the cells of producers will run out of energy.

_____   __+__   3. All producers and consumers ultimately depend on the sugars that are produced during photosynthesis.

Stated in the reading

_____   __−__   4. Cellular respiration is the process by which oxygen enters the lungs.

Cellular respiration is the process used by cells to break down complex molecules, such as sugars, to release energy.

_____   __−__   5. Photosynthesis occurs in many types of cells in a producer.

Photosynthesis occurs only in certain cells of producers that contain the pigment chlorophyll. The cells are in the leaves of the plants.

_____   __+__   6. Cellular respiration occurs in many types of cells in producers and consumers.

Stated in reading

_____   __−__   7. Oxygen is needed for every reaction of cellular respiration.

Oxygen is needed for the electron transport chain in aerobic respiration.

_____   __−__   8. Photosynthesis and cellular respiration both require pigments.

Only photosynthesis requires pigments, which absorb light energy.

_____   __+__   9. Photosynthesis and cellular respiration both require a number of specialized enzymes.

Stated in reading

_____   __+__   10. Photosynthesis converts solar energy into chemical energy.

Photosynthesis begins with light energy and results in the production of glucose.

13 The Cell Cycle

INVESTIGATION • 1–2 CLASS SESSIONS

OVERVIEW

Students play a board game that simulates the cell cycle, with each student in a group of four taking the role of a specific type of cell. As they progress through the cycle, students learn about the phases and events of the cycle.

KEY CONTENT

1. Cell functions are regulated to control and coordinate cell growth and division.

2. The cell cycle is the complete sequence of phases from the end of one cell division to the end of the next.

3. When normal cell regulation is disrupted, serious consequences, such as cancer, result.

4. Some types of cells, including blood and skin cells, divide more often than other types, such as liver and nerve cells.

KEY PROCESS SKILLS

1. Students record observations and identify trends.

MATERIALS AND ADVANCE PREPARATION

For the teacher
Literary Transparency 3, "Read, Think, and Take Note" (optional)

Scoring Guide: GROUP INTERACTION (GI)

For the class
6 Cell Cycle game key: cancer cell

For each group of four students
Cell Cycle game board

4 9-ounce plastic cups, each containing a different color of modeling clay (red, green, yellow, and blue)*

2 number cubes*

set of four Cell Cycle game keys (blood, liver, nerve, and skin)

For each student
Student Sheet 13.1, "Cell Cycle Record Sheet"

empty 9-ounce plastic cup*

Student Sheet 2.1, "Disease Information" from Activity 2

sticky notes*

Scoring Guide: GROUP INTERACTION (GI) (optional)

Divide the four colors of clay into enough portions so that each group of four students receives one half-full cup of each color.

Masters for Scoring Guides are in Teacher Resources IV: Assessment.

TEACHING SUMMARY

Getting Started

- Introduce the importance of cell division and the cell cycle for normal growth and development of an organism.

Doing the Activity

- (GI ASSESSMENT) Students play the Cell Cycle simulation game.

- (GI ASSESSMENT)(LITERACY) Students discuss what happened to their cell types.

- (LITERACY) Students follow the "Read, Think, and Take Note" literacy strategy as they read a case study about cancer.

Follow-up

- ✓(LITERACY) The class compares the five types of cells.

BACKGROUND INFORMATION

The cell cycle is the subject of intensive scientific and medical research because of its role in growth and cell differentiation, and because disruption of normal regulation of the cell cycle often leads to serious consequences, including cancer.

Cell Division

As an organism grows, its cells become more numerous, but not steadily larger. A cell cannot grow indefinitely because it cannot survive if its surface-area-to-volume ratio becomes too small. When this ratio is too small, there is not enough cell membrane surface to exchange nutrients and wastes and maintain cell homeostasis of the larger volume within. Growth of a multicellular organism, therefore, requires cells to divide. Cell division is the process by which a cell produces two genetically identical offspring, which scientists often refer to as daughter cells. Cell division includes mitosis, in which the replicated chromosomes divide and separate, and cytokinesis, in which the cytoplasm is divided. After division, each daughter cell has a complete set of chromosomes.

The Cell Cycle

Most cells in the human body have exited the cell cycle, and are in the G_0 phase. When protein growth factors or other molecular signals cause them to re-enter the cell cycle, they usually complete the cycle and divide. There are four main phases in the cell cycle. A newly formed cell progresses through these four phases in the following order: G_1, S, G_2, and M. G stands for growth or gap, and cell growth occurs during the two G phases. S is the synthesis phase in which DNA replication occurs. Both mitosis and cytokinesis take place during the M—mitosis—phase. Do not share this information with students until they have finished the game. One object of the game is for them to develop an understanding of these phases. The cell cycle is regulated by many factors, including a group of proteins called cyclins, which fluctuate in concentration and provide a sort of molecular clock for the cell cycle. Cancer results when cell division is no longer controlled. Some cells that have become cancerous do not respond to the protein regulators such as cyclin, and divide more frequently than needed. This kind of growth creates the masses of cells that become tumors, which damage, impinge on, or attach themselves to surrounding tissues. If these cells also lose the controls that determine where in the body they belong, they can migrate to other parts of the body (metastasize). Cancerous tumors, or malignant tumors, are those that grow without limitations, invade surrounding tissues, and metastasize. For example, lung cancer often metastasizes to the brain or bones. In contrast, benign tumors lack these characteristics and are not considered cancerous, although they can cause problems if they interfere with other tissues or organs. Some benign tumors can become cancerous.

GETTING STARTED

1 Begin by comparing a human zygote, embryo, and adult to each other. Explain that a zygote forms immediately upon fertilization. After four days, the human embryo has divided several times and is made of 64 cells. As these cells continue to divide, the embryo develops specialized cells, tissues, and organs. At about eight weeks the human embryo is called a fetus. The fetus develops until a baby is born at about 38 weeks after fertilization, and eventually an adult develops. Ask, *What happens during those days, months, and years to turn those early 64 cells of the embryo into a baby and then an adult?*

Students will likely say that the cells grow or divide and specialize. If not, bring out the idea that for a multicellular organism to grow its cells must divide, because cells cannot enlarge infinitely. Explain that the events that take place from the initial formation of one cell until it completes division to form two new daughter cells is called the cell cycle. Next ask, *Where in the body do you think cells must divide frequently in adults?*

---

13 The Cell Cycle

1 **C**ELL DIVISION IS the basis of reproduction for all organisms, and also for the development and growth of multicellular organisms. The complete sequence of phases from the end of one cell division to the end of the next is called the **cell cycle.** The cell cycle is divided into a sequence of four phases, shown in the diagram below. One of these four phases, called **mitosis,** is the stage at which the cell divides to produce two new—or offspring—cells.

A group of cell-cycle control proteins regulates the phases of the cell cycle to ensure that all events needed for normal cell division take place before division begins. Cell-cycle regulation also ensures that specific cell types divide at the right time and place. For example, in the human body red blood cells must be replaced about every 120 days. If the stem cells that differentiate into red blood cells become under- or over-active, either too few or too many red blood cells are produced. Regulation of the cell cycle also ensures that a cell completes the growth and synthesis phases so that it will divide properly. When cell growth and division proceed abnormally, cancer might result.

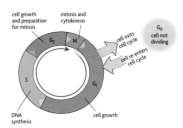

Challenge

▶ What happens during each phase of the cell cycle, and how are the phases regulated?

MATERIALS

FOR EACH GROUP OF FOUR STUDENTS
    Cell Cycle game board
4 cups, each containing a different color of modeling clay (red, green, yellow, and blue)
2 number cubes
    set of four Cell Cycle game keys (blood, liver, nerve, and skin)

FOR EACH STUDENT
    Student Sheet 13.1, "Cell Cycle Record Sheet"
    Student Sheet 2.1, "Disease Information" from Activity 2
    empty plastic cup
    sticky notes

229

Likely answers include the reproductive system, skin, and hair. Tell students that in adults, cells also divide frequently in other locations, for example to replace the linings of the digestive system and blood cells, which last only a few days or months, respectively. Ask, *What problems might result if certain cells in the body divide too slowly, or not at all?*

There will not be enough cells to replace those that die naturally or become damaged and die, and there will not be enough to perform those cells' specialized functions. For example, if red blood cell forming cells, called blood stem cells, did not divide to produce blood cells fast enough or not at all, there would not be enough blood cells to deliver

oxygen to the organs and tissues of the body. Explain also that some tissues and organs rarely need replacement, and so their cells stop dividing. If cells divide too frequently, there may be more than are needed, and they might run out of space or crowd other cells or organs. Then ask, *What preparations do you think are necessary so that a cell can divide to form two daughter cells?*

The cell must have sufficient numbers of organelles and enough cytoplasm to split between two cells. Also, since every cell has a complete copy of DNA, the DNA must be doubled before the cell divides.

DOING THE ACTIVITY

2 Demonstrate how to make a marble-sized piece of clay, and show how to enlarge it to 1.5 times its original size by adding a smaller piece of clay to simulate growth during G_1. Show how to enlarge it to 2 times its original size by adding more clay, should the cell grow again during G_2. When the cell is approximately twice its original size and its DNA has replicated, it is ready to divide. Demonstrate how students should pinch their cells into two approximately equal-sized daughter cells when the game key instructs them to do so.

3 (GI ASSESSMENT) Distribute the materials for the cell cycle simulation. Review the game board, which is an enlarged version of the cell cycle diagram in the Student Book. Be sure that each student in the group takes one of the four keys (blood, liver, nerve, or skin) and a cup of clay in the color that matches the key. You may wish to tell students that the blood-forming stem cells modeled in this activity are located in the bone marrow, and have not yet been released to the circulating blood. Review the GROUP INTERACTION (GI) Scoring Guide. Tell students this activity is an opportunity for them to demonstrate their ability to work effectively in groups: groups will process and discuss information as they play the game and then meet to discuss their results as described below.

Monitor the groups or work with the whole class as they conduct Procedure Steps 1–5. Make sure each student is clear on the type of cell he or she has been assigned and has the appropriate color of clay according to the key in the Student Book. Allow them to continue working until they complete Procedure Step 9. Some students' cells will become cancerous, and they will ask you for a Cell Cycle game key for cancer. If two or more students in the group have cells that become cancerous, they can share the cancer cell key.

2
3
Procedure

1. You will play the Cell Cycle game in your group of four. Each of you takes one of the four Cell Cycle game keys—blood, liver, nerve, or skin.

2. Based on your game key, you will play the game as a blood, liver, nerve, or skin cell. Record your cell type on Student Sheet 13.1, "Cell Cycle Record Sheet."

3. Distribute the cups of clay according to the key below, with each person taking the color for his or her assigned cell type.

Cell Cycle Game Key	
CELL TYPE	CLAY COLOR
Blood	red
Liver	blue
Nerve	green
Skin	yellow

4. Prepare a clay model of your cell. It should be about the size of a marble.

5. Place your model cell on the game board at the beginning of the game, near the start of the G_1 phase. Each player's cell has just completed the mitosis phase (M) of the cell cycle, and is ready to begin another cycle.

6. Begin round one of the game, with the blood cell person going first, and the rest of the group proceeding clockwise around your group. When it is your turn, roll both number cubes.

7. Look at your Cell Cycle game key to find out what the number you rolled means, and follow that instruction.

8. On Student Sheet 13.1, "Cell Cycle Record Sheet," record what happened to your cell in this round of the game.

9. Tell your group members what happened to your cell.

10. Continue to play the game for at least 20 rounds of rolling the number cubes. Each round, roll the number cubes unless you were told by your Cell Cycle game key to skip the turn. Each time you roll, follow Steps 7, 8, and 9 to find out what happens to your cell, record the outcome, and share it with your group.

4 (LITERACY, GI ASSESSMENT) Set up five areas of the classroom, one for each type of cell: blood, liver, nerve, skin, and cancer. Direct students who represent these cell types to the appropriate area where they can discuss in an Informal Meeting of the Minds what happened to their cell type, as explained in Procedure Step 11. Circulate around the room, and, as needed, ask such questions as: Based on the simulation, does your cell type divide frequently or infrequently? What factors or events controlled whether the cell moved along in the cell cycle? What kinds of things might occasionally go wrong as the cell progresses through the cycle?

5 Have students return to their original groups, and instruct them to work together to prepare a chart (or other format you suggest) to summarize what kinds of things happened to each cell type. A sample is shown on the following page.

6 (LITERACY) If necessary, project Literacy Transparency 3, "Read, Think, and Take Note" guidelines to review with students. If you wish to assign the cancer case study for homework, make sure students take sticky notes with them so they can follow the "Read, Think, and Take Note" literacy strategy. Begin the next class by having students discuss with their partners or groups what they wrote on their sticky notes and the main points of the reading. A sample response for Student Sheet 2.1, "Disease Information" is shown at the end of Activity 13.

---

4 11. Following your teacher's instructions, join a group of other students who had the same type of cell as yours. Discuss with these students, and record in your science notebook, what kinds of things happened to this cell type.

5 12. Rejoin your original group.

13. Work with your group to prepare a chart that summarizes what you learned about each of the four types of cells.

6 14. Follow your teacher's directions for reading the case study about cancer. As you read, use the "Read, Think, and Take Note" strategy.

15. Fill in the information for cancer on Student Sheet 2.1, "Disease Information," after you read the case study.

7 *Analysis*

1. Of the cell types you investigated, which divide:
   a. frequently?
   b. occasionally, as needed?
   c. never, or almost never?
   d. more frequently than normal and without control?

2. What kinds of factors regulate a cell's progress through the cell cycle?

3. Beginning with G_1, list the four phases of the cell cycle in order, and describe what happens in each phase.

4. Why is it important for each of the following to be regulated?
   a. Entry into the cell cycle
   b. Progress from one phase of the cell cycle to the next

5. A cell in the liver divides. Its offspring and all of their offspring continue to divide as fast as they grow and synthesize DNA. Is this likely to be a problem? Why or why not?

6. Many of the drugs given to people to fight their cancers damage the cellular structures involved in mitosis. Explain:
   a. why these drugs kill a higher percentage of cancer cells than normal cells.
   b. whether you would expect the drugs to have more of an effect on normal white blood cells or on normal neurons.

231

FOLLOW-UP

7 ✓ Discuss the similarities and differences in the cell cycles of the five types of cells. Similarities include the phases of the cell cycle, cyclin's role as a regulatory factor, and coordination of cell cycle events and phases. For example, the chromosomes must be copied before a cell enters mitosis so that each daughter cell ends up with a complete copy of the chromosomes. Cells occasionally become cancerous because

Summary of Cell Events

Cell type	Events that happened to the cell		
Liver	• Divided occasionally • Offspring cells often stayed in G_0. • Something went wrong with factors that regulate cell cycle, and cell got stuck in G_2. • Normal mitosis and cytokinesis produced two daughter cells.	• Sometimes mitosis did not work properly and was not completed (chromosomes did not separate) or cytokinesis was not completed. Cell was destroyed. • Cyclin accumulated. • Sometimes a cell became cancerous, and continued to divide.	• Sometimes a cell became cancerous, but was destroyed by the immune system. • Sometimes cancerous cells were destroyed when the chromosomes did not separate.
Nerve	Did not divide and was in G_0 permanently.		
Skin	• Cells grew and divided frequently, although some progressed through the phases faster than others. • Something went wrong with factors that regulate cell cycle, and cells got stuck in G_2. • Normal mitosis and cytokinesis produced two daughter cells.	• Sometimes mitosis did not work properly and stopped (chromosomes did not separate), or cytokinesis stopped. Cell was destroyed. • Cyclin accumulated. • Some skin cells became cancerous and continued to divide.	• A cell that became cancerous was destroyed by the immune system. • Sometimes cancerous cells were destroyed when their chromosomes did not separate.
Blood-forming stem cell	• Cells divided frequently, although some cells progressed through the phases faster than others. • Something went wrong with factors that regulate the cell cycle, and a cell got stuck in G_2. • Mitosis and cytokinesis usually proceeded normally to produce two offspring cells.	• Sometimes mitosis did not work properly and was stopped (chromosomes did not separate), or cytokinesis stopped. Cell was destroyed. • Cyclin accumulated. • Stem cells sometimes became cancerous and continued to divide without normal controls.	• A cell may have become cancerous, but was destroyed by the immune system. • Sometimes cancerous cells were destroyed when the chromosomes did not separate.
Cancer cell	• DNA replicated normally, or an error occurred that was either repaired or not. In both cases cell continued into G_2.	• Normal mitosis and cytokinesis occurred. • Mitosis occurred but cytokinesis did not work properly. Cancer cell was destroyed.	• One time all cancer cells were destroyed, and the cancer cell student started over as his or her original kind of cell.

normal control mechanisms failed. These cancer cells are often destroyed by the immune system. The main difference between the cell types was how long they remained in G_1 (or moved into a permanent G_0) before continuing through the cycle. This rate depends on the body's need for and ability to replace this type of cell. A notable difference was the neuron's inability to divide. Analysis Question 5 is a Quick Check assessment for students' understanding that uncontrolled cell division often leads to formation of a tumor. Be sure to bring out that the cell cycle is regulated by proteins and other molecular factors, including the cyclin proteins. If the cell does not respond to these molecular signals or proceeds even when the cell is not fully prepared, the cell cycle becomes abnormal. This can damage the cell, leading to cell death or formation of cancer cells. Cancer cells lose the normal controls of cell division, which leads to the formation of tumors.

8 Woman 2 develops precancerous tissue at age 30 even though she was vaccinated for HPV at age 16. This is possible because the HPV vaccine does not protect against all types of HPV that can lead to cervical cancer.

SAMPLE RESPONSES

1. a. blood stem cell, skin stem cell

    b. liver

    c. nerve

    d. cancer

2. The factors that control a cell's progress through the cell cycle include whether it has grown and replicated its DNA and the levels of a regulatory protein called cyclin.

3. Stage 1: G_1 (first gap or growth), the cell grows.

    Stage 2: S (synthesis), the cell's DNA replicates.

    Stage 3: G_2 (second gap or growth), the cell grows more, until it is about twice its original size.

    Stage 4: M (mitosis) and cytokinesis, the cell divides. This begins with separation of the chromosomes, and then the two daughter cells separate.

4. a. Cells should only be signaled to enter the cell cycle when the body needs more of them. Otherwise, there is no reason for them to prepare for division.

    b. At each stage of the cell cycle, certain things must happen for a cell to go on to the next stage. For example, the cell's DNA has to be copied so that when the cells divide, each cell has a complete copy of the DNA. Also, if cells don't grow before they divide, they will be too small and may lack needed structures.

---

8 7. Explain the main reasons why the outcomes at age 35 for the two women with cervical cancer vary in the following scenario:

Outcomes for Two Cervical Cancer Patients

AGE	WOMAN 1	WOMAN 2
16	No access to screening for abnormal cervical tissues with a Pap smear test or HPV test No access to vaccine for HPV	Begins regular screening for abnormal cervical tissues with a Pap smear test, and education from the doctor about the risks of cervical cancer Receives HPV vaccine that prevents infection by some types of HPV
30	Abnormal vaginal bleeding begins, indicating the likelihood of early stage cervical cancer. No access to adequate health care to detect and remove any abnormal cervical tissue	Pap smear reveals some precancerous cervical tissue from a type of HPV for which there is no vaccine. Precancerous tissue is removed with a simple surgical procedure to prevent progression to cancer.
35	A progression to advanced cervical cancer begins.	Leading a healthy life
36 and older	Advanced stages of cervical cancer No access to adequate health care, even to ease the pain associated with advanced stages of the cancer	Continues to get regular screening

8. Based on the cancer case study, how is cancer related to the social, economic, and environmental aspects of sustainability?

KEY VOCABULARY

cancer	cytokinesis
cell cycle	daughter cell
chromosome	**mitosis**
cyclin	replication

232

---

5. ✓ The cells will grow and divide so rapidly that there will be too many of them, and they will form a tumor. Often the tumor interferes with the function of the organ.

6. a. The drugs will kill a higher percentage of cancer cells because cancer cells divide more frequently. The drugs will kill them by interfering with the structures that are used for mitosis.

    b. Because white blood cells have to be replaced, the blood stem cells have to divide often, so the drugs will have more of an effect on white blood cells.

7. The two women in the case study had different outcomes because one had adequate health care and the other one did not. Specifically, the girl with access to health care was offered preventive measures: she was screened and vaccinated early to reduce the risk of developing cervical cancer. When she developed precancerous cervical tissue, it was removed and prevented from developing into cancer.

8. Cancer causes anxiety, pain, suffering, and sometimes death, and takes a heavy toll on patients and their families. This is one social impact of the disease. Social factors, such as lifestyle choices and behaviors, can also increase the risk for some cancers, such as smoking, drinking alcohol, dietary selections, being obese, lack of exercise, and engaging in unprotected sex. Cancer has an economic impact on families and society due to the high cost of care, and the lack of productivity if people with cancer cannot work. Environmental factors, such as exposure to tobacco smoke or air and water pollution, increase cancer risk. People may be exposed to these environmental factors based on where they live or work.

REVISIT THE CHALLENGE

Review the phases of the cell cycle with the class. Make sure they understand key events of each phase and their importance in producing normal daughter cells. Emphasize the importance of the role of proteins in coordinating all steps of the cell cycle.

CASE STUDY

Cancer

ONE IN EIGHT deaths worldwide is caused by cancer—more deaths than caused by AIDS, tuberculosis, and malaria combined. Scientists have made great progress in understanding, treating, and curing many types of cancer, but much about cancer is still unknown.

Cancer affects people living in all areas of the world, at all income levels. It usually develops over several years and has various causes, some environmental and some internal.

SYMPTOMS AND DISEASE MECHANISM

The term cancer refers to more than 100 diseases that result when cells lose the normal controls that regulate their growth and division in the cell cycle. These cells continuously divide even when no new cells are needed. In most types of cancer, as an original cancer cell divides through multiple cell cycles, a mass of cells develops to form a tumor. However, some types of cancer, such as leukemia, rarely produce tumors. Leukemia results when abnormal white blood cells are produced too rapidly or do not die within the normal lifetime of white blood cells. These cells crowd the blood and prevent normal blood cells from performing their functions.

Mutations, or errors, in some genes can cause cancer. Some of these genes normally stimulate cell division, while others normally stop cell division. Mutations in these genes can lead to unregulated cell growth and division that result in tumors.

Cervical cancer is an example of a cancer that is linked to an infection from a virus, in this case human papillomavirus (HPV). Women worldwide are at risk of being infected by this sexually transmitted virus. There are more than 100 types of HPV, about 30 types infect the genital regions of men and women, and a few have been shown to cause cervical cancer in women.

(Continued on next page)

Burden of Disease		
	NUMBER OF NEW CASES PER YEAR	NUMBER OF DEATHS PER YEAR
Worldwide	12 million	7 million
United States	1.7 million	570,000

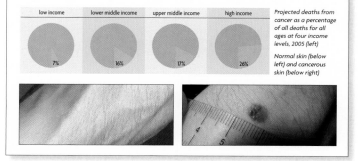

low income 7%   lower middle income 16%   upper middle income 17%   high income 26%

Projected deaths from cancer as a percentage of all deaths for all ages at four income levels, 2005 (left)

Normal skin (below left) and cancerous skin (below right)

233

367

(Continued from previous page)

Cancer sometimes develops when environmental factors or viruses interact with certain genes to cause mutations. Environmental factors that lead to cancer include exposure to such chemicals as tobacco smoke, air pollutants, and asbestos. The chemicals produced when tobacco burns put people who smoke, and who are regularly exposed to tobacco smoke, at a higher risk of developing lung cancer than non-smokers. In fact, approximately 10%–15% of smokers develop lung cancer, and smokers are 10–20 times more likely to get lung cancer than nonsmokers. Other environmental factors, including various kinds of radiation, also cause cancer.

CANCER PREVENTIONS AND TREATMENT

The World Health Organization reports that approximately 30% of cancer cases could be prevented by addressing such risk factors as:

- tobacco use
- being overweight or obese
- lack of physical activity
- lack of fruits and vegetables in the diet
- alcohol abuse
- sexually transmitted HPV infection
- urban air pollution
- indoor smoke from household use of solid fuels, such as wood

There are a number of programs and a few vaccines that help people reduce or eliminate their risk factors for cancer. The table below shows examples.

The main ways that cancers are treated are surgery, chemo-

therapy, radiation therapy, or a combination of those. Surgeries to treat cancer include removing the tumor and surrounding tissues, removing the tumor and the organ it is in, and sometimes removing lymph nodes where the cancer may have spread. Surgeons also might remove just part of a tumor to relieve pain or open any blockages the tumor is causing. Chemotherapy involves taking certain drugs that kill cells, including cancer cells. Chemotherapy might follow surgery or be used alone or in combination with radiation therapy,

Some Preventive Measures for Cancer

PREVENTIVE MEASURE	EXAMPLES
Vaccines	Vaccination for the hepatitis B virus that can cause liver cancer
	Vaccination for HPV, which causes cervical cancer
Tobacco and alcohol-abuse programs	Increase taxes on tobacco and alcohol
	Educate the public about health risks
	Ban smoking in public and commercial areas
Health education in schools and the workplace	Promotion of healthy diet and exercise
Screening	HPV test and pap smear for cervical cancer
	Colonoscopy or other screening for colon and rectal cancer

A diet high in fat and calories and low in fruits and vegetables, as shown at far left, increases a person's risk of developing some cancers, as compared to the diet shown at near left.

234

depending on the cancer. Radiation therapy directs X-rays or other high-energy particles to the area of the tumor to damage the genetic material inside the cancer cells and kill them. Normal cells in the radiated area are sometimes damaged but are usually replaced by division of the normal cells that remain.

CHALLENGES TO PREVENTION AND TREATMENT

Challenges vary depending on the type of cancer. It is often difficult for people to avoid or control environmental risk factors for cancer simply because some of these factors are found in the environment. For example, several industrial chemicals have been associated with increased lung cancer risk, including asbestos, arsenic, nickel, chromium, zinc, and radon. People might be exposed to these chemicals in their work environment or home. Research suggests that up to 15% of lung cancer cases in men and 5% in women are due to occupational hazards. Also, many people cannot avoid exposure to air pollution if they live in urban areas where pollution levels are high. And for many people, making a behavioral change, such as quitting smoking, is very hard to do.

While screening may detect cancer early, it can only be effective if there is a treatment strategy for that cancer. Also, for many cancers, cost-effective early diagnostic tests have not yet been developed. The drawbacks of chemotherapy and radiation therapy are that they kill many normal cells, not just cancer cells. Fatigue, nausea, diarrhea, loss of appetite, and hair loss are just some of the side effects that might be mild or severe, depending on the drugs and course of radiation.

Although cancer might strike anyone, poor people in low-income developing countries have a lower chance of surviving the disease than those in higher-income countries. The preventions and treatments available for cancer are often too expensive in the lower-income countries, and there may be few, if any, accessible hospitals or health care professionals capable of providing the care needed. ■

Disease Information

Disease	Cancer
Description of disease and symptoms	People all over the world, at all income levels get cancer. Cancer refers to any of more than 100 diseases that occur when cells lose the normal controls that regulate growth and division in the cell cycle.
Cellular mechanism of disease	Most cancers grow through a number of cell cycles that results in a mass of cells called a tumor. Mutations in genes that stimulate or stop cell division can cause cancer through unregulated cell growth and division that lead to tumors.
Social factors	Some risk factors for cancer are: tobacco use, being obese, lack of physical activity, diet, alcohol use, infection with a certain virus, urban air pollution, and indoor smoke from burning fuels. Some of these can be difficult to avoid depending on where people live. Behavior can be difficult to change. Screening, education, tobacco/alcohol programs, and vaccination can prevent some cancers.
Economic factors	Preventions and treatments can be expensive for people in developing countries. Some countries may not have hospitals or health care professionals to provide proper treatment or screening.
Environmental factors	Toxicants, tobacco smoke, pollution, asbestos, and viruses in the environment can cause mutations.

14 Stem Cell Differentiation

INVESTIGATION • 1 CLASS SESSION

OVERVIEW

To investigate how embryonic stem cells become specialized cells, students draw from a set of colored chips that represent specific molecular factors that determine the next step of specialization. They discuss the paths stem cells take as they differentiate into specialized cells.

KEY CONTENT

1. Stem cells can produce a variety of specialized cells.

2. The process by which stem cells produce specialized descendent cells is called differentiation.

MATERIALS AND ADVANCE PREPARATION

For the teacher

Transparency 14.1, "The Organization of Multicellular Organisms"

For each pair of students

cup containing 9 chips (3 green, 3 blue, 3 orange)

3 colored pencils*

For each student

Student Sheet 14.1, "Stem Cell Differentiation"

TEACHING SUMMARY

Getting Started

- Discuss the process of differentiation in producing the many types of specialized cells in a multicellular organism.

Doing the Activity

- Students complete the investigation.

Follow-up

- The class discusses the importance of stem cell differentiation.

BACKGROUND INFORMATION

Stem cells and precursor cells

A stem cell produces daughter cells that might remain as stem cells or begin a pathway of differentiation into one of a variety of specialized cell types. Stem cells are classified into three groups, depending on where they are on the pathway toward differentiation. Totipotent stem cells can produce any kind of cell in the body, and have an unlimited ability to self-renew. The embryonic cells that form during the first few divisions after an egg is fertilized are totipotent. Pluripotent stem cells can become almost any type of cell in the body, except the cells of the placenta and certain other uterine tissues. Totipotent stem cells become pluripotent after three or four divisions. Multipotent stem cells produce only certain types of cells. For example, one line of multipotent stem cells gives rise to all the blood cells, including red and white blood cells. Adult stem cells are multipotent.

Precursor (or progenitor) cells are immature cells that are precursors to a fully differentiated cell of the same tissue type. They are in a stage between a stem cell and a fully differentiated cell. Precursor cells are usually unipotent (capable of developing into only one type of cell). They multiply quickly and regenerate tissue, but are limited in the type(s) of cell they produce. For example, a lymphoid precursor cell might be able to make only T lymphocytes.

In this activity students focus on the differentiation of embryonic stem cells. Embryonic stem cells come from five-day-old pre-implantation embryos created at fertility clinics. They develop into the cells and tissues of the three primary germ layers—endoderm, mesoderm, and ectoderm.

GETTING STARTED

1 ◆ Project Transparency 14.1, "The Organization of Multicellular Organisms." Ask students to name some organs in the human body. Likely suggestions are the heart, liver, and kidney. Explain that all of these organs are made of specialized tissues and cells. As students have learned, specialized cells have specialized arrangements of structures and organelles that allow them to perform their specific function. Ask, *How do you think all of the specialized cells that make up your body develop?*

Accept students' ideas. They will likely state that something happens during development of the embryo. Explain that all cells start as identical stem cells in a developing embryo, and that these embryonic stem cells are capable of producing all cell types. The process in which stem cells become specialized cells is called differentiation. Emphasize that a stem cell itself does not become a differentiated cell, but one or both of its daughter cells may change in some way. These cells, in turn, produce daughter cells that are different from the parent cell, until a fully specialized cell results. Explain to students that they will investigate a simplified model of stem cell differentiation in this activity. Instruct them to read the introduction.

---

14 Stem Cell Differentiation

1 **T**HE HUMAN BODY is made of many kinds of specialized cells. Red blood cells, white blood cells, muscle cells, nerve cells, and skin cells are just some examples. Each specialized cell performs a function in the body. You have learned about several conditions that result when cells don't function normally. Diabetes damages the cells in the pancreas that make insulin. Sickle cell disease is a genetic condition that alters the functioning of the hemoglobin protein in red blood cells. And many kinds of cells may become cancerous when they lose their normal cell cycle controls.

Every cell in your body is the offspring of another cell and has the same genetic material as the fertilized egg from which it developed. It is amazing that the many different types of cells all arise from a single fertilized egg cell. Yet that is what happens during embryo development. Initially, all the cells in the embryo are alike. But as they divide, they become more specialized and produce their own characteristic proteins. Cells that have the ability to produce a variety of types of specialized cells are called **stem cells**. The process by which stem cells produce specialized cells is called **differentiation**. As differentiation progresses, segments of the genetic material are either activated or suppressed.

You have probably heard about stem cell research in the news. This is an important area of cutting-edge research. Once we understand exactly how a human develops from a single cell to a multicellular organism we might learn how certain conditions, such as some birth defects, and diseases, such as cancer, develop. Researchers around the world are trying to figure out how stem cells might be used to replace diseased or damaged tissues in any number of diseases.

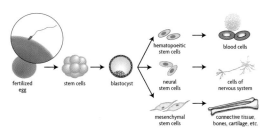

The development of specialized cells from stem cells.

236

DOING THE ACTIVITY

2 Distribute Student Sheet 14.1, "Stem Cell Differentiation." Explain to students that the chart is a representation of some of the types of stem cells in the body and some of the types of cells that differentiate from the stem cells. It does not include every type of stem cell or differentiated cell in the body. Circulate around the room to monitor students' progress through the Procedure, and answer questions when necessary. You may want to tell students that many of the molecular differentiation factors represented by the chips are proteins, and are classified as signaling proteins.

In this activity, you will learn about the differentiation of human stem cells. In the next activity you will have a chance to apply what you learn about stem cells to stem cells' potential for curing diseases.

Challenge

▶ How do stem cells produce specialized cells?

MATERIALS

FOR EACH PAIR OF STUDENTS
    cup containing 9 chips (3 blue, 3 green, 3 orange)
3   colored pencils
FOR EACH STUDENT
    Student Sheet 14.1, "Stem Cell Differentiation"

2 Procedure

1. The colors of the chips in the cup represent the specific protein or chemical factor that directs the differentiation of an embryonic stem cell. You and your partner will share the cup of chips, but you will each draw your own chips and follow your own cell on Student Sheet 14.1, "Stem Cell Differentiation." With your partner, decide who will begin. Take turns drawing one chip from the cup. When drawing a chip, look away to make sure your selection is random. Use the key below to find out how your stem cell differentiates. Put the chip back in the cup before your partner draws a chip. Select a colored pencil. On Student Sheet 14.1, draw a line from the embryonic stem cell to the type of stem cell it produced.

   Note: Differentiation cannot be reversed from this point forward.

Differentiation Key 1	
DIFFERENTIATION PROTEIN (CHIP COLOR)	**STEM CELL TYPE PRODUCED**
Blue	Endoderm—the innermost layer of cells in an embryo
	These cells develop into the linings of the digestive tract and most of the respiratory system.
Green	Mesoderm—the middle layer of cells in an embryo
	These cells develop into muscles and most of the circulatory, reproductive, and excretory organ systems.
Orange	Ectoderm—the outermost layer of cells in an embryo
	These cells develop into sense organs, nerves, and the outer layer of skin.

2. Have the second person draw one chip and repeat Step 1.

237

3. Take turns drawing a second chip from the cup to represent the next step in the pathway of differentiation from the same stem cell. Use the key below to find out how your differentiated cell differentiates further. Sometimes, a protein will have no effect on a certain stem cell. If the factor has no effect, take a chip of another color. Put all of the chips back in the cup before your partner draws again.

Differentiation Key 2

DIFFERENTIATION FACTOR (CHIP COLOR)	ENDODERM	MESODERM	ECTODERM
Blue	no effect	hematopoietic (blood-forming) stem cell	skin precursor cell
Green	pancreas precursor cell	no effect	no effect
Orange	intestinal epithelial stem cell	muscle stem cell	neural stem cell

On your Student Sheet 14.1, "Stem Cell Differentiation," using the colored pencil you used before, draw a line to show the next step in your cell's differentiation.

4. Take turns drawing a third chip. Using the colored pencil you used before, draw a line from your cell from Step 3 to the next type of cell on Student Sheet 14.1, based on the color key below. If the factor has no effect, draw another chip. Put all of the chips back in the cup before your partner draws chips.

Differentiation Key 3

	PANCREAS PRECURSOR CELL	INTESTINAL STEM CELL	MUSCLE STEM CELL	HEMATOPOIETIC (BLOOD-FORMING) STEM CELL	SKIN PRECURSOR CELL	NEURAL STEM CELL
Blue	no effect	no effect	heart muscle cell (differentiation complete)	macrophage (differentiation complete)	hair follicle cells (differentiation complete)	motor neuron (differentiation complete)
Green	alpha (α) cell producing glucagon (differentiation complete)	intestinal epithelial cell (differentiation complete)	no effect	no effect	no effect	no effect
Orange	beta (β) cell producing insulin (differentiation complete)	no effect	smooth muscle cell (differentiation complete)	red blood cell (differentiation complete)	cheek lining cell (differentiation complete)	photoreceptor (differentiation complete)

5. Show the path of differentiation of your embryonic stem cells to your group. Discuss the various paths of differentiation that occurred for each person in the group.

FOLLOW-UP

3 Emphasize that specialized cells each produce specific proteins that they need for performing their specialized functions. In the *Science and Global Issues* "Genetics: Feeding the World" unit, students will learn about the processes that regulate gene expression and determine the proteins a cell produces. Instruct students to go back to the introduction of the activity and re-read the third paragraph. Ask, *Now that you know more about stem cells and differentiation, why do you think scientists think stem cells are the key to replacing diseased or damaged tissues in patients with heart disease, cancer, or diabetes?*

Since stem cells are capable of becoming a variety of specialized cells, if these cells can be put into humans who have diseased cells of a given type, they could develop into healthy cells and perhaps treat or prevent a disease.

SAMPLE RESPONSES

1. Stem cells can become a variety of types of cells, while differentiated cells like red blood cells are fully specialized cell types.

2. a. A stem cell produces a mesoderm cell, which can then further differentiate to form a muscle stem cell. From there it differentiates into a smooth muscle cell.

   b. An embryonic stem cell divides and gives rise to an endoderm cell, which divides and produces a pancreas precursor cell. From there the precursor differentiates into a specialized beta (ß) cell in the pancreas.

3. The replication of DNA in the S phase of the cell cycle and equal division of the chromosomes during mitosis ensure that each cell contains a complete copy of all of the DNA for that individual.

Inset (Student Sheet reproduction):

6. Repeat Steps 1–4 to model a second course of differentiation. On Student Sheet 14.1, "Stem Cell Differentiation," trace the path of differentiation with a pencil of another color.

7. If you have time, repeat Steps 1–4 to model another differentiation process. Use a pencil of a third color.

3 *Analysis*

1. What is the difference between a stem cell and a differentiated cell, such as a red blood cell?

2. Use the information on Student Sheet 14.1, "Stem Cell Differentiation," to describe the pathway for each of the following as it differentiates:

   a. A smooth muscle cell

   b. A pancreatic beta (ß) cell

3. The two types of cells in Question 2 have the same genetic information. What process ensures that all cells get a complete set of the same genetic information?

4. Your friend has just learned that she will be starting erythropoietin treatment for anemia (lowered hemoglobin) that has developed as a result of kidney disease. She is worried because she does not know much about the treatment. The doctor gave her the following information:

   • Erythropoietin is a hormone that is naturally produced in the liver and kidney.

   • Erythropoietin stimulates the differentiation of red blood cells in the bone marrow.

   • Erythropoietin treatment increases red blood cell production in patients with anemia due to kidney disease, and in patients who have had chemotherapy and radiation treatment for cancer.

   Using what you have learned about cell biology and stem cells, explain to your friend how erythropoietin works.

   KEY VOCABULARY

   differentiation   stem cells

239

---

4. Because of kidney disease, your body is not producing erythropoietin, which normally stimulates the production of red blood cells by stem cells in your bone marrow. Without erythropoietin, your body is not producing enough red blood cells, and so you are anemic. Your doctor wants to treat you with additional erythropoietin. This will stimulate stem cells in your bone marrow to produce red blood cells.

REVISIT THE CHALLENGE

Stem cells produce specialized cells in a developing embryo through a number of cell divisions. Differentiation factors stimulate stem cells to give rise to more differentiated stem cells in a process that ends when a cell has become fully specialized.

15 Stem Cell Research

TALK IT OVER • 1 CLASS SESSION

OVERVIEW

Students read about current scientific research on and the social controversy over embryonic stem cells. On a KWL literacy strategy student sheet, they record their initial ideas and what they have learned from the reading.

KEY CONTENT

1. Stem cells produce a variety of types of specialized cells.

2. The process by which stem cells produce specialized descendent cells is called differentiation.

3. An embryonic stem cell has the potential to produce any type of specialized cells, while stem cells from developed organisms can produce a limited set of specialized cell types.

KEY PROCESS SKILLS

1. Students distinguish scientific questions from ethical questions.

MATERIALS AND ADVANCE PREPARATION

For each student

Student Sheet 15.1, "KWL: Stem Cells"

TEACHING SUMMARY

Getting Started

• Review the role of stem cells in the development of specialized cells.

Doing the Activity

• (LITERACY) Using the KWL literacy strategy, students discuss in their groups what they know and want to know about stem cells and stem cell research.

• (LITERACY) Students read about stem cells and stem cell research, and complete their KWLs according to what they learned.

Follow-up

• The class discusses the types of questions that science can and cannot answer about stem cells.

BACKGROUND INFORMATION

In 1998, biologist James Thomson and his group of research scientists at the University of Wisconsin were the first to isolate and reproduce human embryonic stem cells. Scientists are working towards a complete understanding of embryonic stem cells and their role in normal human development, and they think that embryonic stem cells may be harnessed to create better treatments for such diseases as Parkinson's disease, heart disease, Type I diabetes, and rheumatoid arthritis, or reverse damage from spinal cord injuries.

Experimenting with embryonic stem cells currently requires destroying the embryos from which they are derived. This is so controversial in the United States that in 2001, President George W. Bush ordered that no federal funds could be used to develop or conduct research on new embryonic stem cell lines. Research on existing cell lines was allowed with federal funds as long as the embryonic cells were derived from embryos that were created for reproductive purposes and were no longer needed. The policy also required informed consent for the donation of the embryo and that donation must not have involved financial inducements. On March 9, 2009, U.S. President Barack Obama issued an Executive Order titled "Removing Barriers to Responsible Scientific Research Involving Human Stem Cells." The purpose of the order was to remove barriers to scientifically worthy and responsible use of embryonic stem cells. The National Institutes of Health's Stem Cell Information website provides updates on the status of national guidelines and policies for stem cell research.

REFERENCES

National Institutes of Health. 2009. *Stem Cell Information*. Retrieved October 2009 from http://stemcells.nih.gov/

GETTING STARTED

1 Review the function of stem cells in producing the many types of specialized cells in the body. Emphasize to students that the simulation they conducted in the last activity showed that embryonic stem cells pass through a number of stages along the pathway to complete differentiation. Explain that each time it divides, a stem cell might become two more stem cells or one or both of its offspring might enter the next stage of differentiation.

15 Stem Cell Research

1 **B**ECAUSE OF THEIR ability to differentiate into multiple cell types, stem cells hold the potential to treat a variety of human diseases. In fact, several stem cell-based treatments are already in widespread use, including bone marrow transplantation and umbilical-cord-blood stem cell therapy. One area of stem cell research, however, has generated a major social controversy. This is research performed with human embryonic stem cells.

In this activity, you will explore current scientific knowledge and social issues related to stem cell research.

Challenge

▶ What are the current scientific understandings and social debates about stem cell research?

MATERIALS

FOR EACH STUDENT
Student Sheet 15.1, "KWL: Stem Cells"

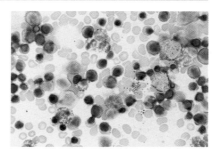

Bone marrow cells from a healthy donor, such as the stained cells shown here, can be transplanted into a patient with a disease such as leukemia.

240

DOING THE ACTIVITY

2 (LITERACY) Distribute copies of Student Sheet 15.1, "KWL: Stem Cells." The letters KWL refer to the three sections of the reading strategy that ask, "What do I Know? What do I Want to know? What did I Learn?" KWLs help students process and apply what they have read. For more information on this strategy, refer to Teacher Resources III: Literacy. Encourage students to listen and respond to each other's ideas about stem cells, based on their current perceptions, and to ask thoughtful questions about what more they want to know about stem cells. It is likely that many students have heard something about stem cell research in the news.

3 (LITERACY) You might assign this short reading for homework. After students have read the text, ask them to complete the "Learned" column on Student Sheet 15.1, "KWL: Stem Cells." A sample KWL is shown at right.

Procedure

2 1. In your group, discuss each of the questions below. Record on Student Sheet 15.1, "KWL: Stem Cells," what you Know and Want to know about each of the questions.

- What is a stem cell?
- What kinds of human stem cells are there?
- Why might stem cells be useful in treating certain diseases?
- What is the debate about stem cell research and stem cell therapy?

3 2. Read the information below about stem cells, and then complete the Learned column of your KWL.

Reading

Several Types of Stem Cells

In the previous activity, you learned that stem cells often differentiate through multiple cell cycles to produce a variety of types of specialized cells. A human fertilized egg, or zygote, can produce cells that differentiate into every kind of specialized human cell. This means the zygote is **totipotent,** totally capable. When the zygote first begins dividing, its cells form a hollow ball, called a blastocyst. The inner cells of this blastocyst will form most types of human cells, and are called **pluripotent embryonic stem cells.**

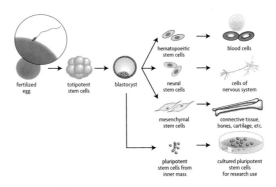

Sample Student Response, KWL: Stem Cells

Know	Want to know	Learned
• Blood is produced from blood-forming stem cells (Activity 13). • Stem cells can differentiate into more than one kind of specialized cell (Activity 14).	• Why can't scientists just use adult stem cells to treat diseases? • What kinds of diseases are treated with stem cells? • At what stage of an embryo's development are stem cells taken from human embryos?	• There are several types of stem cells. • Stem cells vary in the kinds of cells they produce, from totally potent, to pluripotent, to multipotent. • Because embryonic stem cells are totipotent—they can produce any kind of cell—they might be more useful in treating many diseases. • Adult stem cells are usually multipotent, and can only produce certain cell types. • Embryonic stem cells are obtained from early-stage embryos in which the cells have not begun to differentiate. • Getting stem cells from an embryo destroys the embryo. That's why embryonic stem cell research is controversial. • Stem cells are most likely to work at treating or curing non-infectious diseases that affect one kind of cell.

Unlike embryonic stem cells, the stem cells in a human adult—or a child or infant—can differentiate into only a limited number of kinds of cells and are usually found within the tissues that they will renew. Stem cells found in our bone marrow, for example, can form many types of blood cells, but not muscle or nervous tissue cells. These **multipotent stem cells** have a multiple, but limited, potential.

Stem Cell Therapy Today

A frequently used stem cell therapy, bone marrow transplantation, involves injecting blood stem cells from a healthy donor into the bone marrow of a recipient with a blood disease, such as leukemia. Leukemias are a group of cancers that cause an overproduction of white blood cells. The recipient is first treated with radiation and chemotherapy to kill all of the unhealthy bone marrow and blood cells before receiving blood-forming cells from the donor. These cells may be obtained from the donor's bone marrow or circulating blood. There are a number of risks to this procedure, including an immune system attack on the donor cells.

Umbilical cord stem cells are also used to treat leukemia. Like an adult's stem cells, they are multipotent, but they are less likely than fully developed stem cells to cause an immune response in the recipient.

The Potential of Stem Cells for the Future

Many diseases are caused by a problem with one particular cell type. These are the diseases that are current or potential targets for stem cell therapy. One possible target for adult stem cell therapy is diabetes. In Type-I diabetes, the afflicted person's immune system attacks cells in the pancreas that produce insulin, the protein hormone necessary for metabolizing sugars. One approach to treating this disease is to kill the person's immune cells with radiation or chemotherapy, and then provide adult stem cells that will restore a healthy immune system. A group of scientists has reported promising results from trying this treatment on a small number of diabetes patients. This treatment is highly experimental, and even if the results hold up over time, there are risks involved.

Embryonic stem cells can become any type of specialized cells. They are also easier to obtain than some types of adult stem cells, most of which are not easily located and isolated. For these reasons, embryonic stem cells might allow more rapid development of effective treatments.

One area of potential is treating neurological diseases, such as Parkinson's disease. In Parkinson's, the nerve cells in the brain that make the chemical dopamine stop functioning, and the person loses the ability to move properly and might eventually develop mental impairments. If these cells could be replaced in some way, it might relieve the symptoms or cure the disease. Because stable adult nerve cell lines are difficult to produce, using pluripotent embryonic stem cells might allow researchers to find cures more quickly.

FOLLOW-UP

4 Continue the class discussion using the Analysis Questions as prompts. Discuss the types of questions about stem cells that science can and cannot answer. Scientific inquiry can answer questions about the isolation and properties of stem cells at each stage of development, and can investigate stem cells' effectiveness in treating diseases. This information may help an individual understand and form an opinion about stem cell research. Ethical questions enter into decisions about whether or not particular types of stem cells or methods for obtaining them should be used in research or medical procedures.

SAMPLE RESPONSES

1. Scientists can answer questions about the potential of stem cells at different stages and investigate whether stem cells can be used to reduce the symptoms of or cure certain diseases.

2. The types of questions that involve ethical considerations include: Where do the stem cells come from? How were they obtained? These questions apply especially to embryonic stem cells.

3. Stem cell treatments will not kill microbes. Stem cells are useful for treating diseases that involve a problem with a particular type of cell in the person with the disease. In the future, it might be possible to use stem cells to reverse damage that an infection caused. But right now the targets of stem cell treatment are diseases that involve breakdown of human cells from genetic or environmental factors, aging, cancer, and other noninfectious disease mechanisms.

The Stem Cell Debate

Working with stem cells from developed humans is not generally a controversial area of scientific research, but it is more complicated than starting with an embryonic stem cell that might be steered in any direction to re-create specialized cells. In contrast, embryonic stem cell research involves getting an early-stage embryo from a fertility clinic and isolating individual cells. This destroys the embryo. Although the cells of those embryos have not yet begun to differentiate into the specialized cells that will turn into a functioning human being, some people object to destroying any embryo because of its potential to develop into a human being. Another method being researched for creating embryonic stem cells is to take a human egg, remove its nucleus, and insert an adult cell nucleus from the person to be treated. This produces an embryonic stem cell with the same genetic makeup as the recipient, lowering the chance of an immune reaction to the stem cells. However, the same ethical considerations apply.

 Analysis

1. What kinds of questions can scientists answer about stem cells?

2. What kinds of questions about stem cell research involve ethical considerations?

3. Why do you think scientists are not pursuing stem cell research and treatments to reduce deaths from infectious diseases?

KEY VOCABULARY	
multipotent stem cells	**totipotent**
pluripotent embryonic stem cells	stem cell

243

REVISIT THE CHALLENGE

Much of the current scientific research on stem cells revolves around the different types of stem cells and their potential to differentiate into specific cell types. Because those embryonic stem cells that are in the earliest stages of the embryo's development have the potential to form all types of specialized cells, scientists think they provide a faster route to inventing therapies for diseases. People's qualms about stem cell research are related to destroying a human embryo to obtain its stem cells.

16 HIV/AIDS Infection and Cell Organelles

INVESTIGATION • 1–2 CLASS SESSIONS

OVERVIEW

In this activity, students apply their knowledge of the functions of cell organelles to investigate the cell organelles that HIV commandeers in order to reproduce during infection.

KEY CONTENT

1. Cells have particular structures that perform specific functions.

2. To support life cells need thousands of proteins, each with a specialized function.

3. Receptor proteins and enzymes play key roles in viral infections.

4. Cellular organelles, structures, and enzymes make the proteins required by cells.

5. The HIV virus is not a cell and cannot reproduce on its own.

6. When HIV infects a cell, it uses the host's cell organelles and proteins to make more HIV viruses.

MATERIALS AND ADVANCE PREPARATION

For the teacher

Student Sheet 16.1, "HIV Infection" (optional)
Literacy Transparency 3, "Read, Think, and Take Note" (optional)

For each pair of students

set of 13 Cell Structures and Organelles Cards
colored pencils*
computer with internet access*

For each student

Student Sheet 16.1, "HIV Infection"
Student Sheet 2.1, "Disease Information," from Activity 2
sticky notes

Masters for Literacy Transparencies are in Teacher Resources III: Literacy.

Arrange for computers with Internet access for the day(s) students do this activity. Go to the Science and Global Issues *page of the SEPUP website to access the simulation. You may want to bookmark this site for students. Make sure the browsers and supporting software are current and can properly run the simulation.*

TEACHING SUMMARY

Getting Started

- The class reviews the structures and organelles cells need for producing and packaging proteins.

Doing the Activity

- Students complete the investigation.

- (LITERACY) Students follow the "Read, Think, and Take Note" literacy strategy while reading a case study about rotavirus.

Follow-up

- ✔ The class discusses why HIV must infect cells in order to reproduce.

BACKGROUND INFORMATION

HIV

HIV is a retrovirus, which means that it contains ribonucleic acid (RNA) as its genetic material and has an enzyme called reverse transcriptase that transcribes the RNA into DNA. HIV has an envelope made of a bilayer of phospholipids that surrounds the capsid (protein shell). HIV has proteins on its surface that attach to cells that have protein receptors on their surfaces used by HIV to enter the cell. One cell protein receptor is the CD4 receptor found mainly on helper T cells, but it is also present on macrophages and brain cells. There are also other receptors on the cell surface called co-receptors, which the HIV needs for entry into the cell. Once it is inside the cell, the reverse transcriptase transcribes the HIV RNA into DNA in the cytoplasm. This DNA then enters the nucleus, where it is integrated into the cell's genome and directs the synthesis of viral mRNA. This mRNA is transcribed by the cell, leading to the production of viral proteins.

HIV Infection cycle

Production and transport of viral proteins to the membrane rely on the host cell's ribosomes and components of its endomembrane system. The endomembrane system is made of membranes and vesicles within the cell that perform various functions, including protein synthesis and transport, lipid metabolism, lipid transport, and detoxification. HIV harnesses the endoplasmic reticulum, Golgi apparatus, and vesicles of this system to produce and assemble new viruses. As the virus buds from the cell, it is surrounded by part of the cell membrane to produce the viral envelope. Once outside the cell, the newly assembled virus can move on to infect other cells.

Rotavirus

Rotavirus attacks cells that line the small intestine and produces a toxin that causes diarrhea and vomiting. The diarrhea and vomiting cause dehydration, which may lead to death. Almost every child in the world will have been infected with rotavirus at least once by age five. More than 500,000 children die from the infection each year, but only approximately 20–60 of these deaths occur in the United States. The death rate in the United States is low because improved sanitation and vaccination reduce the number of cases, and access to adequate health care prevents death of those who do get rotavirus.

Although rotavirus is also an RNA virus, it has a completely different life cycle than HIV. It does not need reverse transcriptase, but applies its double-stranded RNA genome for reproduction in the cytoplasm of the host cell.

GETTING STARTED

1 Review with students the cell structures and organelles that they learned about in Activity 4, "What Do Cells Do?" Ask students, *Which cell organelles and structures are involved in protein production?*

From their answers develop the idea that the DNA in the nucleus and ribosomes in the cytoplasm are involved in all protein production. The rough endoplasmic reticulum and Golgi apparatus also play a role in the production of membrane proteins and proteins to be exported from the cell. The DNA contains coding for proteins.

Inform students that the genetic material in HIV happens to be RNA instead of DNA. This is true for many viruses that infect animal cells. Because the genetic material in animal cells is DNA, the virus must have a way to change its RNA into DNA in order to use the cell's structures and organelles to make proteins.

---

16 HIV/AIDS Infection and Cell Organelles

1 **A**LTHOUGH MANY OF their characteristics are similar to those of cells, viruses are not cells. They contain genetic material and a few proteins, but they do not conduct cellular functions. For example, a virus can neither metabolize nutrients needed to grow and to develop essential structures, nor can it reproduce on its own. To reproduce, a virus must infect a living host cell. Viruses are specific to their hosts. Some infect one kind of animal, while others infect plants or even bacteria. Once it is inside the host cell, the virus takes over the cell's structures, enzymes, and organelles that will enable it to reproduce.

Challenge

▶ How does HIV take over a cell's structures and organelles during infection and use them to reproduce?

MATERIALS

FOR EACH PAIR OF STUDENTS
set of 13 Cell Structures and Organelles Cards
colored pencils

FOR EACH STUDENT
Student Sheet 16.1, "Scientific Diagram of HIV Infection"
Student Sheet 2.1, "Disease Information," from Activity 2
sticky notes

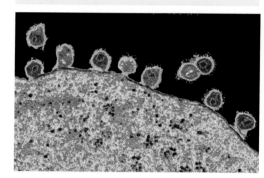

An electron microscope image of HIV virus budding from a human cell membrane

244

DOING THE ACTIVITY

2 Distribute the Cell Structure and Organelle Cards and Student Sheet 16.1, "HIV Infection." The Student Sheet provides a template on which students label the organelles they think are involved in the HIV infection process and describe why. Students might suggest that HIV must use membrane receptors to get into a cell, that ribosomes make viral proteins, and the Golgi apparatus packages the viral proteins. Depending on your curriculum goals, you may wish to make a transparency of the Student Sheet and label all of the structures and organelles together as a class. Alternatively, you can ask student pairs to work together to label the cell structures and organelles on the Student Sheet and then review the labels as a class.

3 Visit the *Science and Global Issues* website *(sepuplhs.org/sgi)* for additional links to HIV/AIDS infection animations.

If necessary, students may go through the simulation more than once. A sample diagram is shown below:

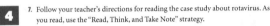

Procedure

1. With your partner, spread out the Cell Structures and Organelles cards on the table. Sort out the cell structures and organelles that you think the HIV virus would directly need in order to reproduce many copies of itself. Set the other Cell Structures and Organelles cards aside.

2. Discuss with your partner the path that you think the HIV virus would take within the cell as it takes over the cell. Lay out the cards in the order you decide on.

3. Pick a colored pencil, and on your Student Sheet 16.1, "Scientific Diagram of HIV Infection," do the following:
   a. Trace the path of the virus infection through the various structures or organelles you decided on in Step 2.
   b. Next to each structure or organelle in the path, write an explanation of why you think that structure or organelle is involved.

4. Visit the *Science and Global Issues* page of the SEPUP website at *sepuplhs.org/sgi.* With your partner, follow the simulation of the life cycle of the HIV virus.

5. Watch the narrated version of the simulation. As you watch and listen, with a different colored pencil add to or change the path you traced, where appropriate, on Student Sheet 16.1, "Scientific Diagram of HIV Infection."

6. For more detail, view the step-through version of the simulation and read the descriptions of each stage of the process. At each step you can click "Play" to watch the animation of only that stage.

7. Follow your teacher's directions for reading the case study about rotavirus. As you read, use the "Read, Think, and Take Note" strategy.

8. Complete the information for rotavirus on Student Sheet 2.1, "Disease Information" after you read the case study.

245

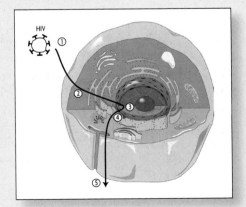

Step 1: HIV enters the cell using proteins on its surface that attach to receptors on the cell surface.

Step 2: Viral reverse transcriptase converts the RNA into DNA in the cell cytoplasm.

Step 3: The DNA enters the nucleus and is integrated into the host DNA. The DNA is transcribed back into multiple copies of viral RNA in order to make viral proteins.

Step 4: HIV viral proteins are made on the host cell's ribosomes. Some are made on free ribosomes, while others are made on the rough endoplasmic reticulum and travel through the Golgi apparatus to the cell membrane.

Step 5: New viruses are assembled and released from the cell through the cell membrane.

4 (LITERACY) If necessary, use Literacy Transparency 3 to review with students the "Read, Think, and Take Note" guidelines. If you assign the rotavirus case study for homework, be sure that students take sticky notes home so they can complete the "Read, Think, and Take Note" literacy strategy. Begin the next class by asking students to discuss the main points of the case study and their comments on their sticky notes with their partners or groups. A sample response for Student Sheet 2.1, "Disease Information," is shown at the end of Activity 16 in this guide.

FOLLOW-UP

5 ✓ Review with students the structure of a virus, such as HIV. HIV and most other viruses are made of a protein coat, or capsid. The capsid encloses genetic information and sometimes a few proteins and lipids. If you wish, project a transparency of Student Sheet 16.1, "HIV Infection," to aid the discussion of how the HIV virus reproduces all of its components during infection.

Students should understand by now that the virus's proteins are made by the cell's ribosomes. Many are transported by the endoplasmic reticulum, Golgi apparatus, and vesicles to the cell membrane. If you want to be sure students understand the role of vesicles, point it out. Because eukaryotic cells have DNA as their genetic material, the HIV RNA must first be transcribed into DNA in order to take advantage of the cell's protein-making machinery. The HIV DNA is then integrated into the cell's DNA, forming what is called a provirus. This makes the genetic material recognizable by the host cell. The DNA is transcribed into multiple copies of RNA that can be used to produce proteins. Protein production then proceeds on the ribosomes. Although the simulation does not show it,

emphasize that the host cell provides many enzymes needed for the production of viral proteins. Newly made viruses are assembled at the cell membrane, where they exit the cell. These viruses can now infect other cells. Analysis Question 6 is a Quick Check assessment of students' understanding of the cell and viral structures HIV needs in order for it to enter a host cell and for the host cell to reproduce the virus.

SCIENCE & GLOBAL ISSUES/BIOLOGY • CELL BIOLOGY

5 *Analysis*

1. Explain why HIV must infect a host cell.

2. Explain how the HIV virus uses specific structures to enter the cell.

3. **a.** List the structures and organelles inside the cell that an HIV virus needs if it is to reproduce.

   b. Describe how HIV uses each structure and organelle during the infection process.

4. In Activity 10, "Functions of Proteins in Cells," you learned about eight classes of proteins.

   a. Which classes of proteins were shown in the HIV infection animation?

   b. What function did each of those classes of proteins perform in the virus infection cycle?

5. How did your ideas about the steps of the HIV infection inside a cell change before and after viewing the simulation?

6. If you were a researcher of HIV/AIDS, explain which part of the infection process you would be most be interested in if you were trying to find a way to:

   a. prevent HIV from entering cells.

   b. prevent HIV from reproducing.

7. HIV infects cells of the immune system, while rotavirus infects cells of the intestine. What structures do you think are responsible for the ability of each virus to only infect specific types of cells?

8. What evidence from the rotavirus case study explains why more than 85% of rotavirus deaths occur in Southeast Asia and Africa?

KEY VOCABULARY

DNA	protein
enzyme	rotavirus
organelle	

246

SAMPLE RESPONSES

1. HIV must infect cells to get access to structures that help them reproduce. Viruses do not have all of the organelles or enzymes needed to reproduce on their own.

2. The proteins on the surface of an HIV virus attach to the CD4 receptor on the membrane of the host cell. The virus then enters the cell.

3. a. DNA in the nucleus, endoplasmic reticulum, Golgi apparatus, vesicles, cell membrane

   b. Viral reverse transcriptase converts the RNA into DNA in the cell cytoplasm. The DNA enters the nucleus and is integrated into the host DNA. The DNA is transcribed back into multiple copies of viral RNA in order to make viral proteins. Some HIV viral proteins are made on the rough endoplasmic reticulum and travel through the Golgi apparatus and in vesicles to the cell membrane.

4. a. Receptors and enzymes

   b. Receptors allow the virus to enter the cell. Enzymes are used to reproduce new viruses.

5. Students' answers will vary. Some might answer that they included more details, such as the receptor on the cell's surface that the HIV uses to enter the cell. Some may not have initially made the Golgi apparatus part of the process. Many students may not have understood that the HIV RNA must be reverse-transcribed or that the viral DNA must integrate into the host DNA.

6. a. ✓ Prevent the HIV virus from attaching to the host cell receptor. You might do this by attacking the protein on the HIV surface that binds to the host cell receptor.

   b. Students' answers will vary. Some may answer that you would need to prevent the HIV RNA from being converted into DNA so that the cell could not use it to make proteins. Some may answer that you must prevent the HIV proteins from being produced or packaged in the Golgi apparatus so that functional viruses would not be made.

7. Each virus has specific surface proteins, and those can interact only with specific receptors that are on specific kinds of cells.

8. Southeast Asia and Africa have the lowest percentages of access to improved sanitation, and rotavirus often spreads through contaminated food and water. Also, children in low-income countries in Africa and Southeast Asia are less likely to get vaccinated or receive medical care if their rotavirus infection becomes severe.

CASE STUDY

Rotavirus

GLOBALLY, ONLY A few infectious diseases cause the majority of deaths for children younger than five years old. Rotavirus, with the severe diarrhea it causes, is one of them.

Rotavirus causes approximately 40% of all cases of severe diarrhea in infants worldwide. More than 85% of rotavirus deaths occur in Asia and Africa.

SYMPTOMS AND DISEASE MECHANISM

The symptoms of rotavirus infection include severe vomiting, fever, abdominal pain, and watery diarrhea over several days. These symptoms are usually milder in adults, who normally recover. Rotavirus is an RNA virus that infects cells that line the small intestine, the ones that absorb nutrients and water.

When the virus infects and kills these cells, unabsorbed nutrients and water leave the body rapidly in diarrhea and vomit, making the patient weak and dehydrated. Rotavirus is transmitted

(Continued on next page)

Burden of Disease		
	TOTAL NUMBER WITH DISORDER	NUMBER OF DEATHS PER YEAR
Worldwide	more than 100 million	500,000
United States	55,000–70,000 hospitalizations	20–60

child deaths per 100,000 population under age five
- < 10
- 10 – 50
- 50 – 100
- 100 – 500

Rotavirus deaths of children younger than five

247

REVISIT THE CHALLENGE

Raise the idea that a virus has a smaller set of genes, and, therefore, fewer proteins than a cell. Because it has only a few of the enzymes essential for its reproduction and lacks such structures as ribosomes, it must exploit the host's enzymes, organelles, and other structures in order to reproduce. These include the cell's chromosomes and machinery for making RNA and proteins, as well as the membranes and organelles that create the new viruses' outer membranes.

(Continued from previous page)

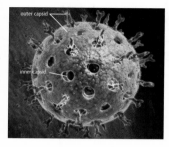

Model of a rotavirus

in contaminated water or food, airborne droplets, and contact with contaminated surfaces. Therefore, safe water, sanitation, and refrigeration of food are important for controlling rotavirus transmission.

ROTAVIRUS PREVENTION AND TREATMENT

Exclusive breastfeeding is a strategy for preventing diarrheal infections, including rotavirus, in infants up to six months old. Exclusive breastfeeding means the baby ingests no food or drink besides its mother's breast milk. The baby is allowed vitamins, minerals, or medicines, but no water. Breast milk contains nutrients, antibodies, and other elements that boost the immune system, and breastfeeding eliminates the need for infants to eat food or take in drink that may be contaminated.

In 2007, a vaccine became available to prevent rotavirus infection, and widespread distribution of the vaccine could be a major

boost for prevention of the disease. Public health care workers estimate that in Asia vaccinations for rotavirus would prevent approximately 110,000 deaths, 1.4 million hospitalizations, and 7.7 million visits to the doctor.

Currently, there is no drug treatment for rotavirus infection. Only oral or intravenous rehydration with electrolytes is prescribed. This maintains homeostasis of water and salts in the blood.

CHALLENGES TO PREVENTION AND TREATMENT

For HIV-positive mothers, breastfeeding is not a good option for preventing rotavirus in their infants because breast milk can transmit HIV. In these cases it is safer to feed babies a breast milk replacement, such as infant formula. But with formula, the baby does not get the antibodies to protect against diseases that breast milk would carry from mother to child.

Currently there are two major roadblocks to global use of a

Distribution of Improved Sanitation (% of population)[1]					
AFRICA	THE AMERICAS	EASTERN MEDITERRANEAN	EUROPE	SOUTHEAST ASIA	WESTERN PACIFIC
33	87	60	93	37	69

1. Data from WHO organization of world regions.

248

17 Disease Interventions

TALK IT OVER • 2–3 CLASS SESSIONS

OVERVIEW

Student groups each construct a poster showing the disease mechanism for one of six diseases: malaria, TB, diabetes, HIV/AIDS, cancer, and rotavirus. They review information about various interventions for each disease and identify what the interventions target in order to prevent or treat the disease. They also determine the trade-offs of each intervention.

KEY CONTENT

1. Abnormal body cells and microbes cause diseases.

2. Disease interventions prevent or treat diseases, and vary in effectiveness, cost, and ease of implementation.

3. Widespread diseases hinder progress toward the goal of sustainable development, which aims to meet the needs of current generations without endangering those of future generations.

KEY PROCESS SKILLS

1. Students use evidence to make conclusions.

2. Students consider the trade-offs of disease interventions.

MATERIALS AND ADVANCE PREPARATION

For the teacher
Scoring Guide: GROUP INTERACTION (GI)
Group Interaction Student Sheet 2, "Developing Communication Skills" (optional)

For each group of four students
sheet of chart paper*
markers*

For each student

Student Sheet 2.1, "Disease Information," from Activity 2

Student Sheet 17.1 a–f, "Disease Intervention Information" for assigned disease

Scoring Guide: GROUP INTERACTION (GI) (optional)

Group Interaction Student Sheet 2, "Developing Communication Skills" (optional)

Not supplied in kit

Masters for Group Interaction Student Sheets are in Teacher Resources II: Diverse Learners. Masters for Scoring Guides are in Teacher Resources IV: Assessment.

TEACHING SUMMARY

Getting Started

• Introduce disease interventions.

Doing the Activity

• (GI ASSESSMENT) Students work in groups to sketch the disease mechanism for one assigned disease.

• Student groups discuss the trade-offs of the interventions for their assigned disease.

• (LITERACY) Student groups create a poster of the disease mechanism for their assigned disease, showing the disease interventions and related sustainability factors.

Follow-up

• ✓ The class discusses how social, environmental, and economic factors influence decisions about disease interventions.

GETTING STARTED

1 Write the following on the board or overhead: flu, strep throat. Ask students if they know what type of microbe causes each disease. A virus causes the flu, and a bacterium causes strep throat. Ask students what types of preventions they know of for each of these diseases. They are likely to say that the flu vaccine prevents the flu. For strep throat, there is no vaccine, and the only preventions are for people who have strep throat to cover their noses and mouths when they sneeze or cough, wash their hands frequently, and stay away from other people, and for uninfected individuals to wash their hands frequently. Next ask what types of treatments students know of for flu and strep throat. Students will likely mention antibiotics or other medications, bed rest, and fluids. This is an opportunity to discuss with students that antibiotics kill bacteria, such as those that cause strep throat, but they do not work against viruses, such as those that cause flus. You may wish to explain to students why this is the case. As described in Activity 4, "What Do Cells Do?" antibiotics work by disabling a cell structure in a bacterium that the bacterium needs for survival. Because viruses are not cells, they have no cell structures for antibiotics to attack. Antiviral drugs have been developed for only some viral diseases so far.

Tell students that in this activity they will examine various interventions for six diseases, and their trade-offs.

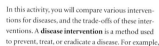

17 Disease Interventions

1 **T**HROUGHOUT THIS Cell Biology unit, you have learned about the devastating impact of diseases worldwide, and about some of the ways to prevent or treat the diseases you have studied. Understanding human cells, microbes, and disease mechanisms helps people make informed decisions about where and how to focus efforts in combating the diseases.

In this activity, you will compare various interventions for diseases, and the trade-offs of these interventions. A **disease intervention** is a method used to prevent, treat, or eradicate a disease. For example, improving sanitation or vaccinating children prevents rotavirus infection. If a child is infected, giving the child fluids to keep him or her hydrated until recovery is another kind of disease intervention.

Challenge

▶ What are the benefits, drawbacks, and trade-offs of some disease interventions?

MATERIALS

FOR EACH GROUP OF STUDENTS
    sheet of chart paper
    markers

FOR EACH STUDENT
    Student Sheet 2.1, "Disease Information," from Activity 2
    version of Student Sheet 17.1 a–f, "Disease Intervention Information"

Procedure

1. Your teacher will assign your group one of the six diseases you studied in this unit—malaria, tuberculosis, diabetes, HIV/AIDS, cancer, and rotavirus. With your group, review the information that you each collected for your assigned disease and noted on your copies of Student Sheet 2.1, "Disease Information."

250

DOING THE ACTIVITY

2 (GI ASSESSMENT) Assign each group a disease to work with in this activity and the next—malaria, TB, HIV/AIDS, diabetes, cancer, or rotavirus. There are six diseases, one per group of four in a class of 24 students. If you have fewer than six groups, be sure to assign at least one noninfectious disease (cancer or diabetes). If you have more than six groups, choose which disease(s) you will assign to two groups. Review the GROUP INTERACTION (GI) Scoring Guide. Tell students this activity is an opportunity to demonstrate their ability to work effectively in groups to process and discuss information and to prepare a poster presentation for the class. Review with students the guidelines for a Level-3 response. Explain that their sketches should show how a person contracts the disease, and show the organs, tissues, and cells involved.

If their entries for Student Sheet 2.1, "Disease Information," do not provide enough information to draw the disease mechanism, students should review the case studies and related activities in the unit to find more information.

3 Before students begin discussing the benefits and drawbacks of the interventions, you may want to provide an example of how to evaluate these benefits and drawbacks. Two interventions for rotavirus infection are vaccination and water sanitation. If one had to choose, he or she might find vaccination cheaper, quicker, and requiring less new infrastructure than sanitation. On the other hand there's still a small risk of children getting sick even if they have been vaccinated, while a water sanitation system may rid a community of many disease-causing microbes.

2. With your group, develop and draw in your science notebook a sketch that shows the infection mechanism of your assigned disease. The sketch should depict what occurs at the cellular level when a person has the disease. If the disease is infectious, also show how it spreads from one person to another.

3. Look over Student Sheet 17.1, "Disease Intervention Information." This sheet contains information on several types of interventions for your assigned disease. With your group, discuss the benefits and drawbacks of each of the interventions.

4. With your group, make a poster about your assigned disease that shows
- the disease cycle you sketched in Step 2.
- where in the disease cycle each prevention or treatment intervenes.
- for each intervention, the cost per person, target age, and infrastructure needed.
- labels for each intervention as "treatment" or "prevention."
- a list of the social, environmental, and economic effects of the disease.

5. Your teacher will provide instructions for sharing your poster with the class.

Analysis

1. What is the difference between prevention and treatment of a disease?

2. Suppose you have enough money from a private foundation to implement one intervention for your assigned disease. Decide which intervention you would choose, and explain why. Be sure to identify the trade-offs of your decision.

KEY VOCABULARY	
disease	trade-offs
disease intervention	

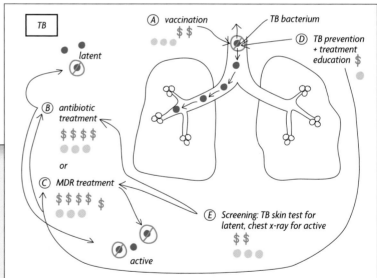

4 (LITERACY) Decide if you want students to create a gallery walk to observe others' posters or to make presentations to the class. If you choose to have students make presentations, you may wish to distribute copies of Group Interaction Student Sheet 2, "Developing Communication Skills," and review it with students. If you choose a gallery walk, remind students to represent the information in a clear manner so that others will be able to understand without narrative. A sample poster is shown on the previous page.

For a gallery walk, decide how you will display the posters, how many students in a group will view each poster, and how much time you will allot for students to spend at each poster. Ask students to carry their science notebooks along and write down what similarities and trends they notice among the interventions for the six diseases. If students conduct a gallery walk, you may wish to build in some time for students to ask clarifying questions of each other, whether with a class discussion or an Informal Meeting of the Minds. If you choose Informal Meeting of the Minds, direct students to find a partner from another group and compare the similarities and trends they notice among the interventions for the six diseases. Ask these pairs to share their discussion with the class. Alternatively, students could have members of each group take turns to stay near the group's poster to answer questions.

FOLLOW-UP

5 ✓ Review with students what the posters demonstrate. Ask students what similarities or trends they noticed about the interventions for the six diseases. They should notice that, in general, treatments are more expensive than preventions. Education is a cost-effective prevention measure across the board. The most expensive interventions are screening, surgery, and antiretroviral therapy. Screening for certain cancers and treatment for TB require the most infrastructure. Next, ask for some students to share with the class some of the benefits and drawbacks they came up with for the interventions they evaluated. For example, oral rehydration therapy replaces electrolytes lost in diarrhea and vomiting, and is a relatively inexpensive treatment for rotavirus. However, it does not remedy the problem of unsafe water systems that transmit rotavirus, and which are expensive to build. Next ask students what social, environmental, and economic factors might complicate any interventions. For rotavirus, for example, it is important to consider the problem of the poor sanitation that often comes with poverty, which is a social and environmental issue. It is also important to consider that it can be hard to get vaccine to remote parts of the world where children are at risk of rotavirus infection, which is both a social factor and an economic factor that affects

the value of vaccine as an intervention. These examples of oral rehydration therapy, sanitation, and vaccination as interventions for rotavirus emphasize the point that you cannot consider interventions in isolation when choosing between them; you must also consider the benefits, drawbacks, and sustainability factors that affect the value of the interventions. Analysis Question 2 is a Quick Check assessment to ensure that students understand the term, and can identify trade-offs, which is a component of the EVIDENCE AND TRADE-OFFS scoring variable.

SAMPLE RESPONSES

1. The difference between a prevention and a treatment is that a prevention blocks the microbe from infecting its host through vaccination or prevents the person from contracting the disease through interventions such as education and lifestyle changes, while a treatment fights the infection or disease once it is contracted.

2. ✓ Students' answers will vary depending on the disease they were assigned. A sample answer for malaria follows.

   The intervention I would choose for addressing the problem of malaria is insecticide-treated nets. Insecticide-treated nets directly kill the mosquitoes that carry the parasite, preventing people from getting malaria. Then there would be no sick people who need treatment with more expensive drugs. A trade-off is that you would not be able to treat people who are already sick with malaria or fund research for things like new drugs.

REVISIT THE CHALLENGE

Students should take away from this activity that there are various interventions—both preventions and treatments—for diseases, but there are trade-offs to consider when choosing one over another. For example, one intervention might be cheaper than another, but would only work if implemented routinely over a long time period (e.g. bed nets). Students should also understand that social, environmental, and economic factors influence the use and effectiveness of a particular intervention. For example, there is an effective antibiotic treatment for malaria, but it is only effective if taken according to the prescribed schedule. If not, people can relapse, or the *Plasmodium* that causes malaria can develop drug resistance. This is a social factor that influences the effectiveness of the antibiotic treatment.

18 World Health Proposal

TALK IT OVER • 2–3 CLASS SESSIONS

OVERVIEW

In this activity, student groups write a world health proposal to address the problems of the disease they each studied in Activity 17, basing the proposal on the disease mechanism and intervention information from the poster they created for that activity. The class then votes on what should be the priorities for funding the proposals. They discuss the tensions that arise when funding is limited, and the trade-offs involved in funding one or more, but not all, proposals.

KEY CONTENT

1. Abnormal body cells and microbes cause diseases.

2. Disease interventions are actions taken to prevent or treat diseases.

3. Less-developed countries tend to have a higher proportion of deaths from infectious diseases than do more-developed countries.

KEY PROCESS SKILLS

1. Students interpret data.

2. Students construct explanations using logic, knowledge, and reasoning.

3. Students consider various perspectives in setting priorities.

4. Students identify and describe trade-offs.

5. Students take positions they can support with evidence.

MATERIALS AND ADVANCE PREPARATION

For the teacher
> Scoring Guide: EVIDENCE AND TRADE-OFFS (ET)

For each group of four students
> disease intervention poster from Activity 17
> chart paper (optional)*

For each student
> Student Sheet 2.1, "Disease Information," from Activity 2
> Student Sheet 18.1, "World Health Proposals"
> Scoring Guide: EVIDENCE AND TRADE-OFFS (ET) (optional)
> > *Not supplied in kit

Masters for Scoring Guides are in Teacher Resources IV: Assessment.

TEACHING SUMMARY

Getting Started

- The class discusses the benefits and limitations of efforts to treat and prevent diseases.

Doing the Activity

- Each group writes a proposal for funding of one intervention they think will be most effective in combating their assigned disease.

- Groups present their proposals to the class.

Follow-up

- (ET ASSESSMENT) The class discusses the trade-offs of funding some but not all proposals, and votes on how to prioritize funding for the proposals.

BACKGROUND INFORMATION

Decisions about which health interventions should be given priority globally are challenging. They require a consideration of the burden of the disease, the infrastructure available, the cost-effectiveness of the interventions, and other social and economic factors. In the late 1980s, the World Bank called for a review of the priorities for the control of some diseases. The review found a need to address undernutrition and infectious childhood diseases along with new epidemics such as HIV/AIDS. It also expressed a concern for the health of lower-income people during economic crisis. It used the information to compare interventions for the diseases and their cost-effectiveness in developing countries, and to help with decision-making about the funding and implementation of the interventions. The information has been periodically updated, with the latest findings and recommendations published in 2006 by a joint project of six influential world-health-policy organizations.

REFERENCES

Disease Control Priorities Project. (2006). D. T. Jamison, et al.,(Eds.) *Disease Control Priorities in Developing Countries,* 2nd edition. Washington DC: Oxford University Press. Retrieved January 2010 from www.dcp2.org/pubs/DCP

World Health Organization. (2006). *WHO Statistical Information System (WHOSIS).* Retrieved September 2009 from www.who.int/whosis/en

GETTING STARTED

1 Ask students which they would focus on to address global diseases—treatment or prevention—if there were limited money to do either. This will initiate a review of some of the larger trade-offs involved in various interventions. For example, students may have noticed from the previous activity that treatments tend to be more expensive than preventions, but treatments might prevent deaths in people who have or will get the disease.

---

18 World Health Proposal

1 **D**ETERMINING THE BEST ways to prevent and treat diseases that affect the global community is not an easy task. As you have learned in this unit, social, economic, and environmental consequences of diseases vary by country, and by region. Such variations create complications when deciding how to allocate funding for disease interventions. For example, if funding were so limited that there was a choice between dedicating it all to cancer research or directing it to several less costly interventions that would prevent thousands of children from dying of malaria or rotavirus, what is the best decision?

Currently a private foundation, whose mission is to fund projects that address problems related to world health, is about to review project proposals. Proposals must relate to prevention or treatment of one of the six global diseases you have studied—malaria, tuberculosis, diabetes, HIV/AIDS, cancer, and rotavirus. Your group will develop a proposal for funding, and then the class will decide how to allocate funding after considering all of the proposals.

Challenge

▶ How should funding be allocated to address sustainability problems related to world health?

MATERIALS

FOR EACH GROUP OF STUDENTS
    disease intervention poster from Activity 17

FOR EACH STUDENT
    Student Sheet 2.1, "Disease Information," from Activity 2
    Student Sheet 18.1, "World Health Proposals"

DOING THE ACTIVITY

2 Students review the scope of the problem of their assigned disease. Depending on the curriculum goals for your class, you may wish to have students do additional research about their assigned disease. For example, you might ask students to research the most recent information about available drug treatments and vaccines and in which regions of the world the disease is most prevalent. You might have students look at the prevalence of their disease over a period of time in the past so that they can predict how many people might be helped if their intervention is put into place over the next 10 years. For suggestions of sites that can help with the research, visit the *Science and Global Issues* page of the SEPUP website (*sepuplhs.org/sgi*).

3 If time and availability of materials permit, groups should present their proposals to the class using such visual aids as posters, presentation outlines, or slide shows. Remind students that when they are not presenting they should note information from the other groups' presentations on Student Sheet 18.1, "World Health Proposals." Instruct the class to take careful notes, as they will rely on that information for the final discussion on the proposals. Sample answers are shown at right.

Procedure

2

1. With your group, review Student Sheet 2.1, "Disease Information," and the poster you created for your assigned disease in Activity 17, "Disease Interventions."

2. From the information you have already accumulated on your assigned disease, write a proposal to obtain funding from the foundation. Be sure to include the following information in your proposal:

   • The number of people affected by this disease and the age groups most affected, if appropriate

   • The number of deaths worldwide

   • Which parts of the world are experiencing more of the burden of the disease

   • Which intervention you chose to implement. Include evidence to support your choice of intervention.

3

3. Follow your teacher's instructions for presenting your proposal to the class. As you listen to the proposals, take careful notes on Student Sheet 18.1, "World Health Proposals."

4

4. The foundation has limited funding and, therefore, cannot fund every proposal. As a class, discuss all of the proposals and come to agreement on how to rank the proposals in terms of priority for funding.

Analysis

1. In Procedure Step 4 what reasoning most convinced the class to determine whether one proposal should be ranked as a higher priority than another?

2. Describe how you think the limited funds from the foundation should best be distributed among the proposals. For example, should all of the proposals receive equal funding, should all of the proposals receive some funding but with some getting more than others, or should one or two receive all of the funding? Explain the evidence and reasoning for your decision, and discuss the trade-offs of your decision.

3. Which do you consider to be a greater world health problem—infectious diseases or noninfectious diseases? Explain your reasoning.

4. How does an understanding of cells and microbes help scientists address world health issues?

Sample Response to Student Sheet 18.1

Disease	Scope of the problem	Intervention
Malaria	Worldwide: 350 million–500 million new cases per year; 1 million deaths per year. Most deaths are children. Africa is experiencing high burden.	Insecticide-treated nets because they are fairly easy to use and distribute, and relatively inexpensive.
Tuberculosis	Worldwide: 2 billion infected; 9 million new cases per year; 1.7 million deaths per year. Africa and Russia are experiencing highest burden.	Treat latent or active TB with a long course of antibiotics that will kill the bacteria. This will help stop the transmission of TB, which is very infectious.
Diabetes	Worldwide: 180 million with disorder; 6.5 million new cases per year; 2.9 million deaths per year. Higher-income countries are experiencing high burden.	Educate people about the connection between diabetes and unhealthy lifestyles. This type of prevention is easy to implement for a reasonable cost.
HIV/AIDS	Worldwide: 30 million infected; 2.7 million new cases per year; 2 million deaths per year. Africa has highest burden.	Educate people about preventions, such as using condoms. Condoms are fairly easy to distribute, and education programs are a relatively inexpensive prevention.
Cancer	Worldwide: 12 million new cases per year; 7 million deaths per year. All areas of world have cancer burden.	Focus on cancers that can be prevented now with immunizations that are fairly easy to administer and are relatively inexpensive. Good choices are vaccines for hepatitis B, which may cause liver cancer, and HPV, which causes cervical cancer.
Rotavirus	Worldwide: more than 100 million with disease; 500,000 deaths per year, mostly children. Asia and Africa have highest burden.	Oral rehydration therapy early in the course of the disease is a fairly inexpensive treatment that keeps the patient strong enough to survive while the immune system works to kill the virus.

FOLLOW-UP

4 (ET ASSESSMENT) Analysis Question 2 is an opportunity to use the EVIDENCE AND TRADE-OFFS (ET) Scoring Guide to assess students' ability to use evidence to prioritize funding and identify trade-offs. If necessary, pass out copies of the Scoring Guide and review the standards for a Level 3 response. Hold a class discussion about prioritizing the proposals for funding. There is no single correct way to rank the proposals for funding, and each way involves trade-offs. For example, the class might decide that it is more important to support a proposal addressing rotavirus, which affects mostly children, and to make diseases that mostly affect older people the lowest priority. Discuss the benefits and trade-offs of such a funding decision: one proposal would help more young children worldwide grow and be healthy, but the costs of treating many cancers are so great that finding ways to prevent them or cure them may save huge amounts of money in the long run. The class may decide to give higher priority to treating infectious diseases rather than treating noninfectious diseases. Because infectious diseases kill mostly people living in developing countries, these countries will get needed funding, but those in more-developed countries, where noninfectious diseases afflict more people, would lose out. Another possibility is that the class decides to focus on funding prevention rather than treatment. This provides benefits for the future but doesn't solve the immediate problem of treating those people who already have a disease. Whatever system the class uses to prioritize the proposals, make sure that all students provide reasons to support the decisions.

SAMPLE RESPONSES

1. Students' answers will depend on how they prioritized the funding. A sample answer follows.

   We decided to prioritize infectious diseases because they affect mostly people living in developing countries, and those countries are in greater need of the funding. We prioritized malaria and rotavirus over HIV/AIDS and tuberculosis because they kill children the most, and we thought it was important to help children live and be healthy.

2. (ET ASSESSMENT) Students' answers will vary. A complete and correct response will include a brief description of each of the proposals, evidence that supports the decision, and a description of the trade-offs.

Sample Level-3 Response

I would choose to fund two proposals: the ones for preventing malaria by providing people with insecticide-treated nets and the one for oral rehydration therapy for rotavirus. I choose these two proposals because they will reduce deaths from diseases that kill mostly children. By preventing malaria with insecticide-treated nets and treating children for rotavirus there is a chance that these children will grow up to be healthy, productive citizens. The trade-offs of funding two proposals as opposed to just the one for insecticide-treated nets is that fewer nets could probably be distributed in a given amount of time if the money is being divided. Also, by focusing on diseases that affect mostly children, the diseases that affect older people in the population might not get funding, which means those people will still be at risk of getting sick or are already sick and suffering.

3. Students' answers will vary. Some might say that infectious diseases are more of a problem because they afflict mostly people in developing countries with fewer economic resources. Some of these diseases, including rotavirus and malaria, kill mostly children. Others might say that noninfectious diseases are more of a problem because most deaths worldwide of both men and women are from noninfectious diseases.

4. An increasing understanding of cells, microbes, and normal cell processes that some microbes interrupt helps scientists develop new and better treatments and prevention strategies to combat diseases.

REVISIT THE CHALLENGE

Review some of the ideas the class discussed in the first activity of the unit. Countries all over the world have disease challenges, but the types, frequency, and severity of the problems differ. Many of these factors are influenced by the country's income level. People in lower-income countries are more likely to die from infectious diseases than people in higher-income countries, and people in higher-income countries are more likely to die from noninfectious diseases. However, all countries experience problems with some diseases, such as cancer, and noninfectious diseases cause the most deaths—6 of 10—worldwide. There is never enough money to address every problem, and there are no simple solutions. Using evidence and weighing the trade-offs of various options can help the global health community make informed decisions about world health issues.

Unit Review: Cell Biology

Cells and Disease

Diseases often hinder a community's or country's progress toward sustainable development. Without a healthy population and environmental, social, and economic conditions that allow children to experience a normal lifespan, a community may not be able to sustain itself. Disease interventions are actions taken to prevent or treat diseases, and they vary in effectiveness, cost, and ease of implementation.

Diseases are classified as infectious or noninfectious. Infectious diseases are transmitted from person to person either directly or by another organism, called a vector. Noninfectious diseases are instead caused by such factors as aging, the environment, behavior, genetics, or a combination of these. Less-developed countries tend to have a greater proportion of deaths from infectious diseases than do more-developed countries. Some human diseases are caused by abnormalities that develop within the body's cells, while others are caused by microbes. Some diseases, including sickle cell disease and malaria, are diagnosed by viewing blood samples from the affected individual through a light microscope.

KEY VOCABULARY	
antibiotic	malaria
cancer	microbe
diabetes	mutation
disease	noninfectious disease
disease intervention	protist
HIV/AIDS	rotavirus
indicator	sickle cell
infectious disease	sustainability
intervention	trade-off
latent	tuberculosis
macrophage	vector

Cell Structure and Function

Every organism is made of one or more cells. All cells maintain homeostasis, a range of internal conditions that allows the cell to live and function. The structure and organization of cells and internal cell parts are essential for the cell to transform and release energy needed for cellular functions. The molecules in a cell form a variety of specialized structures, or organelles, to perform such cell functions as energy production, transport of molecules, waste disposal, synthesis of new molecules, and storage of genetic material. Bacterial cells have neither a nucleus nor other membrane-bound organelles. Multicellular organisms have specialized cells with an arrangement of structures that accomplish a specialized function.

A cell has a membrane that surrounds it and separates it from the outside environment. The cell membrane is a fluid mosaic of molecules, made mainly of phospholipids and proteins, which gives the cell flexibility and strength and controls what enters and leaves the cell. In addition to a cell membrane, plant cells have a cell wall that provides support and additional protection.

A cell also has a cytoplasm that contains a mixture of thousands of molecules. Within the cytoplasm of a eukaryotic cell is a cytoskeleton that provides support and structure for the cell. The cytoplasm of all cells (and the nucleus of eukaryotes) is the site of the reactions of metabolism. Nearly all cells contain genetic information. In eukaryotes, the genetic information is stored in the nucleus.

KEY VOCABULARY	
bacteria	Golgi apparatus
cell	homeostasis
cell biology	lysosome
cell membrane	membrane
cell principle	metabolism
cell wall	multicellular organism
cilium, cilia	nucleus
cytoplasm	phospholipid
cytoskeleton	prokaryote, prokaryotic
deoxyribonucleic acid (DNA)	prokaryotic cell
endoplasmic reticulum	ribosome
eukaryote, eukaryotic	single-celled organism
eukaryotic cell	vacuole
flagellum, flagella	

Cell Transport

The cell membrane is selectively permeable, meaning that only certain substances are able to cross it to move into or out of the cell. Diffusion is the movement of a substance from an area of higher concentration to an area of lower concentration. The diffusion of a liquid, such as water, across a membrane is called osmosis. Some substances diffuse freely across cell membranes, while others must enter through protein channels in a process called facilitated diffusion. Some substances are transported into the cell by transport proteins against, or up, a concentration gradient. This process requires the cell to expend energy and is called active transport.

KEY VOCABULARY	
active transport	osmosis
diffuse, diffusion	passive transport
endocytosis	phospholipid (lipid) bilayer
exocytosis	selectively permeable
facilitated diffusion	semipermeable
fluid mosaic model	transport protein
lipid	vesicle
macromolecule	

Proteins

To support life cells need thousands of proteins, each with a specialized function. Cellular organelles, structures, and enzymes make the proteins cells require. The genetic information stored in DNA directs the synthesis of those proteins. Proteins are often classified according to their functions. Enzymes, for example, are a large group of proteins that act as biological catalysts to speed up the chemical reactions in cells. Enzymes' structures and functions are affected by such factors as temperature and pH.

Receptor proteins and enzymes are also a virus's key to entering a cell, reproducing itself, and spreading infection. The HIV virus, as well as other viruses, is not a cell and cannot reproduce on its own. When HIV infects a cell, it uses the host's cell organelles and proteins to make more HIV viruses.

KEY VOCABULARY

binding site	pH
catalyze	protein
enzyme	receptor
lactase	receptor protein
lactose	signaling protein
motor protein	

Photosynthesis and Cellular Respiration

The energy for life comes primarily from the sun. The structure and organization of cells and internal cell parts transform and release the energy an organism needs for cellular functions. Some plant cells contain chloroplasts, the sites of photosynthesis. In photosynthesis, plants capture energy by absorbing light and using it to form chemical bonds between the atoms of carbon-containing molecules. The chemical bonds of food molecules store energy. Energy is released when the bonds of food molecules are rearranged in the reactions of cellular respiration to form new compounds. Cells temporarily store the energy released by cellular respiration in adenosine triphosphate (ATP) molecules.

KEY VOCABULARY

adenosine triphosphate (ATP)	light-dependent reactions
aerobic respiration	light-indepedentreactions
anaerobic respiration	matrix
Calvin cycle	mitochondria
cellular respiration	mitochondrion
chloroplast	organelle
cristae	photosynthesis
electron transport chain	pigment
glycolysis	stroma
Krebs cycle	thylakoids

Cell Growth, Division, and Differentiation

Cell functions are regulated to control and coordinate cell growth and division. The cell cycle is the complete sequence of phases from the end of one cell division to the end of the next. Some types of cells, including blood and skin cells, divide more often than other types, such as liver and nerve cells. When normal cell regulation is disrupted, serious consequences, such as cancer, may result.

Stem cells produce a variety of specialized cells. The process by which stem cells produce specialized descendent cells is called differentiation. An embryonic stem cell has the potential to produce any type of specialized cell, while stem cells from developed organisms can produce a limited set of specialized cell types.

KEY VOCABULARY	
cancer	mitosis
cell cycle	multipotent
chromosome	pluripotent emryonic stem cell
cyclin	replication
cytokinesis	stem cells
daughter cell	totipotent
differentiation	

Inquiry and the Nature of Science

In an experiment a control provides a standard of comparison for judging experimental effects.

Scientists develop models for representing actual phenomena and to compare theoretical situations to actual situations.

KEY VOCABULARY	
control	hypothesis

Genetics: Feeding the World

REMINDER

Order live materials for Activity 2, following the instructions in your materials kit. Leave ample time for specimen delivery.

FOR THOUSANDS OF years, people have selected crops and animals with desirable traits and have bred them to produce ever more desirable offspring. This selective breeding has produced modern varieties of organisms, such as sweet corn, dairy cows, and domestic pets. It was not until the mid-nineteenth century that scientists began to understand that inherited traits pass from parents to offspring through genes. Modern scientists study genetics to learn more about how genes work and to solve such practical problems as enhancing crop productivity, curing diseases, and producing new fuels.

One dynamic, and sometimes controversial, technology that has emerged from genetics is genetic modification. After learning to manipulate the genes of various species, scientists now can place genes from one species into another to give the target species a specific, desirable trait, such as pest resistance. Many people and some scientists are concerned, however, that this may lead to unintended consequences for the environment or human health.

In this unit you will investigate how genes and patterns of inheritance function in organisms and generations of organisms. You will also learn about the procedures and results of genetic modification, and about some of the benefits and trade-offs of producing specific genetically modified organisms.

260

1 A Genetically Modified Solution?

INVESTIGATION • 1–2 CLASS SESSIONS

OVERVIEW

Students consider the risks and benefits of the genetically modified organism Bt corn as a way to address world hunger and as an element of sustainable agriculture. They listen to scientific panel members advising a country's Office of Agriculture; debate the benefits, risks, and trade-offs of planting genetically modified corn as a food source; and recommend what the country should do.

KEY CONTENT

1. Genetically modified organisms are created through the insertion of particular genes, usually from other species, into the genetic material or through the deletion of particular genes.

2. Many crops have been genetically modified to carry specific desirable traits, such as pest or disease resistance, drought tolerance, and higher nutritional value.

3. The production and use of a genetically modified organism might have unintended consequences for humans and ecosystems.

4. Basic concepts and principles of science and technology contribute to evidence-based debate about the economics, policies, politics, and ethics of various science- and technology-related innovations.

KEY PROCESS SKILLS

1. Students develop conclusions based on evidence and reasoning.

2. Students consider and evaluate multiple perspectives.

3. Students identify and describe trade-offs.

4. Students take a position and support it with evidence.

MATERIALS AND ADVANCE PREPARATION

For the teacher
Scoring Guide: EVIDENCE AND TRADE-OFFS (ET)

For each group of four students
sheet of chart paper*

2 markers of different colors*

For each student
Student Sheet 1.1, "Genetically Modified Corn: Potential Benefits and Risks"

Student Sheet 1.2, "Writing Frame: Letter to Governmental Office" (optional)

Scoring Guide: EVIDENCE AND TRADE-OFFS (ET) (optional)

Not supplied in kit

In SEPUP activities, students work in groups of fours, in pairs, and individually. Organize students into groups of four before the activity begins so they can move from group to pair and to individual work smoothly. Because many activities in this unit require the teacher to use an overhead or data projector, make sure that one is always available. Masters for Literacy Skills Sheets are in Teacher Resources III: Literacy. Masters for Scoring Guides are in Teacher Resources IV: Assessment.

Note: *Activity 2, "Creating Genetically Modified Bacteria," requires live specimens. See your materials kit for ordering information and timelines. Be sure to order materials according to the advised timeframe. Activity 15, "Genetic Modification: Benefits, Risks, and Trade-offs," in this unit involves an independent research project. Decide in advance when you want to assign students to begin researching and developing their projects.*

TEACHING SUMMARY

Getting Started

- Elicit students' ideas about the relationships between agriculture and sustainability and about genetically modified organisms.

- Introduce the SEPUP 4–2–1 cooperative learning model.

Doing the Activity

- (LITERACY) Introduce the use of a science notebook.

- Students read scientists' positions on genetically modified Bt corn.

- (LITERACY) The class conducts a walking debate on Bt corn.

- Students generate questions about genetically modified organisms.

Follow-up

- Introduce the concept of trade-offs.

- (LITERACY) (ET ASSESSMENT) Introduce the EVIDENCE AND TRADE-OFFS Scoring Guide and the SEPUP Assessment System.

REFERENCES

Benbrook, C. (2009). Impacts of genetically engineered crops on pesticide use: The first thirteen years. The Organic Center. Retrieved February 2010, from http://www.organic-center.org/science.pest.php?action=view&report_id=159.

Bessin, R. (2004). Bt-corn for corn borer control. Retrieved December 2008 from http://www.ca.uky.edu/entomology/entfacts/ef118.asp.

Gurian-Sherman, D. (2009). Failure to yield: Evaluating the performance of genetically engineered crops. Union of Concerned Scientists. Retrieved January 2010 from http://www.ucsusa.org/food_and_agriculture/science_and_impacts/science/failure-to-yield.html.

Harwood, J. D., William, G. W., & Obrycki, J. J. (2005). Uptake of Bt endotoxins by nontarget herbivores and higher order arthropod predators: Molecular evidence from a transgenic corn agroecosystem. *Molecular Ecology, 14,* 2815–2823.

James, C. (2005). Global status of commercialized biotech/gm crops. ISAAA Briefs, No. 34. ISAAA: Ithaca, NY.

Nordlee, J. A. (1996). Identification of brazil-nut allergen in transgenic soybeans. *New England Journal of Medicine, 334,* 688–692.

Wraight, C. L., Zangerl, A. R., Carroll, M. J., & Berenbaum, M. R. (2000). Absence of toxicity of *Bacillus thuringiensis* pollen to black swallowtails under field conditions. *PNAS, 97*(14), 7700–7703.

Wu, F. (2006). An analysis of Bt corn's benefits and risks for national and regional policymakers considering Bt corn adoption. *International Journal of Technology and Globalization 2*(1/2), 115–136.

Wu, F. (2006). Mycotoxin reduction in Bt corn: Potential economic, health and regulatory impacts. *Transgenic Research 15,* 277–289.

GETTING STARTED

1 ⬥ Begin the class by asking students, *How do you think food and food production relate to sustainability?*

Have them take a couple of minutes to write down their ideas or discuss them with their partner or group. If necessary, introduce or remind students of the three pillars of sustainability: economic, environmental, and social. For more information on sustainability, see the *Science and Global Issues* page of the SEPUP website *(sepuplhs.org/sgi)*. Students are likely to say that food is a basic need for human survival. Food production also depends on and contributes to a healthy economy. Students, especially in urban areas, may have little idea that large-scale agriculture has often caused serious ecological damage. Elicit their ideas about why this might be so. Their ideas may include the use of large amounts of resources, such as water, hazards of pesticides and fertilizers, production of plant and animal wastes, and energy demands to run farm machinery and transport food.

Explain that in this unit students will investigate genetically modified organisms (often referred to as GMOs), and questions related to their role in ensuring a sustainable food supply. Explain that a genetically modified organism is one that has had a gene from another type of organism inserted into its genetic material. For example, a scientist might insert a gene for a nut or an animal protein into a bean plant, with the goal of creating a strain of beans with higher protein content for human consumption. Inserting a gene into an organism is part of the process of genetic engineering.

---

1 A Genetically Modified Solution?

1 **T**HE **UNITED NATIONS** World Food Program has clearly stated, "Hunger and malnutrition are in fact the number one risk to health worldwide—greater than AIDS, malaria, and tuberculosis combined."

More than 1 billion people in the world today don't get enough nutritious food to lead healthy lives. As shown in the figure at right, this means that more than one in seven people are hungry or malnourished. Widespread sustainable farming practices and broader distribution of food would help meet nutritional needs and promote economic and social well-being of huge numbers of the world's hungry people.

Beginning in 1945, a private program in the United States started developing fast-growing, high-yield rice and wheat seeds and new fertilizers to help other countries grow enough food for their people. Results in Mexico, India, and Pakistan were so successful that in the 1960s the new farming practices became known as the Green Revolution. Those methods, however, included heavy use of fertilizers and pesticides, which caused water pollution and other environmental problems. Today, there is a call for new ways to improve crop yields while not harming the environment. Some people think that genetically modified (GM) crops provide a good solution.

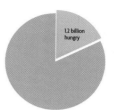

1.2 billion hungry

Hunger is one of the world's greatest sustainability challenges today.

2 To create **genetically modified organisms** (often called GMOs) scientists directly manipulate the genes of an organism, often by inserting or deleting one or more genes. The inserted gene is usually from another species. The purpose of this manipulation is to give the target organism and its offspring a new trait that improves it in some way. The improvement might, for example, give the organism higher vitamin content. The process is called **genetic engineering.**

Genetically Modified Organisms (GMOs)

Statement	Agree	Disagree	Uncertain
1. I have eaten food that contains genetically modified crops.			
2. Genetically modified foods should be available, as long as they are tested before they are sold for human consumption.			
3. The risks of genetically modified foods outweigh the possible benefits.			
4. Genetically modified foods will help provide a sustainable food supply.			
5. I am concerned about eating genetically modified foods.			
6. Farmers should grow corn that is genetically modified to resist insects that damage cornfields.			

⬥ Copy the chart above on the board or on chart paper with the idea of it remaining posted somewhere that students will see it until the end of the unit. Ask students to indicate what they think about each statement by a show of hands. Tell them to write down their responses to each statement in their notebooks. You will return to the results at the end of the unit.

2 Explain that in this activity students will evaluate and give their thoughts on the use of one genetically modified crop, Bt corn. Explain the importance of corn (maize) as a crop in the United States and other countries, especially in South and Central America. Students will learn how to state their opinions in the context of the evidence and reasoning that led them to their decisions. Note that this paragraph of the activity introduces the vocabulary term genetically modified organism. Although the term is in bold and defined in the Student Book in Activity 1, do not expect students to fully understand the concept until later in the unit. It is not necessary at this point to expand on the molecular details of GMOs other than to make sure students understand that GMOs' genes have been directly manipulated, and that genetic modification is sometimes referred to as genetic engineering. In talking about genetically modified organisms it is fine for students to become accustomed to the term GMO (genetically modified organisms) and GM (genetically modified). However, except for in the Procedure sections, the Student Book spells out the term in text sections to avoid too many abbreviations.

ⓘ Students may think genetic modification always results in a harmful or toxic organism. If so, review the definition of GMOs in the introduction to the activity in the Student Book, and explain that a genetically modified organism produces proteins not typical of that organism, but characteristic of the organism that provided the inserted genes. These proteins may or may not be harmful or helpful to humans and other organisms. Stress that toxicity is determined only by toxicity testing; it cannot be assumed.

In the late 1990s, a few countries, including the United States and Brazil, began allowing farmers to grow genetically modified crops. Many other countries, however, were uncertain about the impacts the GMOs might have on human health, the environment, and unmodified crops, and have tightly restricted their import or growth. For example, GMOs have been highly restricted in Japan and several European Union countries. Today, as populations everywhere are growing and needing more food, some governments are considering changing their policies on the growing and importing of genetically modified organisms.

You are advising a country where many people suffer hunger. Corn is an important crop in that country for feeding both people and the animals they rely on for other foods. You have been called to meet with the country's Government Office of Agriculture, which has set up a committee to discuss allowing farmers to raise genetically modified crops. Today, you will examine evidence presented by a scientific panel that evaluated the benefits and risks of growing a genetically modified corn, called Bt corn.

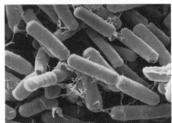

This corn (a) has been modified with a gene from these bacteria (b) to produce an insecticide.

---

3 Activities in *Science and Global Issues* use a 4–2–1 cooperative learning model. Groups of four students share certain materials, pairs of students in the groups work together and discuss issues, and each student is responsible for recording ideas, observations, and thoughts. In this activity, students will work in groups of four to synthesize information from the activity and compose lists of questions about genetic modification. Encourage students to work collaboratively to solve problems and answer questions. Collaboration is essential for developing new ideas and gaining a better understanding of scientific concepts. If necessary, be sure to explain to students your expectations for successful group effort.

DOING THE ACTIVITY

4 If your students worked through the *Science and Global Issues* "Sustainability" Unit, they will be familiar with the use of science notebooks in this course. If not, explain to your students that, as they conduct activities, they will record data, observations, hypotheses, conclusions, and thoughts in their notebooks. Keeping a science notebook helps them track data, note questions as they arise in investigations and discussion, and build science-writing skills. Decide how you would like students to record their work in each of the activities in this unit. For recommendations and more information see "Science Notebooks" in Teacher Resources III: Literacy. As students read, encourage them to ask group members about any ideas that seem unclear and to record questions in their science notebooks. Take time to help clarify words or ideas in a reading when necessary.

5 If you are set up for students or the class to view videos from the Internet, go to the *Science and Global Issues* page of the SEPUP website *(sepuplhs.org/sgi)* for a link to a video that will enhance class discussion about Bt corn.

Challenge

▶ Should your country allow farmers to grow genetically modified corn?

MATERIALS

FOR EACH GROUP OF FOUR STUDENTS
  sheet of chart paper
  2 markers of different colors

FOR EACH STUDENT
  Student Sheet 1.1, "Genetically Modified Corn: Potential Benefits and Risks"

Procedure

1. Read the background information about Bt corn on the next page.

2. When you finish reading, record in your science notebook the two or three questions about Bt corn that you would most like to have answered before you advise this country about growing Bt corn.

3. With your group, review all of your questions, and select the three or four that you think are most important. Record these questions on the top half of the chart paper.

4. With your group, decide who will read which one of the statements on the following pages made by the science panel members. Take turns reading your statements aloud to your group.

5. After each statement is read, record on Student Sheet 1.1, "Genetically Modified Corn: Potential Benefits and Risks," any benefits or risks mentioned in the statement.

6. Based on the information the scientific panel provided, decide if you would support growing genetically modified corn in this country. Be sure to consider the statements from all four scientists. In your science notebook, record your opinion and the evidence and your thinking that led you to your opinion.

7. Share your ideas with the class by conducting a walking debate. Your teacher will explain how to run the debate.

8. With your group, review the questions you listed on the chart you made for Step 3. Check which of those questions have been answered. With another colored pen, add to your chart three or four new questions you have about genetically modified corn and other genetically modified organisms. Be prepared to share any answers you found for your previous questions and your new questions with the class.

263

---

6 Extend the discussion (and prepare students for an EVIDENCE AND TRADE-OFFS (ET) assessment) by conducting a walking debate (see Teacher Resources III: Literacy). This strategy works best when the question or issue has no single correct answer. Designate one corner of the room as "For Growing Bt Corn," and a second area of the room as "Against Growing Bt Corn." Have students stand in the place that they believe best represents their viewpoint. (If most of the students already agree on one option, you may want to assign some of them to the other option to foster the skills of debate and evidence analysis.) Have each group of students discuss with each other, and then explain to the class, why they chose that option. Once each group has explained its choice, allow students to change their minds and move to another area. Record a final tally of students' viewpoints in a different colored chalk or marking pen next to statement 6 on the chart that you posted on the board or transparency as part of the activity introduction. You will return to this information in the final activity as students review what they have learned over the course of the unit.

7 Post the groups' charts in a visible place in the classroom. Students will return to these questions as they conduct independent research in Activity 15, "Genetic Modification: Benefits, Risks, and Trade-offs," and as they work through other activities in this unit.

BACKGROUND INFORMATION

Bt Corn

COMMON SOIL BACTERIA called *Bacillus thuringeinsis (Bt)* produce a protein toxic to the larvae of certain insects, such as the European corn borer. This insect is found throughout Europe, North Africa, Canada, and most of the United States. A single generation of corn borers can reduce by as much as 5% the amount of corn a farm produces. In warm climates up to three generations of corn borers will attack a crop during one growing season, which causes an even greater percentage of crop loss. In the past, many farmers have sprayed chemical insecticides that kill corn borers and many other insects. Many of these insecticides pose health risks to farm workers, consumers, and bees and other beneficial insects. Also, the insecticides are expensive to buy and to spray on crops.

Beginning in Europe in the 1930s, farmers in many regions of the world have sprayed Bt bacteria on fields of plants as an insecticide. The Bt toxin is generally considered safe for people and wildlife. Its drawbacks are that it remains active for no more than a week after it is applied, and it is not effective against all insects.

In 1996, farmers in the United States began growing a new

a

b

The adult corn borer is a moth (a). The corn borer larvae bore into the plant and destroy the corn (b).

genetically modified corn plant, called Bt corn. This corn plant had the Bt gene from *Bacillus thuringeinsis* inserted into its cells. This gene provides information that causes the plant cells themselves to produce the Bt protein. As a result, the offspring of the modified plants are protected from the corn borer.

Today, genetically modified corn is one of four genetically modified crops—along with canola, cotton, and soybeans—grown in huge quantities. The table below shows the top 10 countries that grow genetically modified crops, which crops they grow, and on how much land.

Today, the need for more food to meet the needs of growing populations has led many countries to consider growing genetically modified crops as a way to increase the amounts grown. People in various countries fear that such crops might harm humans, other organisms, and the environment. These concerns have led to debate about which is greater: the benefits or risks of genetically modified organisms. ■

Top 10 Countries Growing Genetically Modified Crops in 2008

COUNTRY	TYPE OF CROP	AREA (MILLIONS OF HECTARES)
United Sates	soybean, corn (maize), cotton, canola, squash, papaya, alfalfa, sugar beet	62.5
Argentina	soybean, corn (maize), cotton	21.0
Brazil	soybean, corn (maize), cotton	15.8
India	cotton	7.6
Canada	canola, corn (maize), soybean, sugar beet	7.6
China	cotton, tomato, poplar, petunia, papaya, sweet pepper	3.8
Paraguay	soybean	2.7
South Africa	corn (maize), soybean, cotton	1.8
Uruguay	soybean, corn (maize)	0.7
Bolivia	soybean	0.6

SOURCE: *International Service for the Acquisition of Agri-biotech Applications Brief 39-2008.*
http://www.isaaa.org/Resources/publications/briefs/39/executivesummary/default.html

Panel Member #1

I think that planting genetically modified crops to improve yield and reduce the need for insecticides will be good for our people and safe for the environment. Bt corn has raised corn yields in the United States. Investigations of Bt corn at a leading university showed that it did not harm monarch butterflies in the field. Bt corn seed might be more expensive, but it may also save farmers money and labor, since they will not need to purchase and spray the insecticides that fight the corn borer. Research has shown that farmers growing Bt corn use fewer chemical insecticides to fight other organisms that attack corn. In addition, one researcher found that Bt corn has lower levels of a fungal toxin that is common in corn.

Because that toxin is harmful to children, Bt corn may be safer to eat than unmodified corn.

Bt corn is just one example of how genetically modified organisms might contribute to the food supply. For example, genetically modified disease- and drought-resistant crops have already been developed. Researchers are also working to improve the nutritional quality of such basic foods as rice through genetic modification. By increasing food production in our country, we can help to end hunger and malnutrition among our people. We would no longer have to import corn, which is more expensive than growing it. We could also make money by selling our corn to other countries.

Panel Member #2

I do not think we know enough about genetically modified crops for our country to invest in any of them at this time. Genetic engineering technology has not always resulted in improved crop yields. A study by the U.S.-based Union of Concerned Scientists found that Bt corn is the only genetically modified crop giving better yields, but the improvements were small. I'm also concerned that it will harm monarch butterflies and other organisms, or cause other environmental damage.

Many people think that changing just one or a few genes is unlikely to cause harm, because a single gene codes for just one protein. But I am concerned because one protein can have multiple effects in the organism. New discoveries in genetics suggest that the effects of inserting a gene from one organism into another organism's DNA are more complex than scientists once thought.

Finally, the continual exposure of insects to insecticides nearly always leads to the development of resistant insect populations. With Bt in the corn itself, the insects are constantly exposed to the toxin, and are more likely to become resistant than when farmers spray it on their crops just a few times. For these reasons, I urge caution. We must feed our children today without harming the environment for the children of tomorrow.

Panel Member #3

Humans have been breeding crops to develop desirable traits for thousands of years. Genetic engineering technology is a faster and more precise way to make these changes. Genetic modification allows scientists to insert beneficial genes from one species into another, and that's not possible with breeding. Several genetically modified organisms have been used for more than 30 years to produce medicines. One example is the modification of *Escherichia coli (E. coli)* bacteria to produce the human hormone, insulin. Before this was produced in 1978, insulin was extracted from pig pancreases, which was time-consuming and more expensive to produce. With the hunger we face, it's time to allow the growth of genetically modified crops here. Corn is a major food for people and livestock. Research shows that Bt corn is most cost-effective in areas like ours, where crop losses to corn borers are large. People in our country are starving, and researchers have shown that Bt corn does improve yields. Research also shows that with Bt corn we do not have to rely as much on chemicals to control insects in the cornfields. I am certain that genetically modified crops will contribute to a sustainable food supply, help our farmers make a better living, and let our children think about schoolwork instead of their empty stomachs.

Panel Member #4

I do not think genetically modified crops should ever be grown or eaten. The impact that they have on ecosystems and humans has not been fully explored. What if the plants breed with wild crops or other plants and spread the inserted genes? This has happened with some genetically modified crops. If it happened here it could be harmful for our native plants. Additionally, what impact will the proteins produced by the modified crops have on the health of humans or animals? There was a case of a soybean plant that was genetically modified to make it more nutritious by adding a gene for a Brazil-nut protein. A study published in the *New England Journal of Medicine* found that the nut protein produced by these soybeans caused allergic reactions in people allergic to Brazil nuts. As a result, the company that developed the modified soybean had to stop its work and not sell the soybeans. I am concerned that there might be other unintended consequences of planting such crops as Bt corn. Much more thorough scientific studies of each product are needed. These studies would divert resources from other approaches to sustainable agriculture, such as better soil management, relying on pests' natural enemies, and other ecologically balanced approaches to pest control.

8 Before students begin answering the Analysis Questions, point out that each activity in this book includes Analysis Questions to help guide them in their learning and provide ways for them to synthesize what they learned in the activity. Many Analysis Questions are designed to extend class discussion on the activity's connection to personal and global issues and sustainability.

FOLLOW-UP

9 (ET ASSESSMENT) One of the goals of *Science and Global Issues* is to teach students that:

1. Decisions often involve trade-offs.

2. Identifying trade-offs involves analyzing evidence.

Explain to students that in this unit they will make several decisions about genetically modified organisms. In this activity they must decide if they support the growing of Bt corn to alleviate hunger. In a decision involving trade-offs, something is given up to gain something else. Since many decisions involve trade-offs, it is important for students to understand that a perfect choice is often not possible. It is possible, however, to recognize and analyze the trade-offs associated with each decision. For example, when asked, "Paper or plastic?" at a store checkout counter, most shoppers make the choice quickly. But there are several trade-offs attached to choosing paper or plastic. A shopper who chooses paper may do so to avoid generating plastic waste or using up petroleum resources. In requesting the paper bag though, the shopper is contributing to other environmental problems, such as increased water and energy usage, and the higher amounts of solid waste and CO_2 emissions associated with making paper bags. Neither choice is particularly beneficial for the environment, and both choices have additional downsides. Identifying the trade-offs helps clarify the reasoning behind a decision, and the strength of the evidence relevant to making the most informed decision.

To further explore trade-offs, brainstorm with the class a list of decisions they make every day. Choose one, and talk through the associated trade-offs of deciding one way or another. This practice will familiarize students with ways of identifying and considering trade-offs for this and subsequent activities.

Students' written work from Analysis Question 4 can be scored with the EVIDENCE AND TRADE-OFFS (ET) Scoring Guide. Provide all students with an ET Scoring Guide, and ask them to keep it with their science notebooks, as they will refer to it several times in this unit, and throughout *Science and Global Issues.* Explain to the class that you will use the ET Scoring Guide to provide feedback on the quality of their work. Let them know that you might

---

8 Analysis

1. What is a genetically modified organism?

2. How might genetically modified food organisms affect each of the three pillars of sustainability:

   a. economic?

   b. social?

   c. environmental?

3. Did your initial ideas about Bt corn change? Explain your initial ideas. If they have changed, explain how and why. If they have not changed, explain why not.

4. Write a letter to the country's Office for Agriculture explaining your views on growing Bt corn. In your letter include

   a. a statement explaining your decision and the evidence and reasoning that led you to your conclusion.

   b. a description of the trade-offs of your decision. A **trade-off** is giving up something in order to gain something else.

5. Currently in the United States, federal law does not require foods containing genetically modified ingredients to be labeled as such.

   a. What would be the advantages of labeling foods that have genetically modified ingredients?

   b. What would be the disadvantages?

   c. Would you recommend labeling of foods that have genetically modified ingredients? Explain.

10	KEY VOCABULARY	
	gene	genetic engineering
	genetically modified organism	trade-off

present their writing from Analysis Question 4 to model how the scoring guide works.

Note: Consider students' writing in Analysis Question 4 as an initial assessment. Inform students that this early assessment will help you gauge their ability to identify trade-offs and support a decision with evidence, and that the score on this will not be used for grading. Instead, their scores on this task will allow you to see how well their analytical skills improve in similar tasks later in this unit and other units in *Science and Global Issues*.

As a class, discuss what a Level-3 response would include. In this case it should include the student's recommendation about Bt corn, a description of at least two appropriate reasons to support the decision, and a discussion of at least one of the trade-offs of their recommendation. You may develop a Level-3 exemplar with the class, or share with students the Level-3 response shown on the next page. Point out the elements that make the example a Level-3 response, and discuss how a Level 1 and a Level 2 are different. Ask students for ideas about how to improve the Level-3 response to make it a Level 4. For more information on the use of the Scoring Guides and the SEPUP Assessment System see Teacher Resources IV: Assessment.

To help students write a letter to the Office for Agriculture in Analysis Question 4 you may wish to pass out Student Sheet 1.2, "Writing Frame: Letter to Governmental Office." This sheet provides a literacy strategy that gives students a structure for communicating their ideas. It helps students organize their ideas into coherent written responses. More information about the writing frame literacy strategy is in Teacher Resources III: Literacy. A sample student response appears in the pages that follow.

10 This box lists the key vocabulary developed in this activity. When words are formally defined in an activity, they appear in bold type in the list. Encourage students to include these words when answering the Analysis Questions. Also, during informal and formal discussions listen for these words and see if students are applying them correctly. Decide how you will support students' understanding of the vocabulary—perhaps with a student glossary, or setting up a class word wall. For more suggestions on ways to develop students' understanding of and proficiency with scientific vocabulary, see the Vocabulary section of Teacher Resource III: Literacy.

EXTENSION

Bt corn is the first of many genetically modified organisms that are discussed in this unit. Encourage your students to look for stories and information about others in the media and to bring those in to share with the class. This will broaden their exposure to current work with genetically modified organisms. Find ways to support your students in seeking more information about the variety of organisms that are genetically modified, and designate a place in the classroom where they can post such information.

SAMPLE RESPONSES

1. A genetically modified organism is one in which scientists have directly manipulated its genes. This can be done by inserting genes, usually from another species, or deleting genes.

2. a. Genetically modified organisms might positively affect the economy of a country by improving farmers' crop yields and in turn their ability to make a living. However, they might negatively affect the economy by harming crops or damaging the ecosystem.

   b. Genetically modified crops could improve the social aspects of sustainability if they provide everyone with enough food to help prevent more deaths from starvation or famine, and prevent wars and crime over food. As above, they could negatively affect social aspects if they threaten human or environmental health.

   c. Genetically modified organisms could harm the environment if they are toxic to other organisms or in other ways disrupt ecosystems. On the other hand, they could have positive effects if they reduce the use of pesticides.

3. Students' answers will vary. Complete and correct responses will compare their ideas at the end of the activity with their initial ideas.

4. (ET ASSESSMENT) Students' responses will vary, but should include a clear position, at least two statements of evidence supporting their position, and one trade-off for their position.

Level-3 Response, Sample 1:

Dear Office of Agriculture,

Your country is considering whether to grow Bt corn. I do not recommend that you grow Bt corn. My recommendation is based on the following evidence:

1. Human health has already been affected with at least one kind of GM plant, and the effects on the environment are not yet fully known. For example, tests on a kind of soybean that was genetically modified by adding a gene from a nut species caused nut-allergy reactions. It seems possible that other GM crops might cause other kinds of allergic reactions.

2. I don't think we know for sure that it doesn't affect other species.

3. Another reason for my recommendation is the fact that Bt corn doesn't increase yields by very much.

From listening to the presentations of the scientific panel members, I think the risks of growing Bt corn outweigh the possible benefits in improving crop yields. A benefit from my recommendation is that you will avoid unintended consequences. A trade-off of my recommendation is that your farmers will have to spray more insecticides to prevent damage from corn borers.

In conclusion, I recommend that Bt corn should not be grown in your country.

Level-3 Response, Sample 2:

Dear Office of Agriculture,

Your country is considering whether to grow Bt corn, and I recommend that you do so. My recommendation is based on the following evidence:

1. Bt corn increases yields of corn, which provides more food for your people and more profits for your farmers.

2. Farmers who use Bt corn use less chemical insecticides, which should be better for human and environmental health. I think the benefits of growing Bt corn outweigh the possible risks.

A benefit from my recommendation is that your country will have more food and use fewer pesticides. A trade-off of my recommendation is that there may be unintended health or environmental consequences.

In conclusion, based on the evidence presented above and the level of hunger in your country, I recommend that Bt corn should be grown.

5. a. An advantage of labeling GM foods is that people would have that information and could make their own decisions about eating them.

   b. A disadvantage of labeling GM foods is that it might cause unnecessary concern and worry people for no reason. It would also cost food producers money to redesign their labels, and people might stop buying their foods.

   c. I think it is a good idea to let people make their own decisions about what they eat. I would recommend labeling foods that have GM ingredients.

REVISIT THE CHALLENGE

Return to students' responses to the six statements they responded to when you introduced the activity. Ask students to respond again to each statement, and use another color of chalk or marker to record their new responses. Have them discuss what they have learned and whether it changed their understanding or their opinions. The sixth statement is directly related to the challenge for this activity. Conclude with a summary of students' thinking at this time, and the questions they would like to have answered about the production and use of genetically modified organisms. As the unit continues, return to students' questions, and add what they have learned.

Genetically Modified Corn: Potential Benefits and Risks

Bt corn	Potential Benefits	Potential Risks
1	Bt corn reduces use of chemical insecticides. Saves money and labor of spraying Decreases a toxin from fungus Fights hunger Boosts income of farmers Does not hurt monarch butterflies	
2	Increases yield	Yield increases are small. Changing one gene might have many effects. May lead to development of insecticide resistance Might harm monarch butterflies or other organisms
3	Genetic modification is faster than breeding. Genes from another species can be added. Has been a safe and effective way to make insulin Bt corn results in higher crop yields.	
4		Ecosystem and human impact not fully studied Might spread genes to other plants Might lead to food allergies Unintended consequences Diverts resources from other better options

2 Creating Genetically Modified Bacteria

LABORATORY • 3–4 CLASS SESSIONS

OVERVIEW

In this activity, students genetically modify a population of *Escherichia coli (E. coli)* by inserting two genes into the bacteria: one for green fluorescent protein (GFP) and one for ampicillin resistance. Once these genes are successfully inserted and expressed, the *E. coli* will be fluorescent and able to grow in the presence of ampicillin. By growing the *E. coli* on plates that contain ampicillin, students screen out the untransformed bacteria and ensure that all bacterial colonies include the inserted genes. This is an opportunity for students to actually use genetic engineering techniques and to work with *E. coli,* which is a model organism for basic genetics research and for developing certain biotechnology applications.

KEY CONTENT

1. Cells store DNA to guide their functions. The genetic information stored in DNA directs the synthesis of the thousands of proteins the cell needs.

2. Scientists alter small pieces of DNA called plasmids to transfer desired genes into bacteria.

3. Through selective breeding and genetic modification of organisms, people can significantly transform the genetic makeup of a population.

KEY PROCESS SKILLS

1. Students make and record observations.

2. Students interpret data.

MATERIALS AND ADVANCE PREPARATION

For the teacher
Transparency 2.1, *"Escherichia coli"*
Transparency 2.2, "Transforming Bacteria"
Student Sheet 2.2, *"E. coli* Growth Observations"
Bunsen burner or candle*
matches*
sterile applicator swab
Luria agar plates without ampicillin (1 per 2 student groups)
tube of *E. coli* culture

Literacy Transparency 3, "Read, Think, and Take Note"
Scoring Guide: GROUP INTERACTION (GI)

For the class
tube of pGLO (GFP) plasmid
waste container*
spray bottle of disinfectant*
supply of paper towels*
10% bleach solution*
UV light*
incubator*

For each group of four students
small container of crushed ice* (beaker or foam cup)
2 microtubes containing 300 μL CaCl$_2$ (prepared by the teacher 1 day in advance)
inoculating loop
4 sterile pipettes
permanent marker*
timer*
2 Luria broth (LB)–ampicillin plates
2 spreaders

For each student
Student Sheet 2.1, "Genetic Modification Procedure"
Student Sheet 2.2, *"E. coli* Growth Observations"
Student Sheet 2.3, "Genetics Case Study Comparison"
3 sticky notes*
Group Interaction Student Sheet 2, "Developing Communication Skills" (optional)
Scoring Guide: GROUP INTERACTION (GI) (optional)
safety goggles*

Not supplied in kit

Masters for Literacy transparencies are in Teacher Resources III: Literacy. Masters for Scoring Guides are in Teacher Resources IV: Assessment.

This laboratory requires extensive advance preparation and ordering of live materials. See your materials kit for instructions on ordering your live materials within an appropriate time for class use. Be sure to read materials requirements at least one week in advance.

Students may need to practice their pipetting skills before starting the Procedure. If your laboratory has an adequate supply of sterile micropipettes of the appropriate size (suitable for measuring 10 and 100 μL), which may be easier for students to use, provide those. If there is no incubator available, the plates can be incubated at room temperature for several days. Monitor closely for bacterial growth. The exact incubation time will depend on the temperature of the room where the plates are stored.

DETAILS FOR PROCEDURE SUPPLIES

Storing Materials

Carefully read the instructions in the kit regarding ordering and storage of live materials. The prepared plates and the *E. coli* bacteria need to be stored in the refrigerator until the start of class. Store the plates upside down.

Safety Note on Sterile Techniques

Students work with live *E. coli* bacteria in this activity. Stress the importance of following proper safety procedures throughout the activity. Students must disinfect work surfaces and wash their hands thoroughly before beginning and immediately after working with the *E. coli*. When the activity is complete, soak all items in 10% bleach solution for at least 10 minutes before placing them in the garbage.

SEPUP recommends that you check your school's and district's safety regulations on use and disposal of live cultures. Follow regulations when cleaning glassware and discarding disposable equipment that has come in contact with *E. coli* and the growth medium. At a minimum, teacher and students must follow the sterile technique practices below during the advance preparation and as students complete the activity. Never store live specimens and agar plates where food products are stored; keep them in a designated lab-only refrigerator.

STERILE TECHNIQUE PRACTICES FOR WORKING WITH *E. COLI*

1. Keep all equipment away from your eyes and nose to avoid contact with bacteria.

2. Wipe all surfaces with a disinfectant solution (10% bleach solution or disinfectant) before and after working with *E. coli*.

3. Wash your hands before and after any work with *E. coli*.

4. Treat all equipment that has been exposed to *E. coli* (pipettes, spreaders, microtubes, etc.) by soaking them in a 10% bleach solution for 10 minutes before placing them in the appropriate waste container.

5. To prevent overgrowth of *E. coli* do not over-incubate culture plates.

ADVANCE PREPARATION SCHEDULE

2–3 days before activity: Streak the bacteria onto the 10 Luria agar plates without ampicillin. This will ensure that there is adequate bacterial growth for the day of the activity.

First day of activity: Prepare containers of ice and microtubes with $CaCl_2$.

2–3 DAYS BEFORE THE ACTIVITY

Streaking the bacteria onto the starter plates

Use the Luria agar plates without ampicillin. You will need at least one plate per 1–2 student groups for each class. Streak each plate with the *E. coli* culture as follows:

Sterilize the work area with a 10% bleach solution. Light a candle or Bunsen burner. Remove the sterile applicator swab from its package, being careful to only touch the stick end. With the thumb and forefinger of the hand holding the applicator swab, unscrew the cap of the tube with the *E. coli* culture with your little finger. Hold the cap with your little finger until you are ready to recap the tube. Slowly wave the opening of the culture tube through the flame twice.

Cover the cotton end of the sterile swab with *E. coli* culture by dragging the swab across the surface of the agar in the bottom of the culture tube. For each agar plate lift the lid of the plate just enough to insert the swab, and streak it in a back and forth motion across the surface of the agar. Do not damage the surface of the agar. Flame the opening of the culture tube again. Screw the cap back on the tube, and set it aside. Place the swab back into the wrapper and dispose of it (see safety guidelines).

Store the plates upside down in an incubator overnight, and then remove them. If an incubator is not available, store the plates at room temperature out of direct sunlight for two to three days. Check daily to see that the *E. coli* are growing. The *E. coli* that grow should form visible white colonies about 1 mm in diameter. They should grow overnight in an incubator, and within three days at room temperature. These colonies consist of hundreds of bacterial clones. You might also see streaks of bacterial colonies. When you see at least 20 colonies on each plate, you are ready to conduct the Procedure for the activity. Store the plates at room temperature until the day of the activity, no longer than 48 hours. Do NOT store the *E. coli* starter plates in the refrigerator. This will cause the bacteria to enter a dormant phase.

FIRST DAY OF THE ACTIVITY

Dispense the CaCl₂ into microtubes

Dispense 300 µL of $CaCl_2$ into sterile microtubes. Each group needs two tubes with 300 µL $CaCl_2$ per tube.

Prepare containers of ice

Each group will need one container of ice in which to place their tubes of bacteria. Each container should hold enough ice for submerging at least 90% of both tubes.

TEACHING SUMMARY

Getting Started

- Introduce the investigation.

- Introduce group communication skills and the GROUP INTERACTION (GI) Scoring Guide.

- Review with students the equipment and procedure for transforming *E. coli*.

Doing the Activity

- (GI ASSESSMENT) Students transform the bacteria with an engineered plasmid that contains the GFP gene.

Follow-up

- After a 24- to 48-hour incubation period, the class observes the *E. coli* plates and discusses their observations.

- (LITERACY) Students read a case study about biofuels.

BACKGROUND INFORMATION

E. Coli

Escherichia coli (E. coli) are bacteria commonly found in the intestines of warm-blooded animals. While some *E. coli* do cause illness, the majority of strains—including the one used in this activity—are nonpathogenic. Scientists have worked

with nonpathogenic *E. coli* for many years. They are model organisms for investigating genetics and techniques for genetic modification because they are easy to grow, their genome is relatively simple (consisting of 4,000 genes), and they are easy to genetically modify.

Steps in Genetically Modifying an Organism

For an organism to be genetically modified, or transformed, the foreign genetic material must somehow get into the organism's cells, be taken up by the cells' genome, and be expressed (through the gene's product, usually a protein). Some bacteria, including *E. coli,* have the natural ability to take up DNA across their cell walls and membranes, making them relatively easy to modify. Modifying cells that lack this ability requires more complex techniques to get the foreign DNA into the cell, as will be discussed in later activities.

Green Fluorescent Protein

In this activity, students engineer a nonpathogenic population of *E. coli* so that it will contain and express the green fluorescent protein (GFP). In 2008, three scientists, Osamu Shimomura, Martin Chalfie, and Roger Y. Tsien, were awarded the Nobel Prize for chemistry for their discovery and work with GFP. With GFP scientists have proof that genes have been successfully inserted into a certain organism. GFP also serves as a molecular tag (screenable marker) for the expression of other proteins when it is inserted into the DNA in a position near the gene of interest. Links to more information are on the *Science and Global Issues* page of the SEPUP website *(sepuplhs.org/sgi)*.

Plasmids

Most plasmids are found in bacteria, although some eukaryotic organisms also have them. Plasmids are composed of DNA that is separate from the organism's chromosomal DNA, and they replicate independently. They are often circular and double-stranded. In genetic engineering, including this laboratory, plasmids serve as vectors. The desired gene is inserted into the plasmid, which then integrates the gene into the cell through transformation. In this activity students work with pGFP (plasmid with green fluorescent protein). The plasmid also contains a gene for antibiotic resistance. This serves as a selectable marker allowing selection of only the transformed *E. coli*.

GETTING STARTED

1 Explain to students that as they genetically modify bacteria to turn them fluorescent they will be executing the same laboratory techniques as genetic engineers. They will work with *Escherichia coli,* an organism used extensively for cell biology studies, genetics research, and biotechnology applications. There are many other research and commercial applications of DNA and RNA technologies. Links to more information on this topic are on the *Science in Global Issues* website *(sepuplhs.org/sgi)*. Emphasize that the *E. coli* strain for this activity does not cause disease. This laboratory occurs early in this unit to provide students with a motivating hands-on experience with genetically modified organisms before they explore the molecular basis of genetics and heredity in later activities. Students will refer back to this activity throughout the unit.

Project Transparency 2.1, *"Escherichia coli,"* and review the cellular structures relevant to this activity. Explain that in *E. coli,* as in all bacteria, the genetic material (DNA) is in a single circular chromosome. Like all cells, the bacterial cell is surrounded by a cell membrane, and like all bacteria, *E. coli* has a cell wall that surrounds the membrane. Explain to students that there are numerous challenges to creating a genetically modified organism. One of these is getting the DNA from another organism into the cells of the organism to be modified. Explain that with *E. coli,* this is relatively easy to do: by shocking the *E. coli* cells with heat and then cold, scientists force the bacteria's cell walls and membranes to allow pieces of foreign DNA into the cell. A second challenge is to prepare small pieces of DNA containing the genes to be inserted. The genes students will insert have already been engineered into small pieces of

DNA called plasmids, also shown on the transparency. A third challenge is to be able to detect whether the genes have been incorporated into the cell and are active. To do this, students will use two genes that are easy to detect: one of these genes makes the *E. coli* resistant to the antibiotic ampicillin, and the other makes the *E. coli* glow under ultraviolet light (UV). At this point you may want to discuss with your students the challenges presented to modern medicine by antibiotic resistance, particularly if they are familiar with it from the "Cell Biology: World Health" unit of *Science in Global Issues.*

---

2 Creating Genetically Modified Bacteria

1 **G**LOW-IN-THE-DARK rabbits, pigs, and mice may sound like something out of a science fiction movie, but because of genetic modification, these animals actually exist. They were the results of scientists inserting a gene from the jelly species *Aequorea victoria* into their DNA. Genes code for the production of specific proteins. *Aequorea* jellies naturally glow in the dark because they have a gene that codes for green fluorescent protein.

The goal of inserting a gene from one organism into another is for the modified organism to make the protein coded by the inserted gene and express the new trait. For example, a certain gene in *Bacillus thuringiensis* bacteria produces the Bt pesticide protein. When this gene is inserted into corn, the resulting Bt corn produces the Bt pesticide. This production of a protein is called **gene expression.**

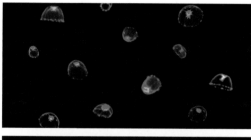

A gene from an Aequorea jelly (a) has been inserted into the DNA of the mouse (b), causing it to glow.

a

b

269

DOING THE ACTIVITY

2 Stress the importance of adhering to sterile techniques throughout this laboratory. These techniques ensure that the *E. coli* won't become contaminated with other bacteria and that the work area does not become contaminated with *E. coli*. Students should sterilize their workspace before they begin and again when they finish the activity. Review all safety procedures with students, as spelled out in the "Sterile Technique and Safety Note" in the beginning of this activity. Explain the procedure for washing or disposing of contaminated equipment. Be sure students wash their hands with soap and water after the activity.

3 (GI ASSESSMENT) Throughout this unit students will engage in small-group work and discussions. Good group communication skills will assist them in gaining a better understanding of content and having more meaningful discussions that support their learning. You may wish to use Group Interaction Student Sheet 2, "Developing Communication Skills," which gives students suggestions for communicating well when in a group. Consider using the GROUP INTERACTION (GI) Scoring Guide throughout the course to provide students feedback about their interaction within groups. For more information about ways to support group interactions see the Facilitating Group Interaction section of Teacher Resources II: Diverse Learners.

In order to produce a genetically modified organism, scientists insert the desired gene into the DNA of eggs from the target organism. Scientists often include the gene for an *Aequorea* jelly's green fluorescent protein, in addition to the desired gene. If they can successfully raise these eggs to adult organisms, and if that organism glows, scientists know that they have inserted the genes correctly. The green fluorescent protein acts like a marker that shows the genes have been inserted into the target organism and that the organism can express the trait.

In this activity, you will genetically modify a population of *Escherichia coli (E. coli)* bacteria. Geneticists study *E. coli* because, even though it is a simple organism, it uses the same cellular processes for gene expression as do more complex organisms. You will insert two genes into *E. coli*: one for green fluorescent protein (GFP), and one that will make the *E. coli* resistant to the antibiotic ampicillin. Because the plates on which you will grow the bacteria contain ampicillin (which normally kills *E. coli*), only the successfully modified *E. coli* will grow.

Challenge

▶ How do scientists genetically modify an organism?

MATERIALS

FOR THE CLASS
4–6 *E. coli* starter plates
    tube of pGLO (GFP) plasmid
    waste container holding 10% bleach solution
    spray bottle of disinfectant
    ultraviolet (UV) light
    supply of paper towels

FOR EACH GROUP OF FOUR STUDENTS
    container of crushed ice
2 microtubes containing 300 μL $CaCl_2$
    inoculating loop
4 sterile pipettes
    permanent marker
    timer
2 Luria broth (LB)—ampicillin plates
2 spreaders

FOR EACH STUDENT
    Student Sheet 2.1, "Genetic Modification Procedure"
    Student Sheet 2.2, "*E. coli* Growth Observations"
    Student Sheet 2.3, "Genetics Case Study Comparison"
3 sticky notes
    safety goggles

Provide all students a copy of the GROUP INTERACTION (GI) Scoring Guide, and ask them to keep it with their science notebooks, as they will refer to it several times in this unit, and throughout *Science and Global Issues.* Let them know that you will use this throughout the unit at specific times to provide feedback on their work within their groups of four and with their partners. Take this opportunity to explain your expectations for group effort, and to discuss as a class what successful group work looks like. For more information on scoring how well students work together, see Teacher Resources IV: Assessment.

4 Before students begin the laboratory, project Transparency 2.2, "Transforming Bacteria," which shows an abbreviated flow chart of the procedure students will carry out. You may choose to photocopy this transparency and pass it out for students to reference. Have students read the Procedure and familiarize themselves with the terminology, equipment, and techniques they will use.

5 If you need to break because of time constraints, you may stop at this Procedure step and ask students to continue working through Procedure Step 18 the next day. If so, you will need to keep the tubes on ice, in a designated lab-only refrigerator or cooler, until students are ready to work on them again. Tubes should not sit longer than 24 hours, and should never be stored in an area where food products are stored.

Procedure

2

3

1. Follow your teacher's instructions for recording notes on this laboratory.

2. Read the entire procedure to familiarize yourself with the steps. After doing so, on Student Sheet 2.1, "Genetic Modification Procedure," write a summary of the purpose of this activity and the experimental design you will follow to transform the *E. coli* bacteria.

4

3. Sterilize your table surface with disinfectant. It is important to work on sterile surfaces during this investigation so that your bacteria do not become contaminated.

4. Label one of the microtubes containing $CaCl_2$ "+ pGFP," and label the other "Control." Place both tubes in your beaker of crushed ice.

5. With the inoculating loop carefully scrape about ¼-loop-full of *E. coli* bacteria from the starter plate. To prevent contamination touch only the handle of the loop. Be careful not to damage the agar plate while harvesting the bacteria.

6. Place the loop with the bacteria into the $CaCl_2$ solution in tube + pGFP, and twirl it back and forth in the liquid for a few seconds to be sure the bacteria have come off the loop. Remove the loop, and place it on a clean paper towel. Do not touch the loop—touch only the handle—to prevent contamination.

7. Your solution should turn cloudy with *E. coli*. If not, use a sterile pipette to mix the cells by gently suctioning the solution into the pipette and then pushing it back out into the microtube. Repeat the mixing 4 to 5 times. Place the pipette on the paper towel with the loop. Close the tube, and put the tube back on ice.

   Note: Touch only the bulb end of the pipette, to avoid contamination. Be careful to only suction the solution far enough to remove it from the tube; do not let any get into the bulb of the pipette. Do this gently to prevent any bubbles from forming in the solution.

8. Repeat Steps 5–7 for the Control tube. You may use the same loop and pipette, as long as they have been kept on a clean paper towel.

9. Obtain the pGFP plasmid according to your teacher's instructions. With a new pipette, transfer 10 µl of pGFP plasmid to the + pGFP tube. Close the tube. Mix the contents by flicking the tube vigorously with your forefinger several times, then tap the end of the tube on the table to make sure the contents are all at the bottom of the tube. Do NOT add plasmid to the Control tube.

5

10. Place both tubes on ice, and let them sit for 15 minutes.

11. Label the underside of your Luria broth (LB)–ampicillin plates with your group's initials and the date. Label one "+ pGFP" and the other "Control."

Safety ⚠️

Be cautious when working with live organisms. If there are any spills, or if any substances come in contact with your skin, notify your teacher immediately, and wash with soap and water. Wash your hands at the end of the investigation. Do not look directly at the UV light source, as it might damage your eyes.

Follow the sterile technique procedures outlined in the box on the next page.

271

6 Place all plates in an area in the classroom where they can sit undisturbed for 24–48 hours. If you have access to an incubator, incubate the plates at 37°C until you see bacterial growth. During this incubation period, you should see bacterial colonies begin to grow on the plates. When sufficient growth is observable, resume the activity at Procedure Step 18.

On the day in between, have students read and discuss the case study as described below for Procedure Step 19.

FOLOW-UP

7 Decide how you want students to share data on the numbers and sizes of their bacterial colonies. You may want to have students post their information on the board. Discuss with students why different groups have different results. Include in your discussion the concept of experimental error, and have students brainstorm what kinds of experimental error might have occurred in the activity (e.g., not timing accurately or not streaking enough bacteria onto the plate). Students will need the information to answer Analysis Question 1.

Sterile Technique Practices for Working with *E. Coli*

1. Keep all equipment away from your eyes and nose to avoid contact with bacteria.

2. Wipe all surfaces with a disinfectant solution before and after working with *E. coli*.

3. Wash your hands before and after any work with *E. coli*.

4. Treat all equipment that has been exposed to *E. coli* (pipettes, spreaders, microtubes, etc.) by soaking them in a 10% bleach solution for 10 minutes before placing them in the appropriate waste container.

5. To prevent overgrowth of *E. coli* do not over-incubate culture plates.

12. The next step is to shock the bacteria with heat. Heat shock causes the bacteria cells to take in the plasmid with the GFP gene. Rub your hands together rapidly to be sure they are warm. Remove both tubes from the ice, and hold them in your hands to incubate them. Shake your hands gently for 2–3 seconds to mix the fluid in the tubes. Incubate EXACTLY 3 minutes, and immediately put the tubes back on ice for 1 minute.

13. With a new sterile pipette transfer 100 µl of the mixture from the Control tube to the control plate. Use one of the spreaders to spread the liquid across the entire plate, taking care not to damage the agar. Discard the pipette in the waste container.

14. With another new sterile pipette and the other spreader, repeat Step 13 to transfer the contents of the + pGFP tube to the + pGFP plate.

15. Let the plates sit for 3 minutes to allow the agar to absorb the liquid that contains the bacteria.

6 16. Turn the plates upside down. Your teacher will give you instructions for storing the plates.

17. On Student Sheet 2.2, "*E. coli* Growth Observations," record your observations of each plate on the section of the Student Sheet designated, "time = 0 hours."

18. After 48 to 72 hours, observe the plates under a UV light. *Keep the lids on the plates. Do not look directly at the UV light source, as it might damage your eyes.* In your science notebook, record your observations of the plates your team prepared. Be sure to record the number of bacterial colonies on each plate, and to sketch each plate and the colonies.

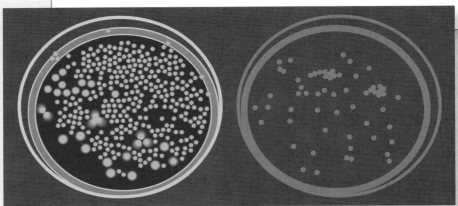

8 Throughout this unit, case studies highlight particular research and issues surrounding genetically modified organisms. With each case study, students will follow the "Read, Think, and Take Note" literacy strategy. "Read, Think, and Take Note" is an opportunity for students to record thoughts, reactions, or questions on sticky notes as they read. The notes serve to make concrete the thoughts arising in their minds and then serve as prompts to generate conversation or write explanations. Throughout this unit and the rest of *Science and Global Issues* you will see multiple opportunities for students to employ and become comfortable with this strategy. Explain to students that through these literacy strategies they are learning the ways in which proficient readers think while reading. Display the guidelines shown on Literacy Transparency 3, "Read, Think, and Take Note," in your classroom for students to refer to. Look for additional occasions for students to apply this strategy when reading text. For more information on "Read, Think, and Take Note," see the Teacher Resources III: Literacy.

7

19. Following your teacher's instructions, compare the results from your plates with the number of colonies on plates that other groups grew.

20. Dispose of all materials as instructed by your teacher, and sterilize your table surface.

21. Wash your hands thoroughly with soap and water.

8

22. Throughout this unit, you will read case studies about genetic modification. You will use the information you collect on Student Sheet 2.3, "Genetics Case Study Comparison," to answer Analysis Questions in a number of activities.

23. Follow your teacher's directions for reading the case study about biofuels. As you read, follow the "Read, Think, and Take Note" strategy. To do this:

   • Stop at least three times during the reading to mark on a sticky note your thoughts or questions about the reading. Use the list of guidelines below to start your thinking.

   • After writing a thought or question on a sticky note, place it next to the passage in the reading that prompted your note.

   • Discuss with your partner the thoughts and questions you had while reading.

24. Complete the information for "Biofuels from Bacteria" on Student Sheet 2.3, "Genetics Case Study Comparison."

Read, Think, and Take Note: Guidelines

As you read, from time to time, write one of the following on a sticky note:

• Explain a thought or reaction to something you read.

• Note something in the reading that is confusing or unfamiliar.

• List a word that you do not know.

• Describe a connection to something you learned or read previously.

• Make a statement about the reading.

• Pose a question about the reading.

• Draw a diagram or picture of an idea or connection.

Sample notes for this section of Student Sheet 2.3, "Genetics Case Study Comparison," are shown at the end of this activity.

CASE STUDY

Modifying Bacteria to Produce Biofuels

CITIES, HOMES, FACTORIES, cars, and trucks throughout the world are powered primarily by fossil fuels. Concerns about the availability of these fuels and the environmental impacts of producing and using them have led to a search for alternatives. One of these alternatives is a group of fuels called biofuels. **Biofuels,** including bioethanol and biodiesel, are compounds that are produced from renewable biological sources. Plants high in starch and sugar are made into ethanol, while vegetable oils and other fats are made into biodiesel. Both of these fuels may be burned in combustion engines in place of fossil fuels. Research on alternative fuels and the role of genetically modified organisms in producing them is rapidly expanding in the United States.

Scientists are currently working on ways to overcome several obstacles to the sustainable production of biofuels. They hope to improve the plants themselves to get high yields of fuel, and to improve the

Many farm machines at the Agricultural Research Service's Beltville Agricultural Research Center are running on a mixture of diesel fuel and biodiesel, which is made from soybean oil.

technology for extracting fuel from the plants. Much of the research focuses on the development of genetically modified microorganisms. Currently, most bioethanol is generated by fermenting corn or sugar cane with yeast or bacteria. Those crops, however, are also important food crops, and the starchy and sugary edible parts of these plants are the parts needed to make bioethanol. If too many farmers dedicate too much agricultural land to producing biofuel plants, supplies of basic foods will shrink. For this reason, scientists are trying to find efficient ways to make biofuels from the waste stalks and leaves of crops and from grasses that don't require the high-quality soil that food crops need.

The difficulty in making fuel from grasses and inedible parts of crops is that they contain two substances —lignin and cellulose—that are very hard to break down. These substances add strength to the plants' cell walls, but cause problems in the production of biofuels. The solution might be found in bacteria that live in such places as compost piles or in the digestive systems of termites and other organisms. Enzymes that break down wood and the tough parts of plants have been identified in these bacteria. A current approach scientists are pursuing is to insert genes from these bacteria into other bacteria that grow well on the large scale needed for producing commercial ethanol. One such bacterium is the very well understood *E. coli*. Scientists are working on a genetically modified *E. coli* that can break the lignin and cellulose into sugars that can then be converted to ethanol.

Another potential use of genetically modified microorganisms is to improve the quality of the fuel produced from sugars. Typically, yeast or bacteria break down sugars and starch to produce ethanol, a two-carbon fuel. Ethanol's shortcomings, however, are that it doesn't have a

Ethanol is currently used as a fuel, but has some shortcomings.

high energy content, it binds to water, and it corrodes metals, including those with which storage tanks and cars' gas tanks are made. One research group has modified *E. coli* to produce fuels that have longer carbon chains and are similar to gasoline. These longer-chain alcohols store more energy than ethanol, are easier to separate from water, and perform better in engines.

(Continued on next page)

(Continued from previous page)

Currently, other types of microbes can produce these fuels, but the yield is low. The fuels can also be produced through breaking down the plant matter with chemicals, but this is expensive and requires a lot of energy. To harness *E. coli* to produce fuels scientists have deleted several genes in *E. coli* and replaced them with genes from other organisms. These efforts have been somewhat successful. The modified *E. coli* produces longer-chain alcohols, but not enough for commercial use. Some researchers are trying to determine how to balance each step of the reaction pathway in the *E. coli* to maximize production of the fuels. Other research is looking at performing a similar genetic modification in yeast and other microbes that are often used in converting plant material into other types of biofuel.

A third research group has genetically engineered *E. coli* that are able to both break down cellulose and turn that product into biodiesel and related compounds. They have done this by deleting two *E. coli* genes and adding genes from several other organisms. Although these modified *E. coli* produce less fuel than needed for commercial use, they produce enough that the results are promising.

Longer chain alcohols, such as octanol, may perform better than ethanol as a fuel.

Some scientists question the safety of modifying bacteria and other microbes to produce biofuel. They think there has not been enough safety testing done on genetically modified organisms, and suggest that there may be unintended consequences for human health or the environment. Although the *E. coli* needed to make biofuels would be grown only in laboratories, there might be problems if some were accidentally transferred to other environments.

Alternatives to developing genetically modified organisms for producing biofuels include:

- Improving the fuel quality of plants by selective breeding.
- Weakening plants' cell walls through selective breeding.
- Improving the process of chemically breaking down plant matter.

Both scientific advances and policy decisions will play a role in decisions about pursuing these approaches to producing biofuels. ∎

SAMPLE RESPONSES

1. Four groups had at least 25 colonies of bacteria that grew and glowed on the +pGFP plates, and 0–2 colonies on the control plate. Based on this my group concluded that the insertion of the genes for GFP and ampicillin-resistance worked. However, one group had +pGFP plates on which no bacteria grew. The lack of growth might have been caused by the heat shock not being warm enough, or by incorrect timing so that the bacteria did not have enough time to transform. Another group had a few colonies on the control plate, which might have become contaminated.

2. If ampicillin had not been added, all bacteria—both genetically modified and not modified—would have grown. The ampicillin served as a selection agent that prevented those bacteria that did not take up the engineered plasmid from growing.

3. Nothing would grow on this plate. The ampicillin would prevent the growth of the *E. coli* since the *E. coli* do not contain the engineered ampicillin-resistant gene.

4. The possible benefits of using GMOs to produce biofuels from plant waste products are that biofuel crops would not compete with food crops for cropland, the fuels would be renewable, and we would not have to rely on oil. The possible risks are if the GMOs were somehow released into the wild and transferred genes to wild populations.

CREATING GENETICALLY MODIFIED BACTERIA • ACTIVITY 2

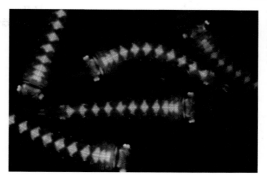

These mosquito larvae have been genetically modified with GFP. Scientists hope to one day genetically modify mosquitoes so they cannot carry the protozoa that cause malaria. This could save millions of lives.

Analysis

1. Analyze your work in this activity and that of the other groups, according to your teacher's instructions. Analysis should include a summary of the data collected and conclusions you and your group draw from the data about the bacteria on the plates. Explain possible sources of experimental error.

2. How would your results differ if you had not added ampicillin to any of the plates but kept all other variables the same?

3. What results would you expect if you had created a Luria–ampicillin plate containing *E. coli* that were not transformed?

4. What are the possible benefits and risks involved in developing genetically modified organisms to produce biofuels?

KEY VOCABULARY	
biofuel	gene expression
DNA	genetic modification
gene	

277

REVIST THE CHALLENGE

Students should be able to articulate that there are several technical challenges involved in modifying *E. coli* to express the green fluorescent protein. These include isolating the gene from the jelly that produces it, producing a small piece of DNA (called a plasmid) that contains the gene to be inserted, getting the bacteria to take up the plasmid, and detecting the presence of the protein.

A sample response to Student Sheet 2.1, "Genetic Modification Procedure," is shown at the end of this activity.

Genetic Modification Procedure

In the second column of the table below, record a one-to-three-sentence summary for each group of procedure steps.

Procedure Steps	Summary of purpose of these steps
1–5	In these steps we prepare for the investigation, set up our notebooks, sterilize the work area, and label the growth plates.
6–9	In these steps we add bacteria to two tubes.
10–13	The plasmid with the GFP gene is added to one of the two tubes, and the tubes are shocked with heat so they will take up any plasmid that is present.
14–18	The bacteria are streaked onto plates that contain ampicillin and incubated to give them time to grow.
19–22	We observe the results of the investigation and then clean up.

E. Coli *Growth Observations*

Directions: Record your observations for the growth on each plate in the space provided below.

	Observed Growth Time = 0 hours	Observed Growth Time = _48 hours_
Control **LB/ampicillin**		
+GFP **LB/ampicillin**		

Genetics Case Study Comparison

Case study	Type of genetic modification	Benefits	Risks and concerns	Current status of research and development	Other solutions?
Modifying bacteria to produce biofuels	Genes to produce butanol from plant matter are inserted into E. coli bacteria.	Alternative fuel to gasoline Less cost and chemical waste than with other biofuel production	Unintended consequences, such as gene transfer and ecological impacts, if GMOs released to environment	Bacteria have been modified but are not yet producing enough Trying to modify yeast	Make chemical processes more efficient Selective breeding of microbes such as bacteria or yeast
Golden rice					
History of selective corn breeding					
Fast-growing salmon					

3 Mitosis and Asexual Reproduction

MODELING • 1–2 CLASS SESSIONS

OVERVIEW

In this activity, students work with an online simulation and chromosome models to learn about mitosis and asexual reproduction. From their understanding of mitosis they predict the percentage of asexually produced offspring that will inherit an inserted gene from a genetically modified parent.

KEY CONTENT

1. Asexual reproduction produces genetically identical offspring from a single parent.

2. Genes are organized in larger structures called chromosomes.

3. Mitosis is the process by which replicated chromosomes divide and, following cytokinesis, form two identical daughter cells.

KEY PROCESS SKILLS

1. Students make and record observations.

MATERIALS AND ADVANCE PREPARATION

For the teacher

Student Sheet 3.1, "Mitosis"
(available online only: see note at the end of the Materials section)

Scoring Guide: UNDERSTANDING CONCEPTS (UC)

For each pair of students

set of 2 pop-bead chromosome models:

> 16 blue pop beads
>
> 16 green pop beads
>
> 2 orange pop beads
>
> 2 blue centromeres
>
> 2 green centromeres

computer with internet access*

For each student

Student Sheet 3.1, "Mitosis"
(available online only: see note below)

Scoring Guide: UNDERSTANDING CONCEPTS (UC) (optional)

Not supplied in kit

Masters for Scoring Guides are in Teacher Resources IV: Assessment.

Note: *Student Sheet 3.1, "Mitosis," is found only on the* Science and Global Issues *website (sepuplhs.org/sgi). Sample student answers are also available on the website. Both are located in the teacher's section. Arrange for computers with Internet access for the day(s) students do this activity. Go to the* Science and Global Issues *page of the SEPUP website to access the simulation. You may want to bookmark this site for students. Make sure the browsers and supporting software are current and can properly run the simulation.*

TEACHING SUMMARY

Getting Started

- Discuss the issue of genetically modified organisms passing inserted genes to unmodified populations of the species.

Doing the Activity

- Students work with an interactive online mitosis simulation.

- Students model mitosis.

Follow-up

- (UC ASSESSMENT) Students determine the probability that an organism carrying an inserted gene will pass the gene to future generations through asexual reproduction.

GETTING STARTED

1 Remind students that in Activity 1, "A Genetically Modified Solution?" they read about scientists' concerns that genetically modified organisms might breed with a wild organism, passing the inserted gene to future generations of the wild organism. Point out to students that this concern is frequently raised in debates about genetic modification. Remind students that corn reproduces sexually, while the *E. coli* they were working with in the previous activity reproduces asexually.

Be sure students understand that in this activity they will study asexual reproduction, and what they are learning will apply to the *E. coli* they have genetically modified with GFP. The simulation introduces students to chromosomes and their structure and function. If students are completely unfamiliar with chromosome structure and function, you may want to first review briefly as a class the packaging of genes into chromosomes. This unit does not discuss polyploidy or organisms with more than two sets of chromosomes. This is common in plants, and is found in some animals, such as goldfish. You may want to review this phenomenon if it is required by your state or local standards.

DOING THE ACTIVITY

2 If your class completed the "Cell Biology: World Health" unit of *Science and Global Issues,* students will be familiar with the term mitosis and its place in the cell cycle. Explain that the other three phases of the cell cycle—G1, S, and G2—are often referred to together as interphase.

---

3 Mitosis and Asexual Reproduction

1 **WHEN SCIENTISTS GENETICALLY** modify an organism, it is important that they be able to predict how many of the offspring of the modified organism will contain the newly inserted gene. This prediction depends on how the organism reproduces. In this activity you will investigate how a single-celled organism, in this case *E. coli*, reproduces asexually.

In **asexual reproduction** it takes only one parent to produce offspring. The parent's cells undergo **mitosis,** in which a single cell divides to produce two identical daughter cells. When humans and other multicellular organisms grow, their new cells are also products of mitosis.

You will model mitosis and compare the genetic makeup of a parent cell and its daughter cells. Then you will predict the chance of an inserted gene being passed on to next generations through asexual reproduction.

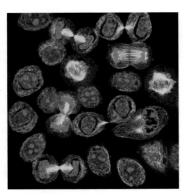

Some of these human cells are undergoing mitosis. At bottom left and top, the cells are in the last stages, and will soon form two daughter cells.

278

Tell students how you would like them to work with the online simulation. Either direct them to the bookmarks you have already set on the computer or to go to the *Science and Global Issues* page of the SEPUP website *(sepuplhs.org/sgi)* and look for the link to Genetics, Activity 3, "Mitosis and Asexual Reproduction."

3 As students work with the simulation, you may find it necessary to direct them to observe the position and action of the chromosomes in each step of the simulation. Ask them to note in each phase the chromosomes' shapes, position within the cell, and movement. If time permits, locate additional simulations, and ask students to compare their observations of the first with subsequent simulations. It may help students to see more than one representation of mitosis. A sample response to Student Sheet 3.1, "Mitosis," is available at *sepuplhs.org/sgi*.

Review students' observations and the work they have recorded on Student Sheet 3.1, "Mitosis." Project a transparency of Student Sheet 3.1. Starting with two pairs of chromosomes in prophase, ask students to describe what occurs at each phase, and what you should next add to the transparency. This is an opportunity to check students' understanding of the key events of mitosis. Ensure that students understand that each x represents a duplicated chromosome. The parent chromosome and the new chromosome are linked at a structure called a centromere, which produces the x-shaped structure of the replicated chromosome. When linked, the two chromosomes are each called chromatids. Stress that these linked chromatids are identical. If students have trouble summarizing the events, you may want to record a summary of the key events on a blank transparency, such as "Interphase—DNA Replicates and Chromosomes Condense." If your state and local standards require that students be familiar with additional new vocabulary, such as **centrioles** and **cytokinesis,** this is an appropriate time to introduce and review those terms.

Challenge

▶ If a genetically modified cell undergoes mitosis, how likely is it that the daughter cells will contain the inserted gene?

MATERIALS

FOR EACH PAIR OF STUDENTS

    set of 2 pop-bead chromosome models

16 blue pop beads

16 green pop beads

2 orange pop beads

2 blue centromeres

2 green centromeres

    access to online mitosis simulation

FOR EACH STUDENT

    Student Sheet 3.1, "Mitosis"

Procedure

2 1. Observe the mitosis simulation on the *Science and Global Issues* page of the SEPUP website *(sepuplhs.org/sgi)*. Determine what happens to the genetic material of the cell at each phase.

3 2. On Student Sheet 3.1, "Mitosis," draw what happens to the chromosomes during each of the phases shown.

3. In your science notebook, write a description summarizing the key events of each stage of mitosis.

4 4. With your partner, use the pop-bead model chromosomes to show what happens when a cell with one pair of chromosomes undergoes mitosis. To do this:

   a. Make two strands of four blue pop beads, and attach them to the blue centromere. Repeat this process for green. This represents one pair of chromosomes.

   b. Simulate the replication of each chromosome during prophase. To do this, repeat Step 4a. With the centromeres, form the shape of a replicated chromosome as shown in the illustration on the next page. Note that the X shape is a replicated chromosome, and that the model demonstrates one pair of replicated chromosomes.

   c. Refer to Student Sheet 3.1, "Mitosis," to determine how to move the chromosomes as they would move through each phase—prophase, metaphase, anaphase, and telophase. Determine the genetic makeup of the cells that result.

279

4 Check that students understand that DNA is replicated during interphase. The mechanism of DNA replication will be formally introduced and explored in Activity 12, "DNA Replication," and DNA replication during meiosis will be discussed in Activity 13, "Meiosis and Sexual Reproduction." This is an appropriate time to review the vocabulary terms **centromere** and **chromatid.** Check that in their models students end up with two cells in telophase, each containing one pair of chromosomes. You might challenge students to repeat the procedure without the assistance of Student Sheet 3.1, "Mitosis."

5 ⬥ This can be used as a Quick Check on whether students correctly concluded that the genetic makeup of the daughter cell is identical to that of the parent cell. You may point out that each daughter cell is a clone of the parent cell.

6 (UC ASSESSMENT) Encourage discussion that incorporates the terms DNA, chromosomes, parent cell, daughter cell, and gene. If necessary clarify that the cellular mechanisms of mitosis and asexual reproduction are the same. This is also an appropriate time to point out to students that if a mutation were to occur in an organism, it would be inherited in a similar way to the modified gene they are discussing. Students do not need to understand the mechanism of genetic mutation at this time, but should be aware that it is an important source of genetic diversity.

Students' responses may be scored with the UNDERSTANDING CONCEPTS (UC) Scoring Guide. A sample response is shown below.

Level-3 Response

Before a genetically modified cell undergoes mitosis, its DNA is replicated. This means that the newly replicated chromosome and the original chromosome will contain the inserted gene. All of those chromosomes then go through the stages of mitosis: prophase, metaphase, anaphase, and telophase. The result is a daughter cell that is genetically identical to the parent cell, and it will include the inserted gene. There is a 100% probability that a genetically modified cell that undergoes asexual reproduction will produce offspring that contain the inserted gene as well.

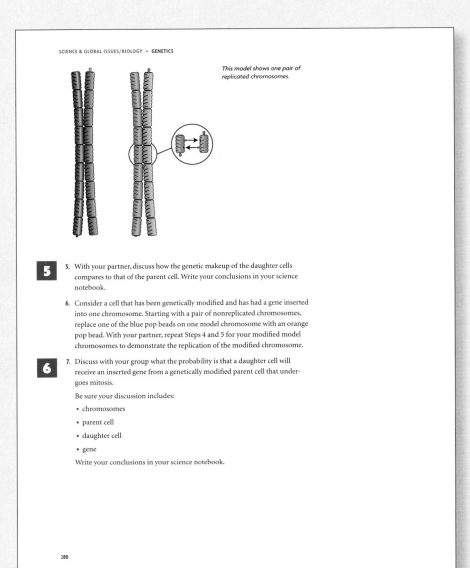

This model shows one pair of replicated chromosomes.

5 5. With your partner, discuss how the genetic makeup of the daughter cells compares to that of the parent cell. Write your conclusions in your science notebook.

6. Consider a cell that has been genetically modified and has had a gene inserted into one chromosome. Starting with a pair of nonreplicated chromosomes, replace one of the blue pop beads on one model chromosome with an orange pop bead. With your partner, repeat Steps 4 and 5 for your modified model chromosomes to demonstrate the replication of the modified chromosome.

6 7. Discuss with your group what the probability is that a daughter cell will receive an inserted gene from a genetically modified parent cell that undergoes mitosis.

Be sure your discussion includes:
• chromosomes
• parent cell
• daughter cell
• gene

Write your conclusions in your science notebook.

280

FOLLOW-UP

7 In the scenario described in the Analysis question, if the insertion is made into the bacterial chromosome, or in eukaryotic organisms where the genetic modification occurs in the chromosomes, all inserted genes will be passed on to the daughter cells. Note for students that if the gene were inserted into the plasmid, for example in a bacterium genetic modification, the plasmid DNA is usually (but not always) passed on to all offspring. This unit does not cover plasmid DNA replication in detail, and assumes genetic modification is occurring in the chromosomes, except where noted.

SAMPLE RESPONSES

1. Mitosis involves the separation of replicated chromosomes from a parent cell to form daughter cells. The DNA is replicated in interphase, and then chromosomes condense in prophase, line up in metaphase, are separated into chromatids in anaphase, and begin to separate into two cells in telophase. After the cytoplasm pinches and divides during cytokinesis, two genetically identical daughter cells are formed.

2. The chromosomes are identical to the parent cell's.

3. This is a valid claim. When mitosis occurs, identical daughter cells are formed that contain each gene that the parent cell contained. This means that the daughter cells will include the inserted gene as well.

4. Since all of the daughter cells will contain the inserted gene, scientists will only need to modify a starting population of an organism, and all descendants of this population will contain the inserted gene as well. On the other hand, there is a chance that the genetically modified organism could be introduced to unmodified organisms in a nearby farm or wild ecosystem and multiply. It would be difficult to eliminate future generations that contain the modification.

Analysis

1. Explain mitosis. In your explanation include the preparations that take place during interphase and each of the four phases of mitosis (prophase, metaphase, anaphase, and telophase).

2. In mitosis, how does each daughter cell's chromosomes compare to the chromosomes of the parent?

7 3. A friend of yours claims that every genetically modified single-celled organism that reproduces asexually would pass along the inserted gene to its daughter cells. Based on your work in this activity, is that claim valid? Explain.

4. Based on your answer in Procedure Step 7, what benefits and risks might the asexual reproduction of a genetically modified organism or cell pose?

KEY VOCABULARY	
asexual reproduction	cytokinesis
centrioles	daughter cell
centromere	**mitosis**
chromatid	parent cell
chromosomes	

281

REVIST THE CHALLENGE

Refer back to Analysis Question 4, which addresses one concern often raised about growing genetically modified organisms. Ask students to share their ideas with the class. They should incorporate evidence from their work in this activity to support their ideas about the potential benefits and risks associated with the genetic modification of an organism that reproduces asexually.

4 Breeding Corn

INVESTIGATION • 1–2 CLASS SESSIONS

OVERVIEW

Students observe two generations of corn crosses to investigate basic concepts of heredity. They use Punnett squares to analyze and predict the results of genetic crosses for one trait—corn kernel color—and are introduced to selective breeding as a way to improve crops.

Key Content

1. Cells contain two copies of each gene. These copies are called alleles. In organisms that reproduce sexually, one allele of each type of gene is inherited from each parent.

2. Punnett squares are models of the transmission of alleles from one generation to the next.

3. A Punnett square demonstrates the possible phenotypic and genotypic results of a cross and how likely it is that each genotype and phenotype will occur from that cross.

4. Studying and observing the results of sexual reproduction of a model organism provide information about the behavior of genes and the relationship between genotype and phenotype.

5. Selective breeding influences the phenotypes and genotypes of offspring.

KEY PROCESS SKILLS

1. Students make predictions.

2. Students interpret data.

3. Students identify and describe trends in data.

MATERIALS AND ADVANCE PREPARATION

For the teacher
Color Transparency 4.1, "Breeding Corn: First Generation"
Color Transparency 4.2, "Breeding Corn: Second Generation"
Transparency 4.3, "Corn Reproductive Structures"
Transparency 4.4, "Creating a Punnett Square"
Scoring Guide: ANALYZING DATA (AD)
Scoring Guide: UNDERSTANDING CONCEPTS (UC)
Scoring Guide: GROUP INTERACTION (GI)

For each pair of students
cardboard corn ears A and B
set of P/p allele cards

For each student
Student Sheet 4.1, "Traits and Heredity"
Student Sheet 4.2, "Practice Punnett Square Problems" (optional)
Scoring Guide: ANALYZING DATA (AD) (optional)
Scoring Guide: UNDERSTANDING CONCEPTS (UC) (optional)
Scoring Guide: GROUP INTERACTION (GI) (optional)

You may want to laminate the cardboard corn ears and provide students with dry-erase markers to keep track as they count the corn kernels.

Masters for Scoring Guides are in Teacher Resources IV: Assessment.

TEACHING SUMMARY

Getting Started
- Introduce corn as a selectively bred plant.
- Discuss the usefulness of corn in studying heredity.

Doing the Activity
- Explore students' ideas about traits and heredity.
- (AD, GI ASSESSMENT) Students observe corn ears to predict the genotypes of the parent plants.

Follow-up
- (UC ASSESSMENT) The class discusses the crosses that produced corn ears A and B.

BACKGROUND INFORMATION

Corn as a Model Organism

Corn has been extensively bred over many centuries to develop the sweet kernels of today's corn. Corn, peas, fruit flies, and yeast are some of the organisms that geneticists have focused on and have provided a great deal of our general understanding of the behavior of genes. These organisms are easy to breed and grow, have short generation times, multiple offspring, and other traits that make them ideal models for genetic studies.

Basic Genetics

Most phenotypic traits are polygenic—determined by the interaction of a number of genes—and, in many cases, by environmental factors as well. For the purposes of this unit, assume that corn kernel color is determined by one gene. This activity asks students to work backward to determine the genotypes of the parents based on their observations of offspring (kernel) phenotypes. Students inquire into the results of heredity and work to explain why they observe specific ratios of kernel phenotypes.

Note that the ratios produced by Punnett squares are predicted outcomes, not actual outcomes. Just as coin tossing does not always produce the 50% heads and 50% tails predicted mathematically, genetic crosses do not usually produce the exact ratios predicted. The larger the sample size of offspring to be analyzed, the more likely it is that the ratio of phenotypes produced will be near the predicted ratio.

GETTING STARTED

1 This is the start of a series of activities about selective breeding. Students will compare selective breeding to genetic modification for producing organisms with traits that might help address sustainability challenges.

Explain to students that they will investigate the results of two crosses of corn. Project Transparency 4.3, "Corn Reproductive Structures." Emphasize that corn reproduces by sexual reproduction, not through asexual reproduction, which was discussed in Activity 3, "Mitosis and Asexual Reproduction." Explain how sexual reproduction in corn happens. The sperm cells are in the pollen contained in the tassel that grows from the top of the plant. The ear of corn is the female part of the plant, and contains up to 1,000 eggs. Each egg produces a silk—the hair-like structure that grows from the egg under the husk to the tip of the ear, where it is exposed to the air. When pollen falls on the silk, fertilization occurs. Each fertilized egg creates an individual kernel, inside of which an embryo is formed.

◆ Note: It is a common misconception that corn kernels are gametes. Make sure your students understand that each kernel is a fertilized offspring, or embryo. Corn ears are particularly useful in this activity because each ear shows the results of hundreds of fertilization events, thus providing a large sample size for analysis.

---

4 Breeding Corn

1 FARMERS THROUGHOUT THE world grow crops and raise animals to sustain their families and communities, and to earn a living. Livestock and most crops reproduce by **sexual reproduction**—in which two parents contribute genetic material to the offspring. Farmers practice selective breeding to improve livestock and crops. In **selective breeding,** organisms with desirable traits are mated with the goal of producing even more desirable offspring. For example, farmers have bred apples for different colors, tastes, and types of consumption, such as baking, juicing, and eating. Before the development of biotechnology methods that allow scientists to alter plants and animals on a gene-by-gene basis, selective breeding was the only way people could develop varieties of crops and livestock that had traits they wanted or needed.

In this activity, you will explore the results of selectively breeding two varieties of corn.

Challenge

▶ How can information about the genetic makeup of plants help farmers breed plants for desirable traits?

MATERIALS

FOR EACH PAIR OF STUDENTS
cardboard corn ears A and B
set of P/p allele cards

FOR EACH STUDENT
Student Sheet 4.1, "Traits and Heredity"

Breeding yellow-kernelled corn and purple-kernelled corn will produce a first generation of purple-kernelled offspring. Breeding those offspring will produce corn with kernels of both colors.

DOING THE ACTIVITY

2 (GI ASSESSMENT) Student Sheet 4.1, "Traits and Heredity," and students' responses in Procedure Steps 1–6 will allow you to assess their background knowledge of heredity and alleles. Sample student answers appear later in the activity. Do not correct any student's misconceptions about heredity and alleles at this point. Procedure Steps 1–14 are an opportunity for you to use the GROUP INTERACTION (GI) Scoring Guide to assess students' group interaction skills.

3 Project Transparency 4.1, "Breeding Corn: First Generation." This transparency shows the cross that students are asked to consider in Procedure Step 2. Pedigrees are introduced formally in Activity 8, "Interpreting Pedigrees." Refer to the transparency to clarify students' questions before they begin work in Procedure Step 2. As they work, circulate around the room and listen to groups' discussions. Determine if all students understand that some traits may be hidden and that each parent contributes genetic information to the offspring. If students do not understand these concepts, lead a class discussion, basing it on questions you devise that are related to any misconceptions that you have heard. Remind students that corn reproduces sexually, which means that each parent provides genetic information through an egg and a sperm. At this point do not introduce any new vocabulary.

Procedure

2 1. Read the questions posed on Student Sheet 4.1, "Traits and Heredity." Fill in the "I think" column with a response to each question.

3 2. The figure below shows a cross between a corn plant that produces ears with purple kernels and a corn plant that produces ears with yellow kernels. The resulting offspring have ears with only purple kernels.

PARENT GENERATION

plant that produces
purple kernels

plant that produces
yellow kernels

plant that produces
purple kernels

With your group, discuss what you think is happening in the above cross. Share your ideas with the class, as directed by your teacher.

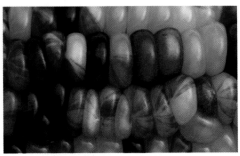

The corn shown above has been selectively bred to exhibit many kernel colors.

284

4 Be sure students understand clearly the terms allele, dominant, and recessive and how to depict genes with letters before they move on to Punnett squares. If necessary, guide a discussion. Some sample questions and answers might be: What does each letter represent? An allele. How many alleles does each parent give to the offspring? One. Which allele represents the dominant trait? The one that is a capital letter. The recessive trait? The lowercase letter. What will occur if an offspring has one dominant and one recessive allele? Only the dominant trait will be seen.

5 Check students' Punnett squares, and correct them as needed. The correct answers are:

	P	p
P	P P	P p
p	P p	p p

The allele combinations are PP, Pp, and pp. The PP and Pp offspring would be purple, and the pp offspring would be yellow.

If necessary, project Transparency 4.4, "Creating a Punnett Square," and review how to show the results of a cross. Point out where a square shows the allele combinations and which trait will be seen in possible offspring that may result from a cross. The terms genotype and phenotype will not be introduced until the next activity.

6 Take this opportunity to ensure that students understand how to calculate a ratio, reduce it to its lowest terms, and represent it in writing. You might provide practice problems, such as those that follow, and ask students to reduce to the lowest ratio.

---

4 **3.** Read the information on the next page in the text box, "Basic Genetics," that you will need for the rest of the procedure. Record information in your science notebook, as instructed.

4. With your partner, and based on what you know about the heredity of traits, use the P and p allele cards to discuss why the corn kernels (offspring) were all purple. Discuss your ideas with the other pair in your group. Record a summary of your discussion in your student notebook.

5. Record your group's ideas from Step 4 in the second column of Student Sheet 4.1 in the "My group thinks" column. You will return to these questions later to see how your ideas and understanding of traits and heredity have changed.

5 **6. a.** A **Punnett square** is a tool that shows and helps predict the possible offspring when two organisms reproduce sexually. The Punnett square below shows a cross between a purple corn plant that has PP alleles and a yellow corn plant that has pp alleles.

	P	P
p	P p	P p
p	P p	P p

The alleles written along the top and side of the square are the alleles from each parent organism, in this case the purple corn and the yellow corn. The allele combinations inside the square show the possible combinations that could be found in the offspring of this cross.

b. Draw a blank Punnett square in your science notebook, and show what a cross would look like between two parent corn plants with the genes Pp. Note the allele combinations and what color the offspring would be for each combination.

6 **7.** Determine the predicted ratio of the different-colored offspring in the Punnett square you drew in Step 6b. How is this different from the ratio for the Punnett square shown in Step 6a?

285

Ratio	Ratio reduced to lowest terms
1,020 red : 510 blue	2 red : 1 blue
2,415 crooked : 345 straight	7 crooked : 1 straight
1,040 rough : 52 smooth	20 rough : 1 smooth

Students should calculate that the ratio for the corn offspring in Procedure Step 6 is 3 purple offspring to 1 yellow offspring, which differs from the 100% purple offspring in Procedure Step 7.

7 Sample results for Procedure Steps 10 and 11 appear below. Expect that students' results may deviate by plus or minus 5 kernels.

Assist students as necessary in calculating the ratio of kernels produced. Students should divide both numbers of kernels by the smaller number of kernels and then round their answers. For example, for ear A, students would divide 116 by 114 and 114 by 114, producing a ratio of approximately 1 : 1.

BACKGROUND INFORMATION

Basic Genetics

- An organism has two copies of the gene for each of its traits. These copies are called **alleles.**

- Some traits are either **dominant,** meaning they will mask another version of the trait, or they are **recessive,** meaning that they will be hidden by a dominant trait.

- In scientific writing a dominant trait is represented with a capital letter, which is underlined to be easy to distinguish. A recessive trait is shown with a lower-case letter. For example, in corn the allele for purple kernel color is P̲, and the allele for yellow kernel color is p. The possible allele combinations for a corn plant are P̲P̲, P̲p, or pp.

8. Read the scenario that follows.

   Shauna is a gardener who would like to produce bicolored (two-colored) corn like some samples she got from a friend. In her garden, she has corn with purple kernels and corn with yellow kernels, but no bicolored corn. Shauna begins by crossing the plants with yellow kernels with those with purple kernels. The offspring produced have all purple kernels, as shown in the Punnett Square in Step 6a. Help Shauna figure out what to do next to produce corn like corn ears A and B.

9. In your science notebook, make a data table like the one below.

7

10. Count the number of purple kernels and the number of yellow kernels on corn ear A. Record them in your data table.

Corn Breeding Data

	Number of purple kernels	Number of yellow kernels	Ratio of purple kernels to yellow kernels	Ratio rounded to the nearest whole number
Kernels on ear A				
Kernels on ear B				

Sample Results for Procedure Steps 10 and 11: Corn Breeding Data

	Number of purple kernels	Number of yellow kernels	Ratio of purple kernels to yellow kernels	Ratio rounded to the nearest whole number
Kernels on ear A	116	114	1.0175 : 1	About 1 : 1
Kernels on ear B	170	58	2.931 : 1	About 3 : 1

11. Count the number of purple kernels and the number of yellow kernels on corn ear B. Record them in your data table.

12. With your group, discuss what the ratio of purple to yellow kernels tells you about the genetic information that was passed from the parent generation to each of these corn kernels. Remember: In corn, the trait for purple is dominant over the recessive trait for yellow.

13. From the data you recorded in Steps 10 and 11 calculate the ratio of purple kernels to yellow kernels. To do this, divide the number of purple kernels by the number of yellow kernels. Enter your results on the data table. Then divide the smaller number by itself, to produce 1. The ratio of purple to yellow kernels would be $x : 1$. Round the ratio to the closest whole numbers.

14. With your partner, discuss what the genes of the parent corn must have been to produce the corn kernels on ears A and B. Record your ideas in your science notebook.

15. Based on the ratio of kernels counted, Shauna constructed three Punnett squares to show the possible crosses she thinks may have produced the corn on ears A and B.

	P	p
P	$P\,P$	$P\,p$
P	$P\,P$	$P\,p$

PUNNETT SQUARE X

8 (AD ASSESSMENT) As students discuss which Punnett square shows the cross that produced the kernels on ear A, make sure students refer to the kernel ratios. If they need a hint, have them work backward to compare the ratios they calculated in the chart, "Corn Breeding Data," with the ratios shown in the offspring in each Punnett square from Shauna's notes. Students' responses to Procedure Steps 16 and 17 may be scored with the ANALYZING DATA (AD) Scoring Guide. Students should conclude that the cross shown in Punnett square Z —Pp × pp—produced the kernels on ear A and the cross shown in Punnett square Y—Pp × Pp—produced the kernels on ear B.

FOLLOW-UP

9 Have the class conduct an Informal Meeting of the Minds. Direct students to find a partner from a different group and compare their groups' results and conclusions. Ask pairs to share their discussions with the class. Ask for volunteers to share their conclusions about the parent plants that produced ear A and ear B. Survey the class to determine which groups came to the same conclusion. If groups are not in agreement, project Transparency 4.2, "Breeding Corn: Second Generation," and review what students know about each cross, including the allele combinations of the parents and the offspring.

Note: The term homozygous will not be introduced until the next activity.

10 (UC ASSESSMENT) Students' answers to Analysis Questions 1 and 3 will help you gauge their understanding of heredity and the use of Punnett squares. Students' work for Analysis Question 4 may be scored with the UNDERSTANDING CONCEPTS (UC) Scoring Guide. To give your students further practice with Punnett squares, have them complete Student Sheet 4.2, "Practice Punnett Square Problems." Sample student responses to the Student Sheet are found at the end of this activity.

PUNNETT SQUARE Y

PUNNETT SQUARE Z

8 **16.** Given the data you collected in Step 10, which of the three Punnett squares shown in Shauna's notes—X, Y, or Z—best describes the cross that produced ear A? Record your reasoning in your science notebook.

17. Given the data you collected in Step 11, which of the three Punnett squares—X, Y, or Z—best describes the cross that produced ear B? Record your reasoning in your science notebook.

9 **18.** Follow your teacher's instructions to discuss your ideas from Steps 16 and 17 with the class. Determine if your ideas agree. If not, discuss why, and try to come to agreement.

288

SAMPLE RESPONSES

1. A Punnett square shows the alleles of the parents and all of the possible allele combinations that can occur in a cross between the two parents. These allele combinations are what potential offspring could have.

2. We counted the offspring (kernels) of the corn and calculated a ratio of the two colors present. From this ratio we were able to determine the ratio of phenotypes the Punnett square should show, then we worked backwards from that to determine which Punnett square was the best match. From that Punnett Square, we could infer the parent's genotypes. That confirmed the validity of the Punnett square tool.

3. All of the offspring will be purple. This can be determined because each offspring will get an allele for the dominant purple trait (<u>P</u>) from the <u>PP</u> parent. However, half of the offspring will be <u>PP</u> and half will be <u>Pp</u>, as shown by the Punnett square.

	<u>P</u>	<u>P</u>
<u>P</u>	<u>P</u> <u>P</u>	<u>P</u> <u>P</u>
p	<u>P</u> p	<u>P</u> p

4. To breed plants that can resist drought, scientists would first have to find some plants proven to grow with less water than most plants of their type. Then they would need to breed them with each other to see if the offspring were able to withstand drought. By continuing this process with plants that have some resistance to drought, they might be able to produce plants that are even more resistant.

REVIST THE CHALLENGE

Return students to Student Sheet 4.1, "Traits and Heredity," and ask them to complete the "Now we know…" column. Sample student responses are shown at the end of this activity. Be sure students fully understand the concepts of dominant and recessive genes, and how to use a Punnett square, as they will work with them in the activities that follow. Reinforce the idea that selective breeding takes advantage of traits that already exist in the population, and brings them together in new combinations.

---

10 Analysis

1. How does a Punnett square show the possible results of a cross between two individuals?

2. Describe how your observations of offspring (corn kernels) allowed you to determine the genetic makeup of the two parents. Discuss how you used ratios in this process.

3. What do you predict will happen if a purple corn plant with the genes <u>Pp</u> is bred with a corn plant with purple kernels and the genes <u>PP</u>? Explain your answer, and include a matching Punnett Square.

4. How could scientists use selective breeding to help solve a sustainability challenge such as breeding a crop that can survive drought?

KEY VOCABULARY

allele	selective breeding
dominant	sexual reproduction
Punnett square	trait
recessive	

Traits and Heredity

Two mice, one female and one male, have black hair. They have a litter of six baby mice. Four of the baby mice have black hair. Two have white hair.

Based on this information, answer the questions in the left hand column below.

Questions	I think . . .	My group thinks . . .	Now we know . . .
1. **What information determines a trait, such as hair color?**	*It is passed on from parents to babies.*	*The alleles determine it.*	*The allele combination, one from each parent and whether there are dominant or recessive alleles*
2. **Explain how traits like hair or whisker color are passed from one generation to the next.**	*They get the genes from their parents.*	*Alleles are passed from parents to offspring.*	*Each parent passes down one allele for the trait to the offspring.*
3. **Choose which of the two images below best depicts how the trait for white hair was passed from the parent mice to their offspring.**	*Image A*	*Image B*	*Image B*

A.

B.

Practice Punnett Square Problems

Directions: Use the Punnett square below to answer Questions 1 and 2.

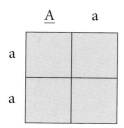

1. a. What are the alleles of parent 1?

    Aa

    b. What are the alleles of parent 2?

    aa

2. a. What are the possible allele combinations of the offspring of a cross between parent 1 and parent 2?

    Aa, aa

    b. What are the ratios of the possible allele combinations of the offspring?

    1 Aa : 1 aa

3. The trait for black fur in bears (<u>B</u>) is dominant over the one for brown fur (b). A bear with black fur (parent 1) mates with a bear with brown fur (parent 2). If there is a 100% chance that the offspring will be black, what are the allele combinations of parent 1 and parent 2? Explain why.

    Black parent 1 would be <u>BB</u>, and brown parent 2 would be bb. The brown parent 2 must have the genotype bb, because brown is recessive and will only appear if the parent has two alleles for the recessive trait. If all of the offspring must be black, then they must inherit the dominant trait from the black parent 1. That means that the black parent 1 is <u>BB</u>. If this black bear had a <u>Bb</u> genotype, then 50% of the offspring would be expected to be brown.

(continued on next page)

Practice Punnett Square Problems *(continued)*

4. In a certain type of plant the allele for orange flowers (F) is dominant over white flowers (f). Two orange-flowering plants that have the alleles Ff are crossed.

   a. What are the possible allele combinations of the offspring that may result from the cross?

   FF, Ff, ff

   b. What are the possible colors of the offspring that may result from the cross?

   orange and white

   c. What ratio of allele combinations would you predict would occur from the cross?

   1 FF : 2 Ff : 1 ff

   d. What ratio of colors would you predict? *3 orange : 1 white*

5. Cystic fibrosis is a chronic recessive genetic disorder that affects the respiratory and digestive systems. Jaren was diagnosed with cystic fibrosis when he showed such symptoms as a persistent cough and an excessive appetite with little weight gain. Neither of his parents shows symptoms of the disease. Use C to represent the normal allele and c to represent the recessive cystic fibrosis allele.

   a. What are the allele combinations of Jaren's parents? How do you know?

   Both are Cc, because each had to give Jaren a c allele, but they don't have symptoms so they must have a C as their second allele.

   b. What is Jaren's allele combination?

   cc

   c. What are the chances that any future child of Jaren's parents will NOT inherit cystic fibrosis?

   75% or three in four

   d. What are the chances that any future child of Jaren's parents WILL inherit cystic fibrosis?

   25% or 1 in four

   e. Explain why you think Jaren's parents do not show symptoms.

   Because they both have one allele for the dominant C (no cystic fibrosis) trait.

5 Genes and Traits

READING • 1 CLASS SESSION

OVERVIEW

Students read about Gregor Mendel and his early studies of heredity. The reading also covers common heredity patterns in sexually reproductive plants, animals, and humans.

KEY CONTENT

1. Heredity is the passage of genetic traits from one generation to the next.

2. Gregor Mendel (1822–1884) was a monk, teacher, and scientist, who studied the relationship between heredity and traits, mainly by experimenting with pea plants.

3. According to the laws of simple dominance, dominant traits will appear in the phenotype of an organism, while recessive traits are masked by the presence of a dominant trait.

4. Genes are sequences of DNA that encode for a particular trait.

5. Dominance is not always complete. Incomplete dominance refers to two traits that result in a third, intermediate trait, while codominance refers to the full expression of both traits in a heterozygote.

6. Some traits are determined by one gene, and others are determined by multiple genes.

KEY PROCESS SKILLS

1. Students make accurate interpretations, inferences, and conclusions from text.

TEACHING SUMMARY

Getting Started

- Students discuss why people who are related have similar traits.

Doing the Activity

- (LITERACY) Students use the literacy strategy Stopping to Think as they read about genes and traits.

Follow-up

- Clarify students' ideas about heredity and inheritance of traits.

GETTING STARTED

1 ◆ Ask students, *Why do people who are related often have similar characteristics?*

Encourage students to build on their understanding from Activity 4, "Breeding Corn," and share ideas about heredity—the passing of genetic material from two parents to offspring during the process of sexual reproduction.

---

5 Genes and Traits

1 F YOU EXAMINE a family photograph of relatives from three or four generations, you may notice similar traits among the people, such as a certain eye or hair color. When people began growing crops and breeding animals, they noticed patterns in the traits of parent plants and animals and their offspring. These patterns of traits passing from one generation to the next helped farmers decide which animals to breed and which seeds of which plants to grow to obtain the qualities they wanted in their farm products. More recently, scientists began studying these patterns in human families to track and understand such traits as those that cause genetic diseases.

In the previous activity, you modeled the possible combinations of traits passed on to sexually reproduced corn plants. In this activity, you will learn more about the mechanism of **heredity,** the passing of genetic traits from one generation to the next.

Challenge

▶ What can we infer about genes and traits based on heredity patterns?

Due to many generations of selective breeding, domestic carrots (Daucus carota) (on the right) show many traits that differ from those of wild carrots (on the left).

290

DOING THE ACTIVITY

 (LITERACY) The reading is supported with a literacy strategy called Stopping to Think, which helps students process the information they read. In this activity, Stopping to Think questions focus students' attention on important ideas they encounter in the text. These questions do not require a written response and are different than the Analysis Questions found at the end of the activity. Depending on students' reading level, it may be helpful to have students discuss the answers to the questions either in pairs, small groups, or as a class. For more information on this strategy, see the Literacy section of Teacher Resources III: Literacy. Sample responses to each question are part of the discussion of the reading below and on the following pages.

3 The study of heredity and specific traits is important because it teaches breeders how to select parent organisms that will produce offspring likely to have traits the breeder wants. It is also very helpful in studying genetic conditions.

Procedure

 1. The reading below involves a strategy called Stopping to Think questions. Occasionally, in between paragraphs, there will be a question. As you read, stop and answer these questions in your mind. They can help you determine the main ideas of the reading. Follow your teacher's instructions on further exploration of these questions in discussions.

Reading

Early Breeding Practices

Farmers learned thousands of years ago that by selecting which parent plants and animals to breed, those parents would produce offspring with characteristics people wanted. Through this selective breeding, farmers' improvements in farm products have helped sustain human communities. The potato, for example, was first discovered as a food source in South America more than 10,000 years ago. Native South Americans who started farming potatoes quickly learned that they would lose fewer potatoes to disease if they grew several kinds. Through selective breeding, potato farmers around the world now grow thousands of varieties. A few traits of those varieties are size, color, and how long they can be stored. Such progress in agriculture led to the modern study of heredity.

3
> **STOPPING TO THINK QUESTION 1**
>
> *Why is the study of heredity and traits important?*

Gregor Mendel was a 19th century monk, teacher, and scientist, who set out to systematically explore the relationship between traits and heredity. He worked mainly with pea plants, which he could grow easily and which showed several traits clearly. Among the pea traits Mendel analyzed were seed color (yellow or green) and stem length (long or short). Over several years, he conducted carefully controlled experiments and kept detailed records of the traits inherited by offspring from parent pea plants. A summary of Mendel's findings is shown in the table on the following page.

291

---

4 The idea of calculating ratios to discuss probability of traits in offspring was introduced in Activity 3, "Mitosis and Asexual Reproduction." For further practice, ask students to reduce the ratios found in the last row of the table to lowest terms. Answers are shown below:

Ratios Reduced to Lowest Terms

Ratio	Ratio reduced to lowest terms
705 purple : 224 white	Approximately 3 : 1
6,022 yellow : 2,001 green	Approximately 3 : 1
5,474 smooth : 1,850 wrinkled	Approximately 3 : 1
428 green : 152 yellow	Approximately 3 : 1

---

4 Mendel's Results for Three Generations of Pea Plant Crosses

	FLOWER COLOR	SEED COLOR	SEED SURFACE	POD COLOR
Original cross	purple × white	green × yellow	wrinkled × smooth	green × yellow
F₁ generation	all purple	all yellow	all smooth	all green
F₂ generation	705 : 224 (purple : white)	6,022 : 2,001 (yellow : green)	5,474 : 1,850 (smooth : wrinkled)	428 : 152 (green : yellow)

Mendel crossed hundreds of pea plants, and observed and counted phenotypes of traits related to seeds, pods, and flowers in thousands of offspring. The **phenotype** of an organism is its physical characteristics, which result from the organism's genes and their interaction with the environment. For example the color of some flowers depends on both the genes they carry and the soil conditions in which they are grown. He then analyzed the results and applied his knowledge of statistics to figure out the patterns associated with individual genes and the probability of such patterns occurring.

Painting of Gregor Mendel working with pea plants

As he looked at the data, Mendel noticed an interesting relationship. With seed color, if the original cross (parent generation) was a purebred green seed with a purebred yellow seed, he found that all of the offspring (F_1 generation) had yellow seeds. When he bred the F_1 seeds together, their offspring (F_2 generation) still had many yellow seeds, but some were green. Calculating the ratio of the two traits in the F_2 generation, he obtained a ratio very near to 3:1. This means that for every one green-seeded plant, there were approximately three yellow-seeded plants in the third generation. For example, for color in 8,023 pea seeds he calculated the ratio of yellow to green seeds as

$$\frac{6{,}022 \text{ yellow}}{2{,}001 \text{ green}} = \frac{3.01 \text{ yellow}}{1 \text{ green}}$$

This is almost exactly a 3:1 ratio of yellow : green.

Mendel observed that the green-color trait was absent in the F_1 generation, but reappeared in the third generation, and that the probability of the seeds of an F_2 generation plant having the trait was one in four—that is, about one green-seeded plant for every four plants produced overall. Mendel found the same ratio for several other characteristics involving the same number of generations. The 3:1 ratio was the clue to how the parents' genes combine in their offspring. Based on his analysis, he proposed three principles of heredity:

- Each characteristic that appears in the F_1 generation is the dominant version of the trait. A dominant trait, when present in an individual, will always appear in that individual. The trait that is "hidden" in the F_2 generation is called recessive. It can be present but does not appear if there is a dominant trait masking it.
- Every plant has two copies, alleles, of the gene for each trait.

    Note: The terms "allelle" and "gene" were proposed long after Mendel's research.

- Every offspring receives only one allele for each trait from each parent.

5 Answers are shown below.

- The purple allele is dominant for flower color.

- The yellow allele is dominant for seed color.

- The smooth allele is dominant for seed surface.

- The green allele is dominant for pod color.

These are dominant since they were the only traits expressed in the second-generation offspring. The other traits (white flower color, yellow seed color, wrinkled seed surface, and yellow pod color) are all recessive. They were all hidden by the dominant traits in the F_1 generation.

STOPPING TO THINK QUESTION 2

5 *Look at the information presented in the table, "Mendel's Results," on the previous pages. Based on these results, which allele for each trait is a) dominant? b) recessive? What evidence supports your claim?*

The work of Mendel and other scientists has provided evidence that supports his basic ideas about heredity. Today, scientists know that heredity is controlled through genes. A **gene** is a segment of an organism's genetic material, or DNA. Each gene is present in an individual in two versions, called alleles. We now know that when organisms reproduce sexually, each parent donates a gamete. A **gamete** is a sexual reproductive cell, such as a sperm or an egg, which contains genetic material of the organism. The gamete from each parent carries one allele for each trait. During sexual reproduction the two gametes, one from the female and one from the male, fuse together and create a new cell with two alleles for each trait. This new cell eventually grows into a fully developed organism.

Consider the corn ears in the last activity. You worked with two alleles for corn color—purple and yellow. Each kernel (offspring) received one allele for color from each parent to make a complete set of two alleles. This genetic makeup for an organism is its **genotype.**

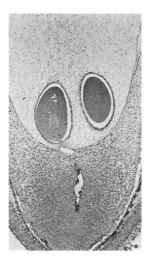

In sexual reproduction, a gamete from a male parent carrying one allele for every trait fuses with the gamete of a female parent, also carrying one allele for every trait as shown in the ovule of a plant at left and in the human sperm and egg above. Once fused, the fertilized egg contains a complete genetic set of alleles—one from each parent.

6 Answers are shown below.

- Homozygous purple: <u>PP</u>

- Homozygous yellow: pp

- Heterozygous purple: <u>P</u>p

In the simplest cases, there are two types of alleles, and the gene can produce only two traits, one of which is dominant over the other. An example of this in Mendel's pea plants is flower color. Based on the results of breeding plants with purple flowers with plants with white flowers, Mendel inferred that a pea plant having two copies of the allele for the white color trait will have white flowers, while a plant with two copies of the allele for the purple color will have purple flowers. However, a pea plant with one allele for the purple color and one allele for the white color will always have purple flowers. This evidence led to the conclusion that the purple flower trait is dominant and the white trait is recessive.

For corn kernel alleles, we can designate <u>S</u> for smooth and s for wrinkled. The allele pair—whether <u>SS</u>, <u>S</u>s, or ss—is the kernel's genotype. Genotypes that have two identical alleles, such as <u>SS</u> or ss, are called **homozygous.** The prefix homo means "same." Genotypes with two different alleles, such as <u>S</u>s, are referred to as **heterozygous.** The prefix hetero means "different." The kernels with homozygous recessive alleles will express the recessive phenotype (ss = wrinkled kernels), those with homozygous dominant alleles will express the dominant phenotype (<u>SS</u> = smooth kernels), and kernels with heterozygous alleles will express the dominant phenotype (<u>S</u>s = smooth kernels).

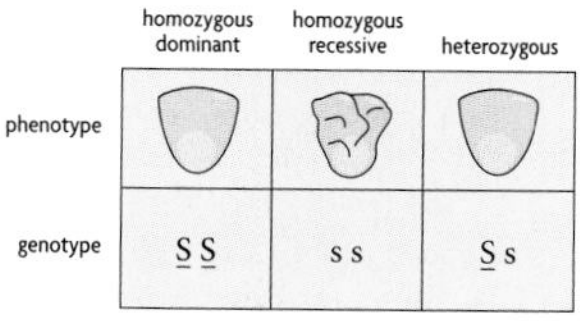

	homozygous dominant	homozygous recessive	heterozygous
phenotype			
genotype	<u>S</u> <u>S</u>	s s	<u>S</u> s

STOPPING TO THINK QUESTION 3

6

If <u>P</u> represents the dominant purple allele for corn color and p represents the recessive yellow color allele, what letters would represent a kernel that has the following genotypes:

- *Homozygous purple?*
- *Homozygous yellow?*
- *Heterozygous purple?*

7 The genes for curly hair are somewhat more complex than this suggests, and some of the genes involved exhibit incomplete dominance. If you choose to discuss other examples of codominance and incomplete dominance with your students, be aware that many traits are now known to be complex polygenic traits and subject to environmental influence (e.g., height, eye color.) Visit the *Science and Global Issues* page of the SEPUP website (*sepuplhs.org/sgi*) for links to more information.

8

	C^R	C^W
C^W	$C^R C^W$	$C^W C^W$
C^W	$C^R C^W$	$C^W C^W$

The possible genotypes are $C^R C^W$ and $C^W C^W$, and the possible phenotypes are pink and white. The ratio of the genotypes and phenotypes are both 1 : 1.

Since the time of Mendel's work, scientists have continued to explore patterns of heredity in organisms. For some traits, the patterns follow the rules of simple dominance, as Mendel observed. However, some traits are not so simple.

Consider flower color in snapdragons. When red snapdragons are crossed with white snapdragons, pink flowers result, as shown in the Punnett square below.

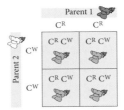

Parent 1

	C^R	C^R
C^W	$C^R C^W$	$C^R C^W$
C^W	$C^R C^W$	$C^R C^W$

Parent 2

SNAP DRAGONS:
A CASE OF INCOMPLETE DOMINANCE

7 This is called **incomplete dominance,** and it occurs when neither trait is dominant. The result is a blending of the two traits that produces a third trait. In humans, the trait for curly hair shows a type of incomplete dominance. If a person inherits one allele for straight hair and one allele for curly hair, he or she will have the intermediate trait, wavy hair.

STOPPING TO THINK QUESTION 4

8

What are the possible phenotypes and genotypes of offspring from a cross between a pink snapdragon and a white snapdragon? What percentage of each phenotype and genotype would you expect to find?

A third type of dominance occurs when more than one trait is dominant, and each is expressed instead of the two blending into one trait. This is called **codominance.** Blood type in humans is a trait that exhibits codominance. Humans who have the allele for type A red blood cell proteins and the allele for type B red blood cell proteins will have red blood cells that express both proteins, type AB blood. This means that the traits produced by the A and B alleles are equally dominant, or codominant. However, there is a third blood trait, type O, which is recessive to both A and B. The box on the next page explains codominance and human blood types in more detail.

BACKGROUND INFORMATION

Codominance of Human Blood Types

Human Blood Type Alleles

ALLELE	CODES FOR PHENOTYPE	RED BLOOD CELL SURFACE PROTEINS
I_A	Type A surface proteins on red blood cells	
I_B	Type B surface proteins on red blood cells	
i	No surface proteins on red blood cells	

THERE ARE THREE possible alleles for human blood type; each person carries two alleles of the gene, which may be two of the same, or any combination of two out of the three possible alleles.

Figure 1 shows the red blood cells of a person who has type A blood and has the genotype $I_A I_A$.

1

Figure 2 shows the red blood cells of a person who has type A blood and has the genotype $I_A i$.

2

NOTE: *Cell surface proteins not drawn to scale.*

Figure 3 shows the red blood cells of a person who as type B blood and has the genotype $I_B I_B$.

3

Figure 4 shows the red blood cells of a person who has type AB blood and the genotype $I_A I_B$.

4

Figure 5 shows the red blood cells of a person who has type O blood and the genotype ii.

5

9 As needed, explain to students that the capital I represents a dominant allele for both type A or type B blood, as noted by the subscript. The lowercase i represents an allele for type O blood (often called type zero in languages other than English.)

Parents could have any of the following combinations:
$ii \times ii$
$I_A i \times I_A i$
$I_B i \times I_B i$
$I_A i \times I_B i$

Each parent must donate an i allele to the offspring for the offspring to have type "O" blood.

10 This unit does not cover epistasis or pleiotropy in detail, but if it is part of your state or local standards this would be a good point to discuss it.

FOLLOW-UP

11 Students may need guidance in reaching the conclusion that the production of the Bt toxin in Bt corn is a genotypic and phenotypic change. If necessary, discuss with your students that we don't see most traits. For example, blood type is not a visible trait, nor are most of the traits that genes code for in organisms.

STOPPING TO THINK QUESTION 5

9

If a child has type O blood, what blood types might his or her parents have? Explain.

If a parent with type A blood and the genotype $I_A i$ and a parent with B blood and the genotype $I_B i$ have children, four possible phenotypes may result, as shown in the Punnett square below.

	I_A	i
I_B	$I_A I_B$	$I_B i$
i	$I_A i$	i i

10

An understanding of genes, alleles, and recessive and dominant traits allows scientists to predict the outcome of many genetic crosses. This information is the basis for both selective breeding and modern biotechnology research. Some traits are determined by only one gene, as illustrated in the cases above. A majority of traits are determined by a combination of many genes. Then again, many traits are also determined by the interaction of one or more genes with environmental conditions. For example, both genes and nutrition determine size in dogs. A Chihuahua that is poorly fed will be smaller than a well-fed Chihuahua. However, because of their genes a Chihuahua cannot be the size of a Great Dane no matter how well it is fed. There are also genes that control more than one phenotype. For example, if a gene controls the production of an enzyme needed by multiple organs, one mutation in that gene that changes the enzyme could affect each organ that uses the enzyme. For most traits, an organism's phenotype is determined by multiple genes and a combination of environmental conditions.

Analysis

1. Explain the difference between an organism's phenotype and its genotype. Include an example in your answer.

2. Explain the difference between simple dominance, incomplete dominance, and codominance.

SAMPLE RESPONSES

1. Genotype refers to the set of alleles that an organism inherits. Phenotype refers to the traits exhibited by the organism based on the alleles (genotype) it has inherited. For example, a corn kernel that is heterozygous for corn color has a genotype of Pp and a phenotype of purple kernels.

2. Simple dominance occurs when, of two possible traits, one is recessive and one is dominant. A heterozygous individual will have the phenotype of the dominant trait. Incomplete dominance is different in that neither trait is dominant. If an organism is heterozygous, the trait will be a blend of or intermediate between the two. In codominance a heterozygous organism will express the phenotype of both traits.

3. In most cases, both phenotype and genotype are altered. A new gene is inserted, which changes the corn's genotype, and the insertion of the gene causes a change in a trait, which is an organism's phenotype. Thus, both the Bt corn's phenotype and genotype were altered.

4. Samples of students' answers are shown at right in the third column.

REVISIT THE CHALLENGE

Students should be able to articulate that observing the traits of offspring over multiple generations provides information about the genetic makeup of parents and shows how those specific traits are inherited. Students modeled this process in Activity 4, "Breeding Corn," when they counted the corn kernels by color and with that determined the genotype of the parent corn. Mendel used this same process to propose the fundamental rules of heredity, which explain how traits are passed from one generation to the next. Students should also be able to explain that not all traits are simply dominant and recessive, and that other patterns, such as codominance and incomplete dominance, are exhibited with many traits. Emphasize that most traits are influenced by multiple genes and by environmental factors.

---

11 3. Think back to the Bt corn you considered in Activity 1, "A Genetically Modified Solution?" When an organism is genetically modified, which of the following is changed: genotype, phenotype, both, or neither? Explain.

4. The following is a list of a few traits in plants and animals. Determine if the traits described are examples of simple dominance, codominance, or incomplete dominance. Explain your reasoning.

Trait	Description	Type of dominance and reasoning
Feather color in chickens	The feathers of a species of chicken can be black, white, or "erminette." Erminette chickens have both black feathers and white feathers, but not gray feathers.	
Sweet pea tendrils	When sweet pea plants with tendrils (structures that grow from the stem and help the plant attach and climb) are crossed with sweet pea plants without tendrils, all of the resulting sweet peas have tendrils.	
Rabbit hair length	Longhaired rabbits crossed with shorthaired rabbits produce offspring that have medium-length hair.	

KEY VOCABULARY

allele	homozygous
codominance	incomplete dominance
dominant	phenotype
gamete	Punnett square
gene	recessive
genotype	selective breeding
heredity	trait
heterozygous	

Sample Student Response to Analysis Question 4

Trait	Description	Type of dominance and reasoning
Feather color in chickens	The feathers of a species of chicken can be black, white, or erminette. Erminette chickens have both black feathers and white feathers, but not gray feathers.	Codominance because both traits are expressed (feathers are white and black), and they do not blend as they would with incomplete dominance (no gray feathers)
Sweet pea tendrils	When sweet pea plants with tendrils (structures that grow from the stem and help the plant attach and climb) are crossed with sweet pea plants without tendrils, all of the resulting sweet peas have tendrils.	Simple dominance because the dominant trait (tendrils) masks the recessive trait (no tendrils)
Rabbit hair length	Longhaired rabbits crossed with shorthaired rabbits produce offspring that have medium-length hair.	Incomplete dominance because the offspring have medium-length hair which is a blend of the two traits (long and short)

6 Breeding Corn for Two Traits

MODELING • 1–2 CLASS SESSIONS

OVERVIEW

Students continue their investigation of the basic concepts of genetics as they model patterns of heredity in corn crosses involving two traits: kernel color (purple and yellow) and texture (smooth and rough). Groups create a plan to determine the unknown genotype of a corn plant.

KEY CONTENT

1. In all organisms, genes carry the instructions for specifying the characteristics of the organism.

2. Cells contain two copies of each gene. These copies are called alleles.

3. Breeding generations of model organisms, such as corn, provides extensive information about the behavior of genes and the relationship between genotype and phenotype.

KEY PROCESS SKILLS

1. Students make and record observations.

2. Students identify and describe trends in data.

3. Students develop conclusions based on evidence.

MATERIALS AND ADVANCE PREPARATION

For the teacher
Scoring Guide: GROUP INTERACTION (GI)

For each pair of students
set of P/p and S/s Allele cards
cardboard corn ear C
cardboard corn ear D

For each student
Student Sheet 2.3, "Genetics Case Study Comparison," from Activity 2

Student Sheet 6.1, "Dihybrid Punnett Square" (optional)

Student Sheet 6.2, "Dihybrid Punnett Square Practice Problems" (optional)

3 sticky notes*

Scoring Guide: GROUP INTERACTION (GI) (optional)

You may want to laminate the corn ears and provide students with dry-erase markers to keep track as they count the corn kernels.

Masters for Scoring Guides are in Teacher Resources IV: Assessment.

TEACHING SUMMARY

Getting Started

• Introduce corn crosses for two traits.

Doing the Activity

• (GI ASSESSMENT) Students observe the results of corn crosses and compare the data with the result predicted by a Punnett square.

• Students devise a plan to determine the genotype of smooth purple kernels.

• (LITERACY) Students follow the literacy strategy "Read, Think, and Take Note" as they read a case study on Golden Rice.

Follow-up

• The class discusses the results of the dihybrid crosses.

BACKGROUND INFORMATION

This activity models the heredity of two genes over three generations. The crosses students investigate involve traits that are determined by genes on different chromosomes. Students will observe that these genes are inherited independently of each other. Because they are on different chromosomes they follow Mendel's law of independent assortment, which states that pairs of alleles of different genes separate independently during the formation of gametes.

In future activities, students learn that genes located on the same chromosome are often inherited together and that analysis of the actual behavior of genes and chromosomes reveals a significant complication: chromosomes often cross over when they are passed from one generation to the next. In a crossover a piece of one chromosome is exchanged with a similar piece on the homologous chromosome during meiosis, as chromosome pairs separate to form eggs and sperm.

Transposable elements, or "jumping genes," first discovered in corn, are not discussed in *Science and Global Issues.*

REFERENCES

Domingo, J. L. (2007). Toxicity studies of genetically modified plants: A review of the published literature. *Critical Reviews in Food Science and Nutrition. 47,* 721–733.

Enserink, M. (2008). Tough lessons from golden rice. *Science. 320*(5875), 468–471.

Task Force of the ILSI International Food Biotechnology Committee. (2008). Chapter 5: Golden Rice 2. *Comprehensive Reviews in Food Science and Food Safety. 7*(1), 92–98.

World Health Organization. (1995). Global prevalence of Vitamin A deficiency in populations at risk 1995–2005. Retrieved online March 2010 from http://www.who.int/vmnis/vitamina/prevalence/en/index.html.

GETTING STARTED

1 Explain that up to this point, students have considered only one corn trait, kernel color. Farmers, however, often want to breed crops for several specific traits. Breeding for many traits presents more possibilities for variation in trait combinations from one generation to the next.

6 Breeding Corn for Two Traits

1 **WHEN FARMERS BREED** plants, they often are trying to produce plants with more than one new and specific trait. The more traits they try to introduce, the more complicated the breeding becomes.

In Activity 4, you considered the heredity in corn of one trait: kernel color. In this activity, you will explore patterns of heredity for two traits: kernel color and texture. You will examine the results of a cross between two purple smooth-kernelled corn plants. This type of cross is referred to as a **dihybrid cross.** You will complete Punnett squares to predict the heredity of these two traits and compare the predicted and actual results.

Challenge

▶ How do scientists predict the results of crossing corn for two kernel characteristics: color and texture?

MATERIALS

FOR EACH PAIR OF STUDENTS
P/p and S/s Allele Cards
cardboard corn ears C and D

FOR EACH STUDENT
3   sticky notes
Student Sheet 2.3, "Genetics Case Study Comparison," from Activity 2

300

DOING THE ACTIVITY

2 (GI ASSESSMENT) Note that an organism with the genotype PpSs is an offspring of two parents that are homozygous for individual traits (possibilities include PPSS × ppss or PPss × ppSS), which is similar to the monohybrid cross students worked with in Activity 4, "Breeding Corn." There are four possible allele combinations (gametes) that can be formed by the parent that is heterozygous for two traits (PpSs). If necessary, remind students that each parent contributes to its gametes one allele for each trait. The possible gametes are: PS, Ps, pS, and ps. As students work through this step, listen for them to correctly use the words gamete, allele, dominant, recessive, phenotype, and genotype. If necessary, review these concepts before continuing with the activity.

This is an opportunity to use the GROUP INTERACTION (GI) Scoring Guide to assess how well students work in pairs. If necessary, review your expectations with the students.

3 Distribute Student Sheet 6.1, "Dihybrid Punnett Square," if your students will be using it.

Note: If students need additional practice, pass out Student Sheet 6.2, "Dihybrid Punnett Square Practice Problems."

BREEDING CORN FOR TWO TRAITS • ACTIVITY 6

Procedure

Part A: Breeding Corn

1. In the crosses that you are about to work with, you will examine kernel color and shape. Note the following:

   Kernel color: You will consider two possible alleles—purple (P) and yellow (p). Purple is dominant over yellow.

   Kernel texture: You will consider two possible alleles—smooth (S) and wrinkled (s). Smooth is dominant over wrinkled.

2. With your partner use the P/p and S/s Allele Cards to model the gametes that might be produced by a parent with purple and smooth kernels and the genotype PpSs (heterozygous for both traits). Record each possible gamete in your science notebook. (Remember, each gamete should include one of the alleles for the gene for color and one of the alleles for the gene for smoothness.)

3. In your science notebook, make a copy of the Punnett Square shown below. Write the possible allele combinations you determined in Step 2 on your Punnett square in place of the dotted blanks.

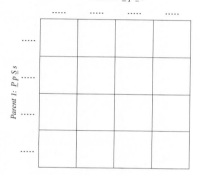

Parent 1: P p S s

301

467

4 A completed Punnett square for Procedure Step 4 is shown on optional Student Sheet 6.1, "Dihybrid Punnett Square," at the end of this activity.

5 There are nine genotypes that may result: PPSS, PPSs, PPss, PpSS, PpSs, Ppss, ppSS, ppSs, ppss.

There are four kernel phenotypes that may be observed: purple smooth, purple wrinkled, yellow smooth, and yellow wrinkled.

6 Students should determine that the ratio of the four possible phenotypes is as follows:

9 purple smooth : 3 purple wrinkled : 3 yellow smooth : 1 yellow wrinkled.

Note: A 9 : 3 : 3 : 1 ratio of offspring genotypes is the expected result from a cross between two parents that are heterozygous for two traits that are not linked on the same chromosome.

7 Students should count kernel phenotype numbers within five kernels of the amounts shown in the table at right.

Students should translate the number of observed kernels into the lowest ratio by dividing each by the lowest number of observed kernels. For the data in this table, that would mean dividing each number by 14 to provide the ratio 9 : 3 : 3 : 1. In this case, the observed results are close to those predicted by the Punnett square. Expect that students' numbers will not match exactly, due to counting errors. Also, emphasize that Punnett squares predict the probability of cross outcomes. Actual results usually differ from those predicted by a small percentage.

8 Students' plans should include the genotype of the plant they choose to cross with the purple smooth corn. Encourage students to suggest a number of possible

---

4 4. Complete the Punnett square for the cross described in Step 3.

5 5. Base your answers to the following questions on your Punnett square. Record your answers in your science notebook. According to your Punnett square:

- How many genotypes are possible in the kernels produced by the cross in Step 4?

- How many phenotypes are possible in the kernels produced by the cross in Step 4? List them in your science notebook.

6 6. From your Punnett square predict the ratio of phenotypes predicted for the cross performed in Step 4. Express your ratio in this form:

purple smooth : # purple wrinkled : # yellow smooth : # yellow wrinkled

7. In your science notebook make a data table like the one below.

Corn Cross Offspring: Color and Smoothness

	Number of purple smooth kernels	Number of purple wrinkled kernels	Number of yellow smooth kernels	Number of yellow wrinkled kernels
Ear C				
Ear D				

7 8. Obtain ear C from your teacher. This ear is the result of a cross between two of the PpSs plants you worked with in Steps 3–6. Count, and record in your data table the number of each of the four kernel types found on ear C. Determine ratios by dividing all numbers by the least amount in each row and reducing to the lowest ratio.

9. How closely did the ratios of phenotypes from ear C in your data table correspond to the ratios predicted by the Punnett square? With your partner, discuss possible reasons for any differences.

8 10. Imagine you have several corn plants that have produced only purple smooth kernels. You want to determine whether these plants are homozygous (PPSS) for the dominant purple and smooth kernel traits. What type of crosses could you do to find out if your plants are homozygous?

Corn Cross Offspring: Color and Smoothness

	Number of purple smooth kernels	Number of purple wrinkled kernels	Number of yellow smooth kernels	Number of yellow wrinkled kernels
Ear C	127	42	42	14
Ear D	56	55	55	56

---

crosses and to think through which would provide the most conclusive results. This can be done by completing a Punnett square for each cross and comparing the possible offspring. The simplest cross to perform is with a homozygous recessive plant (ppss). This is called a test cross. Offspring that are all purple smooth indicate that the first parent was homozygous dominant for each trait (PPSS). Offspring that show a mixture of phenotypes for both traits indicate the parent was heterozygous (PpSs).

9 Students' results from counting the kernel phenotypes for ear D should fall within five kernels of the data shown in the table above.

10 After reducing this data to the lowest ratio, students should infer that the parent corn is heterozygous for both traits (PpSs), as indicated by the 1 : 1 : 1 : 1 ratio of the four phenotypes. Half of the offspring are yellow, which indicates that the parent was heterozygous and it contributed either a P or p allele to offspring. In addition, half of the offspring are smooth and half are wrinkled, meaning the parents must have contributed either S or s. Since the homozygous recessive parent donated only s, the second parent must have been the source of S. Therefore, the genotype of the purple smooth-kernelled parent is PpSs. This may be illustrated with the Punnett square at right that shows the cross of the PpSs with ppss.

11 (LITERACY) If necessary, remind students that the guidelines for the "Read, Think, and Take Note" literacy strategy are in Activity 2, "Creating Genetically Modified Bacteria." Sample student responses for the Golden Rice case study summary are shown below.

12 (LITERACY) Conduct a class discussion during which you ask students to share their thoughts from the sticky notes with the class. Summarize all the ideas. This is an opportunity to discuss the benefits and risks associated with growing and eating Golden Rice 2.

With your group, develop a plan.

- Record your plan for the cross in your science notebook.
- Construct a data table to show the ratio of kernel phenotypes.
- Construct a Punnett square to show the possible results if the plants are homozygous PPSS.
- Include a description of the possible results and an interpretation of what they indicate.

9

11. Imagine that the way you carried out the procedure you proposed for Step 10 produced corn ears similar to ear D. Obtain ear D from your teacher. Count and record the number of each type of kernel found on ear D.

10

12. Analyze the data (color and smoothness of each kernel) from ear D to determine if the parent plants are homozygous or heterozygous for the two traits. Explain your answer in your science notebook.

Part B: Golden Rice Case Study

11

13. Individually read the case study on the next pages. As you read, follow the literacy strategy, "Read, Think, and Take Note."

14. Share your thinking with your group. Place your sticky notes on the table in front of you. Look for connections between your notes and those of others in your group.

12

Hint: Were there common questions people asked? Were people unfamiliar with the same words? Did people react differently to statements in the reading?

15. Place your sticky notes in your science notebook. Below them write a short summary of what your group discussed and any conclusions the group came to.

16. Record the appropriate information from the Golden Rice case study on Student Sheet 2.3, "Genetics Case Study Comparison."

303

Gametes from parent 1
(P p S s, purple smooth-kernelled)

	P S	P s	p S	p s
p s	PpSs	Ppss	ppSs	ppss
p s	PpSs	Ppss	ppSs	ppss
p s	PpSs	Ppss	ppSs	ppss
p s	PpSs	Ppss	ppSs	ppss

Gametes from parent 2 (p p s s, yellow wrinkled)

Sample Case Study Summary for Student Sheet 2.3, "Genetics Case Study Comparison"

Case study	Type of genetic modification	Benefits	Risks and concerns	Research/stage of development	Other solutions?
Golden rice	Gene from daffodil or maize (corn) inserted into rice.	Rice produces beta-carotene.	Not sure it produces enough beta-carotene to be of value nutritionally Environmental and toxicity testing has been limited.	They still need to test if there is enough Vitamin A and if it can be absorbed.	Make sure people have leafy, green vegetables and other sources of Vitamin A to include in their diets.

CASE STUDY

Golden Rice

EVERY DAY 3,000 people in the world die from having too little vitamin A in their bodies. Half a million infants become permanently blind each year from the same deficiency. Some geneticists claim to have found a solution, but others argue that what those geneticists are doing is more problematic than helpful.

Vitamin A is essential for the human body to function. Proper functioning of the immune system, vision, gene transcription, and bone metabolism all rely on vitamin A. The human body converts beta-carotene—a pigment found in carrots, leafy green vegetables, sweet potatoes, and many other foods—into vitamin A.

To combat vitamin A deficiency, experts in biotechnology have developed a way to deliver vitamin A to more people through rice. For more than 3 billion people, white rice is their main food.

The geneticists have inserted genes from plants with high levels of beta-carotene into the gene sequence of rice plants. These are the genes that cause the plants to produce beta-carotene, and the hope is that the rice will now produce beta-carotene. In their first attempts to genetically modify the rice, they inserted a daffodil gene. This modification, however, did not produce enough beta-carotene in the rice to meet a human body's daily needs.

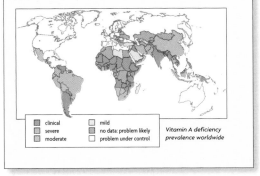

■ clinical	□ mild
■ severe	■ no data: problem likely
■ moderate	□ problem under control

Vitamin A deficiency prevalence worldwide

In their second attempt, geneticists used a maize (corn) gene. The resulting strain of genetically modified rice, called Golden Rice 2, may succeed in reducing the numbers of people with vitamin A deficiency. The rice still has to be tested to determine how well the human body can absorb the beta-carotene in the rice. One concern is that the rice still may not contain enough beta-carotene. Another is that human bodies need protein and fat in their diets for converting beta-carotene to Vitamin A. Malnourished people, however, only rarely eat protein and fat.

Some groups object to the possible use of Golden Rice 2 to address Vitamin A deficiency. They argue that vitamin A deficiency would be better treated by increasing people's consumption of foods that naturally contain beta-carotene.

Eating more leafy greens, sweet potatoes, and other beta-carotene rich foods would alleviate other nutritional deficiencies as well. In addition, there are concerns that there has not been sufficient long-term testing for potential health side effects from genetically modified foods on humans and other organisms.

There are also objections to farming Golden Rice 2 because of the potential for cross-pollination with existing crops. Many rice farmers, particularly in areas where vitamin A deficiency is high, save and then plant their rice's seed from one season to the next, instead of buying new seed. They would have to buy genetically modified rice seed, which is expensive for them, unless the seed is donated by international aid agencies. ∎

White and golden rice

FOLLOW-UP

 Students might need to be guided to the understanding that as the number of traits studied increases, the possible number of variations in allele combinations increases exponentially. For example, with three traits there are 8 (2^3) combinations possible for each parent, which means 8×8 (64) total possible offspring genotypes. For four traits there are 16 (2^4), or 16×16 (256) total possible offspring genotypes. The exact number of possible offspring genotypes is not as important as knowing that the number increases exponentially, making the simultaneous study of multiple traits very complex.

Analysis

13

1. Compare the Punnett squares you constructed in Activity 4, "Breeding Corn," with the Punnett squares you constructed in this activity. By answering the following questions, show how the possible outcomes of a cross for one trait helps in analyzing two traits.

   a. How did you need to change the Punnett square to consider two traits?

   b. How would you need to change the Punnett square if you were to consider three traits?

2. Use the terms below to describe the information given in the Punnett square.

	R	r
R	R R	R r
r	R r	r r

   a. Genotype

   b. Phenotype

   c. Offspring

   d. Allele

3. In what ways might the planting and consumption of "golden rice" affect the sustainability of a community? Discuss it in terms of all three pillars of sustainability: economic, social, and environmental.

KEY VOCABULARY	
allele	phenotype
dihybrid cross	Punnett square
gamete	selective breeding
genotype	trait

SAMPLE RESPONSES

1. a. In Activity 4, the Punnett squares were divided into four smaller squares. This was because we considered one trait, and there were two possible alleles to consider from each parent. In this activity, we considered two traits, and there were four possible allele combinations from each parent. To consider the four possible gametes from each parent, the Punnett square had to have 16 squares.

   b. Considering three traits would mean up to eight possible allele combinations from each parent. The Punnett square would need to be eight squares wide and eight squares deep—64 squares—to show all possible gamete combinations from the parents.

2. Students' answers will vary but should accurately describe the terms listed in the Student Book. Some suggested answers follow.

   • The alleles donated by each parent in sexual reproduction are shown by each letter outside of the larger box of the Punnett square.

   • The possible allele combinations, or genotypes, for offspring are shown in the small boxes of the Punnett square.

   • The phenotypes of the possible offspring and the parents are shown by the combination of alleles listed on the outside of the square for the parents, and within the squares for the offspring.

3. Golden Rice 2 might contribute to economic sustainability if it is donated where it is needed, if it provides enough beta-carotene to be of nutritional value, and if the farmers don't have to buy the seed. If it is not donated it may be too expensive for farmers to grow. The social benefit is that if it provides the necessary beta-carotene, it would combat malnutrition. But leafy, green vegetables might be a more sustainable answer if they grow as well, are as low in cost, and people will eat them. Leafy greens also provide more nutrients than just beta-carotene. Also, if golden rice produces health side effects, or if it cross-pollinates other crops, it could be environmentally unsustainable.

REVISIT THE CHALLENGE

Be sure students understand that the greater the number of traits being studied, the more complex the prediction becomes. Discuss how the complexity changed from studying the heredity of one trait in corn to the heredity of two traits. Discuss implications of this with regard to the study of genetically modified organisms (e.g., if an inserted gene changes multiple traits, it is more difficult to study and might produce unintended consequences.)

Dihybrid Punnett Square

Parent 1: $\underline{P}$ p $\underline{S}$ s

	$\underline{P}\,\underline{S}$	$\underline{P}$ s	p $\underline{S}$	p s
$\underline{P}\,\underline{S}$	$\underline{P}\,\underline{P}\,\underline{S}\,\underline{S}$	$\underline{P}\,\underline{P}\,\underline{S}$ s	$\underline{P}\,p\,\underline{S}\,\underline{S}$	$\underline{P}\,p\,\underline{S}$ s
$\underline{P}$ s	$\underline{P}\,\underline{P}\,\underline{S}$ s	$\underline{P}\,\underline{P}$ s s	$\underline{P}\,p\,\underline{S}$ s	$\underline{P}\,p$ s s
p $\underline{S}$	$\underline{P}\,p\,\underline{S}\,\underline{S}$	$\underline{P}\,p\,\underline{S}$ s	p p $\underline{S}\,\underline{S}$	p p $\underline{S}$ s
p s	$\underline{P}\,p\,\underline{S}$ s	$\underline{P}\,p$ s s	p p $\underline{S}$ s	p p s s

Parent 2: $\underline{P}$ p $\underline{S}$ s

Dihybrid Punnett Square Practice Problems

Directions: Answer the questions that follow in your science notebook.

1. For a particular plant, the allele for tall (T̲) is dominant over the allele for short (t). For the same plant, the allele for colored flowers (C̲) is dominant over white flowers (c). A farmer crossbreeds the hybrid plants as shown in the Punnett square below.

Parent 1: T̲ t C̲ c

	T̲ C̲	T̲ c	t C̲	t c
T̲ C̲	T̲ T̲ C̲ C̲	T̲ T̲ C̲ c	T̲ t C̲ C̲	T̲ t C̲ c
T̲ c	T̲ T̲ C̲ c	T̲ T̲ c c	T̲ t C̲ c	T̲ t c c
t C̲	T̲ t C̲ C̲	T̲ t C̲ c	t t C̲ C̲	t t C̲ c
t c	T̲ t C̲ c	T̲ t c c	t t C̲ c	t t c c

Parent 2: T̲ t C̲ c

What ratio of each phenotype should the farmer expect from this cross?

9 tall plants, colored flowers : 3 tall plants, white flowers : 3 short plants, colored flowers : 1 short plant, white flowers

2. For a particular rodent, black fur (B̲) is dominant over brown fur (b), and a long tail (L̲) is dominant over a short tail (l). Create a Punnett square that shows the genotypes of all the possible offspring that could result from the breeding of two of the rodents that are heterozygous for both traits.

	B̲ L̲	B̲ l	b L̲	b l
B̲ L̲	B̲ B̲ L̲ L̲	B̲ B̲ L̲ l	B̲ b L̲ L̲	B̲ b L̲ l
B̲ l	B̲ B̲ L̲ l	B̲ B̲ l l	B̲ b L̲ l	B̲ b l l
b L̲	B̲ b L̲ L̲	B̲ b L̲ l	b b L̲ L̲	b b L̲ l
b l	B̲ b L̲ l	B̲ b l l	b b L̲ l	b b l l

(continued on next page)

Dihybrid Punnett Square Practice Problems (continued)

3. For the same type of rodent as in question 2, consider a cross between a male heterozygous for both black fur and a long tail, with a female homozygous for black fur and a short tail:

	_B_ _L_	_B_ _l_	_b_ _L_	_b_ _l_
_B_ _l_	_B_ _B_ _L_ _l_	_B_ _B_ _l_ _l_	_B_ _b_ _L_ _l_	_B_ _b_ _l_ _l_
_B_ _l_	_B_ _B_ _L_ _l_	_B_ _B_ _l_ _l_	_B_ _b_ _L_ _l_	_B_ _b_ _l_ _l_
_B_ _l_	_B_ _B_ _L_ _l_	_B_ _B_ _l_ _l_	_B_ _b_ _L_ _l_	_B_ _b_ _l_ _l_
_B_ _l_	_B_ _B_ _L_ _l_	_B_ _B_ _l_ _l_	_B_ _b_ _L_ _l_	_B_ _b_ _l_ _l_

a. What ratio of genotypes would result? Show your work.

BBLl 25%, BBll 25%, BbLl 25%, Bbll 25%, or 1 : 1 : 1 : 1

b. What ratio of phenotypes might be produced? Show your work.

50% black fur, long tail : 50% black fur, short tail, or 1 : 1

7 Breeding Better Rice

MODELING • 1–2 CLASS SESSIONS

OVERVIEW

Students apply what they have learned about selective breeding in Activities 4–6 as they model the selective breeding of a strain of rice.

KEY CONTENT

1. Cells contain two copies of each gene. These copies are called alleles.

2. Selective breeding develops organisms with desirable traits.

3. Punnett squares predict the phenotypes and genotypes of a cross between two parents for two traits that are not linked.

KEY PROCESS SKILLS

1. Students collect and record data.

2. Students interpret data.

3. Students identify and describe trade-offs.

MATERIALS AND ADVANCE PREPARATION

For the teacher

transparency of Student Sheet 7.1, "Breeding Rice—Class Data"

For each pair of students

2 green flood-tolerant allele cards (F)
2 green flood-intolerant allele cards (f)
2 yellow nonaromatic allele cards (A)
2 yellow aromatic allele cards (a)

For each student

3 sticky notes*

Student Sheet 2.3, "Genetics Case Study Comparison," from Activity 2

Student Sheet 7.1, "Breeding Rice—Class Data"

Separate and sort the allele cards so that each group has a set of two of each allele.

TEACHING SUMMARY

Getting Started

- Introduce rice as a crop that has been modified through both conventional breeding and genetic engineering.

Doing the Activity

- Students analyze the results of a first-generation rice cross.

- Students analyze the results of a second-generation cross.

- (LITERACY) Students follow the literacy strategy "Read, Think, and Take Note" as they read a case study on selective breeding in corn.

Follow-up

- The class discusses the results of the crosses.

7 | Breeding Better Rice

RICE PROVIDES MORE than 20% of the calories consumed worldwide, and in some countries accounts for more than 90% of the agriculture. A grain of rice is the seed of the *Oryza sativa* plant. There are more than 100,000 varieties, differing in texture, color, grain length, and taste. To grow rice takes a lot of water. Some varieties, however, suffer damage in floods, while others are flood-tolerant and can be submerged in water for up to two weeks and remain unharmed.

Imagine you are a university professor studying food crop genetics. Your team specializes in selective breeding to produce crops with specific traits. The team has been studying flood tolerance and flavor in rice strains and is working with two strains of rice plants, which are described in the table below.

Rice Strains		
STRAIN	AROMATIC (PLEASANT AROMA AND FLAVOR)	FLOOD-TOLERANT
1	yes	no
2	no	yes

Your team would like to selectively breed a variety of rice that tastes good and can be grown in flood-prone areas of the world.

This photograph shows 12 types of rice, each with a different genotype and phenotype. They vary in taste, nutritional value, optimal growing conditions, and other characteristics.

GETTING STARTED

1 As necessary, review alleles with students. In each cross each parent donates one allele for each trait to its offspring. Support students as needed in determining the correct answers for the dominant and recessive traits and appropriate notation for each. The desired aromatic trait is recessive, and should be represented by a. The flood-tolerant trait is dominant and should be represented by $\underline{F}$.

DOING THE ACTIVITY

2 If necessary, help students determine the genotypes of the two parent strains (Strain 1 is aaff and Strain 2 is $\underline{AAFF}$). You may need to remind students of the chart in the introduction, which explains the traits found in the two rice strains. The genotype for Strain 1 must be aaff because this strain exhibits both recessive traits. The genotype for Strain 2 must be $\underline{AAFF}$ because it exhibits both dominant traits, and when bred with Strain 1 (homozygous recessive) all of the F_1 offspring exhibit the dominant traits.

3 The genotype for all offspring from this cross is $\underline{A}a\underline{F}f$ as shown in the Punnett square at right.

SCIENCE & GLOBAL ISSUES/BIOLOGY • GENETICS

Challenge

▶ What trade-offs are involved in selectively breeding a desirable strain of rice?

MATERIALS

FOR EACH PAIR OF STUDENTS
2 yellow allele cards ($\underline{A}$)
2 yellow allele cards (a)
2 green allele cards ($\underline{F}$)
2 green allele cards (f)

FOR EACH STUDENT
Student Sheet 7.1, "Breeding Rice—Class Data"
Student Sheet 2.3, "Genetics Case Study comparison," from Activity 2

Procedure

Part A: The First Generation of Rice

1 1. Your research team breeds plants from Strain 1 with plants from Strain 2. After cross breeding the plants and allowing the offspring (F_1 generation) to grow, you find that none of these offspring are aromatic, but 100% are flood-tolerant. Based on these results, determine which traits are dominant and decide

   a. whether $\underline{A}$ or a represents the aromatic trait.

   b. whether $\underline{F}$ or f represents the flood-tolerant trait.

   Write your responses and your key to the alleles in your science notebook.

2 2. a. Based on the team's results, what is the genotype for both traits (aromatic and flood-tolerant) for the parent plant from Strain 1?

   b. Based on the team's results, what is the genotype for both traits (aromatic and flood-tolerant) for the parent plant from Strain 2?

3 3. Based on the genotypes you determined above for the parent plant from Strain 1 and the parent plant from Strain 2, what genotypes do you predict for the F_1 offspring described in Step 1? Construct a Punnett square to model your prediction.

4. Compare your work with the work done by the other pair in your group. If there are differences, discuss why the results do not agree.

	af	af	af	af
$\underline{A}\,\underline{F}$	$\underline{A}\,a\,\underline{F}f$	$\underline{A}\,a\,\underline{F}f$	$\underline{A}\,a\,\underline{F}f$	$\underline{A}\,a\,\underline{F}f$
$\underline{A}\,\underline{F}$	$\underline{A}\,a\,\underline{F}f$	$\underline{A}\,a\,\underline{F}f$	$\underline{A}\,a\,\underline{F}f$	$\underline{A}\,a\,\underline{F}f$
$\underline{A}\,\underline{F}$	$\underline{A}\,a\,\underline{F}f$	$\underline{A}\,a\,\underline{F}f$	$\underline{A}\,a\,\underline{F}f$	$\underline{A}\,a\,\underline{F}f$
$\underline{A}\,\underline{F}$	$\underline{A}\,a\,\underline{F}f$	$\underline{A}\,a\,\underline{F}f$	$\underline{A}\,a\,\underline{F}f$	$\underline{A}\,a\,\underline{F}f$

4 The Punnett square below shows that there are nine possible genotypes and four possible phenotypes. The Punnett square also shows that phenotypes are likely to occur in the ratio of 9 : 3 : 3 : 1. Nine are nonaromatic and flood-tolerant; three are nonaromatic and flood-intolerant; three are aromatic and flood-tolerant; and one is aromatic and flood-intolerant. There is a three in 16 (about a 19%) chance that each plant produced from the cross will have both of the desirable traits indicated by red circles in the Punnett Square below.

5 Record data collected from all student groups on the transparency of Student Sheet 7.1, "Breeding Rice—Class Data." Project this information for the class to discuss in Procedure Step 13. Sample data appears on Student Sheet 7.1, "Breeding Rice Class Data," at the end of this activity.

Tally each column and record the total per genotype. Then determine the total per phenotype. For the bottom row, reduce the numbers to the lowest terms to determine the ratio of one phenotype to the next. The ratio of the four phenotypes should be close to 54 : 18 : 18 : 6, which may be simplified to 9 : 3 : 3 : 1. The class ratio is unlikely to be exactly the same as the predicted ratio. Discuss the idea that the predicted ratio is the most likely ratio, just as one would predict that the most likely outcome of flipping a coin 10 times would be heads five times and tails five times. However, the actual outcomes will vary.

Part B: The Second Generation of Rice

Now that you have determined the genotypes of the parent and F_1 generations, you will simulate the results (F_2 generation) of a cross between two F_1 generation plants. The goal is to produce rice that contains both desired traits.

5. Prepare a Punnett square to show all of the possible F_2 generation genotypes that could result from breeding two plants from the F_1 generation.

   a. What types and ratio of phenotypes would you expect from the cross?

   b. What percentage of the offspring do you predict will have the desired traits?

6. Create the chart shown below in your science notebook. Make rows for 10 offspring.

F_2 Generation Rice Plants

Offspring	Genotype (aromatic gene, flood gene)	Phenotype (aromatic trait, flood trait)
1		
2		

7. With your partner, simulate a cross between two F_1 generation rice plants. Each person should place four allele cards—A, a, F, and f—face down on the table and mix them up. Now, each of you takes one of the green cards and one of the yellow cards. Pair your two cards. You now have a gamete from one of the parent rice plants, and your partner has a gamete from the other parent rice plant. Individually your cards are the alleles. Lay your cards face up.

8. The four cards that are face up represent the genotype of an F_2 generation plant. Record the phenotype and genotype in your chart.

9. Reset by placing the cards you turned over back in the original pile and mixing them up.

10. Repeat Steps 7–9 until you have phenotypes and genotypes for 10 F_2 generation plants.

5 11. Add all of your results to the results of the other pair in your group, and record the data for the 20 offspring on Student Sheet 7.1, "Breeding Rice—Class Data."

	$A\underline{F}$	$A f$	$a\underline{F}$	$a f$
$A\underline{F}$	$A A \underline{F} \underline{F}$	$A A \underline{F} f$	$A a \underline{F} \underline{F}$	$A a \underline{F} f$
$A f$	$A A \underline{F} f$	$A A f f$	$A a \underline{F} f$	$A a f f$
$a\underline{F}$	$A a \underline{F} \underline{F}$	$A a \underline{F} f$	$a a \underline{F} \underline{F}$	$a a \underline{F} f$
$a f$	$A a \underline{F} f$	$A a f f$	$a a \underline{F} f$	$a a f f$

6 Discuss with the class what percentage of the F_2 generation rice plants had both desirable traits. The percentage should be close to $\frac{3}{16}$ or 19%. Point out that this is close to 20%, or one-fifth, of the total number of plants produced. However, only the plants with genotype aa<u>FF</u> would always breed true for (produce offspring with) the desired phenotype. This would be about one in 16, or 6.25% of the plants.

7 (LITERACY) If necessary, remind students that the guidelines for the "Read, Think, and Take Note" literacy strategy are in Activity 2, "Creating Genetically Modified Bacteria." As necessary, assist students in adding information from the corn-breeding case study to Student Sheet 2.3, "Genetics Case Study Comparison." While selective breeding is considered by some scientists to be a form of genetic modification, for the purposes of this unit the phrase "genetic modification" refers only to the insertion of genes from other organisms, as described earlier in the unit. Sample student responses for the History of Breeding Corn case study summary are shown at right.

FOLLOW-UP

8 Start a class discussion by asking students to share their thoughts from their sticky notes with the class. Summarize the ideas generated by the class. Take this opportunity to discuss the differences between genetic modification and selective breeding.

SCIENCE & GLOBAL ISSUES/BIOLOGY • GENETICS

12. Fill in the data from all the other groups on Student Sheet 7.1, and add the numbers of each type of gamete.

6 **13.** Discuss the class's results according to your teacher's instructions.

7 **Part C: Selective Corn Breeding Case Study**

14. Individually read the case study on selective breeding at right. Follow the literacy strategy, "Read, Think, and Take Note," as you read.

8 **15.** After reading, share your thinking with your group. Place your sticky notes on the table in front of you. Look for connections between your sticky-note comments and those of others in your group.

Hint: Were there common questions people asked? Were people unfamiliar with the same words? Did people react differently to statements in the reading?

16. Place your sticky notes in your science notebook. Below them, write a short summary of what your group discussed and any conclusions the group came to.

17. Record the appropriate information from this case study on Student Sheet 2.3, "Genetics Case Study Comparison."

Corn is the most widely grown crop in the United States.

310

Sample Case Study Summary for Student Sheet 2.3, "Genetics Case Study Comparison"

Case Study	Type of genetic modification	Benefits	Risks and concerns	Research/ stage of development	Other solutions?
History of corn breeding	None, all selective breeding	Took teosinte, a small, not very tasty plant, and bred to get today's large, tasty corn with hundreds of large kernels	Took a long time to get to today's corn	Other goals of selective breeding in corn are breeding for biofuels, textiles, and renewable fibers. Genome is now known.	Genetic modification

CASE STUDY

History of Selective Corn Breeding

TODAY, THE UNITED STATES grows more corn than any other crop, and produces much more corn than any other country in the world. In 2009, farmers in the United States planted 90 million acres of corn and harvested 13.2 billion bushels, worth billions of dollars. The largest percentage of this corn is for feeding to livestock. The remainder is for humans' consumption, corn-based biofuel, and other products. The following is a list of some of the products derived from corn: corn, corn meal, corn oil, corn starch, high fructose corn syrup, fuel alcohol, beverage alcohol, and corn feed. The ups and downs of corn-crop yields from year to year have a major impact on the U.S. economy and the availability and cost of food. Growing all of this corn also has a major environmental impact.

Corn has been grown in southern Mexico for more than 6,000 years. Both anthropological and genetic evidence suggest that corn is descended from the wild grass teosinte. Teosinte is native to Mexico and parts of Central America, and produces small hard kernels that people once cooked and ate. Some scientists think that the selective

(Continued on next page)

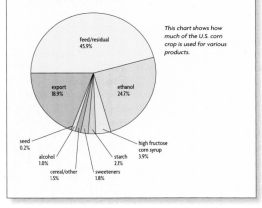

This chart shows how much of the U.S. corn crop is used for various products.

(Continued from previous page)

Teosinte plant

leaves of teosinte have high sugar content, and may have been chewed like chewing gum. People farming teosinte began to purposefully select and breed plants with desirable traits. They cultivated plants that produced more kernels per cluster and were resistant to drought and disease. Over the centuries, farmers continued to select and breed the plants that had traits that best suited their needs. As humans took the plants throughout North America, they selected plants that grew faster in the shorter summers and could withstand drought, while farmers who carried corn to the Caribbean islands selected plants that could withstand heavy rainfall. Today, because of human manipulation,

breeding of teosinte by native Mexican farmers eventually produced plants that we would recognize today as corn.

The differences between corn and teosinte are remarkable. Teosinte produces ears with a few seeds that each have a hard outer coating and are easily separated. In contrast, the corn you are familiar with produces hundreds of kernels per ear. These kernels are much larger, softer, and sweeter than teosinte kernels. Without human cultivation, current-day corn kernels would remain attached to the cob, and would not be dispersed or able to produce new plants.

At some point humans started to farm teosinte for food and other purposes. Anthropologists hypothesize that mashed dried kernels were used as a type of baby powder and as a healing substance. The

9 Note that the increase in corn yields is only partially a result of closed pollination. Other factors that have contributed to increased yield include application of chemical fertilizers and pesticides and other aspects of industrialized agriculture. These factors are not addressed in this unit except in the discussion of pesticides and Bt corn.

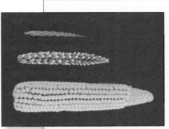

At the top is a Teosinte ear (Zea mays ssp mexicana); at the bottom, an ear of modern corn. In the middle is the F1 hybrid of these two species from the University of Wisconsin-Madison.

there are hundreds of varieties of corn. One type may be 2 feet tall while another grows to 12 feet tall; ears range from 1 to 18 inches long; and while some types grow with as little as 5 inches of rain in a season, others thrive in as much as 150 inches of rain in a growing season.

Corn became a key crop in the United States in the mid-1800s as settlers' push westward vastly increased farmlands. Farmers continued to selectively breed corn for desirable traits. Some developed plants with low moisture in their kernels so they would be less likely to rot when stored for the winter. Since each farmer owned a limited amount of land and wanted to maximize the yield from each plant, they bred plants that produced more ears per plant. In the 1920s, farmers began to control which plants pollinated each other, and to improve their selection process, allowing

(Continued on next page)

9

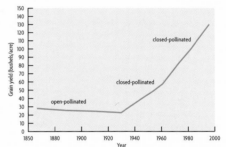

MODIFIED FROM: Lamkey, K. R. and J. W. Edwards. (1999.) *The quantitative genetics of heterosis*. Retrieved June 2010 from http://www.agron.iastate.edu/corn/Lamkey/Publications/PDF/heterosis.pdf, p. 2.

313

SAMPLE RESPONSES

1. Students' ratios should be approximately 9 flood-tolerant, nonaromatic : 3 flood-tolerant, aromatic : 3 flood-intolerant, nonaromatic : 1 flood-intolerant, aromatic.

2. Approximately 3/16 or 19% of the class's second-generation offspring are flood-tolerant and aromatic.

3. The university research team would probably breed Strain 1 and 2 plants, then breed the offspring. From those offspring, they would select the plants that have the aromatic and flood-tolerant traits and breed those to each other. They would continue this for several generations, until nearly all of the offspring had the aromatic and flood-tolerant traits.

4. It would take a longer time to breed offspring with more desirable traits. They would have to cross more plants, and it could take additional generations to get exactly what they are looking for. And it might take crossing several different strains over many growing seasons, as the desirable traits are unlikely to all be found in only two parent plants.

   Note: Students do not need to produce Punnett squares for this cross, but they should be able to infer that the fraction, or percent, of desirable offspring from each cross will be much lower. With three traits, they would have to construct an eight-by-eight Punnett square.

5. Students' results will vary. Most likely, none of the experimental ratios will equal the theoretical ratio provided by the Punnett square, but most should be close. The pooled class data is more likely than most sets of individual data to result in a ratio that is closer to the prediction. Students should explain that any differences were likely due to the small sample size and the fact that random outcomes do not always match the predicted ratio.

6. The time to reach maturity will affect how many generations can be produced in a specific period. For example, a cow takes one year to reach maturity. If you are working with corn or rice, however, you can produce more offspring in a much shorter amount of time. This is advantageous since it takes many generations to produce offspring with desirable traits using selective breeding. In addition, the greater number of offspring an organism produces, the more likely it is that the offspring will have the desirable traits. Therefore, it is easier to selectively breed rice and corn, than to breed cows.

SCIENCE & GLOBAL ISSUES/BIOLOGY • GENETICS

(Continued from previous page)

them to increase the amount of grain produced per plant. This is shown in the graph below. By the middle of the century such controlled pollination, instead of natural pollination by wind, rain, and birds, began to show much higher yields. Today, an average corn plant in the United States produces up to 800 kernels per ear of corn.

Today, farmers and agricultural scientists across the globe continue to breed corn to produce for certain purposes, such as feed corn or biofuel corn. New genetic technologies may lead to further improvements

in selective breeding. One such development is the mapping of the corn genome completed in 2009. This map provides the location of each gene within corn's genetic material. It is hoped that this information will help model the results of crosses in laboratories. As this technology is further developed, it could significantly reduce the time it normally takes to selectively breed corn with a new trait. More breeding innovations may also help relieve sustainability challenges by enhancing not only the yield of corn for human consumption, but corn's use in other products, such as biofuel, textiles, and renewable fibers. ∎

Analysis

Apply the data on Student Sheet 7.1, "Breeding Rice—Class Data," to answer Questions 1 and 2.

1. Based on the class's data, what is the ratio of the phenotypes expressed by the second-generation (F_2) offspring?

2. What fraction and percentage of the second-generation (F_2) offspring had the desired aromatic and flood-tolerance phenotype?

3. Based on what you have learned in this activity, describe and explain the procedure the university research team might follow to produce rice plants that are all aromatic and flood-tolerant.

4. In this activity, you considered breeding rice for two desired traits. Imagine that you would like to selectively breed rice for three or more traits. How would this affect your breeding efforts?

5. Look at the class's data on Student Sheet 7.1, "Breeding Rice." Compare the ratio of genotypes produced by the class with the ratio predicted by the Punnett square in Procedure Step 5 of Procedure Part B. Did the results follow those predicted by the Punnett square? Explain why the predicted outcome might be different from the actual outcome.

314

REVISIT THE CHALLENGE

As they experienced in this activity, students should be able to explain that selective breeding can take many—sometimes tens or hundreds of—generations to produce offspring with desirable traits, especially when more than one trait is targeted. This means that it can take substantial time to produce strains with desirable traits, especially with organisms that take several months or years to grow to reproductive maturity. Discuss with students why actual breeding situations, in contrast to those modeled in this activity, are quite complex: a desirable strain of rice must have favorable phenotypes for many genes, not just the two considered in this activity.

6. Examine the following table, listing the reproductive characteristics of three organisms. In the context of selective breeding, explain why a geneticist would need to understand each of these characteristics.

Reproductive Characteristics of Selected Organisms

ORGANISM	MODE OF REPRODUCTION	AGE OF SEXUAL MATURITY	TOTAL POSSIBLE NUMBER OF OFFSPRING PRODUCED PER REPRODUCTIVE CYCLE
Rice plant	sexual reproduction	2–3 months	50 grains (seeds)
Corn plant	sexual reproduction	2–3 months	Up to 800 kernels (seeds) per ear Sweet corn has been bred to produce up to 6 ears per plant.
Cow	sexual reproduction	1 year	1

KEY VOCABULARY

allele	Punnett square
gamete	selective breeding
genotype	trait
phenotype	

315

Breeding Rice Class Data

Group	Nonaromatic, flood-tolerant				Aromatic, flood-tolerant		Nonaromatic, flood-intolerant		Aromatic, flood-intolerant
	AAFF	_AAFf_	_AaFF_	_AaFf_	_aaFF_	_aaFf_	_AAff_	_Aaff_	_aaff_
1	0	2	1	4	1	2	1	3	2
2	1	2	3	3	1	1	2	2	1
3	3	2	2	2	2	2	1	1	1
4	2	1	3	5	1	1	1	1	1
5	1	2	2	4	1	2	1	2	1
6	2	3	1	2	1	3	1	3	0
Total per genotype	9	12	12	20	7	11	7	12	6
Total per phenotype	53				18		19		6
Ratio	9				3		3		1

8 Interpreting Pedigrees

INVESTIGATION • 1–2 CLASS SESSIONS

OVERVIEW

Students learn how to analyze pedigrees to infer the genetic mechanism of inheritance for certain traits. They then work with pedigrees to determine if a fictional trait for a risk factor of heart disease is likely to be dominant, recessive, or sex-linked.

KEY CONTENT

1. Cells contain two copies of each gene. In organisms that reproduce sexually, one allele for each gene is inherited from each parent.

2. According to the laws of simple dominance, dominant traits will appear in the phenotype of an organism, while recessive traits are masked by the presence of a dominant trait.

3. From pedigrees scientists can infer the genetic mechanism of inheritance of single-gene traits.

KEY PROCESS SKILLS

1. Students develop and test a hypothesis.

2. Students interpret data.

3. Students develop conclusions based on evidence.

4. Students apply logic, knowledge, and reasoning to construct explanations.

MATERIALS AND ADVANCE PREPARATION

For the teacher
Transparency 8.1, "Analyzing Pedigrees"

For each pair of students
Family Risk Factor Data card
card with additional risk factor data

For each student
Student Sheet 8.1, "Family Pedigrees"

TEACHING SUMMARY

Getting Started
- Introduce pedigrees.

Doing the Activity
- Students analyze pedigrees, tracing the inheritance of dominant, recessive, and sex-linked traits.
- Students analyze pedigrees to determine the mechanism of inheritance for certain traits.
- Students discuss results of their analyses and come to agreement on the type of mechanism shown in the pedigree.

Follow-up
- Students consider the role of pedigrees for investigating the genetic basis of traits.

BACKGROUND INFORMATION

Pedigree charts have historically been used to trace ancestry, particularly in animals that are bred for showing or racing, such as dogs and horses. In the United Kingdom some human family pedigrees trace lineages as far back as the Middle Ages. In selective breeding, pedigree charts are used for tracing the inheritance of specific traits and to breed offspring accordingly. A racehorse breeder, for example, may look for speed and endurance, and a dog breeder may seek a certain coat color for show dogs. For humans breeding experiments are considered unethical. However, the information from human pedigree charts has taught geneticists a great deal about genetic mechanisms of inheritance in humans.

GETTING STARTED

1 ◆ Project Transparency 8.1, "Analyzing Pedigrees," and point out the features of pedigrees. Ask students, *What can you say about the individuals shown in the pedigree?*

Have the class generate a list of ideas, and take this opportunity to gauge students' understanding of pedigrees. As needed, review with students the symbols that represent biological parents, offspring, male, female, affected individuals, and generations.

---

8 Interpreting Pedigrees

SCIENTISTS ARE STUDYING *a recently discovered risk factor for heart disease, known as factor Z. Scientists have developed a test for factor Z, which they are currently using in a small island community with a high incidence of heart disease. In this community, where much of the population is related, a high percentage of the people also test positive for factor Z. Scientists have evidence that factor Z is likely a genetically inherited trait. The people on the island have agreed to participate in a study of the genetic basis of factor Z.*

In this activity, you will analyze data collected over several generations to determine the genetic mechanism of this trait. The mechanism of inheritance will be dominant, recessive, or sex-linked recessive.

Challenge

▶ What information can geneticists obtain by analyzing a pedigree?

MATERIALS

FOR EACH PAIR OF STUDENTS
Family Risk Factor Data card
card with additional risk factor data

FOR EACH STUDENT
Student Sheet 8.1, "Family Pedigrees"

Procedure

Part A: How to Read a Pedigree

1 1. When geneticists want to track a trait over several generations, they often use a diagram called a pedigree. Similar to a family tree, a **pedigree** shows generations and relationships among biological parents and offspring. It also tracks which of those individuals have a specific trait. Shown on the next page is a pedigree tracing the appearance of black coats in a family of mice. With your partner, discuss the information shown in the pedigree and in the background information box below it.

316

DOING THE ACTIVITY

2 Monitor students' discussions with their partners to be sure they understand the basic structure of the pedigrees. Students should be able to identify all key features of the mouse pedigree before continuing the procedure.

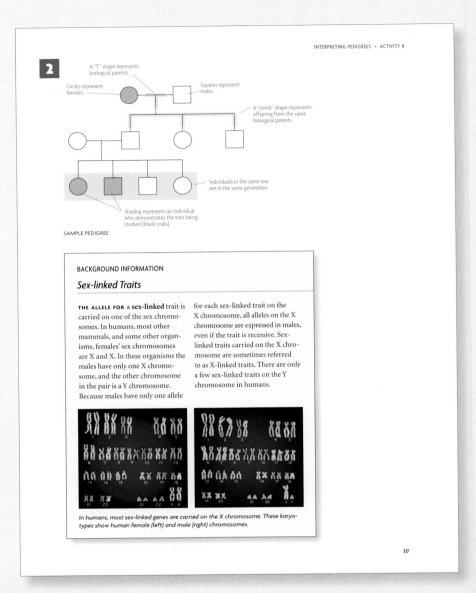

2

A "T" shape represents biological parents.

Circles represent females.

Squares represent males.

A "comb" shape represents offspring from the same biological parents.

Individuals in the same row are in the same generation.

Shading represents an individual who demonstrates the trait being studied (black coats).

SAMPLE PEDIGREE

BACKGROUND INFORMATION

Sex-linked Traits

THE ALLELE FOR a **sex-linked** trait is carried on one of the sex chromosomes. In humans, most other mammals, and some other organisms, females' sex chromosomes are X and X. In these organisms the males have only one X chromosome, and the other chromosome in the pair is a Y chromosome. Because males have only one allele for each sex-linked trait on the X chromosome, all alleles on the X chromosome are expressed in males, even if the trait is recessive. Sex-linked traits carried on the X chromosome are sometimes referred to as X-linked traits. There are only a few sex-linked traits on the Y chromosome in humans.

In humans, most sex-linked genes are carried on the X chromosome. These karyotypes show human female (left) and male (right) chromosomes.

317

490

3 Students may need support in determining the correlation between the types of inheritance (dominant, recessive, sex-linked) and the patterns seen on the pedigrees.

Depending on their level of understanding, you may need to point out to students that a recessive gene can skip generations when it is "hidden" in a heterozygous individual who mates with an individual who is heterozygous or homozygous recessive for the trait being examined.

Make sure students understand that tracing a pedigree does not determine with 100% certainty that a trait is dominant, but if there is enough information on enough individuals over multiple generations it can be inferred with a fair degree of certainty.

Also, be sure students understand that a sex-linked trait will present in male offspring most of the time, unless a female carrier mates with an affected male and the resulting female offspring is homozygous recessive. Point out to students that this is why sex-linked traits are much more commonly observed in, but not exclusive to, male offspring. Some examples of this are color-blindness and male-pattern baldness.

---

2. Scientists think that factor Z may be one of the following types of genetic traits: dominant, recessive, or sex-linked recessive. With your group, discuss what it would mean over several generations for the populations that have factor Z if it were

a. a dominant trait.

b. a recessive trait.

c. a sex-linked recessive trait.

Write your ideas in your science notebook.

3 **3.** Pedigree A below shows where Huntington's disease appeared in several generations of one family. People who suffer from Huntington's disease are afflicted with severe muscle degeneration and dementia, usually starting in middle age. With your partner examine pedigree A. Record in your science notebook your answers to the following questions:

a. What patterns do you notice about which offspring have the trait? Can you tell from the pedigree which parents passed the allele for the trait to the affected offspring?

b. What evidence do you have that suggests the trait is dominant, recessive, or sex-linked recessive?

KEY
□ unaffected males
○ unaffected females
■ affected males
● affected females

PEDIGREE A: HUNTINGTON'S DISEASE
Shading indicates that the individual is affected by Huntington's disease.

4. With your group, repeat Step 3 for pedigrees B and C shown below.

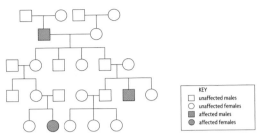

PEDIGREE B: PKU
Shading indicates the individual has PKU, or phenylketonuria. PKU, if not treated, causes mental retardation, seizures, and brain damage in the people who are afflicted by it.

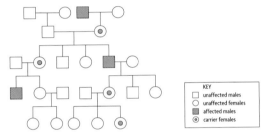

PEDIGREE C: HEMOPHILIA
Shading indicates individual with hemophilia: small circle (○) indicates an individual is a carrier of the trait, but is not afflicted. Generally a carrier can only be identified through genetic testing. Hemophilia is a disease that prevents a person's blood from clotting or coagulating properly. In a severe case, if a hemophiliac who is not receiving clotting treatment is injured, even slightly, the bleeding might not stop for hours, days, or longer and can be fatal. Carriers show no symptoms of the disorder.

4 Discuss with the class their conclusions about the inheritance of dominant, recessive, and sex-linked recessive traits, making sure students understand the patterns these types of traits demonstrate in pedigrees. Pedigree A tracks Huntington's disease, which is a dominant trait. The pedigree supports this because the trait occurs in each generation and in both genders, although the evidence does not rule out a recessive trait. Pedigree B examines phenylketonuria (PKU), a recessive trait. This is supported by the pedigree showing that it skips generations and is found in both genders. Pedigree C follows hemophilia, which is sex-linked recessive. The pedigree shows that only sons of carriers express the condition. You may want to emphasize that only genetic testing identifies carriers of hemophilia, and that the evidence does not rule out a recessive trait.

5 Sample student answers for Student Sheet 8.1, "Family Pedigrees," are shown at the end of this activity. You may want to tell students that factor Z is fictional, but is based on genetic risk factors for disease. You may also need to clarify for students that "genetic mechanism" is also referred to as "pattern of inheritance."

SCIENCE & GLOBAL ISSUES/BIOLOGY • GENETICS

4

5. Based on your conclusions, with the other pair in your group, compare the inheritance of dominant, recessive, and sex-linked recessive traits. Record your comparisons in your science notebook.

Part B: Using Pedigrees to Investigate Factor Z

6. In an attempt to determine what type of genetic mechanism causes factor Z, the genetic research scientists have interviewed families from two of the island's communities where there is a high number of people testing positive for factor Z. The scientists plan to create a pedigree showing who in each family expresses factor Z. Obtain a Family Risk Factor Data card for one of the families from your teacher. Take only one card for yourself and your partner, and together review the information on that card.

5

7. From the information on your Family Risk Factor Data card, fill in the pedigree for your assigned family on Student Sheet 8.1, "Family Pedigrees," including a key and indicating who in the family tests positive for factor Z. Be sure to use only the data shown on your card.

8. With your partner, discuss whether factor Z is a dominant, recessive, or sex-linked recessive trait.

9. Write a hypothesis in your science notebook stating whether the trait is dominant, recessive, or sex-linked recessive. Support your hypothesis with evidence from your pedigree and the Family Risk Factor Data card. If you determine that it is NOT one of these three mechanisms, cite evidence to support your reasoning.

10. Compare your pedigree and hypothesis with those of the other pair in your group, who have data on a different family. Discuss the similarities and differences between your data and hypotheses.

11. Predict the traits that would be exhibited in their offspring if Lynn, from the Sabah-Inde family, or Jackie, from the Brune-Pala family, had three children with an unaffected male, and if the trait were

    a. recessive.

    b. X-linked recessive.

12. Obtain an additional risk factor data card for your assigned family from your teacher. Does this additional data support your hypothesized mechanism for factor Z? Explain.

6 13. As a group,

    a. reach a consensus about the genetic mechanism of factor Z.

    b. revise your hypothesis if necessary to express the ideas of your group.

320

FOLLOW-UP

6 Hold a class discussion to review students' conclusions about what kind of inheritance mechanism factor Z displays. Students should conclude that it is a recessive trait and not sex-linked. Encourage students to support their conclusions with evidence. The fact that it skips generations but reappears indicates that it must be recessive; if a parent has a dominant trait to pass to its offspring, the parent will display the trait. Factor Z's appearance in both male and female offspring indicates that is it unlikely to be a sex-linked recessive trait carried on the X chromosome.

7 ✓ Analysis Question 2 is a Quick Check for you to monitor students' understanding of pedigrees and the information they convey. Discuss students' responses to Analysis Questions 3 and 4, and how this information relates to the issue of genetically modified organisms.

SAMPLE RESPONSES

1. Analyzing a pedigree shows patterns of inheritance of a genetic trait in a family. From it you can determine if the trait is recessive or sex-linked recessive. You may also suspect, but not conclude with complete certainty, that a trait is dominant, because you can't tell from a pedigree, or from an individual's phenotype, if the person is homozygous dominant or heterozygous for a trait. You can also use pedigrees to predict if traits will be inherited by offspring of two individuals.

2. This trait is recessive, but not sex-linked, because it skips generations (recessive) and because it affects both males and females.

3. With a pedigree farmers and geneticists can trace how often a trait occurs in multiple generations of a crop. This information helps them to improve crops.

4. The pedigree shows that the trait is recessive because it is hidden in the third generation and returns in the fourth generation. You can't tell from just the pedigree evidence in the third generation if the gene is still present. The individuals could be homozygous or heterozygous.

5. By understanding how the genetic disease is inherited, scientists can control which birds mate so that the disease is less likely to occur. For example, if the disease trait were recessive, controlling the breeding so that two heterozygous individuals do not mate would help to halt the disease within the population of endangered birds.

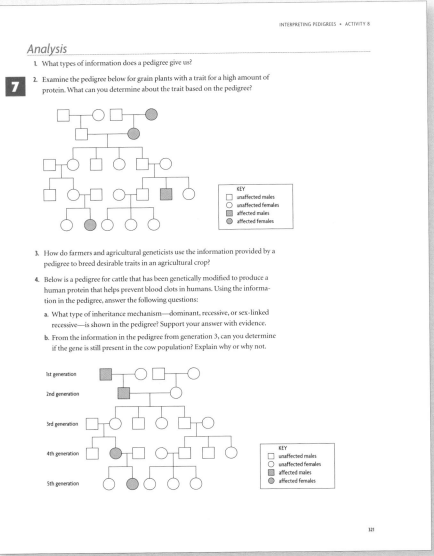

Analysis

1. What types of information does a pedigree give us?

7 2. Examine the pedigree below for grain plants with a trait for a high amount of protein. What can you determine about the trait based on the pedigree?

KEY
☐ unaffected males
○ unaffected females
■ affected males
● affected females

3. How do farmers and agricultural geneticists use the information provided by a pedigree to breed desirable traits in an agricultural crop?

4. Below is a pedigree for cattle that has been genetically modified to produce a human protein that helps prevent blood clots in humans. Using the information in the pedigree, answer the following questions:

    a. What type of inheritance mechanism—dominant, recessive, or sex-linked recessive—is shown in the pedigree? Support your answer with evidence.

    b. From the information in the pedigree from generation 3, can you determine if the gene is still present in the cow population? Explain why or why not.

1st generation

2nd generation

3rd generation

4th generation

5th generation

KEY
☐ unaffected males
○ unaffected females
■ affected males
● affected females

321

6. Parasite resistance in biting flies and abnormal immune cell receptors in guinea pigs are recessive, but not sex-linked. The evidence supporting this is that both of these traits skip generations, and are present in both male and female offspring. White eyes in fruit flies is sex-linked recessive. The evidence supporting this is that only the male offspring exhibit the trait.

REVISIT THE CHALLENGE

Students should be able to articulate that pedigrees allow scientists to trace traits over multiple generations within a family. They should also be able to explain how to analyze a pedigree to infer the genetic mechanism of inheritance for a given trait.

5. Imagine a population of endangered songbirds that are part of a captive breeding program at a zoo. If this population is known to have individuals with a genetic disease, how might an understanding of the mechanism of inheritance of this disease help scientists sustain this population?

6. Pedigrees for three traits—parasite resistance in biting flies, abnormal immune cell receptors in guinea pigs, and white eyes in fruit flies—are shown below. With your partner, determine the inheritance mechanism—dominant, recessive, or sex-linked recessive—that you think is supported by the pedigree. Write your answers in your science notebook. Include evidence to support your conclusions.

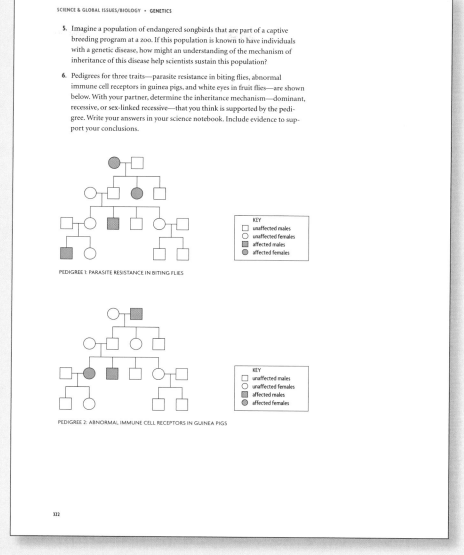

KEY
□ unaffected males
○ unaffected females
▨ affected males
● affected females

PEDIGREE 1: PARASITE RESISTANCE IN BITING FLIES

KEY
□ unaffected males
○ unaffected females
▨ affected males
● affected females

PEDIGREE 2: ABNORMAL IMMUNE CELL RECEPTORS IN GUINEA PIGS

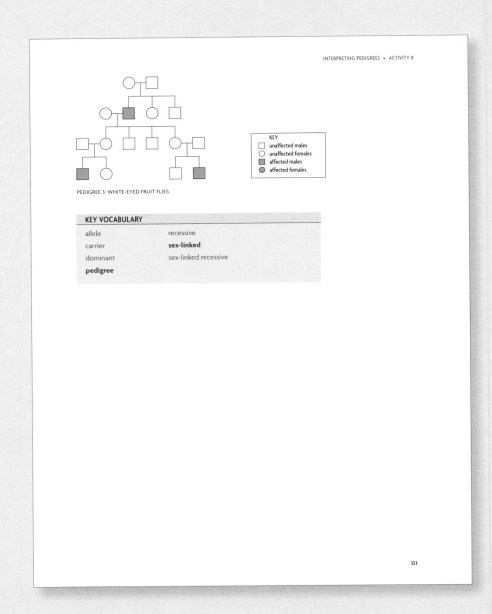

KEY
□ unaffected males
○ unaffected females
■ affected males
● affected females

PEDIGREE 3: WHITE-EYED FRUIT FLIES

KEY VOCABULARY

allele	recessive
carrier	**sex-linked**
dominant	sex-linked recessive
pedigree	

323

Family Pedigrees

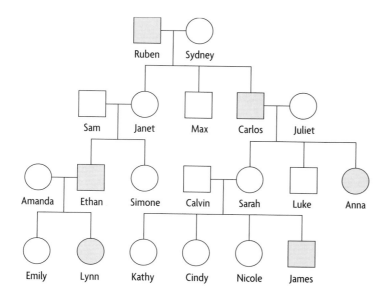

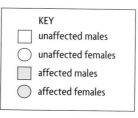

KEY
☐ unaffected males
○ unaffected females
▨ affected males
⬤ affected females

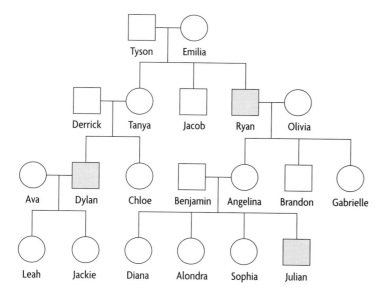

KEY
☐ unaffected males
○ unaffected females
▨ affected males
⬤ affected females

9 DNA Isolation

LABORATORY • 2 CLASS SESSIONS

OVERVIEW

Students isolate and compare the DNA of several organisms. They discuss two reasons for isolating DNA: to study its structure and function and to isolate desired genes for developing genetically modified organisms.

KEY CONTENT

1. DNA is the genetic material in all cells.
2. DNA is isolated from cells by breaking the cells and adding chemicals that precipitate the DNA.

KEY PROCESS SKILLS

1. Students conduct investigations.
2. Students make and record observations.

MATERIALS AND ADVANCE PREPARATION

For the teacher

Transparency 9.1, "Three Types of Cells"
Scoring Guide: GROUP INTERACTION (GI)
transparency marker*
opaque box (optional)*
plastic bag (optional)*
several pipe-cleaner pieces (optional)*

For the class

container for waste*
container of ice or designated laboratory-use freezer to chill bottles of DNA precipitation solution*
test-tube holder or beaker to hold test tubes containing isolated DNA*
masking tape*
marker*
mortar and pestle (optional)*

For each group of four students

bottle of cell lysis solution (detergent solution)
bottle of chilled DNA precipitation solution (100% ethyl alcohol)

For each pair of students

2 test tubes*
2 short SEPUP graduated cylinders
dropper*
funnel*
sealable plastic bag*
square of cheesecloth*
timer*
organism sample (approximately 5 g)*

For each student

Student Sheet 9.1, "DNA Isolation Procedure"
Scoring Guide: GROUP INTERACTION (GI) (optional)
safety goggles*

Not included in kit

For Procedure Step 2 decide if you will provide samples for the isolations or ask students to bring some in. Strawberries, bananas, and other fruits that can be mashed by hand work well. Wheat germ also works well. Dried corn and split peas are good options if they are soaked in warm water for at least 12 hours. Raw onions or liver also work very well, if first macerated in a blender, but many people find their odors unpleasant. For leafy green vegetables, it helps to macerate the tissue with a mortar and pestle. Providing different kinds of organisms allows for comparisons. Decide where you will store the samples until you will need them. Each group should have about five grams of a sample.

Chill the DNA precipitation solution bottles in a container of ice. Check your local, district, and state guidelines for the disposal of solutions and substances used in the laboratory. In many areas with sewage treatment systems, these solutions may be poured down the drain, but in some areas this is not permitted. Based on the relevant guidelines, decide whether to provide a waste bucket for students to dispose of the liquids.

Masters for Scoring Guides are in Teacher Resources IV: Assessment.

TEACHING SUMMARY

Getting Started

- Review the location of DNA in prokaryotic and eukaryotic cells.

Doing the Activity

- The class discusses the DNA isolation procedure.
- (GI ASSESSMENT) Student groups isolate DNA.

Follow-up

- The class compares DNA samples and discusses the necessity of isolating DNA as a first step in genetically modifying organisms.

GETTING STARTED

1 Introduce the term deoxyribonucleic acid (DNA). This was informally introduced in earlier activities, but the chemical name appears here as students begin to explore the molecular nature of DNA.

2 Review the location of DNA in a cell. Project Transparency 9.1, "Three Types of Cells." Ask students, *Where is DNA located in each of these cells?*

With a transparency marker highlight that DNA is in the nucleus of the plant and animal cells (and in protists and fungi, which are not investigated in this activity), and in the cytoplasm of the prokaryotic cell in both the chromosome and plasmid. Prokaryotic cells contain anywhere from zero to several plasmids. Point out that DNA is also found in chloroplasts and mitochondria, however in this unit students will only study nuclear DNA.

Ask students, *How might you remove DNA from a plant or animal cell nucleus?*

Help them visualize the process by making a model cell. Put several pipe cleaner pieces in a baggie, and place it in a box. The baggie represents the nucleus, and the box represents the cell membrane. You might coil one of the pipe cleaners to represent DNA, fold several other pieces to represent proteins, and include small pieces to represent small molecules. Close the box.

Ask the class, *What steps would it take to isolate the DNA contained in the nucleus of the cell, represented by the box?*

Students are likely to respond that first the box, and then the baggie representing the nucleus must be opened, releasing the DNA. The process of breaking a cell apart is

9 DNA Isolation

1 **A**S YOU EXPLORED in earlier activities, the process of making a genetically modified organism begins by identifying a desirable trait in another organism. The second step is to isolate the specific piece of DNA—the gene—that codes for that trait. Genes are made of **deoxyribonucleic acid** (**DNA**), a molecule that is present in every cell of every living organism.

2 In this activity, you will isolate DNA in various organisms by following a laboratory procedure developed by a team of scientists who isolated DNA from spinach. They published their results, and now other scientists are building on their work.

Challenge

▶ How is DNA isolated from an organism?

324

called lysis, and this is the first process students will execute in the laboratory procedure. After the DNA is released, it must be separated from the other cellular molecules.

Remind students that scientists commonly build on each other's work. Students will model this as they follow a protocol designed by a group of scientists who isolated DNA from spinach, and apply that procedure to several other organisms.

DOING THE ACTIVITY

3 As student groups summarize the isolation steps on Student Sheet 9.1, "DNA Isolation Procedure," clarify the purpose of each step and the equipment. Introduce the following key concepts:

- Lysis: Lysis is the process of breaking cells apart. In this activity students use both mechanical (smashing the sample) and chemical means (detergent contained in the DNA lysis solution) to break up cell tissue and cell membranes and release DNA into a solution, which is called the lysate.

- Precipitation: Precipitation occurs when a dissolved substance is made insoluble, usually by adding a chemical. Since it is no longer soluble, the substance becomes a solid and precipitates out of the solution. In the DNA isolation procedure, DNA is not soluble in the ethyl alcohol solution. This causes the insoluble DNA molecules to collect at the alcohol–lysate interface. This separates the DNA from other substances dissolved in the cell lysate, such as carbohydrates and proteins.

Sample student responses for Student Sheet 9.1 appear at the end of this activity.

4 (GI ASSESSMENT) Procedure Step 2 is an opportunity to apply the GROUP INTERACTION (GI) Scoring Guide to assess students' group interaction skills. For more information on this assessment, see Teacher Resources IV: Assessment. Provide warm soapy water for students to use to clean all equipment. Make sure the class understands your requirements for appropriate behavior and safety procedures in the laboratory before allowing them to begin their work. For resources to support and develop a plan for working safely in the science laboratory, see the Lab Materials and Safety section of Teacher Resources I: Course Essentials. Provide cleanup instructions.

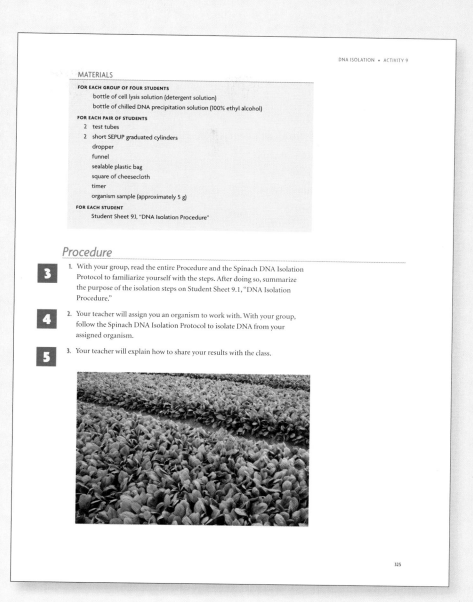

MATERIALS

FOR EACH GROUP OF FOUR STUDENTS
    bottle of cell lysis solution (detergent solution)
    bottle of chilled DNA precipitation solution (100% ethyl alcohol)

FOR EACH PAIR OF STUDENTS
2   test tubes
2   short SEPUP graduated cylinders
    dropper
    funnel
    sealable plastic bag
    square of cheesecloth
    timer
    organism sample (approximately 5 g)

FOR EACH STUDENT
    Student Sheet 9.1, "DNA Isolation Procedure"

Procedure

3 1. With your group, read the entire Procedure and the Spinach DNA Isolation Protocol to familiarize yourself with the steps. After doing so, summarize the purpose of the isolation steps on Student Sheet 9.1, "DNA Isolation Procedure."

4 2. Your teacher will assign you an organism to work with. With your group, follow the Spinach DNA Isolation Protocol to isolate DNA from your assigned organism.

5 3. Your teacher will explain how to share your results with the class.

325

FOLLOW-UP

5 When students complete the isolation, ask for volunteers to display their DNA. Label the test tubes of DNA, and place them in a test-tube holder or beaker for the class to view. Ask students to observe and compare the physical properties of each sample. Make sure students see that the DNA from each organism has the same physical characteristics: it is a wet, whitish, globular mass resembling a clump of white glue. Students will further investigate the molecular structure of DNA, which confers these properties, in Activity 10, "Modeling DNA."

6 DNA isolation is an essential step in the genetic engineering of an organism. Before a gene from one organism can be placed into another, it must first be isolated, characterized, and copied. Students conducted the isolation step in this activity. Ask students to think back to Activity 2, "Creating Genetically Modified Bacteria," when they genetically modified *E. coli*. Explain to them that the DNA containing the target gene—the gene for green fluorescence—was isolated from jellies, inserted into a plasmid, and copied for students before they began the process of inserting the gene to produce genetically modified bacteria. Point out that scientists who study proteins and other cellular molecules also often begin by separating these molecules from other substances in the cell.

SAMPLE RESPONSES

1. Mashing the sample in the plastic bag begins the breakdown of the tissue and cell membranes in the sample.

2. The lysis solution broke down the cells and their nuclear membranes. The DNA precipitation solution caused the DNA to clump at the interface of the precipitation solution.

3. It is important that scientists record specific and detailed procedures so that other scientists can replicate or verify their work. It also helps scientists to build on each other's work.

4. The DNA samples were similar in color and consistency. They were all a translucent white and clumped together like white glue.

5. To genetically modify an organism's DNA scientists first need to isolate the DNA from the organism.

Spinach DNA Isolation Protocol

1. Place the spinach sample into a plastic bag, seal the bag, and with your fingers mash the sample into a uniform pulp.

2. Add 10 mL of cell lysis solution to the bag, and reseal it, pushing out most of the air. Gently squeeze the mixture (without creating bubbles) for 1 minute.

3. Filter the mixture to separate the solids from the liquids. To do this:

   a. Set up the filtering equipment. Place a funnel in a graduated cylinder, as shown at right. Place a piece of cheesecloth in the funnel.

   b. Slowly pour the mixture into the funnel. Let the liquid drip into the cylinder for approximately 5 minutes. (Be careful not to allow any solids to fall into the cylinder.)

4. Remove the funnel from the graduated cylinder.

5. Fill a test tube approximately half-full with DNA precipitation solution. Pick up the test tube, and hold it at a 45° angle. Using a dropper, slowly add the filtered liquid down the inside surface of the side of the test tube until both solutions fill ¾ of the test tube.

6. Let the solutions in the test tube sit for at least 3 minutes. A white layer of DNA should appear at the boundary between the two solutions.

REVISIT THE CHALLENGE

Students should be able to name and discuss the purpose for each main step involved in isolating DNA from organisms' cells. These are breaking cell membranes to release the DNA, separating the solution (lysate) containing the DNA from solid cellular material, and precipitating the DNA out of solution to separate it from other molecules in the lysate.

Analysis

1. What was the purpose of mashing the sample in the plastic bag?

2. Describe the purpose of the cell lysis solution and the DNA precipitation solution.

3. Explain why it is important that scientists record detailed and specific procedures.

4. Compare the properties of DNA isolated from different organisms. What similarities did you observe?

 5. How is the mechanism for isolating DNA from an organism connected to the mechanism for genetically modifying that organism?

KEY VOCABULARY	
cell	gene
deoxyribonucleic acid (DNA)	isolation

327

DNA Isolation Procedure

In the second column of the table below, record a one-to-three sentence summary for each group of Procedure Steps.

Procedure Steps	Purpose of Steps
1–3	These steps break up the sample's tissues and cells. The cell lysis solution breaks down the cell and nuclear membranes so that the DNA is released from the cells.
4–6	In these steps the solution containing the DNA is filtered to separate dissolved materials from solids. Then precipitation solution is added. This causes the DNA to collect between the two solutions.

10 Modeling DNA Structure

MODELING • 2 CLASS SESSIONS

OVERVIEW

Students investigate the molecular structure of DNA. They analyze historical base-pairing data and draw conclusions from the data to construct DNA models. They also compare their models to several images of DNA and discuss what each conveys about the molecular structure of DNA.

KEY CONTENT

1. The genetic material of cells is deoxyribonucleic acid (DNA).

2. DNA is a macromolecule composed of nucleotide subunits.

3. DNA is composed of two complementary strands, each made of a sequence of nucleotides.

4. Each strand of DNA has a sugar–phosphate backbone and a sequence of nitrogenous bases. Two strands of DNA together form a double helix.

KEY PROCESS SKILLS

1. Students identify and describe trends in data.

2. Students interpret data.

MATERIALS AND ADVANCE PREPARATION

For the teacher

    Transparency 10.1, "DNA Structure"
    Transparency 10.2, "DNA Nucleotides"
    Transparency 10.3, "Antiparallel DNA"
    Transparency 10.4, "DNA Images"

For each group of students

    set of colored pencils

For each pair of students

    DNA model kit containing:

        plastic bag*

    36 black deoxyribose sugars*

    36 white phosphate tubes*

        orange, yellow, blue, and green nitrogenous base tubes*

    18 white hydrogen bond rods*

Note: *This activity is written to use the SEPUP DNA modeling kit. If you will be using a different kit, adjust the instructions as appropriate.*

The DNA model kits contain pieces for this activity, and additional pieces to model protein synthesis later in the unit. For each kit separate the pieces needed for this activity, as noted above, and place them into one of the plastic bags. Label the bag DNA Subunit Models. Store the remaining parts for use in Activity 12, " DNA Replication."

TEACHING SUMMARY

Getting Started

- Students discuss their ideas about the structure of DNA.

Doing the Activity

- Students build a DNA model.

Follow-up

- ✓Students analyze the strengths of various DNA models.

BACKGROUND INFORMATION

DNA Structure

Deoxyribonucleic acid (DNA) is a large polymer, or macro-molecule, made of numerous repeating monomers, or sub-units. These subunits of nucleic acids are called nucleotides. Each nucleotide in DNA consists of the five-carbon sugar deoxyribose, a phosphate group, and one of four nitrogenous bases. Because they all contain deoxyribose, the nucleotides in DNA are more specifically called deoxyribonucleotides. However, most of the time they are simply referred to as nucleotides. Note that RNA and ribonucleotides will be discussed in the Teacher's Edition Background Information for Activity 16, "Protein Synthesis: Transcription and Translation."

The nitrogenous bases are heterocyclic organic molecules, which means that they are made of ring structures that include both carbon and another element—in this case, nitrogen. Two of the four nitrogenous bases in DNA are purines and two are pyrimidines, as shown below.

The complete atomic structure of a nucleotide containing thymine is shown below. The phosphate group is attached to carbon 5 of the deoxyribose sugar, and the bases are attached to carbon 1.

In a DNA molecule, the sugar and phosphate group of successive nucleotides link together to form a sugar–phosphate backbone, as shown at right. The nitrogenous bases project from this backbone. Each base hydrogen bonds to only one other nitrogenous base to form a base pair. The purine adenine pairs only with the pyrimidine thymine via two hydrogen bonds. Similarly, guanine pairs with cytosine via three hydrogen bonds. These hydrogen bonds between complementary nucleotides link two DNA strands together, making the resulting DNA molecule double-stranded. This double-stranded molecule takes on a helical shape called a double helix. It resembles a ladder, with the sides formed by the sugar phosphate backbones and the rungs formed by successive base pairs.

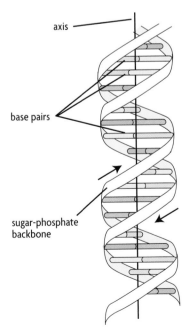

Because the phosphate groups are always on carbon 5 of the deoxyribose sugar, a single strand of DNA has a polarity. The end that terminates with a phosphate group is called the 5' end, while the other end is the 3' end. In a double-stranded DNA molecule, the 5' end of one strand is opposite the 3' end of the other strand. Thus, the two strands of DNA in a double helix are said to be antiparallel.

The Work of Erwin Chargaff

In the late 1940s, Erwin Chargaff, an Austrian biochemist working at Columbia University in New York, was spurred into action after reading the scientific findings of Oswald Avery. Avery was an American physician renowned for his studies on disease-causing bacteria. Avery's research supported the hypothesis that genes are made of DNA. At the time many leading scientists believed cellular proteins served as the genetic material because they couldn't figure out how such a simple molecule as DNA, with only four different nucleotide subunits, could carry genetic information. Chargaff, in an effort to support Avery's findings, changed the work focus of his research team and began investigating the biochemical composition of DNA.

Chargaff's team used two biochemical analysis techniques that were new at the time: chromatography, to analyze the nucleic acid content of a sample, and ultraviolet spectrophotometry, to measure the amount of each nitrogenous base in a DNA sample. These techniques allowed the group to characterize the ratio of DNA nucleotides in various DNA samples. Chargaff published his first papers describing their work in 1950.

The research group further refined its analysis methods to determine the nitrogenous base composition of DNA from several organisms, including plants, animals, and bacteria. From the data generated, the team concluded that the amounts of adenine and thymine in a DNA sample were approximately equal and that the amounts of cytosine and guanine were also approximately equal. In addition, the data disproved a widely held idea that DNA is the same in all organisms. The data supported the idea that the DNA of different organisms is composed of unique ratios of nitrogenous bases.

The work of Chargaff and his team provided critical evidence for the discovery of the double-helical structure of DNA. James Watson and Francis Crick realized that the data Chargaff collected could be the result of pairing between A and T and between G and C in complementary strands of DNA. Thus, what later became known as Chargaff's rules, that A bonds with T and C bonds with G, were an essential piece of evidence in Watson and Crick's discovery of the double-helical structure of DNA.

REFERENCES

Chargaff, E. & Davidson J., eds. (1955). The nucleic acids. New York: Academic Press.

Chargaff, E., Zamenhof, S., & Green, C. (1950). Human desoxypentose nucleic acid: Composition of human desoxypentose nucleic acid. *Nature 165*, 756–757.

Chargaff, E., Lipshitz, R., & Green. C. (1952). Composition of the desoxypentose nucleic acids of four genera of sea-urchin. *Journal of Biological Chemistry 195*(1):155–60.

Chargaff, E., Lipshitz, R., Green, C., & Hodes, M. E. (1951). The composition of the desoxyribonucleic acid of salmon sperm. *Journal of Biological Chemistry 192*, 223–230.

GETTING STARTED

1 ◆ Write the word *genes* on the board, and ask students to describe what they know about them. List students' ideas on the board. If necessary, encourage them to add information about what genes are made of and where they are located. Students' answers will likely indicate that genes, in conjunction with environmental factors, determine traits in an organism's phenotype. They also will likely point out that all organisms have DNA, and, therefore, all organisms have genes. If they completed the "Cell Biology: World Health" unit of *Science and Global Issues,* they may remember that the genetic material is in the cell nucleus. They will explore the relationship between genes and DNA, as well as chromosomes, in this and future activities. This is an opportunity to find out their ideas so that you may address any misconceptions or gaps in basic knowledge of genes throughout the remainder of the unit.

DOING THE ACTIVITY

2 Project Transparency 10.1, "DNA Structure." Explain that DNA has the shape of a double helix, and that despite its size, it is relatively simple in structure. It is made of only four subunits and always takes on a double-helical shape. Refer to the diagram in the Student Book to show students additional detail, but do not explain base pairing rules at this point. If students completed the "Cell Biology" unit of *Science and Global Issues,* remind them about proteins, which are polymers made of long chains built from 20 amino acid monomers and take on a wide variety of shapes. For a long time, scientists assumed that only proteins were complex enough to carry the genetic material. It was after they gained a more detailed understanding of the structure of DNA that scientists figured out how it could carry genetic information.

10 Modeling DNA Structure

1 **D**NA IS THE genetic material of all living organisms. Like proteins, carbohydrates, and lipids, DNA is a polymer—a large molecule made of many repeating subunits, called monomers. The subunits of DNA are nucleotides.

2 DNA contains information that codes for life's processes. Understanding the chemical structure of DNA allows scientists to understand how DNA codes for proteins. Scientists also need to understand the structure of DNA to determine how to isolate a specific desirable or undesirable gene from an organism.

In this activity, you will model the structure of DNA and explore how it provides information that directs the processes in a cell.

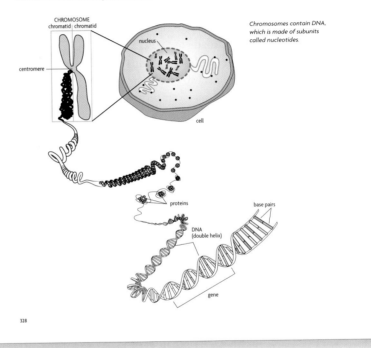

Chromosomes contain DNA, which is made of subunits called nucleotides.

328

3 DNA is a polymer that is made of repeating monomers (nucleotide subunits) that vary in one distinct way—the nitrogen bases that the nucleotides carry. Connect this back to what students learned in the "Cell Biology" unit about polymers and subunits in cells. Show students the deoxyribose sugar, the phosphate group, and the nitrogenous-base pieces from the DNA model kit. Explain that each kit piece represents a nucleotide structure but does not show its detailed atomic structure.

4 With Transparency 10.2, "DNA Nucleotides," show the class four nucleotides—adenine, cytosine, guanine, and thymine—and their corresponding kit pieces. Point out that each nucleotide has the same deoxyribose sugar and phosphate group, but the nitrogenous (nitrogen-containing) base attached to the sugar–phosphate backbone can vary. Depending on your instructional goals, you may wish to explain that each of the four nitrogenous bases has its own molecular structure, but all are based on cyclic molecules made of carbon and nitrogen rings, as shown on the bottom half of Transparency 10.2.

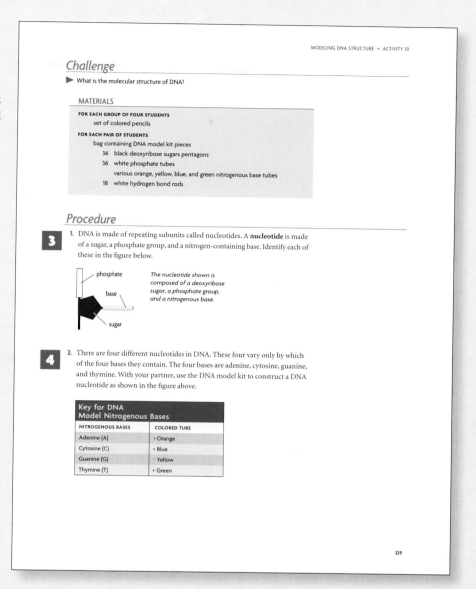

Challenge

▶ What is the molecular structure of DNA?

MATERIALS

FOR EACH GROUP OF FOUR STUDENTS
set of colored pencils

FOR EACH PAIR OF STUDENTS
bag containing DNA model kit pieces
36 black deoxyribose sugars pentagons
36 white phosphate tubes
various orange, yellow, blue, and green nitrogenous base tubes
18 white hydrogen bond rods

Procedure

3 1. DNA is made of repeating subunits called nucleotides. A **nucleotide** is made of a sugar, a phosphate group, and a nitrogen-containing base. Identify each of these in the figure below.

phosphate
base
sugar

The nucleotide shown is composed of a deoxyribose sugar, a phosphate group, and a nitrogenous base.

4 2. There are four different nucleotides in DNA. These four vary only by which of the four bases they contain. The four bases are adenine, cytosine, guanine, and thymine. With your partner, use the DNA model kit to construct a DNA nucleotide as shown in the figure above.

Key for DNA Model Nitrogenous Bases	
NITROGENOUS BASES	**COLORED TUBE**
Adenine (A)	• Orange
Cytosine (C)	• Blue
Guanine (G)	• Yellow
Thymine (T)	• Green

329

509

5 Discuss the role of hydrogen bonds in DNA. Explain that hydrogen bonds form between two nitrogenous bases on two strands of DNA. This is shown on Transparency 10.1, "DNA Structure." The diagram shows the two hydrogen bonds that connect A and T and the three that connect C and G. In their models, students make one connection to represent these bonds. When hydrogen bonds link two nitrogenous bases, the result is a base pair.

6 Use this opportunity to discuss the historical discovery of the structure of DNA. For additional information, see the links on the *science and Global Issues* page of the SEPUP website (*sepuplhs.org/sgi*).

7 Students should conclude that since the amount of adenine (A) and thymine (T) are practically equal in each organism, adenosine pairs with thymine. They should draw the same conclusion for cytosine (C), which pairs with guanine (G). If students need assistance processing the data you might ask, What patterns do you notice? What does this data set show about the percentages of bases in different organisms? What does it tell you about the relative ratio of A, T, G, and C in DNA? Help students see that the percentages of adenine (A) are close to those of thymine (T) and the percentages of guanine (G) are close to those of cytosine (C) for each organism on the table. Explain that the reason the percentages in Chargaff's data are not exactly equal is most likely a matter of experimental errors resulting from the very new procedures that Chargaff and his laboratory developed. This is a good time to introduce students to the common convention of noting the nitrogenous base adenine as A, guanine as G, thymine as T, and cytosine as C.

8 As students build their models, check them to see that students have paired adenine with thymine and cytosine with guanine. Listen for and discuss as necessary students' correct usage of the key terms: sugar–phosphate backbone, base pair, nucleotide, and hydrogen bond.

---

3. Continue to build and connect a single chain of eight nucleotides, using any sequence of bases.

5 4. DNA occurs in its natural state as two strands linked down the middle by hydrogen bonds. Identify the two strands and the location of the hydrogen bonds in the figure below.

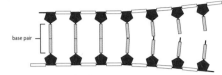

base pair

*A **base pair** is two nucleotides in double-stranded DNA connected by hydrogen bonds.*

6 BACKGROUND INFORMATION

Discovering the Structure of DNA

IN THE 1950S, discovering the structure of DNA became a subject of intense scientific investigation and rivalry. Several research groups competed to be the first to find the answer. These groups included the laboratory of Linus Pauling (who had earlier determined the structure of proteins) at the California Institute of Technology; scientists at Cambridge University in England; and another group of scientists at Kings' College of the University of London.

James Watson and Francis Crick of Cambridge University won the race. In 1953, after careful analysis of structural and chemical data— much of which was provided by Maurice Wilkins and Rosalind Franklin at Kings' College—Watson and Crick published a scientific paper that proposed that DNA is made of two strands spiraling to form a double helix. This structure not only accounts for the chemical makeup of DNA, but also allowed Watson and Crick to predict how DNA replicates when a cell divides. Their discovery opened up the field of molecular biology, which provides insights into the molecular basis of genetics, development, evolution, and other biological processes. Watson, Crick, and Wilkins were awarded the Nobel Prize in 1962, for their breakthrough. Unfortunately, Rosalind Franklin did not share in the prize because she had died in 1958, and the Nobel Prize is not awarded to someone who has died. The story of these scientists and their work is the subject of a number of books and articles.

330

---

9 Develop the concept of antiparallel strands of DNA. Project Transparency 10.3, "Antiparallel DNA." Explain that the 5' end of a DNA strand terminates with a phosphate group. The 3' end terminates with a deoxyribose sugar. Both of the complementary DNA strands in double-stranded DNA have a 5' and 3' end, but in opposite orientations. Therefore, the two complementary strands of DNA are said to be antiparallel. This aspect of DNA structure becomes more important to students as they learn about DNA replication in Activity 12, "DNA Replication."

10 Students' drawings should identify the key components of DNA listed in the Student Book, as shown in the sample image on the next page.

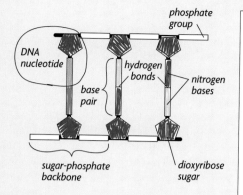

11 Connect three or four of the students' completed DNA models end-to-end. Twist this longer model to demonstrate the double-helix structure of DNA. Explain that this represents a minute portion of the 3.3 billion DNA base pairs contained in an average human cell. Tell students that it is the sequence of nitrogenous bases in an organism's DNA that provides the genetic information that determines an organism's phenotype, in conjunction with environmental factors.

Emphasize again that a gene is a segment of DNA with a unique base sequence that encodes for a specific protein that influences an organism's phenotype. Genes for different proteins vary tremendously in length, both within an organism and from one organism to another. Human genes have from 1,000 to hundreds of thousands or even millions of base pairs, with the average human gene being 10,000–15,000 base pairs in length. Genes in prokaryotes tend to be shorter than the comparable genes in eukaryotes.

Connect this to the DNA students observed in Activity 9, "DNA Isolation." Explain that although the physical characteristics of the DNA they observed from different types of organisms are the same, the DNA from each organism contains a unique sequence of nucleotides characteristic of that species.

Note: At the end of the activity, store the complete longer model to use again in Activity 12.

---

7 5. In the mid-1940s, Erwin Chargaff, an Austrian scientist, analyzed the percentages of each of the four nitrogenous bases in DNA. A summary of his findings is shown in the table below. With your group, review the data, and search for patterns. Discuss what these patterns might suggest about the nucleotides in DNA.

Percentages of DNA Nucleotides in Selected Organisms				
SOURCE OF DNA	ADENINE (A)	CYTOSINE (C)	GUANINE (G)	THYMINE (T)
Human	30.2%	18.8%	18.8%	32.2%
Rat	28.6%	21.6%	21.4%	28.4%
Sea Urchin	31.2%	19.1%	19.2%	30.5%
Salmon	29.2%	20.8%	21.9%	28.1%

8 6. Based on your conclusions from the data in Step 5, construct a second strand of DNA that pairs with the strand you built in Step 3.

9 7. Connect the two strands down the middle with hydrogen bonds.

10 8. With colored pencils sketch the resulting double-stranded DNA model in your notebook. On your sketch, label the following:

- Phosphate group
- Deoxyribose sugar
- DNA nucleotide
- Nitrogen base
- Hydrogen bond
- Base pair
- Sugar–phosphate backbone

11 9. At this point, your piece of DNA should resemble a ladder. Watch as your teacher connects several DNA models and demonstrates the shape of a DNA molecule.

12 10. With your group, look at the series of DNA models shown in the figures on the next page. Compare your DNA Model with the DNA in each image. Discuss what each model demonstrates about the structure of DNA. Record your ideas in your science notebook.

331

---

12 Encourage students to identify the DNA characteristics shown by the physical model and each of the figures in the Student Book. Prompt them to discuss the similarities and the differences they observe between the images and their model. All five models show the overall double-helix structure of DNA, and the structure of the sugar–phosphate backbone. The individual components emphasized in each vary from image to image. The figures at the top of the page clearly show nucleotides in the center of the helix. The figure at the top left shows the nucleotides in a base pair bonded by hydrogen bonds. Discuss which images are computer-generated models and which are scientific drawings. (The figures at the bottom of the page are computer generated. The figures at the top are schematic drawings of DNA.)

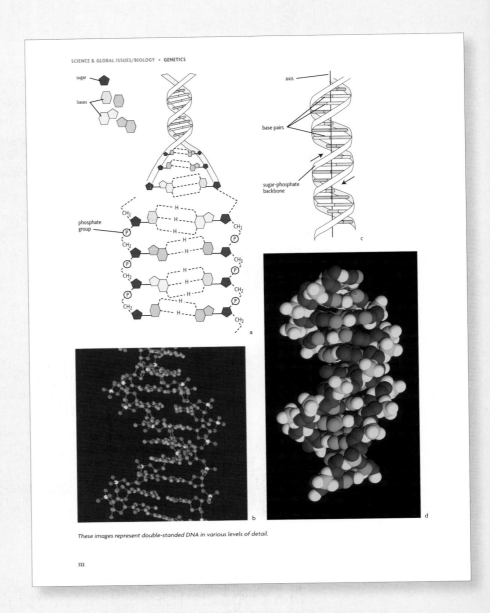

These images represent double-standed DNA in various levels of detail.

FOLLOW-UP

13 ✓Procedure Step 11 serves as a Quick Check to assess students' grasp of the structure of DNA and to make sure they can describe the shape and key structural components of DNA. Showing Transparency 10.4, "DNA Images," will help in this assessment.

14 To provide students with a sense of the amount of DNA contained in an average human cell, explain that the model they built was eight base pairs (bp) in length. The combined length of all of the DNA in the 23 human chromosome pairs (46 chromosomes) is approximately 3 billion base pairs.

SAMPLE RESPONSES

1. Students' answers should explain the double-helical structure of DNA and that it is composed of repeating subunits that contain one of four bases. One possible response is:

   DNA is shaped like a ladder that is twisted. It has rungs that are the same shape that repeat over and over. Each rung is made when two molecules called bases bond together. There are four possible bases, and they carry the genetic information.

2. 3' TAGCGG 5'

3. gene   DNA   chromosome   cell

4. The amount of DNA in an average human cell is more than 1,000 times the amount of DNA in an *E. coli* cell.

---

13 **11.** With your partner, identify the following in the images of DNA shown on the previous page:

- Phosphate group
- Deoxyribose sugar
- DNA nucleotide
- Nitrogen base
- Hydrogen bond
- Base pair
- Sugar–phosphate backbone

Analysis

1. How would you describe the structure of DNA to a 10-year-old?

2. What nucleotide sequence would bond with the following strand?
   5' ATCGCC 3'

3. Arrange the following cell structures from the smallest to the largest, left to right:
   DNA
   chromosomes
   gene
   cell

14 4. The table below shows the number of base pairs in the DNA of selected organisms. From the data in the table, what can you say about the amount of DNA contained in the cells of these three organisms?

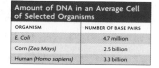

Amount of DNA in an Average Cell of Selected Organisms	
ORGANISM	NUMBER OF BASE PAIRS
E. Coli	4.7 million
Corn (Zea Mays)	2.5 billion
Human (Homo sapiens)	3.3 billion

KEY VOCABULARY	
base pair	hydrogen bond
double helix	**nucleotide**
deoxyribonucleic acid (DNA)	sugar–phosphate backbone

333

REVISIT THE CHALLENGE

Students should be able to explain the overall molecular structure of DNA as a repetition of subunits called nucleotides. They should understand that there are four possible nucleotides, and that pairing of A with T and G with C links two strands of nucleotide subunits. They should be able to explain that DNA has sugar–phosphate sides that run along the outer edge of the DNA molecule like a ladder, with the nitrogenous bases forming the rungs that connect the two helical sides.

11 Genomics

READING • 1 CLASS SESSION

OVERVIEW

Students read about the field of genomics, including its history, goals, and accomplishments. The reading discusses the Human Genome Project and other genome projects. Students are also introduced to current and future applications of genomics as ways to address sustainability challenges.

KEY CONTENT

1. Genomics is the study of the entire genetic makeup of an organism. This field has expanded rapidly over the past four decades.

2. The Human Genome Project successfully cataloged the human genome. The information generated by the project has allowed scientists to explore the role of genes in human diseases and healing and new approaches to finding cures.

3. Genomics has the potential to contribute to solving sustainability problems related to biodiversity, alternative energy, and human and animal health.

KEY PROCESS SKILLS

1. Students make accurate interpretations, inferences, and conclusions from text.

MATERIALS AND ADVANCE PREPARATION

For each student
Student Sheet 11.1, "Three-level Reading Guide: Genomics"

TEACHING SUMMARY

Getting Started

- Revisit the relationship between genotypes and phenotypes.

Doing the Activity

- (LITERACY) A Three-level Reading Guide literacy strategy helps students comprehend the concepts presented in the reading.

Follow-up

- The class discusses the applications of genomics in exploring the mechanisms of heredity, as well as addressing sustainability challenges.

REFERENCES

ArgosBiotech. (n.d.). Historical timeline of genomic sequencing projects. Retrieved April 10, 2010, from http://www.argosbiotech.de/700/omics/genomics/genometer.htm.

Functional and comparative genomics fact sheet. (n.d.). U.S. Department of Energy Office of Science, Office of Biological and Environmental Research, Human Genome Program. Retrieved April 2010 from http://www.ornl.gov/sci/techresources/Human_Genome/faq/compgen.shtml.

GETTING STARTED

1 🛈 Write the terms *DNA* and *genes* on the board, and ask pairs of students to come up with a description of each word and explain how the two are related. Students should be able to explain that DNA is the genetic material of a cell and to describe its major structural components and physical characteristics. As they learned in Activity 10, "Modeling DNA Structure," a gene is a specific region of DNA that codes for a phenotype or trait. The DNA in each chromosome contains many genes. If students need additional instruction, spend time clarifying the relationship between the two. You might sketch a long double helix on the board, and remind students that a gene is a segment of this DNA.

DOING THE ACTIVITY

2 After students have completed the reading, pass out Student Sheet 11.1, "Three-Level Reading Guide: Genomics." The reading guide presents students with statements that require three levels of understanding: literal, interpretive, and applied. Students are asked to determine which statements are supported by the text.

Possible responses to the reading guide are shown at the end of this activity on Sample Student Sheet 11.1. Note that the statements under number 3 (applied) do not have a single correct response. Students may interpret information differently and agree or disagree with each statement. Regardless of their perspectives, it is important for students to be able to explain and support their positions. Clarifying notes are provided for the statements that do not accurately represent the content in the reading. Note that this strategy is not asking students to discern which of the statements are true or false, as many of them are true. It is asking them to determine which are portrayed in the content of the reading.

---

11 Genomics

1 UNDERSTANDING THE PHYSICAL characteristics and molecular structure of DNA is a start to understanding the connections between an organism's genotype and phenotype. But these are only two pieces of the puzzle. By sequencing an organism's genetic material, and mapping the DNA contained in that material, scientists have begun to understand the bigger pictures, including the evolution of organisms and the genetic causes of some human diseases. In this activity, you will read about the field of genomics.

Challenge

▶ How has genomics contributed to our understanding of heredity?

MATERIALS

FOR EACH STUDENT
Student Sheet 11.1, "Three-level Reading Guide: Genomics"

Procedure

2 1. Complete the reading below. When you have finished, complete Student Sheet 11.1, "Three-level Reading Guide: Genomics."

Reading

DNA: Information for Life

Every organism contains genes, which, along with environmental factors, control every process necessary for life. Scientists are only beginning to understand how phenotypes arise from genotypes, but they do know that genes play a central role. These genes are coded in molecules of DNA. Since the 1944 discovery of DNA as the molecule of heredity, scientists have investigated how the information encoded in DNA directs the way cells reproduce, grow, and function. Even viruses, which are not cells, contain genetic material in the form of either DNA or RNA, the same genetic code used by organisms. This basic understanding is helping us tackle issues related to sustainability. In recent years, new biotechnology tools have helped scientists explore DNA and genes in ways never before possible.

334

These researchers are monitoring the amplification of DNA. In this process, many copies of a DNA strand are made and used to sequence the DNA. By sequencing the order of the DNA, scientists hope to learn more about how the DNA determines an organisms's traits.

Scientists are using DNA from many organisms including people, corn, and termites to learn more about the connections between an organisms's phenotype and genotype.

335

The Field of Genomics

The complete sequence of an organism's genetic material is called its **genome**. **Genomics** is the study of this sequence and its organization. Since the role of DNA as genetic material was first discovered, scientists have learned a tremendous amount about it. Genomics aims to determine the sequence of bases in an organism's DNA, where the genes are located in that sequence, and how genes work together along with environmental factors to produce different phenotypes. Genomics research also determines which sections of genomes do not code for genes. In fact, current research indicates that in a typical eukaryotic genome, only 1%–5% codes for genes. Genomics has helped scientists to read the information in the DNA and begin to figure out its role in determining an organism's traits.

As you learned in Activity 10, "Modeling DNA Structure," DNA is a very long double-stranded molecule made of nucleotide subunits. Each nucleotide contains a sugar, a phosphate group, and one of four nitrogenous bases—adenine (A), thymine (T), cytosine (C), and guanine (G). The number and sequence of these bases varies from species to species. Variations in the size of genomes of several species are shown in the table below.

Selected Genome Sizes

ORGANISM OR VIRUS	ESTIMATED SIZE OF GENOME (BASE PAIRS)	ESTIMATED NUMBER OF GENES	NUMBER OF CHROMOSOMES
Amoeba (Amoeba dubia)	670 billion	Unknown	Unknown
Human (Homo sapiens)	3.2 billion	20,000–25,000	46
Mouse (Mus musculus)	2.6 billion	20,000–25,000	40
Fruit fly (Drosophila melanogaster)	137 million	13,000	8
Mouse-ear cress plant (Arabidopsis thaliana)	100 million	25,000	10
Roundworm (Caenorhabditis elegans)	97 million	19,000	12
Yeast (Saccharomyces cerevisiae)	12.1 million	6,000	32
Bacteria (Escherichia coli)	4.6 million	3,200	1
Bacteria (Haemophilus influenzae)	1.8 million	1,700	1
Rotavirus	18,555	11	—
Human immunodeficiency virus (HIV)	9,749*	9	—

*This number represents single nucleotides, not base pairs, because the genome for HIV is single-stranded.

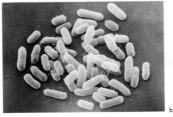

Scientists have sequenced the genomes of many organisms, including mice (a), E. coli (b), and A.Thaliana (c), which are frequently used in research.

Sequencing and Mapping a Genome

Analyzing an organism's genome involves several steps, each of which requires biotechnology tools developed over the past 30 years. First, scientists must isolate the DNA from the many other molecules in a cell of the organism. Next, they make multiple copies of the DNA through a process called polymerase chain reaction (PCR). They then sequence the DNA to determine the total number and order of each base. With this information, scientists can look for the locations of specific genes within the sequence. This is called gene mapping. They can also begin to identify which sections of the DNA do not code for genes. When sequencing and mapping are finished, scientists have the genome of the organism.

THE KEY STEPS TO ANALYZING A GENOME

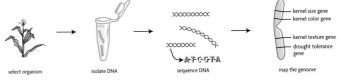

select organism   isolate DNA   sequence DNA   map the genome

kernel size gene
kernel color gene
kernel texture gene
drought tolerance gene

A·T·C·G·T·A

The History of Genomics

In 1972, molecular biologist Walter Fiers and his research team at the University of Ghent in Belgium completed the first sequence of an individual gene in an RNA virus. In 1976, Fiers and his team sequenced the complete genome of the same virus. A year later in 1977, Frederick Sanger in the United Kingdom and Allan Maxam and Walter Gilbert in the United States independently developed sequencing methods that allowed scientists to sequence longer stretches of DNA or RNA. In 1977, Sanger published the first complete sequence of a DNA viral genome. Although the genome of a virus is very small compared to those in such organisms as plants and animals, these were major accomplishments.

TIMELINE OF SELECTED DNA GENOME SEQUENCING PROJECTS

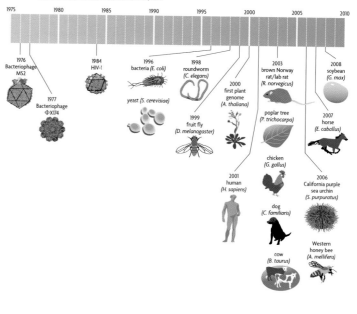

As time progressed, scientists developed faster and cheaper technology for sequencing genomes. This allowed them to map and sequence the genomes of a wide range of viruses and organisms. On the previous page is a timeline of the completion of major genome sequencing projects. As more and more genomes were sequenced, the amount of information available for new directions in research increased rapidly. Scientists can now search for the location of genes within a genome, explore how genes work together, and compare genomes both within a population of organisms and between species.

The Human Genome Project

A monumental achievement was the sequencing of the human genome. In 1990, the United States Department of Energy and the National Institutes of Health co-sponsored the international Human Genome Project, with partner countries including the United Kingdom, Japan, France, and Germany. As stated on the project's website, the goals of the project were to

- *identify* all the approximately 20,000–25,000 genes in human DNA.
- *determine* the sequences of the 3 billion chemical base pairs that make up human DNA.
- *store* this information in databases.
- *improve* tools for data analysis.
- *transfer* related technologies to the private sector.
- *address* the ethical, legal, and social issues that may arise from the project.

It took 14 years of data collection and analysis to determine the human genome sequence. In 2000, the first rough draft of the human genome was published. Overall, the project determined basic information about the human genome, as shown in the box below. Before the completion of the Human Genome Project, it often took researchers years to identify genes associated with a disease or phenotype. With the information made available by the Human Genome Project, this can now be done much more rapidly.

Findings from the Human Genome Project

- The human genome contains 3.2 billion nucleotide base pairs.
- The total number of genes in the human genome is 20,000–25,000. This is much lower than numbers predicted previously, which estimated 80,000–100,000 human genes.
- Genome sequences are 99.9% the same from one person to the next.
- Only 2% of DNA codes for the synthesis of proteins.

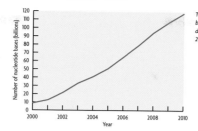

The number of nucleotide bases sequenced increased dramatically between 2000 and 2010.

The Human Genome Project was historic in many ways. It was the first major global project in which all results were made public. The entire human genome sequence was released in an online database. Researchers developed ways to catalog the vast amounts of data so that it could be easily used in future research projects. In addition, committees of scientists, ethicists, attorneys, and policy makers worked together to write guidelines for the use of human genetic data.

The techniques and information developed through the Human Genome Project have inspired a host of new projects that explored the connection between an organism's genome and its phenotype. One was the HapMap project that compared the DNA sequences of people from around the world. HapMap scientists collected DNA samples from populations having Asian, African, or European ancestry. They sequenced specific regions of each person's genome and entered the information into a database freely available to all researchers. With these data scientists are studying the similarities and differences between the populations sampled. From this information, they hope to study human variation and determine which specific gene sequences in human populations contribute to diseases.

Genomics and Sustainability

Since its first applications in the 1970s, genomic technology has advanced rapidly. Scientists have devised ever better equipment and methods for sequencing the genomes of most major model research organisms, and they continue to sequence and map more genomes each year. Genomics data are now freely available to researchers worldwide.

Advances in genomic technology have led to investigations beyond medical applications in a wide range of areas, such as alternative energy sources, ecosystem biodiversity, and evolution. Sample projects include:

- **ALTERNATIVE ENERGY:** Scientists have sequenced the genomes of bacteria found in termite digestive tracts. These bacteria break down the cellulose in the wood that termites ingest. From this information scientists hope to find ways to easily break down cellulose to produce ethanol for biofuel.

FOLLOW-UP

3 Starting with students' responses to Analysis Question 5, discuss with the class the ethical and social issues that are associated with the collection of human genomic data. Students' ideas will likely differ as to whether they would like to have access to their own genetic profile. Some may reason that the more you know, the better informed you will be about your own health. Others may reason that knowledge of this information might be troublesome, and, therefore, they would rather not have their genome sequenced. For example, the information could be alarming or it may not be useful if there are no actions that can be taken to reduce the risks associated with developing a genetic condition.

This is also a good opportunity to discuss with students the issues of who is doing genetic research and how it might be used. For example, while there was a great deal of collaboration between governments, nonprofit and academic institutions, and industrial institutions on the Human Genome Project, much of the genetic modification research on crops, such as Bt corn, has been performed by the companies that sell the corn for profit.

• **ECOSYSTEM BIODIVERSITY:** A team of scientists circumnavigated the world by sea, taking ocean water samples every 200 miles. They sequenced the DNA found in each sample to construct a genomic profile of each sample and chart the biodiversity and dynamics of the ecosystems of the world's oceans. Similar investigations of the genomic profiles of organisms in terrestrial and other aquatic ecosystems worldwide are also under way.

• **EVOLUTION:** Scientists continually add new material to the database of genomes from living and extinct species. With that information they can compare species and organisms of the same species to investigate evolutionary relationships. This is called comparative genomics.

• **HUMAN HEALTH:** The Human Genome Project so far has identified and sequenced the genes for such diseases as cystic fibrosis, types of blindness and deafness, and certain cancers. This information helps identify individuals' risk for a disease and could help develop therapies and cures for various conditions.

Genomics may help scientists understand the evolution of species, such as these two Hawaiian honeycreepers.

341

SAMPLE RESPONSES

1. Genomics is the sequencing, mapping, and analysis of the genetic material of an organism.

2. Technological advances since the mid-1970s have made the sequencing of genomes faster and cheaper, so that today much more is known. Today, a great deal of genomic data is available to researchers through online databases.

3. The Human Genome Project was an international collaboration that sequenced and mapped the entire human genome. Those who contributed to it helped determine basic information about the human genome, such as the number of base pairs in the genome (3 billion) and an estimate of the number of genes in the human genome (20,000–25,000).

4. Genomic research provides the nucleotide sequence and a map of where genes are located within an organism's genome. This is the first step toward understanding how a genome influences an organism's phenotype.

5. Scientists have used genomics to research human disease, alternative energy sources, ecosystem biodiversity, and evolutionary relationships.

REVISIT THE CHALLENGE

Emphasize that the field of genomics has provided a large body of data about the genomes of humans and other species. These include a complete sequence and map of the human genome, and some comparative studies. This field has begun to provide information about human health and genetic diseases, and about sustainability issues, such as ecosystem diversity. Stress that there is, however, still a great deal more work to be done for us to understand how a genome works. In particular, make sure students understand the importance of environmental influence on phenotype, and that mapping genomes is only the beginning of determining how genes and the environment influence phenotype.

The Future of Genomics

The Human Genome Project is complete, but our understanding of how genes are read, how they interact, how they are influenced by environmental factors, and how they produce both normal human traits and disease is far from complete. Many years of additional work and international collaboration are needed to understand the human genome.

Mapping genomes and understanding the role of genetic information in all realms of life presents astounding possibilities. This information combined with extensive further research about the interaction of genes with the environment, may lead to a much more sophisticated understanding about how phenotypes arise. For example, scientists might apply this research to answer questions that may contribute to sustainable solutions for societal problems, such as

- How does a cancer patient's genome affect which anti-cancer drugs are most likely to be effective in that patient?

- How can understanding genetic risk factors for disease lead to more effective methods of disease prevention and treatment?

- How can microbes be engineered to help clean up toxic wastes?

Analysis

1. What is genomics?

2. How has the field of genomics developed over the past 40 years?

3. Describe the Human Genome Project and its major accomplishments.

4. How can genomic research help scientists understand the mechanisms of heredity?

3 5. What types of sustainability challenges have scientists researched using genomics?

KEY VOCABULARY	
DNA	**genomics**
gene	nucleotide
genome	

Three-level Reading Guide: Genomics

1. Check the statements below that you believe say what the reading says. Sometimes the exact wording from the reading is used. At other times, other words may communicate the same meaning as the words in the text.

   __X__ a. Genomics is the field that studies the sequence of the genetic information and location of specific genes in an organism.

   _____ b. The first genome sequenced was from a plant.

   The first genome was sequenced from a bacteriophage.

   __X__ c. Scientists from the around the world worked together to complete the Human Genome Project.

2. Check the statements below that you believe represent the intended meaning of the reading.

   _____ a. Since the first genome was read in the 1970s, it has become more costly to map and sequence a genome.

   It has become less costly as techniques have improved.

   __X__ b. Each year the volume of genomic information available online increases.

   __X__ c. The genomes from two people are more similar than they are different.

   _____ d. Complex organisms have larger genomes than simpler organisms.

   The size of a genome does not necessarily correlate to complexity of the organism.

   __X__ e. There is still a lot left to learn about how genomes function.

3. Check the statements below that you agree with, and be ready to support your agreement or disagreement with ideas from the reading and from your own knowledge and ideas.

   _____ a. Genomics will provide answers to sustainability challenges.

   Those who agree with this statement may cite the projects discussed in the reading, which are working toward solving sustainability challenges, such as the production of biofuel and understanding the biodiversity of the world's oceans. Those who do not agree with this statement may cite alternative solutions to those challenges that do not involve genomics or genetic research, for example alternative modes of producing fuels or other methods of tracking biodiversity.

   _____ b. The Human Genome Project will aid in the study of human disease.

   Those who agree with this statement may cite the accomplishments of the Human Genome Project that have assisted the study of human disease, including the identification of genes that cause certain human diseases, the creation of an online genome database to assist future research, and the worldwide collaboration of scientists to achieve project goals. Those who do not agree may explain that the information from the project in itself does not treat or cure any of the diseases, and therefore, while important, has not revolutionized this field.

(continued on next page)

Three-level Reading Guide: Genomics (continued)

_____ c. There are many benefits to individuals having their genomes sequenced.

Those who agree with this statement may say that sequencing someone's genome allows for the identification of genetic diseases or other health risks, such as increased cancer risk. Those who do not agree may say that determining that an individual has the genes for a disease does not cure or treat the disease and that because individuals cannot change their genes, there is little benefit to having their genome sequenced.

12 DNA Replication

INVESTIGATION • 1–2 CLASS SESSIONS

OVERVIEW

Students observe simulations of three hypothetical modes of DNA replication. They compare these to the results of Matthew Meselson and Franklin Stahl's 1950 DNA replication experiment on those hypotheses and determine which kind of replication is supported by the results.

KEY CONTENT

1. In all organisms, the coded instructions for specifying the characteristics of the organism are carried in DNA, a molecule formed from a sequence of nucleotide subunits.

2. The nucleotide subunits found in DNA are adenine, guanine, cytosine, and thymine, represented as A, G, C, and T.

3. The chemical and structural properties of DNA are the basis for how the genetic information that determines heredity is both encoded in genes (as a string of molecular "bases") and replicated by means of a semiconservative template mechanism.

KEY PROCESS SKILLS

1. Students predict the outcome of an experiment.

2. Students interpret data.

3. Students develop conclusions (claims) based on evidence and reasoning.

4. Students recognize and analyze alternative explanations and models.

5. Students express and defend a scientific argument.

MATERIALS AND ADVANCE PREPARATION

For the teacher
Student Sheet 12.1, "Investigating DNA Replication"
Scoring Guide: UNDERSTANDING CONCEPTS (UC)
computer with Internet access* (optional)

For each pair of students
DNA model set containing:

    plastic bag*

36 black deoxyribose sugars*

36 white phosphate tubes*

    orange, yellow, blue, and green nitrogenous base tubes*

18 white hydrogen bond rods*

computer with Internet access*

For each student
Student Sheet 12.1, "Investigating DNA Replication" (available online only: see note below)

Scoring Guide: UNDERSTANDING CONCEPTS (UC) (optional)
Not supplied in kit

Masters for Scoring Guides are in Teacher Resources IV: Assessment.

Note: *This activity is written to use the SEPUP DNA modeling kit. To use a different kit, adjust the instructions as appropriate.*

Note: *Student Sheet 12.1, "Investigating DNA Replication," is found only on the* Science and Global Issues *website (sepuplhs.org/sgi) in the teacher's section. Sample student answers are also on the website. Arrange for computers with Internet access for the day(s) students do this activity. Go to the* Science and Global Issues *page of the SEPUP website to access the simulation. You may want to bookmark this site for students. Make sure the browsers and software are current and can properly run the simulation.*

TEACHING SUMMARY

Getting Started

- Students propose a model of DNA replication.

Doing the Activity

- Students explore three DNA replication hypotheses.

Follow-up

- (UC ASSESSMENT) Students analyze Meselson and Stahl's experimental results and discuss which hypothesis the evidence supports.

- The class reviews the mechanism of DNA replication.

GETTING STARTED

1 Return to the DNA model set from Activity 10, "Modeling DNA Structure." Bring out the model you built to demonstrate the double-helix shape of DNA, and ask students to suggest how the DNA could be copied, given that each time a cell divides an exact copy of the cell's DNA is produced. Provide time for students to discuss their ideas with their partners, and then ask for volunteers to share their ideas with the class.

◆ This is an opportunity to explore students' ideas about the mechanism of DNA replication. Record a list of students' ideas on the chalkboard or on an overhead transparency. You will revisit these at the end of the activity when students have learned more about semiconservative replication.

---

12 DNA Replication

1 IN ACTIVITY 10, "Modeling DNA Structure," you learned about the work of Watson, Crick, Wilkins, and Franklin that led to the discovery of the structure of DNA (deoxyribonucleic acid). Based on their proposed structure of DNA, Watson and Crick also hypothesized how DNA is replicated. **Replication** is the process by which DNA is copied within each cell. Without replication, cells would not be able to make and then pass on to daughter cells copies of chromosomes and the genes they carry.

In the late 1950s, several hypotheses that described DNA replication had been proposed. To test these hypotheses, two American scientists, Matthew Meselson and Franklin Stahl, performed an experiment with the bacteria *E. coli.*

In this activity you will read about the three hypotheses that Meselson and Stahl tested, weigh the evidence that they gathered from their experiments, and decide which DNA replication hypothesis their results support.

Challenge

▶ How does DNA replicate?

MATERIALS

FOR EACH PAIR OF STUDENTS
bag containing DNA model kit pieces
   36 black deoxyribose sugars pentagons
   36 white phosphate tubes
         various orange, yellow, blue, and green nitrogenous base tubes
   18 white hydrogen bond rods
access to online simulation, "DNA Replication"

FOR EACH STUDENT
Student Sheet 12.1, "Investigating DNA Replication"

343

DOING THE ACTIVITY

2 Pass out a DNA model set to each pair of students. This is an opportunity to review information learned in Activity 10, "Modeling DNA Structure," and to reinforce students' understanding of the structure of DNA. Review base pairing rules as necessary.

3 Sample student results for Student Sheet 12.1, "Investigating DNA Replication," are on the *Science in Global Issues* page of the SEPUP website *(sepuplhs.org/sgi)*. Once groups have had a chance to discuss their ideas and come to a conclusion, ask, *Which proposed mechanism of replication is supported by Meselson and Stahl's experimental results? How do your results on Student Sheet 12.1, "Investigating DNA Replication," support this?*

Ask students to talk about the evidence from the results that supports the mechanism of semiconservative replication. Refer to the sample student results to help guide the students through this discussion.

Links to more information on the Meselson–Stahl experiment are on the *Science in Global Issues* page of the SEPUP website *(sepuplhs.org/sgi)*.

Procedure

1. With your group, read the description and examine the images of each of the three possible hypotheses for DNA replication below. Discuss the differences between the three hypotheses, and in your science notebook summarize the result of replication according to each hypothesis.

Hypothesis 1: Conservative DNA Replication

The original DNA strand "unzips" down the center. Individual nucleotides link together to make a copy of each strand. The new strands unbind from the original strands, allowing the original strands to bind back together.

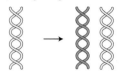

original DNA double helix   conservative DNA replication

Hypothesis 2: Semi-conservative DNA Replication

The original DNA strand "unzips" down the center. Individual nucleotides link together to make a copy of each strand. The DNA formed contains one old and one new strand.

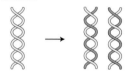

original DNA double helix   semi-conservative DNA replication

Hypothesis 3: Dispersive DNA Replication

The original DNA strand "unzips" down the center. Individual nucleotides link together to make a copy of the original strand. The original pieces and the new pieces join in random combinations.

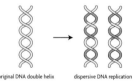

original DNA double helix   dispersive DNA replication

344

FOLLOW-UP

4 Return to the list of students' ideas generated in Teaching Step 1 about the mechanism of replication, and revise the list with the class to reflect what they have learned. Explain that based on the structure of DNA, Watson and Crick had proposed a mechanism similar to the one shown by Meselson and Stahl. Although this seemed like the most plausible mechanism, it was not considered proven until Meselson and Stahl provided experimental data to support it.

✓ Analysis Question 1 is a Quick Check opportunity to check students' current understanding of semiconservative replication.

SAMPLE RESPONSES

1. DNA replication occurs when a strand of DNA is unzipped down the middle between its hydrogen bonds. When the double-stranded DNA is unzipped, each side serves as a template, and free nucleotides bind to each of the single strands. Two double strands of DNA are made, each containing the same nucleotide sequence. Each is composed of one original strand and one new strand.

2. Alternate hypotheses give scientists a framework for designing their experiments. They can try to design an experiment that will provide clear evidence about which hypothesis is correct.

3. Students' answers will vary, based on the initial class brainstorming and their understanding of replication when they began this activity. Their answers should reflect a more detailed understanding of DNA replication.

---

2 2. With your group, construct a DNA model to show the result of replication described by each of the three hypotheses. Start by assembling a double-stranded sequence of DNA that is three nucleotides long and contains the nucleotide sequence ATG on one of its strands.

   Note: Refer to Activity 10, "Modeling DNA Structure," if you need help assembling the DNA.

3. With your group decide which of the three proposed replication methods you think is correct. Record your choice and the reasoning for it in your science notebook.

3 4. Find the "Replicating DNA" simulation on the *Science and Global Issues* page of the SEPUP website *(sepuplhs.org/sgi)*. With your partner, complete the simulation, referring to Student Sheet 12.1, "Investigating DNA Replication," to guide you.

4 *Analysis*

1. Describe how DNA replicates.

2. How does identifying alternate hypotheses help scientists design and analyze experiments?

3. Return to the list of ideas your class generated at the beginning of this activity to explain ways DNA might replicate. How did your ideas change?

KEY VOCABULARY	
DNA	**replication**
nucleotide	

345

REVISIT THE CHALLENGE

Students should be able to explain the basic mechanism of DNA replication and that it is semiconservative. Additionally, students should be able to provide a basic explanation of the evidence and line of reasoning Meselson and Stahl used to support the hypothesis of semi-conservative DNA replication.

13 Meiosis and Sexual Reproduction

MODELING • 1 CLASS SESSION

OVERVIEW

Students follow an online computer simulation to investigate how chromosomes divide during meiosis. They learn about crossing over and how it increases the variability of possible gametes produced by a parent. They also apply what they have learned about meiosis to establishing the probability that an inserted gene is passed from parent to daughter cell through meiosis.

KEY CONTENT

1. Most of the cells in an organism are diploid: they contain two copies (a pair) of each kind of chromosome.

2. Gametes are formed through meiosis, which creates four haploid sex cells, each containing only one copy of each kind of chromosome.

KEY PROCESS SKILLS

1. Students make predictions.

2. Students develop conclusions based on evidence.

MATERIALS AND ADVANCE PREPARATION

For the teacher
transparency of Student Sheet 2.3, "Genetics Case Study Comparison," from Activity 2

For each pair of students
set of two pop-bead chromosome models:

    16 blue pop beads

    16 green pop beads

     2 orange pop beads

     2 blue centromeres

     2 green centromeres

colored pencils (blue, green, orange)*

computer with Internet access*

For each student
Student Sheet 13.1. "Meiosis"
(available online only: see note below)

Student Sheet 13.2, "Mitosis and Meiosis Comparison"

Student Sheet 2.3, "Genetics Case Study Comparison," from Activity 2

Not supplied in kit

If microscope slides of meiosis or mitosis are available (e.g., onion root tip, grasshopper testes, etc.), you may want to set them up for students to view during this activity.

Note: *Student Sheet 13.1, "Meiosis," is found only on the* Science and Global Issues *website* (sepuplhs.org/sgi). *Sample student answers are also available on the website. Both are located in the teacher's section. Arrange for computers with Internet access for the day(s) students do this activity. Go to the* Science and Global Issues *page of the SEPUP website to access the simulation. You may want to bookmark this site for students. Make sure the browsers and supporting software are current and can properly run the simulation.*

TEACHING SUMMARY

Getting Started

• Introduce questions about the location of genes in gametes.

Doing the Activity

• Students view simulations, sketch the phases of meiosis, and model the behavior of chromosomes during meiosis.

Follow-up

• The class discusses the relationship between the behavior of chromosomes and patterns of inheritance.

• (LITERACY) Student read a case study about genetically modified fish.

BACKGROUND INFORMATION

Using microscopes scientists identified the physical processes of mitosis and meiosis in 1875 and the 1890s, respectively. At the time, the importance of these cellular activities to heredity was not apparent. In the early 1900s, scientists noticed that chromosomes seemed to behave similarly to the units of heredity (what we now know as genes) studied by Mendel. They could see the presence of pairs of chromosomes in diploid cells, the halving of the normal number of chromosomes during the formation of gametes by meiosis, and the restoration of chromosome pairs during fertilization. From these observations, they inferred that chromosomes carried the hereditary material.

Soon after that Thomas Hunt Morgan, an American embryologist, confirmed this hypothesis when he identified the chromosomal location of particular traits in the fruit fly, Drosophila. He also established the existence of linkage groups—traits that do not show independent assortment because they are linked on the same chromosome. On top of all that he proposed crossing over was the mechanism for the recombination sometimes observed among genes on the same chromosome. One of his students tracked the frequency of crossovers in order to create linkage maps, which gave information about the locations and distances between genes on the same chromosome.

Because the frequency of crossovers varies in different regions of a chromosome, linkage maps of chromosomes give only approximate locations of genes. With today's equipment and techniques scientists now create accurate maps of chromosomes by tagging specific genes and determining their exact locations on the chromosomes.

REFERENCES

The Center for Food Safety. Transgenic fish. Retrieved April 2010 from http://www.centerforfoodsafety.org/pubs/transgenic%20fish%20fact%20sheet.pdf.

Reichhardt, T. (2000). Will souped-up salmon sink or swim? *Nature 406*(6791) 10–12.

GETTING STARTED

1 Explain to students that before the discovery of DNA and genes, scientists knew that hereditary information passed from parents to offspring, and so they assumed this information was present in eggs and sperm. However, they did not know where this information was located in those cells. Today it is common knowledge that the location of genes is in the DNA on the chromosomes of all cells, including eggs and sperm. In eukaryotes, the DNA is in the nucleus of the cell. Determining that genes were located on chromosomes helped scientists begin to understand how genes are inherited during sexual reproduction. In this activity students investigate how genes are inherited. If the students have not completed the "Cell Biology: World Health" unit of *Science and Global Issues,* you may want to briefly review cell differentiation with them before they begin the Procedure.

2 Review the photographs with the students. Point out that some of the cells have nuclei, but in others the nuclei have broken down and the cells are undergoing division. Have them look for the darkened thread-like structures near the centers of the cells. Point out that scientists realized that these structures appeared when nuclei broke down and cells began to divide. Also, those structures seemed to be divided evenly between newly forming cells. The scientists named the darkly stained structures that appeared just before and during cell division chromosomes, which means "colored bodies." Explain that scientists also noticed that when gametes, or sex cells

---

13 Meiosis and Sexual Reproduction

1 **A**s **YOU LEARNED** in Activity 5, "Genes and Traits," Gregor Mendel explained the results of his pea plant crosses by saying that each parent contributed a unit of information to each offspring. These units of information came to be known as genes. Mendel knew that the genes had to be in the male and female sex cells—the sperm (or pollen) and the egg. For the next 50 years, scientists did not know where in the cell the genes were located, but they continued to breed improved crops and livestock.

As microscope technology improved, scientists discovered small dark structures in cells that they named chromosomes. As scientists watched the behavior of chromosomes during the formation of sex cells, or gametes, they made a significant observation: in the sex cells the number of these chromosomes was reduced to half the normal number in other cells. They realized that the chromosomes must carry the genes. The process that results in this halving of the chromosome number is called meiosis. **Meiosis** is the process of cell division that occurs in developing sex cells. In human males, meiosis occurs in those cells that differentiate into sperm in the testes. In human females, meiosis occurs in the cells that differentiate into eggs in the ovaries. It is only after egg and sperm are joined at fertilization that the full number of chromosomes the new offspring needs is restored.

2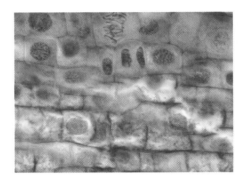

Onion root tips undergo mitosis to make new cells. The new daughter cells are identical to the parent cell.

346

(egg and sperm cells), formed the cells went through two divisions so that the number of chromosomes in the resulting four gametes became half the normal number. This suggested that the chromosomes carried the genes, because the scientists expected that each organism inherited half of its genes from each parent. Scientists named the process that results in half the normal number of chromosomes in gametes meiosis.

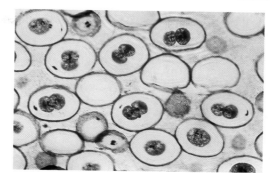

These Ascaris (roundworm) cells are undergoing meiosis. This produces gametes (sex cells) with half the number of chromosomes of the parent cells.

Challenge

▶ How do chromosomes divide during the formation of egg and sperm cells?

MATERIALS

FOR EACH PAIR OF STUDENTS

　　 set of 2 pop-bead chromosome models
16　blue pop beads
16　green pop beads
　2　orange pop beads
　2　blue centromeres
　2　green centromeres
　　 colored pencils
　　 access to online meiosis simulations

FOR EACH STUDENT

　　 Student Sheet 13.1, "Meiosis"
　　 Student Sheet 13.2, "Mitosis and Meiosis Comparison"
　3　sticky notes
　　 Student Sheet 2.3, "Genetics Case Study Comparison," from Activity 2

347

DOING THE ACTIVITY

3 The names of the different phases of meiosis are introduced in the simulations, but are not listed as key vocabulary that all students must know. You may wish to stress these terms if they are important in your local or state standards. They will be discussed again in Activity 14, "Genes and Chromosomes." Sample answers to Student Sheets 13.1, "Meiosis," and 13.2, "Mitosis and Meiosis Comparison," are on the *Science and Global Issues* page of the SEPUP website (*sepuplhs.org/sgi*).

4 Support students in understanding that the inserted gene, present in one of the parental chromosomes, will end up in two of the four gametes produced through meiosis. As they work, listen for, and encourage students to use the words DNA, chromosome, parent cell, daughter cell, and gene.

5 ✓ You may use students' responses to Procedure Step 11 for a Quick Check to monitor their understanding of mitosis and meiosis. As students describe what they see, they may struggle to come up with the best words to use. If so, you might introduce the terms chromatid, bivalent chromosome, and homolog. The initial and replicated parts of a doubled chromosome are called chromatids, and the doubled chromosome before it splits is called a bivalent chromosome. The two chromatids of a recently replicated chromosome are joined by the centromere. The replicated chromosomes then line up so that each is opposite to its similar (homologous) chromosome, or homolog.

Procedure

Part A: Modeling Meiosis

1. Observe the meiosis simulation on the *Science and Global Issues* page of the SEPUP website *(sepuplhs.org/sgi)*. Determine what happens to the genetic material of the cell at each phase.

2. On Student Sheet 13.1, "Meiosis," draw what happens to the chromosomes during each phase shown.

3 3. In your science notebook, write a description summarizing the key events of each stage of meiosis.

4. With your partner, use the pop beads to model chromosomes and show what happens when a cell with two chromosomes—one pair—undergoes meiosis. To do this:

   a. Make two strands of four blue pop beads and attach them to the blue centromere. Repeat this process for green. This represents one pair of chromosomes.

   b. Simulate the replication of each chromosome during prophase I. To do this, repeat Step 4a. Use the centromeres to form the shape of the replicated chromosome shown below. Note that the X shape is a replicated chromosome, and so the model demonstrates one pair of replicated chromosomes, with a total of four sister chromatids.

5. **Crossing over** is a phenomenon that might happen, but only during prophase in meiosis I. During crossing over, homologous chromosomes exchange portions, as shown below. With the pop-bead model demonstrate crossing over between the replicated chromosomes you built in Step 4b. In your science notebook, describe crossing over.

maternal paternal

homologous chromosomes paired during prophase I of mesiosis I

crossing over

6. Move the chromosome models through each remaining phase of meiosis to show what occurs as they move through prophase, metaphase, anaphase, and telophase of meiosis I and II, and the cells that result. In your science notebook, use colored pencils to sketch the chromosomes at each stage.

In the simulation, the similarities between the two homologs are shown by their similar sizes and shapes, and in some cases by colors, such as different shades of blue. These represent the fact that while these homologs have the same genes, they are likely to have different alleles for at least some of these genes. Be sure students understand that one member of each pair in a cell that is dividing came from the maternal parent, and another from the paternal parent. Point out that the way in which the chromosomes line up, and which goes in each direction, is random. In Activity 14, "Genes and Chromosomes," students will learn that this independence of different chromosome pairs leads to independent segregation of the chromosomes.

6 After they finish the reading students should record its key information on Student Sheet 2.3, "Genetics Case Study Comparison." A sample summary is provided below. Project a transparency of Student Sheet 2.3, and discuss students' summaries.

4

7. Repeat Steps 4–6 with the following modification:

    Model a chromosome in a cell that has been genetically modified to contain a new gene. Take an orange pop bead, and switch out one segment of one chromosome. With your partner work with your pop-bead model chromosomes and your understanding of meiosis to determine:

    • What is the probability that a daughter cell will receive a gene that was inserted into one chromosome in a parent cell?

    In your discussion, incorporate the terms that follow:

    DNA   daughter cell
    chromosome   gene
    parent cell

8. Share your model and your reasoning from Step 7 with the other pair in your group. Discuss any differences in your ideas.

9. In your science notebook, write an answer to the question posed in Step 7. Incorporate each of the terms from the list above in your writing.

10. Return to the computer simulation on the *Science and Global Issues* page of the SEPUP website *(sepuplhs.org/sgi)*. Proceed to the page comparing mitosis and meiosis, and complete the simulation.

5

11. In your science notebook, write a description summarizing the similarities and differences between mitosis and meiosis.

Part B: Fast-growing Salmon Case Study

12. Individually read the case study on the following pages. As you read, use the literacy strategy, "Read, Think, and Take Note." To do this:

    • Stop at least three times during the reading to mark on a sticky note your thoughts or questions about the reading.

    • After writing a thought or question on a sticky note, place it next to the passage in the reading that prompted your note.

13. Share your thinking with your group. Place your sticky notes on the table in front of you. Look for connections between your notes and those of others in your group.

    Hint: Were there common questions people asked? Were people unfamiliar with the same words? Did people react differently to statements in the reading?

14. Place your sticky notes in your science notebook. Below them write a short summary of what your group discussed and any conclusions your group came to.

6

15. Record the appropriate information from this case study on Student Sheet 2.3, "Genetics Case Study Comparison."

Sample Case Study Summary for Student Sheet 2.3, "Genetics Case Study Comparison"

Case Study	Type of genetic modification	Benefits	Risks and concerns	Research/stage of development	Other Solutions?
Fast-growing salmon	Gene for growth hormone from one species of salmon inserted into another species of salmon	Fish grow faster, leading to more supply for consumers, and more profits from selling the fish.	The impact of GM fish on wild populations is unknown and may harm wild populations.	Still studying possible effects on wild salmon population	Farm non-GM salmon Prevent escapes Make sterilization 100% effective

CASE STUDY

Fast-growing Salmon

THE AQUACULTURE INDUSTRY has long been on the lookout for ways to grow fish faster while spending less money. Industry leaders hope to meet the increasing demand for fish, increase profits, and reduce the environmental impact of fishing. In recent years they have teamed up with genetic scientists to find ways to speed up fishes' growth rates. Geneticists are currently researching methods to genetically modify a number of farmed fish species, including members of the salmonid family (salmon and trout) and other commercially important species like catfish and tilapia.

One promising idea involves inserting a growth-hormone gene from the Pacific chinook salmon *(Oncorhynchus tshawytscha)* into the Atlantic salmon *(Salmo salar)*. Like humans, salmon produce a growth hormone that signals their bodies to grow. Normally the fish grow at a certain rate, depending on environmental conditions, including food availability. If the genetic modification works as intended, the growth rate of the genetically modified fish should increase so that they grow large enough to be sold four times faster than unmodified salmon. Geneticists have succeeded in producing this genetically modified salmon, but, along with success, there has been controversy.

One concern about genetically modified salmon is that if they escape from their net pens, they could breed with wild salmon and make those salmon less fit. Wild female salmon are most likely to mate with larger males. Studies have shown that in some fish species females mate more frequently with the genetically modified males. Studies of genetically modified fish have also shown that in some species genetically modified males breed offspring that do not survive as well in the wild and are

A gene from the Pacific Chinook salmon, above, has been inserted into the Atlantic salmon, right, to make them grow much faster than unmodified salmon.

MEIOSIS AND SEXUAL REPRODUCTION • ACTIVITY 13

more likely to be eaten by predators. This also prevents the unmodified, wild males from having as many mating opportunities, which depletes the wild populations of fish.

A group of scientists at Purdue University in Indiana created a computer model to examine what would happen if 60 genetically modified fish were released into a population of 60,000 wild fish. They used a species of fish called medaka. The computer model predicted that if the genetically modified medaka and wild medaka successfully reproduced, within 30 generations the wild fish would be extinct. One option to prevent genetically modified fish from disrupting wild populations is to make them sterile. Salmon eggs

may be treated just after fertilization so that they grow into sterile adult fish, but this technique is not always 100% effective.

Another concern is how much genetically modified salmon eat. Some studies show that they eat the same amount as wild salmon, and therefore would not out-eat the wild fish if they escaped. Other studies, however, have shown that genetically modified salmon eat up to three times as much as the wild fish.

Researchers continue to investigate the possible damage genetically modified salmon might do to wild populations, and how to prevent these kinds of problems. As of 2009, genetically modified salmon have not been approved for commercial sale in the United States. ■

Net pens for growing farmed salmon are often built along the migration routes of wild salmon, which poses a problem if the farmed salmon escape.

351

FOLLOW-UP

7 Students may need support answering this question. You may want to point out that the second round of meiosis resembles mitosis, but with only half the number of chromosomes. Remind them that in meiosis II, each replicated chromosome splits, with one side going to each daughter cell.

SAMPLE RESPONSES

1. The daughter cells contain half of the number of chromosomes of the parent cell.

2. Students' answers should show four different cells that contain PS, Ps, pS, and ps as shown below right.

3. Crossing over, which occurs during prophase I, happens when parts of chromosomes are exchanged between homologous chromosomes. This results in new combinations of genes on the chromosomes that swapped pieces. Crossing over does not always occur. It increases the possibility of new gene combinations forming.

4. Approximately half of the offspring would have the genetic modification, because meiosis creates gametes with only one set of chromosomes, and only the gametes that contained the modified chromosome would be genetically modified.

REVISIT THE CHALLENGE

Students should be able to explain meiosis, including specific details about meiosis I and II. They should also be able to explain how mitosis and meiosis differ and apply what they have learned to describe how specific traits, such as genetically modified traits, are passed from parent to offspring. It is also important that you review with students the difference between DNA replication, which they learned about in the previous activity, and mitosis and meiosis.

Analysis

1. How do the daughter cells that result from meiosis compare to the parent cell?

2. Draw meiosis I and II, starting with the parent cell shown below. What possible allele combinations could form in gametes produced from these cells?

7 3. Explain how crossing over can affect the genetic makeup of the gametes an organism produces.

4. A salmon is genetically modified in a laboratory by inserting one gene into one chromosome of a pair. The salmon escapes, and breeds with a wild, unmodified salmon. Would you expect all of the offspring to be genetically modified? Explain your reasoning.

KEY VOCABULARY	
chromosome	gene
crossing over	**meiosis**
daughter cell	mitosis
DNA	parent cell
gametes	

Sample Student Response to Analysis Question 2

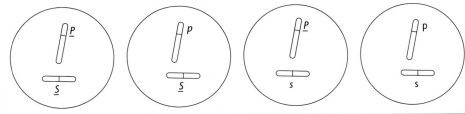

14 Genes and Chromosomes

READING • 1 CLASS SESSION

OVERVIEW

Students read about the role of meiosis and fertilization in maintaining a characteristic number of chromosomes within a species. They also investigate how chromosomal behavior, such as independent segregation and crossing over, explain independent assortment of some traits and linkage of others, and result in human genetic variation. They conclude by investigating nondisjunction and the outcomes of abnormal numbers of certain chromosomes.

KEY CONTENT

1. Gametes—sperm in males and eggs in females—contain half the number of chromosomes found in the somatic cells of the same organism.

2. Fertilization occurs when a sperm and egg unite in sexual reproduction. This produces an offspring with two copies of each chromosome, one from the maternal parent and one from the paternal parent.

3. A karyotype is an image of the stained chromosomes of a cell.

4. The independent segregation of chromosomes during meiosis is the basis for traits that exhibit independent assortment.

5. As a result of independent segregation and crossing over during meiosis, one individual produces an almost limitless variety of gametes.

6. Abnormalities in chromosome number from errors occurring in gamete production often result in loss of viability or abnormal development of affected offspring.

KEY PROCESS SKILLS

1. Students make accurate interpretations, inferences, and conclusions from text.

MATERIALS AND ADVANCE PREPARATION

For the teacher
Scoring Guide: UNDERSTANDING CONCEPTS (UC)

For each student
Student Sheet 14.1, "Three-level Reading Guide: Genes and Chromosomes"

Scoring Guide: UNDERSTANDING CONCEPTS (UC) (optional)

Masters for Scoring Guides are in Teacher Resources IV: Assessment.

TEACHING SUMMARY

Getting Started
• Review the behavior of chromosomes during meiosis and of genes during crosses.

Doing the Activity
• (LITERACY) Students read the text and respond to statements in a Three-level Reading Guide.

Follow-up
• (UC ASSESSMENT) The class reviews concepts introduced in previous activities and now developed more formally in the reading.

GETTING STARTED

1 Review the idea that the traits students investigated in corn and rice follow Mendel's observation when he studied peas: that a number of traits seem to appear independently of each other. In other words, purple smooth corn crossed with yellow wrinkled corn is just as likely to produce purple wrinkled or yellow smooth second generation offspring as it is to produce the parental phenotypes.

DOING THE ACTIVITY

2 Possible responses to the Three-level Reading Guide appear at the end of this activity. Note that the statement under number 3 (applied) does not have a single correct response. Students may interpret information differently and agree or disagree with each statement. Regardless of their perspectives, it is important for students to be able to explain and support their positions. Answers have been provided in the next pages for those statements that do not accurately represent the content in the reading. Note that this strategy is not asking students to discern which of the statements are true or false, as many of them are true. It is asking them to determine which are portrayed in the content of the reading.

---

14 Genes and Chromosomes

1 **A**s you have observed in the previous activities, the behavior of chromosomes in cells helps to explain the behavior of genes that are passed from one generation to the next. Understanding the behavior of chromosomes is also fundamental to learning how inserting genes into an organism might affect the function of the organism's genome.

Challenge

▶ How do genes and chromosomes behave during meiosis and sexual reproduction?

MATERIALS

FOR EACH STUDENT
Student Sheet 14.1, "Three-level Reading Guide: Genes and Chromosomes"

Procedure

2 1. Refer to Student Sheet 14.1, "Three-level Reading Guide: Genes and Chromosomes," to guide you as you complete the following reading.

Humans have 46 chromosomes and the same sequence of genes. Variations in the alleles for same genes, along with environmental factors, cause variation in human phenotypes.

353

Reading

Chromosomes Carry Genes

In each cell of a living organism, DNA carries the genetic information in the sequence of its nitrogen bases. The DNA is wrapped with proteins into structures called chromosomes. A gene is the section of DNA in a chromosome that contains information that influences one or more traits.

The number of chromosomes in each cell of an organism depends on the species. Bacteria, such as *Escherichia coli (E. coli)*, have one circular chromosome that contains about 4,500 genes. In addition, some bacteria also have one or more smaller plasmids that carry a small number of genes. In comparison, a human body cell contains 46 chromosomes, carrying 20,000–25,000 genes. This means that most human chromosomes carry hundreds of genes. Every cell in the human body except for the sex cells contains the same set of 46 chromosomes.

In eukaryotes (organisms with a nucleus in each cell), the chromosomes are present in pairs. Each chromosome in a pair is similar to its partner in size and the genes it carries, except for the chromosome pair that determines the organism's sex. The image at right, called a karyotype, illustrates the 23 pairs of chromosomes in the cell of a human male. Notice that chromosomes in pairs 1–22 are identical in size and shape. The two chromosomes of pair 23 are the sex chromosomes— they determine the individual's sex. In human males, pair 23 has one X chromosome and one Y chromosome. These two chromosomes differ in size and shape. If this were a karyotype for a human female, pair 23 would contain two X chromosomes.

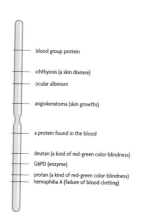

- blood group protein
- ichthyosis (a skin disease)
- ocular albinism
- angiokeratoma (skin growths)
- a protein found in the blood
- deutan (a kind of red-green color-blindness)
- G6PD (enzyme)
- protan (a kind of red-green color-blindness)
- hemophilia A (failure of blood clotting)

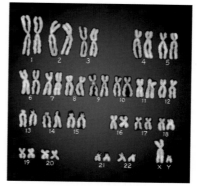

The map of the human X chromosome, top, shows the location of several specific genes and the traits they influence. This male karyotype, above, shows the X chromosome and smaller Y chromosomes present in male cells.

Growth and Reproduction

For organisms to grow and reproduce, cells must divide to form offspring cells, called daughter cells. As you know, during mitosis the chromosomes are divided evenly between the two new cells to produce two daughter cells that are identical to the parent cell. This occurs regularly for cell growth and tissue repair in somatic cells (body cells, but not reproductive cells) in multicellular organisms, such as humans, and in single-celled organisms, such as *E. coli*. In this way, cells in the body of a multicellular organism, except for the sex cells, are exact copies of the parent cell.

How and why are gametes different from the rest of the cells in an organism? The answer lies in the processes of meiosis and sexual reproduction. Sexual reproduction occurs when a male sperm fertilizes a female egg. If these sex cells had a full set of chromosomes, each generation would have twice the number of chromosomes as its parents. Meiosis produces gametes (egg or sperm) that have half as many chromosomes as other cells in the body to prevent this from happening.

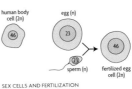

SEX CELLS AND FERTILIZATION

A gamete is **haploid** because it has one set of chromosomes. This is referred to as n chromosomes. Human gametes contain 23 chromosomes (n = 23). A somatic (nonreproductive) cell is **diploid** (has 2n chromosomes) because it has pairs of chromosomes. When a human haploid egg and haploid sperm unite by fertilization, they form a diploid cell with 46 chromosomes (23 pairs). Below is a table showing the number of chromosomes found in several organisms.

Number of Chromosomes in Several Organisms		
ORGANISM	DIPLOID (2n) CHROMOSOMES FOUND IN SOMATIC CELLS	HAPLOID (n) CHROMOSOMES FOUND IN SEX CELLS
Human	46	23
Corn	20	10
Rye plant	14	7
Common fruit fly	8	4
Garden snail	54	27
Gorilla	48	24
Elephant	56	28

Chromosomes and Genes

In the beginning of this unit, you modeled the process of crossing corn plants with such traits as purple or yellow and smooth or wrinkled kernels, which shows independent assortment. When Gregor Mendel was first developing his theories on genetics, he proposed that there is a law of independent assortment. Independent assortment means that it is equally likely for a PpSs corn plant to produce any of four kinds of gametes: PS, Ps, pS, and ps.

Now that scientists have determined that genes are sections of chromosomes, we know that genes on the same chromosome usually stay together during meiosis. These are called "linked genes," and they don't usually show independent assortment. The combination of traits they influence is passed on to the next generation together. For example, in fruit flies the genes for body color and eye color are found on the same chromosome. Therefore, a parent with a grey body and yellow eyes would pass on this combination of genes to its offspring.

In the figure on the next page, "Chromosomes and Meiosis," the red chromosomes represent ones inherited from the female parent, while the blue ones represent those inherited from the male parent. When the chromosomes line up before division, the paternal and maternal chromosomes in the pair line up randomly and separate independently of each other. This is called independent segregation of the chromosomes. Independent segregation of chromosomes explains the behavior of genes that follow Mendel's law of independent assortment. It also accounts for the fact that genes that are linked on the same chromosome don't follow the law of independent assortment, also shown on the next page.

Sexual reproduction and human variation

What happens in meiosis also helps explain why siblings are not identical. In Activity 13, "Meiosis and Sexual Reproduction," you observed the variations in gametes produced by one parent due to both independent segregation and crossing over of chromosomes. New combinations of chromosomes from two different parents produce offspring with a combination of traits from both parents. Notice that the offspring formed by fertilization inherits one set of chromosomes from each parent. This explains why an offspring only inherits one allele for each gene from each parent.

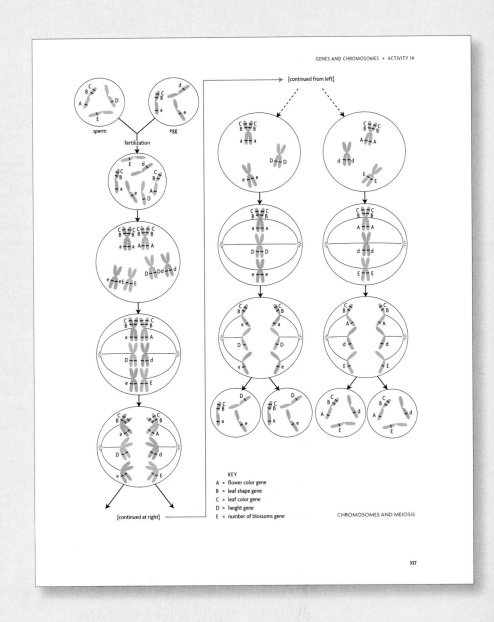

KEY

A = flower color gene
B = leaf shape gene
C = leaf color gene
D = height gene
E = number of blossoms gene

CHROMOSOMES AND MEIOSIS

357

Another source of chromosomal variation in gametes occurs during a process called crossing over. This only happens during meiosis I when chromosomes exchange segments at their ends, as shown in the figure below. Crossing over happens quite frequently and substantially increases the genetic variation of gametes an individual can generate.

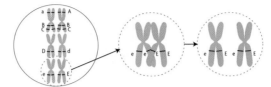

These two chromosomes have exchanged segments of their DNA, through crossing over or a crossover event. Each chromosome now has DNA from both the maternal and paternal parent.

Abnormal meiosis

Meiosis does not always go perfectly. Several human genetic conditions result when errors during meiosis lead to abnormalities in chromosome number, shape, or size. Genetic specialists use karyotypes to test for chromosome abnormalities. To make a karyotype, the white blood cells are separated from a sample of the patient's blood. These cells are placed in a solution with a substance that causes them to divide. Then, another substance is added to stop the cell division in metaphase, when the chromosomes are at their most condensed and easy to see. The cells are then squashed on a microscope slide, stained with a special dye, and photographed. The images of the chromosomes are then arranged in pairs according to size and shape.

One of the most common errors that occurs in meiosis is nondisjunction. **Nondisjunction** is the failure of chromosomes to separate during cell division. If this happens, a gamete can form with an extra chromosome or missing chromosome. Most nondisjunctions result in gametes that either cannot participate in fertilization, or they produce zygotes that do not survive past the initial stages of cell division. In human fertilizations, however, there are instances where chromosomal abnormalities appear in an offspring, as shown in the chart of chromosome-related syndromes on the next page.

FOLLOW-UP

3 Clarify the reading as necessary when students have completed Student Sheet 14.1, "Three-level Reading Guide: Genes and Chromosomes." You may need to further discuss the restoration of the diploid chromosome number when two haploid gametes fuse during fertilization to form a fertilized egg, or zygote. Be sure students understand that the doubled set of chromosomes in a somatic cell includes one of each kind of chromosome from the maternal parent and another set from the paternal parent.

Another point of discussion is the tremendous variety of combinations of traits that can result in gametes, due to independent segregation and crossing over. Without crossing over, an organism with two pairs of chromosomes can produce gametes with four combinations of traits, an organism with three pairs of chromosomes can produce gametes with eight combinations of traits, and a human with 23 pairs of chromosomes can produce gametes with 2^{23} combinations of traits. With crossing over, the number of combination of traits a human can produce becomes much greater.

Lastly, it is important to emphasize that the genes alone do not determine an organism's phenotype. It is the combination of environmental factors and genes that form the traits present in organisms, a process which is still not fully understood. This field, epigenetics, is the subject of much current research. Links to more information on epigenetics are on the *Science and Global Issues* website *(sepuplhs.org/sgi)*.

4 ✓Analysis Question 1 can be scored with the UNDERSTANDING CONCEPTS (UC) Scoring Guide. A sample Level-3 response is shown at right. Analysis Questions 2 and 7 provide a Quick Check opportunity to make sure students understand meiosis and gamete formation.

Chromosome-Related Syndromes

SYNDROME NAME	CHROMOSOMAL ABNORMALITY	COMMON EFFECTS
Down syndrome	Three copies of chromosome 21 (trisomy 21)	Delayed physical and mental development, heart defects
Klinefelter syndrome	Males have extra X chromosome (XXY)	Learning difficulties, sometimes sterility, higher risk for some forms of cancer and heart disease
Prader-Willi syndrome	Missing part of chromosome 15	Reduced muscle tone, short stature, learning difficulties, chronic hunger
Turner syndrome	Females missing all or part of an X chromosome	Short stature, sometimes sterility, sometimes do not enter or complete puberty

The phenotypes produced by these conditions vary. For example, the effects of Down syndrome, one of the most common chromosome abnormalities, are usually mild to moderate, but sometimes severe. Educational interventions and good health care often improve the outlook for affected individuals. Today, most individuals with chromosomal abnormalities live full and productive lives.

Analysis

1. Explain the relationship between genes, chromosomes, and DNA.

2. A species of snail has 24 chromosomes—12 pairs—in each somatic cell. How many chromosomes are there in a snail egg cell? A snail sperm cell?

3. How does the number of chromosomes in gametes of an organism that reproduces sexually differ from the number of chromosomes in its other cells? Explain.

4. Describe how each of the following increases human variation:
   a. Independent segregation of chromosomes during meiosis
   b. Crossing over

5. Define nondisjunction and explain its effect on a sex cell.

359

SAMPLE RESPONSES

1. Students' answers should include a clear description of the relationship between chromosomes, genes, and DNA.

   Level-3 Response
   Each gene is located at a specific place on a chromosome. There are many genes located along each chromosome. Although a chromosome is made of both DNA and proteins, the genes are in the DNA.

2. ✓Each sperm and egg cell will contain 12 chromosomes.

3. The number of chromosomes in gametes is half the number in somatic cells as a result of meiosis. For example, humans have 23 chromosomes in each gamete, but 46 in all somatic cells. This means that when gametes combine during fertilization, the offspring have the normal number of 46 chromosomes.

4. a. Independent segregation of chromosomes allows for exponential variations of gametes because of the number of potential unique combinations of chromosomes.

  b. Crossing over further increases the potential number of unique combinations because it exchanges segments of chromosomes.

5. Nondisjunction occurs when chromosomes do not separate properly during cell division. This can form a gamete with an extra chromosome or one missing part or all of a chromosome.

6. Four gametes are possible in either a male or a female. These are GY, gY, Gy, and gy.

7. ✔ Crossing over could cause alleles that are linked with the color and smoothness genes to be exchanged between the two chromosomes in a pair, resulting in new combinations of alleles.

8. Half of the offspring would have the genetically modified gene for red spots.

SCIENCE & GLOBAL ISSUES/BIOLOGY • GENETICS

6. The chromosomes pictured below are from a fruit fly that is heterozygous for two traits. How many kinds of gametes could form if this were in a male? A female?

7. Consider your answer to Question 6. Explain how crossing over could affect the gametes that result.

8. If the fruit fly from Question 6 also had a gene on that chromosome that was genetically modified to produce red spots on its body, and it mated with a wild fruit fly that was not genetically modified, what would you expect to see in the offspring?

KEY VOCABULARY

chromosome	karyotype
crossing over	law of independent assortment
diploid	meiosis
gamete	mitosis
gene	**nondisjunction**
haploid	somatic cell

REVISIT THE CHALLENGE

Students should be able to explain meiosis and the means by which gametes form with half the normal chromosome number. They should also be able to describe the transmission of chromosomes from parents to offspring and the restoration of diploid chromosome number during fertilization. Students should be able to explain how independent assortment and crossing over lead to human genetic variation. And finally, students should understand that abnormalities in gamete chromosome numbers arising from nondisjunction could have serious effects on the well-being of the offspring.

Three-level Reading Guide: Genes and Chromosomes

1. Check the statements below that you believe say what the reading says. Sometimes exact wording from the reading is used. At other times, other words may communicate the same meaning as the words in the text.

   _X_   a. Sex cells (eggs and sperm) are also called gametes.

   _____   b. Sex cells have twice as many chromosomes as the rest of the cells in your body.
              Sex cells have half as many chromosomes as the rest of the cells in your body.

   _X_   c. Fruit flies have four pairs in each somatic cell. Humans have 23 pairs.

   _X_   d. Human females have two X-chromosomes, while males have one X chromosome and another smaller chromosome, called a Y-chromosome.

   _____   e. Meiosis occurs when two gametes fuse.
              Meiosis occurs when a cell undergoes division to produce four gametes.

2. Check the statements below that you believe represent the intended meaning of the reading.

   _____   a. If a male and female frog each have 26 chromosomes in their somatic cells, their offspring will each have 52 chromosomes
              The offspring would each have 26 chromosomes in their somatic cells.

   _____   b. Alleles on the same chromosome usually show independent assortment in genetic crosses.
              Alleles on the same chromosome are linked and do not sort independently.

   _X_   c. Crossing over increases the varieties of traits in the gametes an organism produces.

3. Check if you agree with the statement below, and be ready to support your choice with ideas from the reading and from your own knowledge and ideas.

   _X_   a. Understanding how traits are passed from one generation to the next can help you predict a child's traits before it is born.

              Students who agree with this statement may say that by knowing parents' traits and the dominant trait, one can predict to a certain degree what a child's traits might be. Students who disagree with this statement are likely to say that this is a prediction based on the genotype of the parents. When fertilization occurs, two gametes create a new combination of chromosomes and the resulting offspring can differ significantly from either parent. Only when the child is born and develops can the traits of the child be determined.

15 Evaluating Genetically Modified Organisms

PROJECT • 4–6 CLASS SESSIONS

OVERVIEW

Each student group researches a genetically modified organism and constructs a poster to inform a decision to allow or prohibit growing or applying a genetically modified organism. The posters present evidence about the development, use, and issues specific to a genetically modified organism that a particular community or region hopes might solve a sustainability challenge. The class conducts an informational poster review session and after considering the evidence, debates the value of the organism in solving a specific problem.

KEY CONTENT

1. Genetically modified organisms are those in which a gene or genes from another organism have been inserted into or deleted from their genetic material.

2. Genetic modification has been used to develop organisms with specific desirable traits, such as pest or disease resistance, drought tolerance, or enhanced nutritional qualities.

3. The production and use of genetically modified organisms might have unintended consequences for humans and ecosystems.

4. Basic concepts and principles of science and technology contribute to evidence-based debate about the economics, policies, politics, and ethics of various science- and technology-related innovations.

KEY PROCESS SKILLS

1. Students apply logic, knowledge, and reasoning to construct explanations.

2. Students distinguish between relevant evidence and irrelevant information.

3. Students identify and describe trade-offs.

4. Students support a position with evidence.

MATERIALS AND ADVANCE PREPARATION

For the teacher

Scoring Guide: GROUP INTERACTION (GI)

Scoring Guide: COMMUNICATION SKILLS (CS)

For each group of four students

access to a library and Internet-based reference materials*

supplies for making either an electronic or a hard copy poster*

For each student

Student Sheet 15.1, "Evaluating Genetically Modified Organisms"

Student Sheet 15.2, "Poster Template"

Literacy Student Sheet 4, "Discussion Web"

Student Sheet 2.3, "Genetics Case Study Comparison," from Activity 2

Scoring Guide: GROUP INTERACTION (GI) (optional)

Scoring Guide: COMMUNICATION SKILLS (CS) (optional)

Not supplied in kit

Masters for Literacy Student Sheets are in Teacher Resources III: Literacy. Masters for Scoring Guides are in Teacher Resources IV: Assessment.

Before students begin this project, determine the following:

Student groups *Decide which four students will be in each group for the duration of the project. Decide how you will assign organisms to each group. SEPUP recommends that you assign a different organism to each group in order to create richer class discussions. If you have more than one class section, consider repeating organisms from one section to the next, as appropriate.*

List of organisms to research *Decide on a list of sustainability issues in areas around the world and the organisms you will assign to groups. One possibility is to assign organisms from the list provided on the* Science and Global Issues *website (sepuplhs.org/sgi). Those organisms illustrate the connection between genetically modified organisms and the sustainability of food systems. They also illustrate issues and complications that arise at different economic and social levels. A second possibility is to generate a list of organisms that relate to your community's or your students' interests.*

When selecting the organisms it is important to keep in mind that it will be more difficult to locate information accessible to your students for some organisms than for others. For this reason, spend time searching for appropriate hard-copy and electronic resources before making assignments. At the very least, students must have access to resources that allow them to answer the questions on Student Sheet 15.1. If necessary, reserve computers and any other helpful resources in advance. You may wish to collaborate with a school librarian and/or media specialist to assist with this project.

Project timeline *SEPUP recommends devoting a minimum of two 50-minute class periods for research, one or two class periods to construct posters, and one or two class periods for the poster session and walking debate. Decide if you will ask students to conduct additional research during out-of-class time. Adjust the project timeline to best suit your instructional needs.*

Students do not need to complete this project before conducting Activities 16–19. SEPUP recommends that the class finish the poster session and walking debate at any point before the start of Activity 20, the final activity of the unit.

Poster construction *Decide if students will construct hard-copy or electronic posters. Collect the appropriate supplies.*

TEACHING SUMMARY

Getting Started

- The class identifies issues associated with genetically modified organisms.

Doing the Activity

- (GI ASSESSMENT) Student groups research a genetically modified organism.

- The class determines what makes a good informational poster.

- Student groups construct informational posters.

- (CS ASSESSMENT) The class conducts a poster session.

Follow-up

- The class discusses the adoption of genetically modified organisms.

15 Evaluating Genetically Modified Organisms

IN THIS UNIT you have read about countries or groups that have considered supporting the development and application of genetically modified organisms to help address sustainability problems. For example, in the first activity you evaluated evidence to determine if a country should grow genetically modified corn to feed hungry people. Central to making a decision about genetically modified organisms is collecting evidence about the organism and weighing the trade-offs of its use.

In this activity, you will research and collect evidence to evaluate potential benefits and problems of a genetically modified organism in solving a specific sustainability issue. You will prepare a poster explaining the possible benefits, risks, and trade-offs associated with the use of the organism. The class will then evaluate the evidence you collected to make a recommendation about the organism.

The growth and harvest of GM organisms has been proposed as a potential solution for many sustainability issues, such as overfishing. However, some people feel the benefits are not worth potential risks.

361

Challenge

▶ What are the benefits and trade-offs of using genetically modified organisms?

MATERIALS

FOR EACH GROUP OF FOUR STUDENTS
　　access to a library and the Internet
　　supplies for making a poster

FOR EACH STUDENT
　　Student Sheet 15.1, "Evaluating Genetically Modified Organisms"
　　Student Sheet 15.2, "Poster Template"
　　Literacy Student Sheet 6, "Discussion Web"
　　Student Sheet 2.3, "Genetics Case Study Comparison," from Activity 2

Drought and crop failure are sustainability issues in many areas worldwide.

GETTING STARTED

1 So far in this unit, students have read four case studies, three of which—engineering of biofuels, golden rice, and faster growing salmon—discuss application of GM organisms to address sustainability issues. As needed, help students pull information from Student Sheet 2.3, "Genetics Case Study Comparison," to construct a list of concerns associated with developing and growing GM organisms. Possible concerns include unintended environmental consequences, toxicity, and effects on humans' health and on native wild organisms.

2 Refer students to their lists of issues from Procedure Step 1 to help them write questions. For example, the toxicity of genetically modified organisms is an issue. Questions students might ask about toxicity include: Is the GM organism toxic to humans? At what level is the GM organism toxic to humans who eat it? Is it toxic to other organisms? For additional question ideas, refer students to the questions they listed in Procedure Step 7 of Activity 1, "A Genetically Modified Solution?"

These researchers are measuring the growth of wheat exposed to elevated atmospheric carbon dioxide levels. Many researchers are concerned that higher levels of atmospheric carbon dioxide will lead to future sustainability issues.

Procedure

Part A: Gathering Information

1
1. With your group make a list of the concerns often associated with genetically modified organisms. To help you generate ideas, refer to Student Sheet 2.3, "Genetics Case Study Comparison."

2. Discuss your ideas with the class, as directed by your teacher.

2
3. With the class, make a list of questions that must be answered if a community is to responsibly evaluate the environmental, social, and economic effects of using a genetically modified organism.

363

DOING THE ACTIVITY

3 The questions and topics the class developed in Procedure Step 3 and those listed on Student Sheet 15.1, "Evaluating a Genetically Modified Organism," will guide students' research. With the class combine the two lists.

4 (GI ASSESSMENT) As students conduct research, you may apply the GROUP INTERACTION (GI) Scoring Guide to provide feedback on the nature and quality of their group work. For more information on the GROUP INTERACTION (GI) Scoring Guide, see Teacher Resources IV: Assessment.

5 Give students a project timeline. Review the electronic and other resources that will be available for their use. In addition, SEPUP recommends providing instruction on the following topics based on your students' research experience:

- How to find quality websites that present evidence-based information, versus websites that are not evidence based.

- How to properly cite an author, reference book, or website and how to paraphrase and use quotations, as opposed to copying and pasting text without providing adequate citations.

As students work, check their progress frequently to ensure that they are able to find sufficient appropriate information. Expect that students will encounter information that is beyond the scope of their understanding. Check frequently to make sure they can comprehend the information they have found, and help them find several different sources of information that discuss the topics at varying levels of complexity.

3

4. Review Student Sheet 15.1, "Evaluating a Genetically Modified Organism," which contains a list of topics and questions to guide your research on your assigned organism. Add to the Student Sheet any questions from Step 3 that are not listed.

5. Your teacher will assign your group a sustainability issue and a genetically modified organism to research.

4

6. Decide who in your group will research each of the items listed on Student Sheet 15.1. Divide the topics among yourselves, making sure each person will contribute evidence to the group poster.

5

7. Your teacher will provide instructions and a timeline for completing your research.

Part B: Preparing the Poster

6

8. As a class, view several examples of posters, and develop a list of criteria for making an effective poster. Keep in mind that the goal of the poster is to offer evidence-based information to help inform a decision on whether or not a genetically modified organism should be used.

7

9. Working with the criteria the class created in Step 8, decide how your group will represent the information you gathered on your poster. To do this
   - review the poster template on Student Sheet 15.2, "Poster Template."
   - decide how you will fit your information into the template.

8

10. Prepare your poster.

Part C: Informational Poster Session

9

11. Your teacher will explain how to present your poster to the class during the poster session.

10

12. As you review other groups' posters, write down on Literacy Student Sheet 6, "Discussion Web," two to three key points from each poster you view.

11

13. Based on the information you recorded on Literacy Student Sheet 6, decide if you would support the use of each genetically modified organism discussed in the poster session. In your science notebook record your opinion, and the evidence and your thinking that led you to your opinion.

12

14. Share your ideas with the class by conducting a walking debate. Your teacher will explain how to run the debate.

---

6 There are links to sample posters on the *Science and Global Issues* website (*sepuplhs.org/sgi*). Decide if you will project the samples or print out examples for students to compare. View the samples with the class, and ask such questions as, What do the posters have in common? How are they different? Are some better than others at conveying information? If so, how? From this discussion make a list of criteria that describe good poster design. Post the list where it can easily be referenced while students work on their posters.

Sample Student Responses for Procedure Step 12
(Note: Students' responses will depend on the information they collect during their research.)

Evidence For	Should the country allow the use of this GM organism?	Evidence Against
GM salmon engineered to grow faster provide more fish to feed people than do wild populations of fish.		GM salmon that escape from fisheries and mate with wild populations survive better than the wild fish. This will lead to a decrease in wild salmon populations.
If farmers grow Bt soy plants they can use smaller amounts of pesticides that may damage other organisms in the ecosystem and protect their crops from certain pests.		The Bt soy itself may be toxic to other organisms in the same ecosystem, and could end up harming organisms all the way up the food chain.

7 Pass out Student Sheet 15.2, "Poster Template," and discuss with students how they might use this format to present the information they found. The template may be used as is or modified.

8 Provide appropriate materials and guidance so that students can construct either electronic or poster-board posters. For electronic posters, make sure students have access to appropriate software.

9 (CS ASSESSMENT) You may apply the COMMUNICATION SKILLS (CS) Scoring Guide to score students' posters and presentations of their posters. If you will assess students' work, make sure that students are aware of your expectations for Level-3 and Level-4 responses. For more information on the COMMUNICATION SKILLS (CS) Scoring Guide, see Teacher Resources IV: Assessment.

One way to conduct the poster session is to display all posters at once, with half of the authors standing by their posters and answering questions while the other half visits each poster. Adapt this process to suit your instructional goals.

10 Direct students to fill in the column headers at the top of Literacy Student Sheet 4, "Discussion Web," as shown in the example above. Students will record evidence for and against this question as they view other groups' posters. This student sheet provides a written record of information students gathered while visiting posters that will serve as evidence during the discussion and debate conducted in Procedure Steps 13 and 14. Sample student responses for Literacy Student Sheet 4 are shown in the Sample Responses section on the next page.

11 Emphasize that students should construct an evidence-based opinion by referring to the evidence they recorded on Literacy Student Sheet 4.

FOLLOW-UP

12 Extend the discussion by conducting a walking debate that asks students to consider a community's acceptance of each organism presented during the poster session. See Teacher Resources III: Literacy for more information on the Walking Debate strategy. Designate one corner of the room as Yes, a second area of the room as No, and a third corner as Maybe. Pose the question, *Should a community accept this genetically modified organism?*

Have students stand in the place that best represents their viewpoint. If most of the students already agree on a particular option, you may assign some of them to the other options to foster the skills of debate and evidence analysis. Have the group standing at each position explain to the class why they chose that option and what was the evidence on which they based their decision. Once each group has explained its choice, allow students to change their minds and move to another area. Repeat this process for each organism presented during the poster session.

13 ✓ Analysis Question 2 is a Quick Check to determine if students are able to support their recommendations with evidence and to identify the trade-offs associated with their recommendations, components of the EVIDENCE AND TRADE-OFFS (ET) Scoring Guide.

SAMPLE RESPONSES

1. When considering genetically modified crops or animals, communities should look at the environmental, social, and economic impacts of farming the organism. Important environmental information would include finding out if people and other organisms can eat the organism safely. If the issue is farming fish, a community should find out if the modified fish would interact with and threaten wild fish populations. In terms of the social and economic effects of the modified fish a country needs to know: Will people buy them? Will raising the fish create jobs? Will it help or hurt the existing fishery? Exploring and evaluating all three facets will help determine if the GM organism is likely to contribute to the community's sustainability.

2. Students' answers should clearly state a position, provide supporting evidence, and discuss trade-offs. For example, a student who researched salmon that are genetically engineered to grow faster than wild salmon may say the

---

Analysis

1. Based on the posters you viewed, what questions should communities ask when considering the sustainability factors involved in using a genetically modified organism?

13 2. Based on your research, would you recommend that a community adopt the use of your assigned genetically modified organism? In your recommendation explain the evidence that supports your decision, and the trade-offs associated with that genetically modified organism.

KEY VOCABULARY	
gene	trade-off
genetic modification	

---

evidence against their use outweighs the benefits of raising the fish. The research shows that they out-compete wild salmon, and in areas where the salmon "escape" from fisheries, the wild populations are decreasing. One trade-off of not using the GM salmon is that there may not be enough salmon to fill consumers' demand, but at least the wild salmon populations will be protected.

REVISIT THE CHALLENGE

Refer to Analysis Question 1, which addresses the benefits and risks associated with the adoption of genetically modified organisms. Ask students to share their ideas with the class. They should incorporate evidence from their work in this activity to support their ideas about the potential benefits and risks associated with the genetic modification of organisms.

16 Protein Synthesis: Transcription and Translation

MODELING • 2–3 CLASS SESSIONS

OVERVIEW

Students use a combination of cards, physical models, and computer simulations to explore the stages of protein synthesis. They work through the steps involved at each stage of transcription and translation. Students also read a case study on gene therapy, which is connected to protein synthesis.

KEY CONTENT

1. Changes in DNA (mutations) occur spontaneously at low rates. Some of these changes make no difference to the organism, whereas others have a variety of effects.

2. In all organisms, the coded instructions for specifying the characteristics of the organism are carried in DNA, a molecule formed from subunits arranged in a sequence with bases of four kinds (represented by A, G, C, and T).

3. The chemical and structural properties of DNA are the basis for how the genetic information that underlies heredity is both encoded in genes (as a string of molecular "bases") and replicated by means of a template.

KEY PROCESS SKILLS

1. Students develop conclusions based on evidence.

2. Students apply logic, knowledge, and reasoning to construct explanations.

MATERIALS AND ADVANCE PREPARATION

For the teacher

Student Sheet 16.1, "Transcription and Translation" (available online only: see note below)

Transparency 16.1, "Protein Synthesis Molecule Key"

Transparency 16.2, "Flow of Genetic Information"

Scoring Guide: UNDERSTANDING CONCEPTS (UC)

For each pair of students

set of 10 Transcription and Translation Cards (A–J)

bag containing DNA model kit pieces:

    36 black deoxyribose sugars pentagons*

    36 white phosphate tubes*

         various orange, yellow, blue, and green nitrogenous base tubes*

    18 white hydrogen bond rods*

bag containing transcription model kit pieces:

     9 purple ribose sugar pentagons*

     5 purple uracil nitrogenous base tubes*

bag containing translation model kit pieces:

     3 purple tRNA molecules (diamond, oval, rectangle)*

     3 black amino acids (diamond, oval, rectangle)*

     2 gray polypeptide bond tubes*

computer with Internet access*

For each student

Student Sheet 16.1, "Transcription and Translation" (available online only: see note on the next page)

Student Sheet 2.3, "Genetics Case Study Comparison," from Activity 2

sticky notes

Scoring Guide: UNDERSTANDING CONCEPTS (UC) (optional)

Not included in kit

Masters for Scoring Guides are in Teacher Resources IV: Assessment.

Note: *This activity is written to use the SEPUP DNA modeling kit. If you will be using a different kit, adjust the instructions as appropriate.*

Note that the DNA model kit from Activity 10 is used in this activity with additional pieces to represent transcription and translation. Transparency of 16.1, "Protein Synthesis Molecule Key," shows which pieces belong in each of the three bags. For ease, label the bags "DNA," "Transcription," and "Translation" respectively.

Note: *Student Sheet 16.1, "Transcription and Translation," is found only on the* Science and Global Issues *website (sepuplhs.org/sgi). Sample student answers are also available on the website. Both are located in the teacher's section. Arrange for computers with Internet access for the day(s) students do this activity. Go to the* Science and Global Issues *page of the SEPUP website to access the simulation. You may want to bookmark this site for students. Make sure the browsers and supporting software are current and can properly run the simulation.*

TEACHING SUMMARY

Getting Started

- Elicit students' ideas about proteins in cells.

Doing the Activity

- (UC ASSESSMENT) Working with cards and an online computer simulation, students investigate transcription and translation.

- Students model the effects of DNA mutations on transcription and translation.

- (LITERACY) Students read a case study about gene therapy.

Follow-up

- Students write about transcription and translation.

BACKGROUND INFORMATION

The Central Dogma of Molecular Biology

Francis Crick introduced the term "central dogma of molecular biology" in 1958 to describe a hypothesis for the flow of information from DNA to proteins. The original version of this hypothesis is summarized as follows:

- DNA serves as a template for the replication of new DNA.

- DNA serves as a template for the production of RNA during transcription.

- RNA serves as the template for the production of proteins during translation.

This traditional view of the central dogma is shown by the blue elements in the figure below. The production of proteins in most cells follows this information flow.

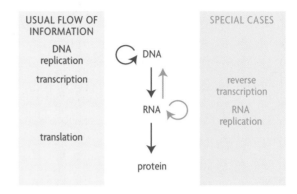

However, as scientists have learned more about the function of the genome in viruses and organisms, they have found numerous exceptions to the dogma. For example, some RNA viruses, called retroviruses, require that their RNA genome first produce DNA, in a process called reverse transcription. Other RNA viruses are able to produce RNA directly from RNA templates. These additional mechanisms are added to the figure above in orange. There is evidence that these mechanisms also take place under special circumstances in eukaryotes, but there are no known cases of protein serving as information for the production of DNA or RNA.

Although the central dogma describes the replication and flow of genetic information, it does not describe completely the functions of DNA and RNA. Not all DNA codes for RNA; some segments of DNA serve structural or regulatory functions. And not all RNA codes for proteins, as RNA includes not only the coding mRNA, but also tRNA, rRNA, and more recently discovered regulatory RNAs.

Ribonucleic Acid (RNA) and Ribonucleotides

Like deoxyribonucleic acid (DNA), ribonucleic acid (RNA) is a large polymer, or macromolecule, made of nucleotide subunits. However, RNA differs from DNA in both subunits and overall structure. There are two key differences between the subunits of RNA and those of DNA. First, the pentose sugar is ribose, rather than deoxyribose, as shown below. For this reason, the nucleotides in RNA are more specifically called ribonucleotides. Second, one of the four bases in RNA is uracil, rather than thymine.

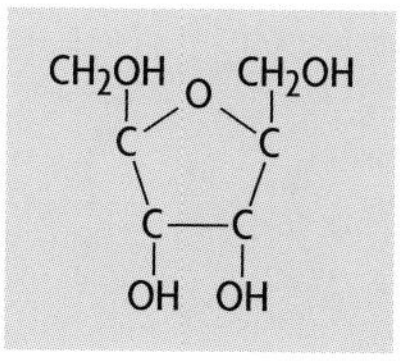

Unlike DNA, RNA is usually single stranded, although it can form loops where one segment of the RNA pairs with a complementary sequence in another segment of the molecule. The base pairing that forms the loops is similar to that in DNA, with base pairs forming between C and G and between A and U.

REFERENCES

Genetics Science Learning Center. (2008). What is gene therapy? University of Utah. Retrieved May 2010, from http://learn.genetics.utah.edu/content/tech/genetherapy/whatisgt/.

Oak Ridge National Lab. (2009). Gene therapy. Human Genome Project Information. Retrieved May 2010, from http://www.ornl.gov/sci/techresources/Human_Genome/medicine/genetherapy.shtml.

National Eye Institute. (2008). Promising results in phase 1 gene therapy trial for blinding disease. Retrieved May 2010 from http://www.nei.nih.gov/news/pressreleases/092308.asp.

GETTING STARTED

1 ◆ Ask students to think of both a corn cell that is genetically modified to contain the Bt gene and a corn cell that is not modified. In what ways are the cells similar? Different? Students' answers should indicate that the cells are the same in all regards, except two. First, the genetically modified cell contains the Bt gene. Second, because it contains this gene, if the gene is expressed, it is able to make the Bt protein. The unmodified cell does not contain the gene, and, therefore, cannot make the protein. Probe students' understanding of the relationship between DNA and proteins in a cell by asking the class, *What is the relationship between DNA and proteins in a cell?*

Use their answers as a starting point to begin discussion about protein synthesis. This is an appropriate time to point out to students that scientists are still working to understand the processes involved in producing proteins from the information in genes (DNA), and that this field is the focus of much current research.

If students had the *Science and Global Issues* "Cell Biology: World Health" unit, you may want to briefly review the main things they learned about proteins before they begin the Procedure. This would include the importance of protein structure and function, that proteins are the "workhorses" of the cells, that proteins have specialized roles, and that all enzymes are proteins.

---

16 Protein Synthesis: Transcription and Translation

1 **G**ENES CARRY THE information that, along with environmental factors, determines an organism's traits. How does this work? Although the complete answer to this question is complex, the simple answer is that genes, along with the influence of environmental factors, direct the production of proteins in cells, and the types of proteins in a cell determine the cell's and organism's structure and function. When scientists set out to genetically modify an organism, their goal is to insert a gene or genes that code for a protein that is not normally in that organism.

While genetically modified organisms produce a protein or proteins that the original organism would otherwise not produce, the process for making the proteins is the same for any and all cells. This process is **protein synthesis.** Protein synthesis has two phases, shown in the figure below. In the first phase, the information contained in DNA is converted into a messenger molecule called messenger ribonucleic acid, or mRNA. The scientific word for this conversion is **transcription.** In eukaryotic cells transcription takes place in the nuclei. The second phase of protein synthesis is **translation,** and this happens on ribosomes in the cytoplasm of a cell. In this phase, the code in the mRNA messenger molecule is translated by transfer RNA (tRNA), which carries the amino acids used to make a protein molecule. In this activity, you will view a computer simulation of both transcription and translation. You will see that these processes occur similarly in both genetically modified and unmodified organisms.

PROTEIN SYNTHESIS

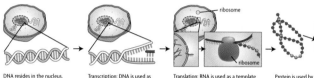

DNA resides in the nucleus.

Transcription: DNA is used as a template to make RNA.

Translation: RNA is used as a template to make proteins.

Protein is used by the organism. For example, an enzyme could be used by the digestive system.

366

DOING THE ACTIVITY

2 The Transcription and Translation Cards prompt students to begin asking questions about these processes. They will explore them further as they go through the online simulations. As students watch the animations, encourage them to talk about what they are viewing, and to record this on Student Sheet 16.1, "Transcription and Translation." The benefit of allowing them to work with both the cards and the computer animations simultaneously is that they can reference the animations as they put the cards in order.

Challenge

▶ How does a cell make proteins with the information from DNA?

MATERIALS

FOR EACH PAIR OF STUDENTS

    set of 10 Transcription and Translation Cards (A–J)

    access to online protein synthesis simulation

    bag containing DNA model kit pieces

        36 black deoxyribose sugars pentagons

        36 white phosphate tubes

            various orange, yellow, blue, and green nitrogenous base tubes

        18 white hydrogen bond rods

    bag containing transcription model kit pieces

         9 purple ribose sugar pentagons

         5 purple uracil nitrogenous base tubes

    bag containing translation model kit pieces

         3 purple tRNA molecules (diamond, oval, rectangle)

         3 black amino acids (diamond, oval, rectangle)

         2 gray polypeptide bond tubes

FOR EACH STUDENT

    Student Sheet 16.1, "Transcription and Translation"

    Student Sheet 2.3, "Genetics Case Study Comparison," from Activity 2

    3 sticky notes

Procedure

2 Part A: Transcription and Translation

1. With your partner spread out the 10 Transcription and Translation cards in front of you on the table. Look closely at the cards. Discuss what each card shows and how the images on the cards differ.

2. To make a protein, a cell must convert the information contained in DNA into a messenger molecule. Then the code in the messenger molecule is translated into a string of amino acids that will make a certain protein. Place the cards in the order that you think shows this process. Record the order of the cards on the back of Student Sheet 16.1, "Transcription and Translation."

3. The first stage of protein synthesis is transcription. During transcription, the information in DNA instructs the cell to make a messenger molecule, mRNA. With your partner, visit the *Science and Global Issues* page of the SEPUP website (*sepuplhs.org/sgi*), and go to the protein synthesis simulation. Student Sheet 16.1, "Transcription and Translation," will guide you through the simulation.

3 The correct order for the Transcription and Translation Cards is D, F, E, J, A, H, B, G, C, I.

Provide students with this order only after allowing them sufficient time to determine the sequence on their own, ideally after Procedure Step 7.

4 Review the information students collected on Student Sheet 16.1, "Transcription and Translation." Suggested answers are on the *Science and Global Issues* page of the SEPUP website *(sepuplhs.org/sgi).*

Note: You may alter the level of specificity and complexity that you want students to learn, based on your state or district standards. For example, if students are expected to learn the names of the enzymes involved in transcription and translation, check to see that they have recorded this information on Student Sheet 16.1.

5 (UC ASSESSMENT) It may be helpful to provide students with photocopies of the cards for them to sequence and tape into their science notebooks, or they may simply write a legend for transcription and translation. A sample summary is shown at right. Note that the letters provided correlate with the letters on the cards. You may score students' work with the UNDERSTANDING CONCEPTS (UC) Scoring Guide.

4. Look at the order in which you placed the cards in Step 2. Based on what you viewed in the animation, was your ordering of the cards correct? If necessary, discuss with your partner any changes you need to make, and rearrange the cards to reflect the correct order of events in transcription. On the back of Student Sheet 16.1, "Transcription and Translation," record the revised order of cards.

5. Based on what you observed in the animation and the information on the cards, fill in the transcription section of Student Sheet 16.1, "Transcription and Translation."

6. The second stage of protein synthesis is translation. During translation, the information in the messenger molecule mRNA translates into a chain of amino acids that will make a protein. Return to the *Science and Global Issues* page of the SEPUP website *(seuplhs.org/sgi)* and the protein synthesis simulation. Again, Student Sheet 16.1, "Transcription and Translation," will guide you through the simulation.

3 7. Look at the order in which you placed the cards in Step 4. Based on what you viewed in the simulation, was your ordering of the cards correct? If necessary, discuss with your partner any changes you need to make, and rearrange the cards to reflect the correct order of events in translation. On the back of Student Sheet 16.1, record the revised order of translation cards.

4 8. Based on what you observed in the animation, and the information provided on the cards, fill in the translation section of Student Sheet 16.1, "Transcription and Translation."

5 9. From the information you recorded on Student Sheet 16.1, in your science notebook write a description of what is shown on each card. Be sure to include

   a. the name of each molecule involved.

   b. a description of what each molecule does.

6 **Part B: Mutations**

As you saw in Part A of this activity, DNA is a template that provides information for creating messenger RNA. The information in mRNA is then converted into an amino acid sequence, which is then turned into a protein. Occasionally during this process a mutation occurs. **Mutations** are changes in the sequence of nucleotides in a strand of DNA. In this part of the activity, you will investigate the effect of DNA mutations on protein synthesis.

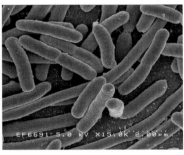

Mutations can be harmful, neutral, or beneficial. Certain strains of E. coli bacteria have mutations that allow them to withstand extreme temperatures.

368

Sample Level-3 Student Response to Procedure Step 9

Card	Legend	Card	Legend
D	This is a cell with DNA in its nucleus. The DNA will be transcribed into RNA, which then might be translated into a protein.	H	The mRNA molecule binds to the ribosome (made of rRNA) in the cytoplasm of the cell. tRNA molecules are nearby.
F	The base pairs of DNA unwind, unzip, and begin to separate so that RNA polymerase can begin pairing RNA nucleotides to the DNA nucleotides.	B	tRNA molecules bind to the mRNA-ribosome complex according to the information contained in the codons (three nucleotides) in the mRNA molecule. Specific tRNAs bind to each codon, and carry an amino acid.
E	Complementary RNA nucleotides match with the DNA bases. The nitrogenous base uracil replaces thymine.	G	The mRNA continues to move along the ribosome and match up tRNA molecules, bringing new amino acids that bond in a chain.
J	RNA nucleotides connect to form a molecule of mRNA that will serve as a messenger carrying the code from the DNA. This occurs in the nucleus of a cell.	C	The amino acid chain continues to grow as the mRNA continues to move along the ribosome, matching the tRNA molecule and bringing new amino acids.
A	The mRNA molecule leaves the nucleus and travels to a ribosome in the cytoplasm of the cell, where it will begin the translation process.	I	The chain of amino acids elongates to become a protein.

6 Students may work with the DNA kit with the protein synthesis pieces, or they may record their work on paper, whichever is easiest for them, to explore the DNA changes. If students use the model, review with them the parts and how they fit together, and how they fit with the purple ribose sugars, purple tubes that represent uracil (U), and the tRNA pieces from the transcription and translation kits. In particular, show how the pieces fit together to accomplish transcription and translation. Remind students that they learned in the simulations that a codon is a series of three nucleotides on the mRNA molecule that codes for a tRNA molecule, carrying with it an amino acid. The series of three nucleotides on the mRNA is the codon, and the corresponding complementary three codons on the tRNA is the anticodon.

7 Students might develop the misunderstanding that protein synthesis begins at the start of the DNA strand and continues from there. It is important for them to see that gene expression begins at the start codons located at specific points along a chromosome.

Students will need to work with the Amino Acid Code Chart in the Student Book.

They should produce an mRNA piece with the nucleotide series 3' AUGGAUCGGUCAGCC 5' and the amino acid sequence methionine–aspartic acid–arginine–serine–alanine (met–asp–arg–ser–ala). If necessary, provide more practice for students to transcribe DNA and translate the mRNA into amino acid sequences.

---

10. Copy the table below into your science notebook.

Mutation	DNA sequence resulting from DNA mutation indicated in table	mRNA transcript	Amino acid sequence	Effect on amino acid sequence
Original strand	5' TACCTAGCCAGTCGG 3'			
Base insertion (frameshift)				
Base deletion (frameshift)				
Substitution				
Three-base insertion				

11. With your partner, select the appropriate pieces of the Protein Synthesis Model, and build a single strand of DNA with the following sequence of bases:

5' TACCTAGCCAGTCGG 3'

Use the Protein Synthesis Model Key below to identify each molecule.

PROTEIN SYNTHESIS MODEL KEY

369

8 Sample Student Work for Procedure Steps 11–13 is shown in the student table below.

Note: The DNA mutation is underlined in the second column.

Discuss students' results. Point out to them that DNA mutations might or might not cause a change in amino acid sequence, depending on the mutation. For example, a CGU codon that mutates to CGC will still code for arginine. To explore the effects of various mutations, ask students to try different sorts of insertions, deletions, substitutions, and frameshifts to see if they can come up with guidelines as to their effects. You may want to discuss mutation rates in different viruses and organisms, shown in the data table at bottom.

12. Work through the steps to translate and transcribe the DNA. Record your results in your data table, using the information in the chart on the next page to identify the amino acids.

Second letter

13. The chart Selected DNA Mutations on the next page describes types of DNA mutations. According to your teacher's instructions, explore how each type of mutation affects the production of an amino acid sequence. To do this

a. as described by each row in the Selected DNA Mutations chart, sequence the DNA mutations.

b. work through the steps to translate and transcribe the DNA. Record in your data table the amino acid sequence that results.

c. repeat Steps 13a and b for each type of mutation listed in the chart, starting each time with the original strand of DNA from Step 10.

Sample Results for Procedure Steps 11–13

Mutation	DNA sequence resulting from DNA mutation indicated in table	mRNA transcript	Amino acid sequence	Affect on amino acid sequence
Original strand	5′ TACCTAGCCAGTCGG 3′	AUGGAUCGGUCAGCC	Met–Asp–Arg–Ser–Ala	—
Base insertion (frameshift)	TACTCTAGCCAGTCGG	AUGAGAUCGGUCAGCC	Met–Arg–Ser–Val–Ser	All amino acids are changed except the first
Base deletion (frameshift)	TACTAGCCAGTCGG (first C deleted)	AUGAUCGGUCAGCC (first G no longer transcribed)	Met–Ile–Gly–Gln	3 amino acids are changed and 4 are sequenced instead of 5
Substitution	TATCTAGCCAGTCGG	AUAGAUCGGUCAGCC	Iso–Asp–Arg–Ser–Ala	1 amino acid is changed
Three-base insertion	TACCTGCTAGCCAGTCGG	AUGGACGAUCGGUCAGCC	Met–Asp–Asp–Arg–Ser–Ala	1 amino acid is inserted

TYPE OF VIRUS OR ORGANISM	ESTIMATED MUTATION RATE PER BASE PAIR PER GENERATION
DNA viruses	10^{-6} to 10^{-8}
RNA viruses	10^{-3} to 10^{-5}
Bacteria	10^{-8}
Eukaryotes	10^{-4} to 10^{-6}
Human (genomic mutation)	2.5×10^{-8}

Students should come to realize that mutations might change an mRNA sequence transcribed from DNA. It is also possible that a mutation will have no impact. The effect of the mutation depends on the type of change it makes to the DNA sequence. Not all mutations are harmful, for example there are hemoglobin mutations that do not affect the function of the hemoglobin. Stress that insertions or deletions of these bases (or multiples of three) will insert or delete a complete codon (or codons), but won't shift the reading frame of the codons that follow.

9 Students should record key information from the case study on Student Sheet 2.3, "Genetics Case Study Comparison." A sample summary is provided below. Project a transparency of Student Sheet 2.3, and discuss students' summaries.

14. Compare the amino acid sequence that resulted from each mutation to the original sequence. Based on your work, what can you say about the effect of DNA mutations on the production of amino acid sequences and proteins? Summarize your ideas in your science notebook.

Selected DNA Mutations

CATEGORIES OF DNA MUTATIONS	CHANGE IN DNA	CHANGE TO DNA MODEL
Base insertion (frameshift)	One nucleotide is inserted into the DNA sequence.	Insert a thymine after the first cytosine.
Base deletion (frameshift)	One nucleotide is deleted from the DNA sequence.	Delete the first cytosine.
Substitution	One nucleotide is substituted for a different nucleotide.	Change the first cytosine to a thymine.
Three-base insertion	Three nucleotides are added or deleted to the DNA sequence.	After TAC, insert three additional nucleotides, CTG.

Part C: Gene Therapy Case Study

9 15. Individually read the case study on the following pages. As you read, follow the literacy strategy, "Read, Think, and Take Note."

16. Share your thinking with your group. Place your sticky notes on the table in front of you. Look for connections between your notes and the notes of others in your group.

    Hint: Were there common questions people asked? Were people unfamiliar with the same words? Did people react differently to statements in the reading?

17. Place your sticky notes in your science notebook. Below each, write a short summary of what your group discussed and any conclusions you came to.

18. Record the appropriate information from this case study on Student Sheet 2.3, "Genetics Case Study Comparison."

Sample Case Study Summary for Student Sheet 2.3, "Genetics Case Study Comparison"

Case study	Type of genetic modification	Benefits	Risks and concerns	Current status of research and development	Other solutions?
Gene Therapy	Replace nonfunctioning gene with functioning gene, add functional genes to nonfunctioning cells, or regulate nonfunctioning genes	Treat or prevent genetic diseases	Isn't always permanent or long-term Might cause immune system responses	Some human trials successful Expanding study to look at more patients, safety, and long-term effectiveness	None presently available for Leber's congenital amaurosis (LCA)

CASE STUDY

Seeing the Results of Gene Therapy

This researcher is in the process of sequencing DNA from an organism.

NORMALLY YOU WOULD not think of a baseball player and the owner of a basketball team working together, but the Chicago Cubs' first baseman Derrek Lee and Boston Celtics owner Wycliffe Grousbeck have teamed up for an unusual reason. Both men have a child who suffers from a rare genetic disease, Leber's congenital amaurosis (LCA), that causes blindness. In 2007, they started a foundation to help those affected in the United States to undergo genetic testing. Because, an estimated 3,000 people in the United States have this disease, the name of the foundation is Project 3000. The foundation works with victims of LCA and raises money for research to identify the genes responsible for LCA and to find ways to treat it.

In most cases, the disease begins in infants, and victims are usually completely blind by age 20. So far there are no treatments for LCA, which is caused by a recessive genetic trait. Researchers have been working to create a gene therapy to treat the disease and restore at least partial sight to children and adults with LCA.

Developing these techniques is not easy. Scientists have been working on various gene therapies for more than 15 years and, as of 2010, there is no method of gene therapy that has been approved for use as a common (no longer experimental) medical treatment. Scientists must ensure that they are targeting the correct cells, that they are correcting the right gene, that the gene is producing the desired protein, that the correction is permanent, and that there are no harmful side effects.

Researchers have not yet determined the best methods of gene therapy. Many of the most promising methods target the various stages of protein synthesis. Some

Research scientists compare mice with one gene removed (left) to normal mice (right) as part of studying possible effects of gene therapy.

PROTEIN SYNTHESIS: TRANSCRIPTION AND TRANSLATION • ACTIVITY 16

Researchers are working on methods for using viruses and bacteria to introduce therapeutic genes into patients.

of the techniques that are being explored are:

1. Targeting the mRNA and repairing the specific section of the mRNA that has the non-functioning gene

2. Preventing the transcription of a specific gene

3. Preventing the translation of a specific gene

In the case of gene therapy for LCA, scientists have run into problems with the treatment not working over the long term. The therapy has also triggered immune system responses, similar to severe allergic reactions, in some patients. The first clinical trials of gene therapy for LCA were halted in 2003, when a patient unexpectedly developed a cancer-like condition. In addition, research is finding that more and more disorders are based on the functioning of multiple genes, making therapies ever more difficult to create. With all the challenges that gene-therapy scientists face, researchers at the National Eye Institute were excited to report in September 2008, that they had successfully completed a gene transfer procedure in three young adults with LCA. All three patients showed partially restored vision over a 90-day study period. Dr. Samuel G. Jacobson of the University of Pennsylvania was the principal investigator of the study. While he was very pleased with the results, he acknowledged that there is still much work to be done. The study is currently being expanded to include more patients, and to further examine the safety and long-term effectiveness of the current therapy. ■

FOLLOW-UP

10 ✓Analysis Questions 1 and 2 are Quick Check assessments of students' understanding of protein synthesis. Analysis Question 2 asks students to practice transcribing and translating sequences of DNA and mRNA. You might also ask them to make up their own sequences to work from. Be sure the sequences they select include a start codon. Analysis Question 4 is a Quick Check to assess students' understanding that DNA mutations might or might not have an effect on transcription and translation, depending on the change made in the DNA sequence.

SAMPLE RESPONSES

1. ✓Protein synthesis is the process by which information contained in the DNA nucleotide series in cells directs the production of proteins. During transcription, the DNA in the nucleus unzips, allowing mRNA to form. The mRNA leaves the nucleus and goes into the cell's cytoplasm for translation. During translation, tRNA uses mRNA as a template from which to synthesize a chain of amino acids on the ribosomes. Those chains are processed and packaged into proteins.

2. ✓Response is shown in the table at right.

3. A two-base insertion or deletion will cause a frameshift, because a codon is three bases. A three-base insertion or deletion adds or deletes an amino acid.

---

10 Analysis

1. Define protein synthesis and describe how it works.

2. Copy the chart below in your science notebook. Fill in the chart to determine the amino acid sequence that results from the transcription and translation of the following nucleotide sequence:

5' TACTCGGCATTGTGA 3'

Nucleotide	Transcription mRNA	Translation Amino Acid
5'		
A		
T		
G		
T		
C		
G		
G		
C		
A		
T		
T		
G		
T		
G		
A		
3'		

Sample Results for Analysis Question 2

DNA nucleotide	Transcription mRNA nucleotide	Translation tRNA anticodon	Amino acid
5'			
T	A	U	Methionine (Met) START
A	U	T	
C	G	C	
T	A	U	Serine (Ser)
C	G	C	
G	C	G	
G	C	G	Arginine (Arg)
C	G	C	
A	U	A	
T	A	U	Asparagine (Asn)
T	A	U	
G	C	G	
T	A	U	Threonine (Thr)
G	C	G	
A	U	A	
3'			

4. This is not true. A DNA mutation might cause damaged proteins, but it also could be beneficial or have little or no impact, depending on the mutation. For example, if the mutation changed the nucleotide sequence, but it still coded for the same amino acid it would not be harmful.

5. Genes contain the instructions for the production of proteins. If there is a mutation in a gene, it can cause problems with the process or product of the protein synthesis because a cell's synthesis mechanism does not have the right code to start from. If scientists can fix the protein synthesis with gene therapy techniques, the correct protein will be produced for the body to use.

REVISIT THE CHALLENGE

Review the role of DNA as the code for the synthesis of proteins. Discuss the steps involved in producing proteins from the information in DNA. You may wish to point out the blue portions of the diagram on Transparency 16.2, "Flow of Genetic Information," to discuss the usual flow of information from DNA to messenger RNA to proteins. The transparency also shows the role of DNA as a template for replication in preparation for mitosis or meiosis. Be sure to also review the roles of codons in DNA and RNA, and the roles of mRNA, tRNA, and rRNA in translation.

You may wish to point out the exceptions to the traditional flow of information, such as reverse transcription, shown in orange on the transparency. If your students have studied the "Cell Biology" unit of *Science and Global Issues*, they have seen examples of RNA viruses that involve RNA to DNA or RNA to RNA information transfers.

---

3. Predict the results of a two-base insertion or deletion to a strand of DNA that codes for a protein. How is this different from a three-base insertion or deletion?

4. One night while watching TV you hear a newscaster say, "DNA mutations cause damaged proteins." Based on your work in Part B, how would you respond to this claim?

5. Describe the relationship between gene therapy and protein synthesis.

KEY VOCABULARY

amino acid	replication
DNA	RNA
mRNA	**transcription**
mutation	**translation**
protein	tRNA
protein synthesis	

17 Cell Differentiation and Gene Expression

INVESTIGATION AND MODELING • 1–2 CLASS SESSIONS

ACTIVITY OVERVIEW

Students investigate gene expression as it relates to cell differentiation in four human cell types. They consider how various physiological events affect gene expression in each of the four cell types.

KEY CONTENT

1. The expression of specific genes regulates cell differentiation and cell functions.

2. Somatic cells in an individual organism have the same genome, but selectively express the genes for production of characteristic proteins.

3. The proteins a cell produces determine that cell's phenotype.

KEY PROCESS SKILLS

1. Students conduct investigations.

2. Students develop conclusions based on evidence.

MATERIALS AND ADVANCE PREPARATION

For the teacher
Student Sheet 2.3, "Genetics Case Study Comparison"

For each group of four students
set of 14 Cellular Event Cards

For each pair of students
3 colored pencils (blue, brown, and orange)*

For each student
model of human chromosome 2
model of human chromosome 11
4 silver binder clips*
7 red paper clips*
7 green paper clips*
Student Sheet 17.1, "Chromosome Map"
Student Sheet 2.3, "Genetics Case Study Summary," from Activity 2
3 sticky notes*

TEACHING SUMMARY

Getting Started

- Elicit students' ideas about the genetic makeup of different cells in a multicellular organism.

Doing the Activity

- Students investigate gene expression.

Follow-up

- The class discusses gene expression and gene regulation.

- (LITERACY) Students read a case study about terminator genes.

BACKGROUND INFORMATION

Gene Expression

Gene expression is the process in which the information stored in DNA is used to produce a functional gene product. Gene products are either proteins or noncoding RNAs, such as tRNA and rRNA, which play essential roles in protein synthesis, but do not code for proteins. Gene expression is regulated throughout the lifespan of an individual cell to control the cell's functions, such as its metabolic activity. Gene expression plays a critical role in the morphological changes that take place in a developing embryo and fetus and in the differentiation of stem cells to form specialized cells.

The expression of protein-coding genes is regulated at a number of steps, including 1) transcription of DNA to form RNA, 2) processing of the RNA product, 3) translation mRNA to produce protein, and 4) post-translational modification of the protein product. This activity introduces students to controls that interact directly with DNA to regulate the transcription of genes into mRNA by RNA polymerase, the enzyme that links ribonucleotides together to form RNA. Transcription is regulated by changes in the DNA and associated histone proteins that affect the condensation of the DNA and by proteins called transcription factors. These transcription factors serve as activators or repressors of transcription. Activators increase the binding of RNA polymerase to the promoter of a gene, thus increasing the rate of transcription. Repressors bind at or near the promoter and interfere with the activity of RNA polymerase.

In prokaryotes, usually clusters of genes are under the control of one promoter that is adjacent to the gene sequences. The promoter is a stretch of DNA where RNA polymerase first binds before the initiation of transcription. These clusters of genes adjacent to a single promoter are called operons. The best-known example of this is the lactose operon of *E. coli*, made up of three genes involved in lactose metabolism. The operon includes the promoter, the three protein-coding genes, and a regulatory sequence called an operator. This arrangement allows the three genes to be turned on or turned off at the same time.

In eukaryotes, the regulation of gene expression is more complex. Genes are generally regulated individually rather than in operons. Each gene has its own promoter and several regulatory sequences called enhancers, some of which may be distant from the gene and its promoter. Multiple activators, co-activators, and repressors might be involved in the regulation of a eukaryotic gene by affecting the condensation of the DNA, by interacting with the promoter, or by interacting with regulatory sequences. This complex regulation allows the rate of transcription to be modulated as needed.

GETTING STARTED

1 Discuss the variety of human cells and the role of proteins in cellular functions. Ask the class to suggest several types of cells that can be found in a human. Record students' responses on the board or chart paper. If students studied the *Science and Global Issues* "Cell Biology: World Health" unit, they should be able to name at least the following: red and white blood cells, skin cells, nerve cells, muscle cells, and liver cells. Next, ask the class to list similarities between these cells. They should be able to name a variety of organelles contained in each, as well as the nucleus and genetic material. Emphasize that every somatic cell in a human contains the same chromosomes with the same set of genes, but the phenotype—expression of the genes—differs from one type of cell to another.

Remind students that in the "Cell Biology" unit they explored the functions of proteins as the "doers" in the cell. Point out that even though every cell contains the same genome, each cell only needs to make those proteins it requires for doing its job in the body. For example, only certain cells in the mouth make salivary enzymes, and no other cell in the body needs to make those. Explain that in this activity, students will investigate how the types and amounts of proteins produced by a cell are regulated.

---

17 Cell Differentiation and Gene Expression

1   **I**N MOST HUMAN cells, the nucleus contains a full set of 23 pairs of chromosomes, which carry 20,000–25,000 genes. These genes are identical from cell to cell. In Activity 16, "Protein Synthesis: Transcription and Translation," you learned that genes are transcribed to produce RNA, and that this RNA is in turn translated to produce proteins. If all cells in the same organism have the same genes, why don't they all make the same proteins?

Some proteins are made by almost every cell because they are needed for basic cell functions. Other proteins are made by only one type of cell or small groups of cells. Only white blood cells, for example, make antibodies, the proteins that help the body fight infections. Each of the more than 220 kinds of specialized cells in the human body makes a characteristic group of proteins.

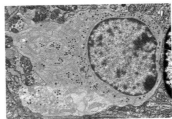

Although the two human cells shown have the same genes in their nuclei, they are specialized to make different proteins. The skeletal muscle cells, top, are specialized for voluntary muscle movement, while the thyroid cell, left, makes large amounts of thyroid hormone.

376

DOING THE ACTIVITY

2 The karyotype image in the Student Book shows the 23 pairs of chromosomes in a human cell. In this activity, students will only work with one chromosome from pair 2 and one chromosome from pair 11, which are sufficient for showing the principles of gene regulation.

In each cell, only some of the genes are active, or **expressed**. The activity of genes in a cell is called **gene expression.** In this activity, you will explore how some genes are turned on and off by molecules called transcription factors. These molecules control the transcription of DNA into RNA.

Challenge

▶ How does the same set of genes direct the activities of 220 human cell types?

MATERIALS:

FOR EACH GROUP	FOR EACH STUDENT
set of 14 Cellular Event Cards	model of human chromosome 2
FOR EACH PAIR OR STUDENTS	model of human chromosome 11
3 colored pencils (blue, brown, and orange)	4 silver binder clips
	7 red paper clips
	7 green paper clips
	Student Sheet 17.1, "Chromosome Map"
	Student Sheet 2.3, "Genetics Case Study Comparison," from Activity 2
	3 sticky notes

Procedure

Part A: Gene Expression in Differentiated Cells

1. You will look at a small number of genes on two human chromosomes: chromosome 2 and chromosome 11. Identify these chromosomes in the diagram below.

2

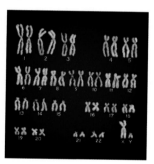

Human male karyotype

3 The genes listed in Tables 1 and 2 are based on actual genes found on human chromosome 2 and chromosome 11. For this activity they have been given generic names that relate to familiar functions. Make sure that the class understands that each gene shown in tables 1 and 2 represents a segment of DNA on chromosome 2 and chromosome 11, respectively.

4 Remind students that they investigated the differentiation of specialized cells from stem cells in the "Cell Biology" unit. As a zygote matures, differentiation factors signal cell lines to differentiate into endoderm, mesoderm, and ectoderm, and eventually into the 220 human cell types. Introduce or review the functions of the four cells students investigate in this activity. Beta cells in the pancreas produce the protein hormone insulin, which regulates cellular uptake and metabolism of sugars and fats. Developing red blood cells produce hemoglobin, a transport protein that carries oxygen to every other cell in the body. This activity specifies developing red blood cells, which still have nuclei and have not yet fully matured. These cells differentiate in the bone marrow. Intestinal lining cells produce enzymes that contribute to specific steps of digestion. And finally, smooth muscle cells in the digestive system contract or relax in waves that move food through the digestive tract.

---

3 2. You will investigate the expression of only 11 of the approximately 25,000 human genes. Review the proteins these 11 genes produce and their functions in the two tables below.

Selected Genes on Human Chromosome 2	
PROTEIN PRODUCED BY THE GENE	**FUNCTION**
Actin, smooth muscle type	Most cells produce actin for cell movement and cell division, but muscle cells produce large amounts of specific types of actin for muscle contraction.
AGA enzyme	Breaks down fats and some toxic substances
Cellular respiration enzyme	Catalyzes reactions for aerobic respiration in the mitochondria
Lactase enzyme	Required for digestion of lactose, the sugar in milk
Protein synthesis initiator	Controls the beginning of protein synthesis
Ribosome protein S7	Needed by ribosomes, which are essential for protein synthesis

Selected Genes on Human Chromosome 11	
PROTEIN PRODUCED BY THE GENE	**FUNCTION**
Cell growth controller	Prevents cells from dividing unless more cells are needed, helps prevent certain cancers
DNA repair	Repairs damage to DNA and helps to prevent certain types of cancer
Fat and protein breakdown enzyme	Catalyzes one step in the breakdown of proteins and fats in the diet so they can be used for energy
Hemoglobin B	Carries oxygen to the cells throughout the body
Insulin	A hormone that regulates the metabolism of sugars and fats

4 3. Each member of your group will look at gene activity in one of four kinds of specialized cells shown below. With your group, decide what kind of cell each of you will investigate.

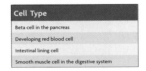

Cell Type
Beta cell in the pancreas
Developing red blood cell
Intestinal lining cell
Smooth muscle cell in the digestive system

378

5 Assist students as they interpret the information in the table, "Genes Expressed in Four Types of Human Cells." Help them to understand that a minus sign indicates that the gene is inactive in that particular cell type, and, therefore, never produces a protein product. A plus sign indicates that the gene is expressed and the cell produces its protein, at least some of the time. As they will learn in Part B, the levels of gene expression and protein production can fluctuate, depending on physiological events.

6 Student Sheet 17.1, "Chromosome Map" is shown at the end of this activity.

Have students compare their results. They should notice that:

1. There is a group of genes that is active in every cell. Stress that these carry out functions that all cells must perform at least some of the time.

2. There is a group of specialized genes (the ones that code for actin, hemoglobin, insulin, and lactase), which are only active in one of the four specific cell types.

3. One of the proteins (the one for AGA enzyme) is not produced by any of their cells. This enzyme helps destroy toxic substances and is found only in the liver.

---

5 4. Read the table below. It shows which of the 11 genes on chromosomes 2 and 11 are expressed in your cell.

Genes Expressed in Four Types of Human Cells

PROTEIN PRODUCED BY THE GENE	BETA CELL IN PANCREAS	DEVELOPING RED BLOOD CELL	INTESTINAL LINING CELL	SMOOTH MUSCLE CELL IN THE DIGESTIVE SYSTEM
Actin, smooth muscle type	–	–	–	+
AGA enzyme	–	–	–	–
Cell growth controller	+	+	+	+
Cellular respiration enzyme	+	+	+	+
DNA repair protein	+	+	+	+
Fat and protein breakdown enzyme	+	+	+	+
Hemoglobin B	–	+	–	–
Insulin	+	–	–	–
Lactase	–	–	+	–
Protein synthesis initiator	+	+	+	+
Ribosome protein S7	+	+	+	+

Key: + = active gene, – = repressed gene

6 5. Based on the information in the table above:

a. On Student Sheet 17.1, "Chromosome Map," find the chromosomes for your cell. Draw a single, dark brown line in the position of each gene that is not expressed in your cell type. These genes are still present, but they are never expressed in your cell, and are permanently turned off, or **repressed.** Your teacher will help you with the first example.

b. On Student Sheet 17.1, "Chromosome Map," draw a single, dark blue line in the position of any gene that is expressed *only* in your cell type. This is one of a number of genes that produce specialized proteins that help your cell perform its role in the human body.

c. On Student Sheet 17.1, "Chromosome Map," draw a single, dark orange line in the position of any gene that is expressed in *all four* cell types. This is a gene that produces proteins that nearly all cells need if they are to function.

d. Compare the chromosomes for your cell on Student Sheet 17.1, "Chromosome Map," with the others in your group. Copy the diagrams from their cells onto Student Sheet 17.1 to have a full set of diagrams.

7 Demonstrate how to place the paper clips over the genes as shown in the image on the next page. Note that since each student is modeling gene expression in one of four types of human cells (as determined in Part A), each student will model a different pattern of gene expression, based on the directions given on each Cellular Event card.

Make sure students understand that silver binder clips represent long-term repressors and have been placed on genes that have been permanently shut off. The paper clips represent activators (green) and repressors (red) that act on a relatively shorter-term basis. Students should record the events that affect gene expression on their chromosome and the result as shown in the sample student tables for gene expression on the next page.

8 Allot time for students to work through the entire deck of cards. If time is limited, SEPUP recommends that students select and work through at least 10 of the 14 cards.

---

6. Obtain a model of chromosomes 2 and 11. Place a silver binder clip over each gene that is permanently repressed in your cell type. This silver binder clip represents a specific **transcription factor**, a molecule that controls the transcription of DNA into RNA. This particular repressor permanently turns off genes that your cell does not need.

Part B: Differentiated Cells at Work

7. Prepare a table like the one below, in your science notebook.

Gene Expression

Cellular event	Affected gene and result

8. Shuffle the deck of Cellular Event Cards, and place it in the middle of your table. Put your models of chromosome 2 and chromosome 11 nearby.

9. Select one member of your group to start. That person will draw a card from the top of the deck and read it to the group.

7 10. Based on the information on the card, each member of the group determines which genes in their cells are activated to make proteins at this time, and which genes in their cells are repressed at this time. Follow directions on the card to place transcription factors that determine whether the genes are expressed, or temporarily repressed. These transcription factors include both activators (green paper clips) and repressors (red paper clips) that bind to portions of the DNA that regulate the gene. Place the paper clips on the appropriate gene on your model chromosomes.

Key: Transcription activator = green paper clip
Transcription repressor = red paper clip

11. For your cell, record the event, the affected gene, and the result in the table in your science notebook.

8 12. The next person, clockwise, in your group selects the next card from the top of the deck. Repeat Steps 10–11.

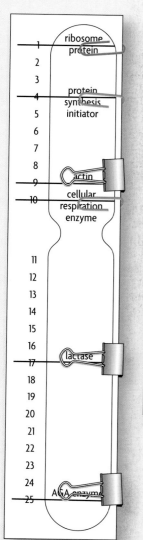

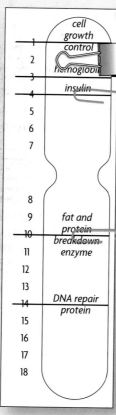

Sample Student Response: Cellular Events Affecting All Cell Types

Cellular event	Affected gene and result
Cell needs energy. (Card 1)	Cell respiration gene is activated to start cellular respiration.
Cells have enough ribosomes for now. (Card 2)	A repressor is attached to the ribosomal protein to decrease production of the ribosome protein.
A full meal of protein and fat (Card 3)	An activator is added to the gene for fat and protein breakdown enzymes.
Proteins are needed. (Card 6)	The protein synthesis initiator gene is expressed.
Meal high in carbohydrates, low in protein and fat (Card 13)	Activator is removed from the fat and protein breakdown enzyme gene.

Sample Student Response: Cellular Events Specific to the Pancreatic Beta Cell

Cellular event	Affected gene and result
Beta cell released its insulin and now needs more. (Card 7)	The insulin gene is activated to make more insulin.
The beta cell has enough insulin. (Card 8)	The insulin gene is repressed.

Sample Student Response: Cellular Events Specific to the Intestinal Lining Cell

Cellular event	Affected gene and result
Milk is present in the small intestines. (Card 4)	The lactase gene is expressed to increase production of lactase enzyme.
There is no milk in the small intestines. (Card 5)	The lactase gene is repressed to decrease production of the lactase enzyme.
No more intestinal cells are needed. (Card 10)	The cell cycle control gene is activated, and prevents the cell from dividing.

Sample Student Response:
Cellular Events Specific to the Developing Red Blood Cell

Cellular event	Affected gene and result
The cell must make a large amount of hemoglobin. (Card 12)	Two activators are placed on the hemoglobin gene so that the gene is expressed at a high level.

Sample Student Response: Cellular Events Specific to the Smooth Muscle Cell

Cellular event	Affected gene and result
Cell is about to start a new cell cycle, when it will replicate its DNA and divide. (Card 9)	The DNA repair protein is activated and suppresses the cell-growth control gene.
Cell is growing and must produce actin. (Card 11)	The actin gene is activated.
The cell is mature. (Card 14)	Activators and repressors are removed from the actin gene.

9 Each of the four students in a group will have observed a different pattern of gene expression because they each modeled a specific differentiated cell. Once groups have compared chromosome 2 and chromosome 11, ask the class to share the basic sorts of events and results that happened to all cells, and then to each cell type. This will be especially useful if students did not work through the entire deck of cards.

FOLLOW-UP

10 Groups should state that a) the types of transcription factors modeled by the paper clips were activators and repressors, and b) physiological events, such as those related to growth, hormone production, energy production, and digestion, caused differences in gene expression.

11 (LITERACY) This case study discusses current technology for engineering genetically modified organisms that do not transfer their traits to wild populations. As students read, encourage them to follow the literacy strategy, "Read, Think, and Take Note." Students should record key information from the case study on their Student Sheet 2.3, "Genetics Case Study Comparison." Project a transparency of Student Sheet 2.3, and discuss students' summaries. A sample summary is shown at right.

13. Continue selecting cards and determining which genes are affected until your teacher tells you to stop.

9 14. Compare your cell's chromosome 2 to those of the other members of your group. Discuss and record in your science notebook any similarities and differences you observe in the genes that are expressed and repressed.

15. Compare your cell's chromosome 11 to those of the other members of your group. Discuss and record in your science notebook any similarities and differences you observe in the genes that are expressed and repressed.

10 16. Discuss with your group

   a. the types of transcription factors that the paper clips represent.

   b. the types of changes in the cell or its environment that led to the need to turn the genes on and off.

11 Part C: Terminator Technology Case Study

17. Individually read the case study on the next pages. As you read, follow the literacy strategy, "Read, Think, and Take Note."

18. Share your thinking with your group. Place your sticky notes on the table in front of you. Look for connections between your sticky notes and the notes of others in your group.

   Hint: Were there common questions people asked? Were people unfamiliar with the same words? Did people react differently to statements in the reading?

19. Place your sticky notes in your science notebook. Below them, write a short summary of what your group discussed and any conclusions you came to.

20. Record the appropriate information from this case study on Student Sheet 2.3, "Genetics Case Study Comparison."

Sample Case Study Summary for Student Sheet 2.3, "Genetics Case Study Comparison"

Case study	Type of genetic modification	Benefits	Risks and concerns	Current status of research and development	Other solutions?
Terminator Technology	GURT: genetic modifications that allow humans to control gene expression in plants It either makes the plants produce sterile seeds, or the GM trait is not expressed unless a chemical is applied.	Provides control of gene expression in GM plants Helps prevent spread of engineered genes to wild plant populations	Not always 100% effective The engineered genes might still be passed on through cross breeding with the second type of GURT technology. Long-term consequences are not known. Farmers must purchase new seeds or chemicals each year to control the GURT plants.	Still being worked on to improve effectiveness Currently plants containing GURT are not sold.	Regulate where and how GM plants are grown to prevent cross-pollination

CASE STUDY

Terminator Technology

WITH GENETICALLY MODIFIED plants, one concern often raised is that they may spread engineered genes into plant populations that are not genetically modified. This can happen when genetically modified (GM) plants crossbreed with non-GM plants and produce hybrids, and may have unintended consequences in non-GM plant populations. For this reason, the United States Department of Agriculture and a private biotechnology company teamed up in the early 1990s to develop genetic use restriction technology, or GURT. GURT is a type of genetic modification that allows people to control gene expression in GM plants, thus earning it the nickname "terminator technology." By engineering GM plants that contain both a set of desired traits and GURT, scientists hope to develop plants that do not spread engineered genes to non-GM populations.

Two main types of GURT have been developed. The first type causes the GM plants to produce sterile seeds. It does this by activating and repressing a series of genes related to seed development. The advantage of this type of GURT is that the genetic modification cannot be passed on to other generations of plants, since the plant cannot reproduce. It is also financially advantageous for the company or group that owns the patent for the GM plant because it ensures that the seeds from one generation cannot be saved and grown again in the following years. Farmers would have to buy new seed each year.

The second type of GURT controls the phenotype of the GM plant. The genetically modified

GURT was developed to help prevent GM plants, such as the rice at left, from breeding with non-GM plants, such as the rice at right, when the GM rice is planted in fields.

382

12 ✓ Analysis Questions 1 and 2 ask students to summarize two key points: 1) all cells in the same organism have the same genes and chromosomes, and 2) even though each student started with the same two chromosomes and 11 genes, through selective gene expression, each of the four cells displayed a specific pattern of gene expression and repression. Analysis Question 5 serves as a Quick Check to assess students understanding of how gene expression is connected to cell function.

SAMPLE RESPONSES

1. a. The chromosomes were identical in each of the four cells.

   b. The genes were identical in each of the four cells.

   c. Gene expression in each of the four cells varied based on the cell type and the events that affected the cell.

2. The types of genes that were permanently inactivated in some cells included the genes for functions unique to certain other cells. For example, the gene for hemoglobin was inactivated in all but the red blood cell. This inactivation takes place because there is no need for a cell to make proteins not needed for its function in the body.

3. The proteins related to cell growth, energy production, DNA repair, fat and protein breakdown, and protein synthesis were made by all four of the cell types. This is because these proteins play an essential role in the growth and survival of all cells.

4. Gene expression was increased or decreased short term by the production of activators that turned on gene expression or repressors that turned off gene expression.

plants would only express the GM gene if the plant were treated with a specific chemical. When the chemical is applied to the plants, the gene for the GM trait is activated. This approach allows seed growers and farmers to control when the GM genes are expressed. It also means that if the GM plants were to crossbreed with non-GM plants, the GM gene would not be expressed unless the chemical was reapplied.

As with any form of technology there are benefits and drawbacks. While scientists have identified genes that can be activated and repressed, field trials have shown that the control of gene expression in GURT plants has not been 100% effective. This means that the seeds will not always be sterile, or that the GM gene is expressed even though the chemical has not been applied. Scientists are also unsure of the long-term performance of terminator technology. They do not yet know what will happen several generations down the line if GURT plants crossbreed with non-GM plants.

Farmers, environmentalists, indigenous-peoples' groups, and some governments have objected to the application of terminator technology for a number of reasons. One is that the farmers who want such plants need to purchase seeds and the activating chemicals from the seed companies each year. Many farmers around the world save seed from one generation of plants to produce the next year's crops. While the terminator technology addresses the fear of gene spread, farmers might not be able to afford to pay for new seeds each year.

Because so many objections were raised, several countries, including India and Brazil, have passed laws prohibiting the planting of GURT seeds. In 2006, the United Nations Convention on Biological Diversity recommended halting all field-testing and commercial release of terminator technology, citing concerns about inadequate research on the unintended spread of the genes into

GURT would prevent gene spread, but would not allow farmers to save seeds from one year's crop to plant the next year's.

non-GM populations of plants. As of mid-2010, seeds engineered to have terminator abilities were still not commercially available. However, research in the development, use, and safety of terminator technology continues. ■

383

5. ✓ Student answers will vary depending on their cell types. One possible response follows.

   Gene expression causes the cell to only make the types and amounts of proteins the cell needs. My cell was a pancreatic beta cell. Gene expression ensured that it made insulin, but didn't make hemoglobin or other unneeded proteins. Gene expression also let the cell respond to short-term changes, such as the need to grow and respire.

6. GURT activates transcription factors that stop GM plants from passing traits to non-GM plants. It does this by activating and repressing genes required for either seed production or trait expression.

7. a. GURT was designed to stop GM plants from transferring genes to non-GM plants. One type of GURT prevents successful breeding with non-GM plants, keeping engineered genes from passing into other crops or wild populations. A second type of GURT allows control of the expression of the gene by requiring application of a chemical to activate the gene. Otherwise the gene is not expressed.

   b. GURT can be beneficial because it allows humans to control the expression of GM genes and to prevent the spread of GM genes into non-GM populations. On the other hand, research studies have shown that GURT is less than 100% effective, and the long-term effects of the technology are uncertain. If GURT is used in crops, there is less chance that the GM genes or traits will spread to non-GM populations. But it will most likely cost more to use the GURT-containing seed.

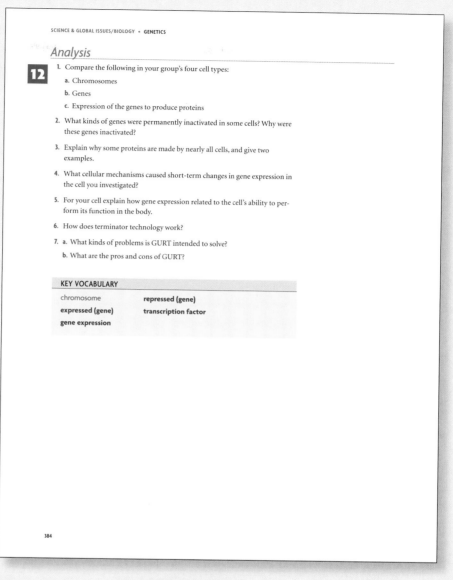

SCIENCE & GLOBAL ISSUES/BIOLOGY • GENETICS

Analysis

12

1. Compare the following in your group's four cell types:
   a. Chromosomes
   b. Genes
   c. Expression of the genes to produce proteins

2. What kinds of genes were permanently inactivated in some cells? Why were these genes inactivated?

3. Explain why some proteins are made by nearly all cells, and give two examples.

4. What cellular mechanisms caused short-term changes in gene expression in the cell you investigated?

5. For your cell explain how gene expression related to the cell's ability to perform its function in the body.

6. How does terminator technology work?

7. a. What kinds of problems is GURT intended to solve?
   b. What are the pros and cons of GURT?

KEY VOCABULARY

chromosome   repressed (gene)
expressed (gene)   transcription factor
gene expression

384

REVIST THE CHALLENGE

Students should be able to explain how the same set of genes can direct the activity of 220 different human cell types by differential gene expression. Students should be able to explain that this process is controlled by transcription factors, proteins that activate and repress the expression of genes. Differential gene expression occurs during development of a cell as it differentiates into an adult cell, and in response to physiological events.

Chromosome Map

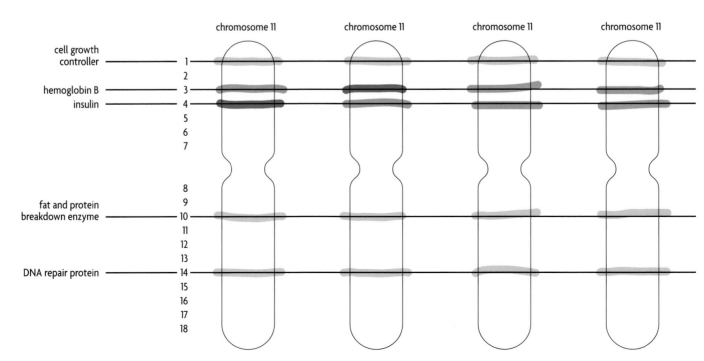

CELL TYPE:	beta cell in pancreas	developing red blood cell	intestinal lining cell	smooth muscle cell
GENE	chromosome 2	chromosome 2	chromosome 2	chromosome 2

ribosome protein — 1
2
protein synthesis initiator — 3
4
5
6
7
actin, smooth muscle type — 8
9
cellular respiration enzyme — 10
11
12
13
14
15
16
lactase — 17
18
19
20
21
22
23
24
AGA enzyme — 25

	chromosome 11	chromosome 11	chromosome 11	chromosome 11

cell growth controller — 1
2
hemoglobin B — 3
insulin — 4
5
6
7
8
fat and protein breakdown enzyme — 9
10
11
12
13
DNA repair protein — 14
15
16
17
18

18 Which Corn Is Genetically Modified?

LABORATORY • 2 CLASS SESSIONS

OVERVIEW

Students run and interpret a gel electrophoresis test to determine which corn samples contain genetically modified Bt corn. Students read a case study on virus-resistant papaya and the benefits and risks of this GM crop.

KEY CONTENT

1. In all organisms, the instructions for specifying the characteristics of the organism are in the genes.

2. Understanding DNA makes it possible for scientists to manipulate genes and thereby create new combinations of traits and new varieties of organisms.

3. DNA electrophoresis separates DNA based on size.

4. DNA electrophoresis is a method of using known samples and markers to match DNA.

KEY PROCESS SKILLS

1. Students conduct investigations.

2. Students make and record observations.

3. Students develop conclusions based on evidence.

4. Students identify and describe trade-offs.

MATERIALS AND ADVANCE PREPARATION

For the teacher
agar*
sodium bicarbonate powder*
gel combs*
electrophoresis trays*
masking tape*
1-L beaker or flask*
large beaker (500-mL or greater)*
hotplate or access to a microwave*
balance*
scoop*

water*
Transparency 18.1, "DNA Fingerprints"
Transparency 18.2, "DNA Electrophoresis Image"
Transparency of Student Sheet 2.3, "Genetics Case Study Comparison"
Scoring Guide: COMMUNICATION SKILLS (CS) (optional)

For the class
access to online DNA gel electrophoresis simulation (optional)*

For every two groups of four students
electrophoresis chamber with lid and power supply*
575 mL of electrophoresis buffer solution (0.2% sodium bicarbonate solution)*
electrical outlet*

For each group of four students
agar gel in electrophoresis tray*
tray for carrying gel*
30-mL bottle of DNA samples from each of the following:
    sample of farm A corn
    sample of farm B corn
    sample of farm C corn
30-mL bottle of Bt DNA
30-mL bottle of glycerin*
30-mL bottle of water*
Chemplate®
4 pipettes (see note below)*
4 SEPUP stir sticks
cup of water*
paper towels*

For each student
Student Sheet 2.3, "Genetics Case Study Comparison," from Activity 2
Scoring Guide: COMMUNICATION SKILLS (CS) (optional)
safety goggles*

Not supplied in kit

Masters for Literacy Student Sheets are in Teacher Resources III: Literacy. Masters for Scoring Guides are in Teacher Resources IV: Assessment.

Note: *Instructions for this activity are based on using SEPUP electrophoresis equipment. If you will be using other equipment, read the entire activity in advance and modify the instructions as appropriate. The simulated DNA samples can be used in any electrophoresis equipment.*

If you have micropipettes of the appropriate size, they may be easier for students to use for loading the gels. If using the provided pipettes, students may need to practice their pipetting skills before starting the lab.

Begin the advance preparation for this activity at least one day before students run their gels. Note that the class will spend one class period preparing prior to running the gels. See Teaching Suggestion 2 for information on how this procedure differs from a typical DNA gel electrophoresis laboratory.

Ideally, you should prepare enough gels for all classes. If classes will not perform the laboratory on the same day, decide how you will stagger when classes conduct the laboratory.

Prepare the buffer

You will need 200 mL of sodium bicarbonate buffer solution to make each gel. You will also need to prepare an additional 575 mL of buffer solution for each two groups that will run a gel. Calculate the total amount of buffer solution you will need. To prepare the buffer, dissolve 2 g sodium bicarbonate in 1 L water.

Prepare the electrophoresis gels

Decide how many gels you will prepare. Prepare several sample gels for demonstration and practice purposes. Create a tight seal at each end of the tray with masking tape, as shown in the photo below. For each gel, dissolve 2 g agar in 200 mL sodium bicarbonate solution. Heat the solution in a beaker until

boiling, stirring frequently. If you have access to a hot plate with a magnetic stirring device, set the stir function on low to medium speed. If you are using a microwave, stop it occasionally, and stir the solution. Once the solution has started gently boiling and the agar is completely dissolved (the solution will become significantly less cloudy), allow the agar solution to cool until you can pick up the beaker. Place the gel comb in the notches in the tray, as shown in the photo below. Pour the warm agar solution into each tray to the fill line. Allow the gel to set with the gel comb in place. With moderate temperature and humidity, this takes approximately one hour but can vary. Gels may be left overnight, but should be used the next day. Do NOT refrigerate the gels. If you plan to store them overnight after they have set, place them in the chambers with buffer solution, cover each with plastic wrap, and keep them in a cool place. Carefully remove the masking tape before using the gels.

To minimize the time needed for this laboratory and avoid the toxic substances and expensive equipment required for a typical DNA gel electrophoresis, this activity has been developed using a mixture of dyes instead of actual DNA. The samples students study in this activity represent samples that have already been cut into pieces by enzymes and are ready to be run through a gel. At some point during the activity you may want to discuss this with the students, being sure to emphasize that the process of electrophoresis is the same, and the dyes separate in the same manner as DNA. The main differences are that the samples do not need to be prepared, cut with restriction enzymes, or tagged (e.g., with ethidium bromide, a mutagen), nor is special viewing equipment (e.g., UV lightbox) needed to see the samples after they have run through the gel. Also, this activity can be run in its entirety within one standard class period if students are introduced to the process and equipment the day before. If your district or state standards require performing a gel electrophoresis laboratory with actual DNA, have students run it with the dyes first to gain experience with the equipment.

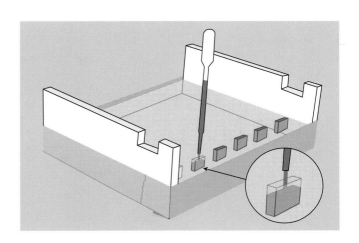

SAFETY NOTE

Most of the solutions for this activity are not considered hazardous. The dye solutions that represent the DNA samples are mild irritants, and proper precautions should be taken. Have students wear goggles while conducting this lab, and tell them to wash their hands after completing the laboratory. The dye solutions will stain clothing and may stain other materials. Check with your local, district, and state standards regarding proper disposal methods. Students should wear safety goggles at all times during this activity.

Check that the lid is properly secured to the electrophoresis chamber before the power supply is plugged in. Do not plug in the power supply without buffer in the chamber.

TEACHING SUMMARY

Getting Started

- Introduce the scenario.

Doing the Activity

- Review how to set up the electrophoresis chamber and run the samples on the gel.

- (LITERACY) Students set up the chamber and run the samples on the gel.

Follow-up

- The class discusses their results.

GETTING STARTED

1 Project Transparency 18.1, "DNA Fingerprints," and review it with the class. Ask the class what conclusions they can draw from comparing the different DNA fingerprints. Students should conclude that the mother's and father's DNA show similarities to about half of their child's DNA, while they show very few similarities to the unrelated child. This is because half of an offspring's DNA comes from each parent.

18 Which Corn is Genetically Modified?

THE GENETICS LABORATORY *you work for has been hired to help solve a dilemma. In your community is a corn silo that holds corn from several farms in the same area. To export the corn, it must be certified as not genetically modified. Local officials hired your lab to test the corn, and it turned out that some kernels in the silo contained a gene from* Bacillus thuringeinsis (Bt), *which is only found in genetically modified Bt corn. Now your lab must trace back the genetically modified corn to determine which farm or farms were growing Bt corn.*

If a gene does not affect the physical appearance of an organism, how do we determine the presence of an engineered gene? One method is through DNA fingerprinting. While all organisms contain DNA, every individual organism contains a unique patern of DNA sequences called a "DNA fingerprint." DNA fingerprints, like those shown below, allow scientists to compare the DNA of one organism to another.

1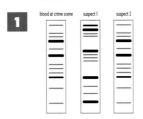

Comparing the DNA fingerprints of blood found at a crime scene to blood samples from two suspects allows investigators to determine if one of the suspects was at the crime scene.

In DNA fingerprinting enzymes cut a sample of an organism's DNA into small pieces, which are then separated, based on their weight, through a process called **gel electrophoresis.** The lighter the DNA, the further it will move through the gel in a fixed amount of time. Pieces of the same size form a band in the gel. The more pieces of the same size, the thicker the band will be. Only samples from the same individual (or identical twins) will have an identical pattern of bands in their DNA. In this activity, you will use gel electrophoresis to analyze DNA samples from several farms. This procedure will allow you to find the source of the Bt corn.

2 Review DNA electrophoresis with the class. You may want to show an online animation to preview the process with the class. A link to a suggested animation is on the *Science and Global Issues* page of the SEPUP website *(sepuplhs.org/sgi)*.

Before they begin the laboratory, be sure students understand that DNA electrophoresis is a technique that separates DNA based on size. DNA is a negatively charged molecule. In the presence of an electric field created with positive and negative electrodes, DNA will move toward the positive electrode (usually indicated with red). The distance a DNA piece travels in an electrophoresis gel is determined by its size. Smaller pieces travel faster and farther in a gel. DNA electrophoresis identifies the presence of a piece of DNA of known size. This is accomplished by running a known sample along with other samples. When bands appear in the same horizontal location on the gel, it can be inferred that the DNA pieces are the same size.

Project Transparency 18.2, "DNA Electrophoresis Image." The "DNA length standard" sample in the left column serves as a ruler. This column shows bands of known length (measured in base pairs). They help determine the size of the other bands that formed on the gel. Students will not have a standard-length ruler when they run a gel in this activity. Direct students' attention to the DNA band in the positive control lane. Explain that this sample contains the Bt gene. Ask students, *According to this gel image, which samples contain the Bt gene? How can you tell?*

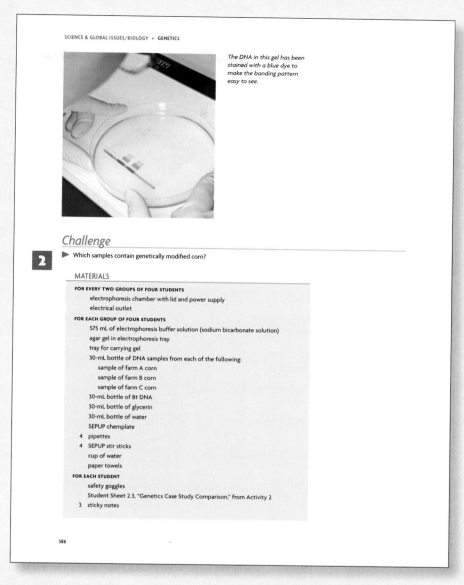

SCIENCE & GLOBAL ISSUES/BIOLOGY • GENETICS

The DNA in this gel has been stained with a blue dye to make the banding pattern easy to see.

Challenge

2 ▶ Which samples contain genetically modified corn?

MATERIALS

FOR EVERY TWO GROUPS OF FOUR STUDENTS
electrophoresis chamber with lid and power supply
electrical outlet

FOR EACH GROUP OF FOUR STUDENTS
575 mL of electrophoresis buffer solution (sodium bicarbonate solution)
agar gel in electrophoresis tray
tray for carrying gel
30-mL bottle of DNA samples from each of the following:
    sample of farm A corn
    sample of farm B corn
    sample of farm C corn
30-mL bottle of Bt DNA
30-mL bottle of glycerin
30-mL bottle of water
SEPUP chemplate
4 pipettes
4 SEPUP stir sticks
cup of water
paper towels

FOR EACH STUDENT
safety goggles
Student Sheet 2.3, "Genetics Case Study Comparison," from Activity 2
3 sticky notes

386

Both of the corn chip and one of the corn meal samples shown on the transparency have the gene. Students should point out that the band with the DNA for the Bt gene is present in these samples. Tell students that they will run a simulated gel that helps them determine which farm or farms were growing Bt corn. You may want to remind them that only in the case of identical twins or clones (e.g., some asexually reproducing species) will the DNA be exactly the same.

DOING THE ACTIVITY

3 Have students read the entire Procedure the day before they do it. They will need as much time as possible to run the gel, and so any structure, such as a flow chart or notes on the procedure steps, that will expedite their work on the day of the laboratory is helpful.

4 Allow sufficient time to review the procedures and techniques students will follow when performing the lab. Prepare a sample dye mixture and gel to demonstrate how to set up a gel for a run. For the mixture take one of the DNA samples and mix 2 drops of that sample with 2 drops of glycerin and 2 drops of water. Let students practice filling the pipette, putting the pipette in the correct position over a well, and filling a well. Show students how to set up the chambers, but do not run the gel.

5 On the day that students run the gel, they should take care but work quickly in setting up their gels according to Procedure Steps 3–7. The electrophoresis chambers are designed for two groups to run their gels simultaneously. Instruct students on how you would like the groups to alternate setting up their gels. The gels must be in place in the chamber with the buffer poured in, before students load any samples. Ask students to notify you when they reach Procedure Step 7. Check their setups before they plug in the power source, and that the lid is properly secured to the chamber. The gels should fit into the notches in the chamber so that the wells are nearest the black end of the chamber. If the chamber lid is fogging up, smear a small drop of liquid dish soap on the inside of the lid. More information can be found in the Advance Preparation section at the beginning of the Teacher's Edition for this Activity.

Procedure

Part A: Analyzing DNA Samples

3 1. Follow your teacher's instructions for recording notes on this laboratory.

4 2. Watch carefully as your teacher demonstrates how to set up the electrophoresis chamber and run the samples in the agar gel.

5 3. According to your teacher's instructions, set up an electrophoresis chamber. Two groups will share this chamber. Place your gel in the chamber. As shown by your teacher, pour approximately 575 mL of buffer solution against the side of the electrophoresis chamber to the fill line in the chamber.

4. With your group, prepare each of the four DNA samples to be loaded into the gel—farms A, B, and C, and a control sample of Bt DNA. To prepare the samples, place 2 drops of each DNA sample into their own cup in the SEPUP chemplate. To each sample, add 2 drops of glycerin and 2 drops of water.

5. Stir the contents of each cup with a clean SEPUP stir stick. Be sure to use a fresh stir stick for each cup to prevent cross-contamination of the samples.

6. With a clean pipette transfer each DNA sample from the SEPUP tray into one well in the gel. Place sample A into well 1. Place sample B into well 2, and so on. To do this hold the pipette that contains the DNA sample directly above the well. With both hands slowly lower the tip of the pipette into the buffer solution, as shown by your teacher.

7. When both group's gels are ready, carefully place the lid of the electrophoresis chamber in place, as shown by your teacher. Make sure to put the lid on the chamber in the correct orientation, as shown by your teacher.

8. Without moving the chamber, check that the lid is on securely. Plug in the power cord to start the flow of electricity.

6 9. Allow the gel to run for 30 minutes, or until you see the samples separate in the gel.

10. Disconnect the power. Carefully take off the lid of the electrophoresis chamber. Remove your group's gel, while holding it level, and place it in the tray for carrying the gel.

11. Compare each lane of the gel to the lane that contains the control sample of the Bt DNA. With your group discuss the results. Draw a sketch of the results in your science notebook.

7 12. With your group, discuss the conclusions you might draw based on the electrophoresis results. In your discussion, explain the evidence that supports your conclusions.

Safety ⚠️

Wear safety goggles at all times during this lab. If accidental spills occur, inform your teacher immediately, and follow his or her instructions to clean up the spill. Do not plug in the power until the chamber is securely closed and keep the lid closed at all times when the power supply is plugged in.

387

---

6 Be sure students allow the gel to run long enough to see the samples separate (approximately 30 minutes), but not so long as to allow them to run off the end of the gel. After running the gel, students should see that the bands produced in the lanes containing samples from farms A and C match those of the Bt DNA sample.

While the gels are running, have students read the case study in Part B of the activity. They should record key information from the text on their copies of Student Sheet 2.3, "Genetics Case Study Comparison." A sample summary is provided on the next page. Project a transparency of Student Sheet 2.3, "Genetics Case Study Comparison," and discuss students' summaries.

Sample Case Study Summary for Student Sheet 2.3, "Genetics Case Study Comparison"

Case study	Type of genetic modification	Benefits	Risks and concerns	Current status of research and development	Other solutions?
Virus-resistant papaya	Insert gene for virus into papaya seedlings so the plant will develop immunity to the virus	Papaya plants are protected from the virus. Fewer crop losses Higher yield and profits	Possible allergic reactions (none documented) Contamination of non-GM crops Reduced diversity if everyone plants one type of GM-papaya	How to prevent contamination of non-GM papaya with GM papaya genes	Isolate the orchards Breed naturally virus-resistant trees Cross-protect the trees by spraying with mild virus so trees develop immunity

FOLLOW-UP

7 Once each student group has had a chance to compare the lanes of its gel, discuss the groups' results with the class. You might want to construct a chart on the board like the one below and tally students' results.

Presence of Bt corn detected

Bt DNA	Sample of farm A corn	Sample of farm B corn	Sample of farm C corn
yes	yes	no	yes

Ask students to describe the evidence from the activity that supports these findings. Student groups should report that the color and formation of bands in the samples from farms A and C matched those that formed in the Bt DNA sample.

Revisit the scenario presented in the introduction. Ask the class, *Where was the GM corn in the silo coming from?*

Students' results should indicate that farms A and C were growing Bt corn.

As a class discuss possible reasons why the samples contain the Bt gene. Answers include: the farm is, in fact, growing Bt corn; the original sample may have been contaminated with other corn; or pollen from a farm growing Bt corn might have traveled to the farms by wind or animal transport and fertilized the non-Bt plants. These all would result in the presence of the Bt gene in farm A's and C's samples.

Take this opportunity to discuss with the class how they could further investigate the presence of the Bt gene in the samples from these farms. Ideas include taking several additional samples and retesting them, talking to the farmer a second time, and mapping the location of farms growing Bt corn near farms A and C to determine if pollen transfer was a possibility.

Part B: Virus-resistant Papaya Case Study

13. Individually read the case study beginning on the next page. As you read, follow the literacy strategy, "Read, Think, and Take Note."

14. Share your thinking with your group. Place your sticky notes on the table in front of you. Look for connections between your sticky notes and the notes of others in your group.

    Hint: Were there common questions people asked? Were people unfamiliar with the same words? Did people react differently to statements in the reading?

15. Place your sticky notes in your science notebook. Below each, write a short summary of what your group discussed and any conclusions you came to.

16. Record the appropriate information from this case study on Student Sheet 2.3, "Genetics Case Study Comparison."

The papaya shown at top is healthy. The one at bottom has ringspot virus.

CASE STUDY

Virus-resistant Papaya

FOR YEARS, THE papaya ringspot virus has destroyed papaya crops in Central American and equatorial countries of the world. Once the virus infects a plant, an entire crop of papayas can be ruined. Traditional methods to handle the disease include isolating papaya orchards to prevent disease transmission, breeding naturally virus-resistant trees, and cross-protection. Cross-protection treats the papaya trees with a mild form of the virus, so that the trees develop immunity to it. All of these techniques have had limited success, and often work best when combined. When nothing works, the farmers' only choice, if they want to continue to grow papaya trees, is to move and start new plantations in a virus-free area.

In 1998, a scientist at Cornell University in New York State sequenced the genome of the papaya virus. Once the genome was completed, the gene that encodes for a protein in the coat of the virus was identified and isolated. Scientists used a gene gun to transport the gene and implant it in papaya seedlings. These GM seedlings grew up to be papaya plants that produced the papaya virus protein. Because the plants produced the virus coat protein, the trees developed immunity to infection by the virus, similar to the way a vaccine works. This protects the crops from ringspot virus, and keeps the crop profitable. Since the development of the genetically modified papaya, many papaya plantations in Hawaii have successfully grown papaya crops without outbreaks of ringspot infection.

(Continued on next page)

A healthy papaya tree

389

(Continued from previous page)

A major concern with genetically modified food is that a person who eats it might have an allergic reaction to the engineered protein. This has happened in other genetically modified crops where genes from one species were inserted into another. For example, a soy plant was modified with a Brazil nut gene in the mid-1990s. In testing the genetically modified soy, it was determined that the modified soy could cause severe allergic reactions in people who were allergic to nuts, and so the project was terminated. Papayas, on the other hand, have been exposed to the ringspot virus for years, which causes them to contain the coat protein. This means that humans have been ingesting the coat protein for years, and thus far there are no documented cases of allergic reaction to the genetically modified papaya.

Non-GM papaya crops in Hawaii have become contaminated by unintentional breeding with GM-papaya crops. Some studies have shown widespread contamination of non-GM papaya crops with the modified gene. This is a problem for Hawaiian farmers because some countries, including those in the European Union, will not allow import of GM crops. Scientists are currently researching the extent of the contamination, and ways to prevent its spread. Many farmers and scientists also worry that if everyone grows GM papaya, there will only be one type of papaya grown. This makes the crop susceptible to devastating losses if a disease were to infect the crop. If all of the plants have the same genome, none would be resistant to the disease. This problem occurs whenever breeding leads to most crops having very similar genomes, even when they are not genetically modified. ■

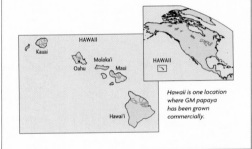

Hawaii is one location where GM papaya has been grown commercially.

8 (CS ASSESSMENT) Analysis Question 2 may be scored with the COMMUNICATION SKILLS (CS) Scoring Guide. As students write their reports, they should reference the information about the scenario in the introduction in the Student Book. You may want students to refer to the CS Scoring Guide for guidance as they write their reports. For more information on scoring guides, see Teacher Resources IV: Assessment.

Analysis

1. Look at the DNA electrophoresis results below.

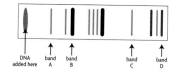

a. Which single labeled band represents the smallest pieces of DNA? Explain how you can tell.

b. Which of the labeled bands represents the most common-sized piece of DNA in this sample? Explain how you can tell.

8 2. Based on your DNA electrophoresis results, prepare a report to the city that hired you to test corn. In the report state your conclusion about which samples have been genetically modified, and explain the evidence that supports your conclusion.

3. DNA electrophoresis is one way to test for a gene in a DNA sample. Additional tests are shown in the table below. A company is deciding which test they will use to certify that the foods they manufacture do not contain genetically modified ingredients. Which test(s) would you recommend they use? In your answer, explain at least two trade-offs associated with your recommendation.

Genetic Modification Detection Tests					
TEST	WHAT IT DETECTS	SPEED OF TEST	EASE OF USE	RELIABILITY	COST
DNA electrophoresis	Inserted gene	1–2 hours	Must be conducted in a laboratory	high	$$$
ELISA protein plate	Amount of protein present	20 minutes	Can be conducted in non-laboratory setting	high	$$
ELISA protein strips	If the protein is present	5 minutes	Can be conducted in non-laboratory setting	low to moderate	$

391

9 You may want to have students discuss their responses to Analysis Question 4 in their groups or as a class. Encourage them to include the information from Student Sheet 2.3, "Genetics Case Study Comparison," in their discussions.

9

4. Policies about labeling genetically modified (GM) foods, such as GM papaya, vary from country to country. Brazil, China, Russia, and Saudi Arabia require labeling of all GM foods and products. Japan requires GM labeling for some products but allows voluntary labeling of others. The United States has a voluntary labeling policy. Certain countries will only import foods that are certified 100% GM free. In countries where labeling is mandatory, consumers often will not buy products that are not certified GM-free. What are the trade-offs of labeling genetically modified foods? Explain at least two trade-offs.

KEY VOCABULARY	
DNA	**gel electrophoresis**

SAMPLE RESPONSES

1. a. The smallest piece is represented by band D. This is the piece that moved the farthest through the gel. The smaller a piece of DNA, the farther it will move through the gel relative to the other pieces in the samples.

   b. The most common length of DNA is represented by band B. It is the thickest band, meaning it has the greatest number of DNA pieces.

2. (CS ASSESSMENT) Students' answers will vary. A complete and correct response will include a description of the data and an interpretation of the results.

Sample Level-3 Response

As requested by the community, we used DNA electrophoresis to see if the Bt gene was present in corn samples from three farms. Our results show that the DNA samples from farms A and C contain the Bt gene.

When we conducted DNA electrophoresis, the samples from farms A and C displayed the banding pattern that matched with the Bt DNA. This means that farms A and C had corn that contained the Bt gene. It's possible that the corn from their farms became contaminated with genetically modified Bt corn at some point.

Our results should be accurate. There is a possibility that we contaminated the samples while performing the investigation. For this reason we recommend running a second gel to confirm our results. Further testing should be conducted to verify the presence of the Bt gene in the farm A and farm C corn.

3. Students' responses will vary, but should include their recommendations and explain at least two trade-offs of their recommendations. A sample response follows.

I would recommend the use of the ELISA protein plate test. It is not the most expensive, has the highest reliability, and can be conducted relatively quickly in the field. One trade-off is that it only tests for the presence of the protein. If the organism contains the gene, but the gene is not expressed, the test will not detect it. Another trade-off is that it is more expensive than the ELISA protein strips.

4. One trade-off of labeling GM foods is that it adds time and cost to the production of these foods. Another trade-off is that people might assume that there is something wrong with the GM foods and not buy them.

REVISIT THE CHALLENGE

Students should be able to explain how to analyze gel electrophoresis results to determine the presence of a specific gene or genes.

19 Biopharming Edible Vaccines

READING • 1 CLASS SESSION

OVERVIEW

Students read about the biotechnology involved in creating vaccines from genetically modified plants, which some scientists hope will one day provide a way to easily deliver vaccinations.

KEY CONTENT

1. Understanding DNA makes it possible for scientists to manipulate genes to create new combinations of traits and new varieties of organisms.

2. The key steps in the creation of a genetically modified organism are: identification of a desirable gene; isolation of the gene; preparation of a DNA construct that contains the desired gene and a selectable marker; delivery of the desired gene into the target organism; and raising the transformed organisms using a selective medium to verify that the gene has been inserted into the target organism.

3. DNA constructs are inserted into organisms in several ways, including shooting them in with a gene gun, bacterial transformation, or delivering them via a virus.

4. Understanding basic concepts and principles of science and technology should precede active debate about the economics, policies, politics, and ethics of various science- and technology-related issues.

5. Human activities have a major effect on other species.

KEY PROCESS SKILLS

1. Students make accurate interpretations, inferences, and conclusions from text.

MATERIALS AND ADVANCE PREPARATION

For each pair of students
    set of 8 Genetic Modification of Lettuce Cards

TEACHING SUMMARY

Getting Started

- Review the process of transferring a gene from one organism to another.

Doing the Activity

- (LITERACY) Students read about genetically modifying plants to carry edible vaccines.

Follow-up

- Students process the information from the reading.

GETTING STARTED

1 Remind students that over the course of the unit they have read about and performed several biotechnology procedures involved in genetically modifying an organism. Ask, *How could you transfer a gene from a fish into a plant?*

Provide time for student pairs to discuss their ideas. Ask them to share their ideas, and, as they do so, record them in a list that is visible to the class. This is an opportunity for students to reflect on what they have learned about biotechnology methods over the course of the unit, and for you to determine what they understand and misunderstand before they complete the reading in this activity. Ask the class to list key things they have learned about genetic modification of organisms, and any questions they still have about them.

Have the class begin a KWL chart about genetic modification. The letters KWL refer to the three sections of a reading strategy that asks, "What do I Know? What do I Want to know? What did I Learn?" KWLs help students process and apply the information that they encountered in the reading. For more information on this strategy, refer to Teacher Resources III: Literacy. At this point the students should only fill out the first two columns. Students will fill in the third column in Procedure Steps 4, 5, and 7. Have each student copy the KWL into their science notebook where they will complete the chart during the rest of the activity. A sample KWL is shown at right.

Note: The Learned column will be filled out in Steps 4, 5, and 7 by the students.

19 Biopharming Edible Vaccines

AS YOU READ in Activity 1, "A Genetically Modified Solution?" scientists have been using genetically modified *E. coli* for more than 30 years to manufacture proteins for medicinal and industrial purposes. In the early 1990s, pharmaceutical researchers began working with genetically modified organisms to insert vaccines against diseases into the foods we eat. Their goal was to find a way to engineer a cheap, easy way to vaccinate people without needles. In many developing countries, making sure that people get their shots has been difficult because there are not enough qualified personnel and equipment. An edible vaccine contained in food would help to address these problems.

1 Throughout this unit you have been learning about genetic modification techniques—the same ones that are involved in the research on edible vaccines. In this activity you will read about how these techniques can be combined to engineer genetically modified organisms that are edible and carry vaccines.

Scientists are researching ways to genetically modify plants, such as this lettuce, to create edible vaccines.

Genetic Modification KWL

Know	Want to know	Learned
• Genes from one organism are inserted into another. Inserted genes cause the GMO to have a desired trait.	• How do the modified genes from one organism get inserted into the other organism?	• There are many methods by which to insert genes into an organism, including gene guns, and through bacteria and viruses that will infect the organism with the new gene.
• Research has shown benefits and trade-offs of GMOs.	• Are there different methods for inserting the genes?	• Scientists are developing GMOs for delivery of vaccines, but there are still problems with the vaccines working properly.
• There are many GMOs that have been developed, such as Bt corn, golden rice, and virus-resistant papayas. Not all of them are in use.	• What other uses are there for GMOs?	• We studied many of the steps for creating a vaccine-carrying GMO in class, including isolating DNA, making modified pGLO bacteria, and running gel electrophoresis.

DOING THE ACTIVITY

2 Clarify questions students may have about the images depicted on the cards as they complete Procedure Steps 1–4 and predict the order in which the cards should be arranged. As needed assist students in completing the table. The sample student response below shows the cards in the correct order. Do not correct students' predicted order until they have completed Procedure Step 7.

3 Students may complete the reading individually, in pairs, or in groups. Determine which is best for your students. Many new words and terms are introduced in this reading to broaden students' exposure to biotechnology processes. However, because they are not key vocabulary words and students are not expected to master them, the words are not included in the Key Vocabulary list. Decide which of the terms you will ask students to be responsible for learning from the following list:

selectable marker
polymerase chain reaction (PCR)
Southern blot

FOLLOW-UP

4 Procedure Steps 6 and 7 help students process the information in the reading by asking them to rearrange the cards to reflect the order presented in the reading. The correct order of the cards is: E, A, H, G, C, B, D, F. Encourage students to refer back to the reading to clarify any questions that arise about the order of the cards.

Challenge

▶ What are the benefits and trade-offs of genetically modifying crops to contain edible vaccines?

MATERIALS

FOR EACH PAIR OF STUDENTS
set of 8 Genetic Modification of Lettuce Cards

Procedure

2
1. Spread the Genetic Modification of Lettuce Cards out on the table in front of you. Each card shows a step required to genetically modify lettuce. With your partner discuss what each card shows.

2. You performed processes similar to those shown on the cards in Activity 2, "Creating Genetically Modified Bacteria," Activity 9, "Isolating DNA," and Activity 18, "Which Corn Is Genetically Modified?" With your partner look back in your science notebooks and this book to identify which of these three activities correlate to which cards. Note that an activity may correlate to just one or to multiple cards, and some cards discuss processes you have not studied.

3. Copy the table below into your science notebook, and write your ideas from Step 2 in the table.

Card	Summary of step	Activity from Genetics unit

4. With your partner, arrange the cards in the correct order for genetically modifying lettuce. Record the predicted order in your science notebook, and add any new information to the KWL chart (What do I Know? What do I Want to Know? What did I Learn?) that your class started at the beginning of the activity.

3
5. Complete the reading that follows. As you read, record any new information or questions you have in your KWL chart.

4
6. When you finish the reading, review the order of the cards with your partner. Revise the order to reflect the information given in the reading. Refer back to the text if necessary.

7. Compare the card order with the other pair in your group. Discuss any differences in the way you have ordered the cards, and come to an agreement about the order. Record the final order your group decides on in your science notebook. Add any new information to your KWL chart.

Sample Student Response for Procedure Steps 1–4

Card	Summary of step	Activity from Genetics Unit
E	DNA from virus is separated, and DNA for gene is cut out.	Activity 9: DNA Isolation (just separated DNA)
A	Add a marker gene to the DNA.	Activity 2: Creating Genetically Modified Bacteria (marker gene was already added)
H	Make copies of the DNA.	Activity 2: Creating Genetically Modified Bacteria (copies were already made)
G	DNA is put into plasmid and then bacterium.	Activity 2: Creating Genetically Modified Bacteria (plasmid was already created)
C	Bacterium transfers DNA into lettuce cells.	Activity 2: Creating Genetically Modified Bacteria
B	Lettuce cells divide.	Activity 2: Creating Genetically Modified Bacteria
D	Lettuce cells grow and make new protein.	Activity 2: Creating Genetically Modified Bacteria
F	Test for new gene in lettuce using gel electrophoresis.	Activity 18: Which Corn Is Genetically Modified?

Reading: Edible Vaccines

Imagine there was a way to be vaccinated against hepatitis B simply by eating a bowlful of lettuce instead of getting a shot. Currently most vaccines come in the form of an injection given by a doctor, nurse, or skilled technician. The vaccines must be kept refrigerated, and some of the shots hurt more than others. Edible vaccines, such as a vaccine in lettuce, would eliminate these problems. Vaccine lettuce is just one example of a genetically modified organism engineered by scientists working in the growing field of molecular farming, also known as biopharming. They are researching ways to insert genes into plants and animals. These genes would cause the organisms to produce proteins for pharmaceutical purposes.

Making an Edible Vaccine

Vaccines have been successful weapons against diseases since the 1800s. They have nearly eradicated polio and smallpox around the world and have prevented millions of children from getting measles, mumps, and rubella. Most vaccines are based on a protein from the virus that causes the particular disease, which triggers an immune system response in our bodies. The virus protein in the vaccine is not enough to actually cause the disease. Instead, when the vaccine is injected the immune system responds the same way it would to fight the disease, eventually making the person immune to the disease.

Creating an edible vaccine from a genetically modified organism relies on the same principles as making other genetically modified organisms. Scientists must first isolate the DNA from the disease agent. Just as you did in Activity 9, "Isolating DNA," scientists lyse (break down) the cell membrane with a detergent and then apply alcohol to precipitate (separate) out the DNA from the other material.

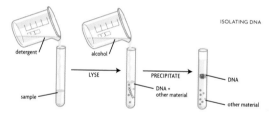

After the DNA is isolated, scientists extract the correct gene from the DNA and make copies of that gene. To do this, they use a process called PCR (polymerase chain reaction). The gene is heated to separate the DNA double helix strand, and then an enzyme and single nucleotides are added. Each separated strand is copied to form a double-stranded segment of DNA. This process is repeated through many cycles to make multiple copies of the gene. The diagram below shows the eight copies produced by three cycles of PCR. After 20 cycles over one million copies of the gene will be produced.

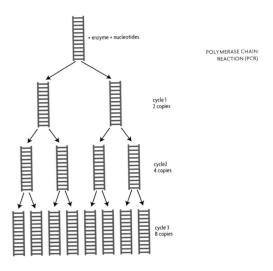

+ enzyme + nucleotides

POLYMERASE CHAIN
REACTION (PCR)

cycle 1
2 copies

cycle2
4 copies

cycle 3
8 copies

Once the gene has been copied, geneticists engineer a DNA construct. A **DNA construct** is a piece of DNA that is made of three specific parts: a start region, the desired gene, and a selectable marker. Antibiotic resistance is a common selectable marker. When you transformed *E. coli* in Activity 2, "Creating Genetically Modified Bacteria," ampicillin resistance was the selectable marker. This meant that only *E. coli* cells transformed with the green fluorescent protein (GFP) protein would grow in Petri dishes with ampicillin in them. In other words, only the bacteria that had taken in the DNA construct containing the ampicillin resistance gene and the gene to make them glow would grow on the ampicillin plates. Bacteria that had not taken up the construct would not grow. Scientists also add a start region, which signals where gene transcription should begin.

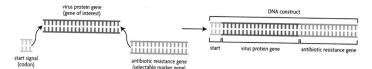

When all of these steps have been completed, scientists insert the DNA construct into the target organism. This can be done in several ways. In Activity 2, "Creating Genetically Modified Bacteria," you worked with a DNA plasmid, a ring of DNA found in bacteria. With bacteria, scientists use enzymes to insert the DNA construct into plasmids. Then the plasmid is introduced to the bacteria, which infects the target organism, bringing along the DNA construct. There are several methods for transmitting the DNA construct into the target organism, three of which are shown in the figure below.

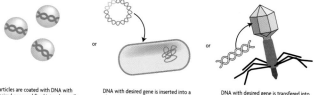

Particles are coated with DNA with desired gene and fired into plant cells using a gene gun.

or

DNA with desired gene is inserted into a plasmid, which is inserted into a bacterium. The bacterium infects the plant cells.

or

DNA with desired gene is transfered into a virus, which infects the plant cells.

After the DNA construct is inserted into the DNA of the target organism, the newly modified organism is grown to mature size. Researchers test for the presence of the new gene using electrophoresis, as you did in Activity 18, "Which Corn Is Genetically Modified?" Scientists also perform a second, more sensitive test, Southern blotting (named for molecular biologist Edward M. Southern), to confirm that the virus protein gene is being created by the cells and is present in the modified organism.

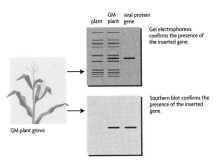

plant | GM plant | viral protein gene

Gel electrophoresis confirms the presence of the inserted gene.

Southern blot confirms the presence of the inserted gene.

GM plant grows

If the modified organism produces the virus protein gene, clinical trials are conducted to see if the protein produces the desired vaccine effect. For example, in the vaccine lettuce that was modified to contain the hepatitis B protein gene, scientists first tested the modified lettuce on mice. The mice were fed the modified lettuce, and then tested to see if their immune systems responded to the hepatitis B protein. Once it was determined that the process does work in mice, similar tests were performed on human subjects. Today, testing and research are continuing and will go on until scientists determine if the lettuce consistently and safely produces the desired result in humans.

Benefits and Trade-offs of Edible Vaccines

The concept of producing edible genetically modified organisms to deliver vaccines has many benefits. Unlike traditional vaccines, many of the plants being tried in this process require little refrigeration, if any. It is easier to grow large amounts of the modified organisms than to produce large amounts of the injectable vaccine. The lettuce could be farmed anywhere that there is adequate soil, sun, and water. Because production does not involve expensive equipment or laboratories, it would cost less than traditional vaccines. There is no need for sterilized needles, or for trained medical staff to administer the vaccine.

SAMPLE RESPONSES

1. The steps involved in creating a genetically modified organism include the following:

   a. Identify a desirable gene.

   b. Isolate the DNA that contains the gene.

   c. Isolate the desirable gene from the DNA.

   d. Make copies of the desired gene.

   e. Insert the gene copies into the target organism.

   f. Verify that the gene has been inserted into the target organism.

2. Both processes are similar because they change the phenotype of a plant by altering the plant's genotype. Selectively breeding the rice involved work with just rice genes. In comparison, engineering the lettuce involved inserting a gene into lettuce cells from a different species, a virus. It also involved laboratory equipment and fairly complex procedures, instead of traditional breeding of plants for desirable traits.

3. Genetic modification allows scientists to chose a desirable trait for an organism, identify the gene(s) in another organism that determine(s) the trait, isolate the gene(s), and insert them into the target organism. It also can mean choosing an undesirable gene and deleting it. Traditional selective breeding can only be performed with reproductively compatible organisms. A benefit of genetic modification is that it allows the engineering of new gene combinations not found in nature. One of the trade-offs of using genetic modification is that inserting gene(s) into organisms can have unintended consequences, such as allergic reactions in consumers.

There are also drawbacks to edible vaccines. Because organisms naturally vary, the dosage of the vaccines may be uneven. This is important because if there is not enough of the vaccine, the immune system will not respond. If there is too much of the vaccine in the organism, the body tolerates the vaccine but the immune system does not respond properly. Also, the edible vaccines still have to be delivered to where they are needed, which is the same problem with the traditional vaccines. Many of the locations where vaccines are most needed are remote areas that are difficult to reach and do not have the farmland needed to grow edible vaccines. Another concern that has been raised is that if the modified organisms are accidentally introduced into regular food crops, there could be unintended consequences.

Several edible vaccines are in the early stages of being tested on humans. Corn and potatoes have been modified to produce a vaccine against a harmful strain of *E. coli*, potatoes have been modified to vaccinate against the Norwalk virus (one cause of the symptoms often called the stomach flu, but not related to influenza), and, as you read earlier, lettuce has been modified to vaccinate against hepatitis B. Other scientists are working on methods to grow the modified plants, and then turn them into vaccine pills, which would help make them easier to distribute and make the doses even. These methods, however, have not yet been fully developed. Currently, there are no edible vaccines approved for use in the United States.

Analysis

1. What are the steps involved in genetically modifying an organism?

2. Compare the genetic modification of "vaccine lettuce" to the process of selectively breeding rice with desirable traits, which you learned about in Activity 7, "Breeding Better Rice." In what ways are the processes similar? Different?

3. What are the benefits and trade-offs of using genetic modification to produce an organism with a specific phenotype?

KEY VOCABULARY	
DNA construct	vaccine
genetic modification	

REVISIT THE CHALLENGE

Students should be able to discuss benefits of edible vaccines, including ease of distribution and administration, as well as trade-offs, such as difficulty controlling dosage and possible side effects or other unintended outcomes.

20 Are GMOs the Solution?

TALK IT OVER • 1–2 CLASS SESSIONS

OVERVIEW

In this culminating activity, students summarize data gathered from four scientific studies on a fictitious genetically modified soybean. Students evaluate and compare the studies, and examine the potential benefits and trade-offs of growing this GM organism. They then make an evidence-based recommendation about whether a country that relies heavily on soybean crops should grow the GM soy.

KEY CONTENT

1. Understanding the relationship between the structure and function of DNA, chromosomes, and genes makes it possible for scientists to manipulate genes and thereby create new combinations of traits and new varieties of organisms.

2. The farming of genetically modified plants or animals poses risks and benefits, and making decisions about them requires trade-offs.

3. Individuals and society must decide on proposals involving new research and the introduction of new technologies into the environment. Decisions require assessment of alternatives, risks, costs, and benefits, and consideration of who benefits and who does not, who pays and who gains, and what the risks are and who or what bears them.

KEY PROCESS SKILLS

1. Students develop conclusions based on evidence.

2. Students analyze claims.

3. Students make accurate interpretations, inferences, and conclusions from text.

4. Students consider and evaluate multiple perspectives.

MATERIALS AND ADVANCE PREPARATION

For the teacher

Student Sheet 20.1, "GM Soybean Study Comparison"

Scoring Guide: ANALYZING DATA (AD)

Scoring Guide: EVIDENCE AND TRADE-OFFS (ET)

For the class

list of statements posed in Activity 1, "A Genetically Modified Solution?"

For each student

Student Sheet 20.1, "GM Soybean Study Comparison"

Literacy Student Sheet 2a, "Writing Frame—Evidence and Trade-offs"

Scoring Guide: ANALYZING DATA (AD) (optional)

Scoring Guide: EVIDENCE AND TRADE-OFFS (ET) (optional)

Masters for Scoring Guides are in Teacher Resources IV: Assessment.

TEACHING SUMMARY

Getting Started

• Introduce the scenario.

Doing the Activity

• Students evaluate the proposals.

Follow-up

• Students recommend whether GM soybeans should be grown.

• (ET ASSESSMENT) The class discusses if the benefits of genetically modified organisms outweigh the risks.

GETTING STARTED

1 Direct students' attention to the list of statements about genetically modified organisms, shown below, that they first responded to in Activity 1.

Revisit the list to determine if students have changed their opinions based on their work in this unit. Have them discuss with a partner, or with the class, why they think their opinions have changed or stayed the same.

20 Are GMOs the Solution?

YOUR COUNTRY IS *facing the possibility of an economic and social crisis. Over the last 40 years, the country has grown more soybeans and fewer other crops. Now, the primary crop grown in your country is soybeans. Only a small percentage of the soybeans are sold within your country for human and animal consumption. Most of the soybeans are exported to other countries, which contributes significantly to your country's economic and social well-being.*

For several years soybean production has been low due to an ongoing drought. Last year a virus, soybean mottling virus (SMV), wiped out two-thirds of the already small soybean crop. SMV is transmitted by aphids and causes plants to grow fewer leaves, smaller pods, and fewer, if any, soybeans. Genomics Unlimited, Inc., has offered to fund the growing of soybeans genetically modified to protect against SMV. The GM soybean, called Soy*, has had a gene inserted from another plant which produces a substance that deters aphids. As a scientific advisor to your government's Panel on Genetic Modification, your job is to recommend what action the government should take.

Some viruses infect up to 94% of a healthy soybean field. The soybeans above are healthy, while the soybeans at left have contracted a virus.

Genetically Modified Organisms (GMOs)

Statement	Agree	Disagree	Uncertain
1. I have eaten food that contains genetically modified crops.			
2. Genetically modified foods should be available, as long as they are tested before they are sold for human consumption.			
3. The risks of genetically modified foods outweigh the possible benefits.			
4. Genetically modified foods will help provide a sustainable food supply.			
5. I am concerned about eating genetically modified foods.			
6. Farmers should grow corn that is genetically modified to resist insects that damage cornfields.			

DOING THE ACTIVITY

2 After students have completed Procedure Step 1, guide a class discussion summarizing the scenario for the activity. Encourage students to identify the likely social, economic, and environmental issues facing the country. Record their thoughts on the board or a poster where students can easily refer to them throughout the activity. Students should reach the conclusion that the country is not in a sustainable situation, given that three key sustainability indicators (crop diversity, profit, and bushels of soy) have shown dramatic declines.

Ask the students to list the characteristics of soybean mottling virus (SMV), as described in the introduction, to ensure they understand the effects of the disease on soybean plants. Students should say that SMV is carried by aphids, causes plants to grow fewer leaves and soybean pods, and, therefore, fewer soybeans.

Discuss briefly with students the importance of the global soybean crop. In 2009 alone, more than 210 million metric tons of soybeans were grown worldwide. More than 35% of that production was in the United States, worth more than 30 billion dollars.

Note: The graphs in this activity are fictitious, based on studies of other crops and GM plants; hence, no actual amounts are used for comparison. Students should instead focus on trends in the data.

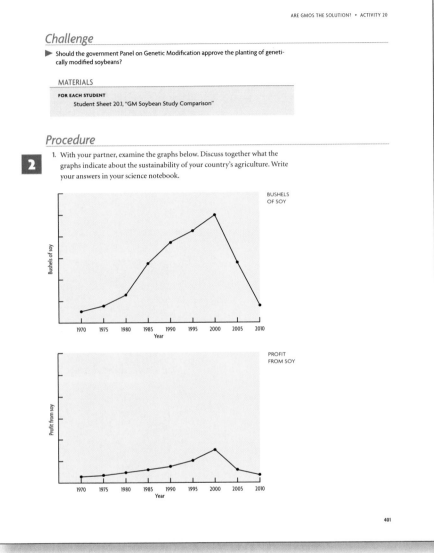

Challenge

▶ Should the government Panel on Genetic Modification approve the planting of genetically modified soybeans?

MATERIALS

FOR EACH STUDENT
Student Sheet 20.1, "GM Soybean Study Comparison"

Procedure

2 1. With your partner, examine the graphs below. Discuss together what the graphs indicate about the sustainability of your country's agriculture. Write your answers in your science notebook.

401

3 After students have read the proposal in Procedure Step 2, hold a class discussion about the benefits and trade-offs for the country if it accepted the proposal. Encourage students to incorporate information from earlier activities that they feel is relevant to this proposal, as well as from the class discussion and their science notebook notes for Procedure Step 2. Students' answers will vary, but should include that benefits of Soy* are that it is resistant to SMV, initial tests show it is safe and effective, and that the country will be getting the seeds at a low price. Trade-offs include that the GM soybeans have not been fully tested, and that because some countries do not allow genetically modified crops, the export of Soy* may not be as profitable for the country as with unmodified crops.

4 You may want to have students read the research summaries in groups or pairs, rather than individually. A second option is to ask each group to read only one summary, and then have the groups compare notes to help each other complete the student sheet. A sample student response to Student Sheet 20.1, "GM Soybean Study Comparison," appears at the end of this activity.

SCIENCE & GLOBAL ISSUES/BIOLOGY • GENETICS

CROP DIVERSITY

3

2. Read the proposal below. In your science notebook, record the benefits and trade-offs of the proposal based on the situation your country is facing.

> ### Proposal by Genomics Unlimited, Inc. to Grow Soy*
>
> Genomics Unlimited, Inc. (GU) has developed a genetically modified strain of soybean called Soy*. Their studies have shown that Soy* resists infection by SMV. They believe that if your farmers raise Soy*, it will restore soybean production in your country to profitable levels.
>
> GU proposes that half of the soybean farmers in your country plant Soy* for this year's crops. Because your farmers have faced such problems with SMV, GU offers your country a low price on the seed for this year. All of their initial effectiveness and safety testing has shown positive results, and they are confident that this GM seed will be a great help in solving your SMV problems.

4

3. Now your group will read four summaries of scientific studies that have been done on Soy*. You will analyze the data and conclusions in these summaries to help you make an evidence-based decision about allowing Soy* planting in your country. With your group, decide who will read which summary. Complete Student Sheet 20.1, "GM Soybean Study Comparison," as you read.

Study conclusions are provided for Study 1. Record your conclusions based on the results for Studies two through four on Student Sheet 20.1. Be sure to consider all study results when you form your conclusions.

402

Study 1: Genetically Modified Soybeans—A Laboratory Study

Study Time Frame: 12 months (January 2008–December 2008)

Research Group: Genomics Unlimited, Inc.

Study Objectives: Test susceptibility of Soy* genetically modified soybeans to SMV transmitted by aphids (common carrier of SMV).

Study Procedures: Twenty test greenhouses were set up, 10 to grow unmodified soybeans and 10 to grow Soy* genetically modified soybeans. Once a week the numbers of leaves and soybean pods were counted on each plant. Half the greenhouses for each type of crop were exposed for two months to aphids carrying SMV. All plants were checked once a week to determine if they had contracted SMV. All crops were watered and fertilized regularly. Trials were repeated three times, for 120 days each. Results were averaged.

Study Results are shown at right.

Study Conclusions: Soy* plants are more resistant to SMV than unmodified soy and have a higher yield than unmodified soy when exposed to SMV. No significant differences in growth and yield result when the plants are not exposed to SMV.

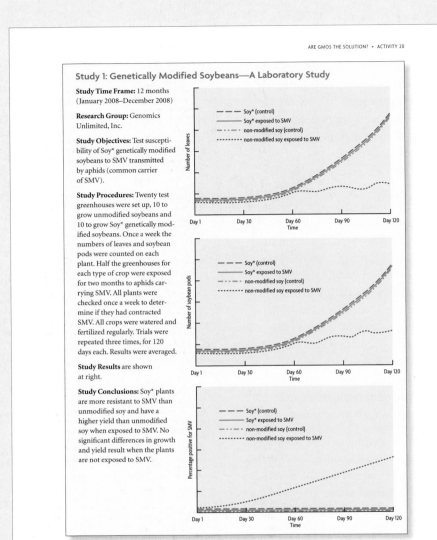

Study 2: Genetically Modified Soybeans—A Field Study

Study Time Frame: 9 months (March 2009–November 2009)

Research Group: State Agricultural University

Study Objectives: Test susceptibility of Soy* genetically modified soybeans to SMV transmitted by aphids (common carrier of SMV) in typical growing conditions.

Study Procedures: Four test fields were set up, two to grow unmodified soybeans and two to grow Soy* genetically modified soybeans. Once a week numbers of leaves and soybean pods were counted for each plant. Half of each type of crop was exposed to aphids carrying SMV. Crops were watered and fertilized regularly. Trials were repeated twice, for 120 days each. Results were averaged.

Study Results are shown at right.

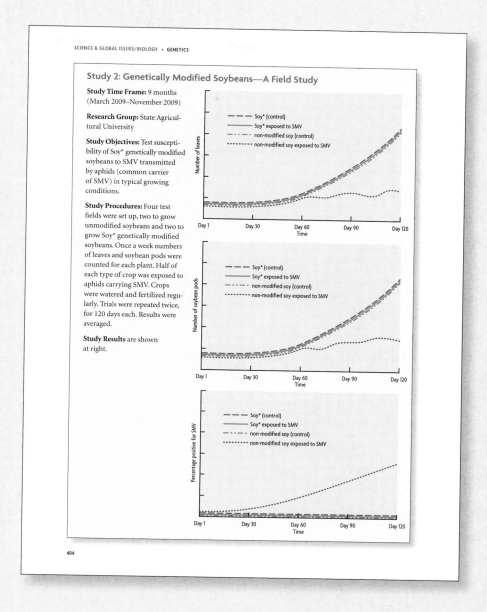

Study 3: Genetically Modified Soybeans—A Field Study

Study Time Frame: 3 years
(October 2006–October 2009)

Research Group: International
Scientific Review Board

Study Objectives: Test susceptibility of Soy* genetically modified soybeans and unmodified
beans to SMV transmitted by
aphids (common carrier of
SMV) in difficult growing
conditions.

Study Procedures: Four test
fields were set up, two to grow
unmodified soybeans and two to
grow Soy* genetically modified
soybeans. Once a week numbers
of leaves and number of soybean
pods were counted for each
plant. Half of each type of crop
was exposed for two months a
year to aphids carrying SMV.
Crops were given limited water
to mimic drought conditions.
Crops were grown in minimally
fertilized soil to mimic poor soil
conditions. Trials were repeated
nine times, for 120 days each.
Results were averaged.

Study Results are shown at
right.

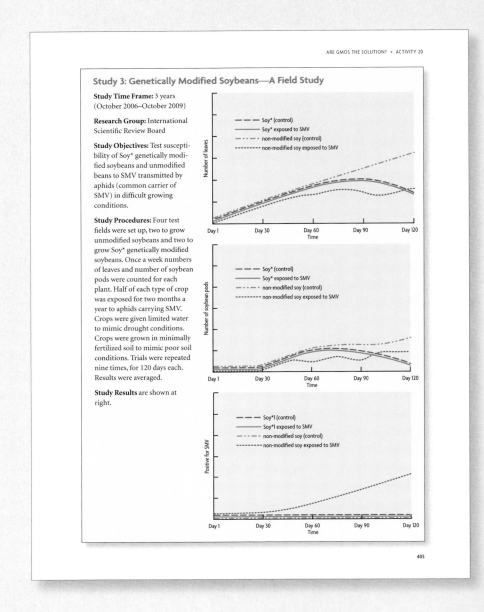

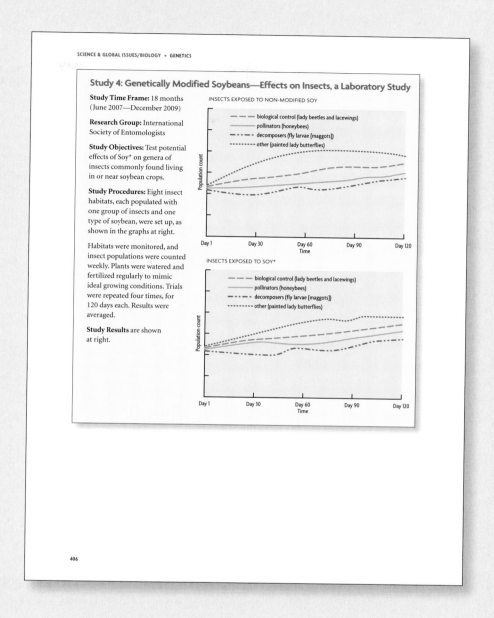

Study 4: Genetically Modified Soybeans—Effects on Insects, a Laboratory Study

Study Time Frame: 18 months (June 2007—December 2009)

Research Group: International Society of Entomologists

Study Objectives: Test potential effects of Soy* on genera of insects commonly found living in or near soybean crops.

Study Procedures: Eight insect habitats, each populated with one group of insects and one type of soybean, were set up, as shown in the graphs at right.

Habitats were monitored, and insect populations were counted weekly. Plants were watered and fertilized regularly to mimic ideal growing conditions. Trials were repeated four times, for 120 days each. Results were averaged.

Study Results are shown at right.

INSECTS EXPOSED TO NON-MODIFIED SOY

- - - biological control (lady beetles and lacewings)
—— pollinators (honeybees)
—·—· decomposers (fly larvae [maggots])
········ other (painted lady butterflies)

Population count / *Time*
Day 1   Day 30   Day 60   Day 90   Day 120

INSECTS EXPOSED TO SOY*

- - - biological control (lady beetles and lacewings)
—— pollinators (honeybees)
—·—· decomposers (fly larvae [maggots])
········ other (painted lady butterflies)

Population count / *Time*
Day 1   Day 30   Day 60   Day 90   Day 120

5 (AD ASSESSMENT) If students have difficulty comparing study summaries, encourage them to look at one element at a time. For example, they could start by comparing the length of the studies and discussing how that might affect the value of the data. After students have completed Student Sheet 20.1, "GM Soybean Study Comparison," project a blank copy of the student sheet, and discuss what the studies show. Fill in the projected student sheet as the discussion progresses. Encourage students to add to their own student sheets any points that they might have overlooked.

Students' responses to the conclusions column of Student Sheet 20.1, "GM Soybean Study Comparison," may be scored with the ANALYZING DATA (AD) Scoring Guide.

6 Survey the class about their recommendations. Ask the class, *Should the government Panel on Genetic Modification allow the growth of Soy* in their country?*

Tally students' responses on the board. Some students will think Soy* should be grown, given its resistance to SMV. Others may feel the risks are too great, and have not been fully investigated. Students may also be unsure, perhaps feeling that there should be more studies such as human or animal toxicity or allergy tests. Encourage students to cite evidence from what they have learned in the unit to support their statements. Consider conducting a walking debate, similar to those in Activities 1 and 15, so students can show their support of, opposition to, or skepticism about the proposal to grow Soy.*

FOLLOW-UP

7 (ET ASSESSMENT) Students' responses to Procedure Step 6 may be scored with the EVIDENCE AND TRADE-OFFS (ET) Scoring Guide. To help them evaluate the trade-offs of the proposal you may wish to pass out Literacy Student Sheet 2a, "Writing Frame—Evidence and Trade-offs."

---

5 4. Share your notes with your group, and complete Student Sheet 20.1, "GM Soybean Study Comparison," for the other three studies. Discuss any questions or thoughts you had while reading the summaries, and write them in your science notebook.

6 5. Discuss the original proposal with the class, following your teacher's instructions.

7 6. Based on the ideas you recorded on Student Sheet 20.1, "GM Soybean Study Comparison," and on the information from your class discussion, decide if you support growing Soy*. In your science notebook write a memorandum to the government Panel on Genetic Modification, in which you state your recommendation, explain the benefits and trade-offs of the proposal, and cite evidence from the summaries that supports your recommendation.

Analysis

1. Explain the similarities and differences in experimental design of the four studies on Soy*.

2. How might the differences in experimental design of the four studies on Soy* affect the outcomes and conclusions of the studies?

3. Describe how your recommendation will affect the social, economic, and environmental sustainability of your country.

4. What information should policymakers evaluate when making decisions about genetically modified organisms?

KEY VOCABULARY	
genetic engineering	trade-offs

This sheet provides a literacy strategy known as a writing frame, which gives students a structure for communicating their ideas. More information about the use of the writing frame literacy strategy is in Teacher Resources III: Literacy. Sample student responses for and against the growing of Soy* are shown on the next page.

SAMPLE RESPONSES

1. All four designs had an unmodified soy control group and a Soy* group. The designs differed in time frame (8 months to three years), location (two were in laboratories, two were field studies), and growing conditions (three were grown under regular conditions, one was grown under drought conditions). Three designs tested plant performance, while one tested effects on insects.

2. Students' answers will vary, but should include explanations of how each of the three main differences between the studies (time frame, where they were conducted, and growing conditions) could affect outcomes and conclusions of the studies.

Sample Student Response

A shorter time frame for a study might mean the study ends before enough time has passed to show accurate results. For example, if studies 1 and 2 continued for three years they might have shown a decrease in yield from Soy* plants. A difference from normal growing conditions might mean that the conclusions from the study are not accurate under normal conditions. Soy* had lower yield than non-GM soy under drought conditions in Study 3, but this outcome was not seen under normal growing conditions in studies 1 and 2. A laboratory study might have different outcomes than a field study because the laboratory has controlled conditions. A field study is exposed to weather and other conditions that cannot be controlled. All of these differences might lead to inaccurate results.

3. Students' answers will vary, but should explain the three pillars of sustainability and use accurate evidence. Even with the same evidence, opinions may differ.

Sample Student Response to Procedure Step 6: Against growing Soy*

We need to decide whether this country should grow Soy* genetically modified soybeans.

I recommend that this country not grow Soy*.

My decision is based on the following evidence:

First, Soy* does not grow well under drought conditions, and our country is experiencing a drought.

Second, the study on the effect of Soy* on insects was only carried out for a short period of time.

Third, if we grow Soy* we may not be able to export as much as we need to because some countries do not accept GM crops.

Some trade-offs of my decision are that several studies showed that Soy* is resistant to SMV, which is a big problem for our country, or that the study on the effects of Soy* on insects showed that it has no effect.

Sample Student Response

I recommend the country grow a small amount of Soy* in a field surrounded by empty fields as a test to make sure that the GM soy is safe for humans and for the environment. This helps the environmental sustainability of the country because it protects the environment. It helps the social sustainability of the country because it is a compromise between the pro- and anti- sides of the debate. If the test shows that Soy* is safe, the country could grow it and that would help the economic sustainability of the country. If the test shows it is not safe, the government will have protected the environment and, perhaps, people's health.

4. Students' answers will vary, but should include several factors that are important in making decisions about genetically modified organisms. Factors include safety, possible toxicity or allergic reactions to the organism, potential economic, environmental or health benefits or risks, how much testing and research has been done on the organisms, and the specifics of any research studies performed on the safety and efficacy of the organism.

REVISIT THE CHALLENGE

Students should be able to summarize the results of the four studies on Soy* and explain how they weighed the benefits and trade-offs to recommend for or against the use of Soy*.

Sample Student Response to Procedure Step 6: For growing Soy*

We need to decide whether this country should grow Soy* genetically modified soybeans.

I recommend that we should grow Soy*.

My decision is based on the following evidence:

First, more studies have shown that Soy* has better yield than non-GM soy when exposed to SMV, and SMV is a big problem in our country.

Second, our country's profits and bushels of soy exported have decreased, which means we need a better strain of soy than what we are growing.

Third, Study 4 showed that insect populations are not harmed when exposed to Soy* and non-GM soy.

Some trade-offs of my decision are that one study showed that Soy* does not grow well under drought conditions or that some countries might not buy our soy if it is genetically modified.

GM Soybean Study Comparison

Study	Where conduct-ed (lab, field)	How long was the study?	Growth condi-tions	Results		Conclusions
				Effects on SMV resistance	**Effects on yield**	
1	Lab	12 months	Good (water and fertilizer)	Soy* shows resistance to SMV. Unmodified soy does not show resistance to SMV.	Number of leaves and soybeans is the same in both Soy* populations. Yield is reduced in unmodified soy population exposed to SMV	Soy* plants are more resistant to SMV than unmodified soy and have a higher yield than unmodified soy when exposed to SMV. No significant differences in growth and yield result when the plants are not exposed to SMV.
2	Field	9 months	Good (water and fertilizer)	Soy* shows resistance to SMV. Unmodified soy does not show resistance to SMV.	Number of leaves and soybeans is the same in both Soy* populations. Yield is reduced in unmodified soy population exposed to SMV.	Soy* are more resis-tant to SMV than unmodified plants and have a higher yield than unmodified soy when exposed to SMV. There is no significant difference between the Soy* and unmodified soy when not exposed to SMV.
3	Field	3 years	Poor (poor soil, drought)	Soy* shows resistance to SMV. Unmodified soy does not show resistance to SMV.	Soy* has lower yield than unmodified soy in control and SMV-exposed populations.	Soy* plants are resis-tant to SMV. Yield is mixed. Soy* does have as high a yield as unmodified soy in drought/poor soil conditions.
4	Lab	18 months	Regular			Soy* showed no significant differ-ence in population levels from control populations.

Unit Review: Genetics

Genetic Modification

Understanding the relationship between the structure and function of DNA, chromosomes, and genes makes it possible for scientists to manipulate genes and thereby create new combinations of traits and new varieties of organisms. Genetically modified organisms are those into which a gene or genes from another organism have been inserted, or organisms which have had one or more of their genes deleted. Through genetic modification scientists have developed organisms with a specific desirable trait, such as pest or disease resistance, drought tolerance, and enhanced nutritional qualities. Potential applications for genetically modified organisms include improving agricultural crops, creating alternative fuels, and treating human diseases. The production and use of a genetically modified organism might have unintended consequences for humans and ecosystems. The farming of genetically modified plants or animals poses risks and benefits, and making decisions about them involves trade-offs.

The sequence of steps involved in creating a genetically modified organism is: identification of a desirable gene; isolation of the gene; preparation of a DNA construct that contains the desired gene and a selectable marker; delivery of the desired gene into the target organism; and raising the transformed organisms using a selective medium to verify that insertion of the gene into the organism was successful. DNA constructs are inserted into organisms in several ways, including shooting them in with a gene gun, bacterial transformation, and delivering them via a virus. Scientists alter small pieces of DNA called plasmids to transfer desired genes into bacteria.

KEY VOCABULARY

biofuel	genetically modified organism
DNA construct	trade-off
genetic engineering	vaccine
genetic modification	

History of the Study of Genetics

Gregor Mendel (1822-1884) was a monk, teacher, and scientist, who studied the relationship between heredity and traits, mainly by experimenting with pea plants. He is credited with much of the early understanding of genetics and heredity.

Much has been learned since Mendel, and a large part of the research focus now is on genomics. Genomics is the study of the entire genetic makeup of an organism. This field has expanded rapidly over the past four decades. In 2003, the Human Genome Project completed its mission to catalog the human genome. The information generated by the project has allowed scientists to explore the role of genes in human diseases and health and new approaches to finding cures. Genomics has the potential to contribute to solving sustainability problems related to biodiversity, alternative energy, and human and animal health.

KEY VOCABULARY	
genome	genomics

DNA and Basic Genetics

In all organisms, genes carry the instructions for specifying the characteristics of the organism. Genes are sequences of deoxyribonucleic acid (DNA) that code for a particular trait. Genes are organized into larger structures called chromosomes. Most of the cells in most eukaryotic organisms are diploid: they contain two copies (a pair) of each kind of chromosome. Cells contain two copies of each gene—one on each chromosome. These copies may code for different versions of the gene, and are called alleles. In organisms that reproduce sexually, one allele of each type of gene is inherited from each parent.

The DNA stored in cells guides the cells' functions. DNA is a macromolecule composed of two complementary strands, each made of a sequence of nucleotide subunits. Each strand of DNA has a sugar-phosphate backbone and a sequence of nitrogenous bases. The nucleotide subunits found in DNA are adenine, guanine, cytosine and thymine, represented as A, G, C, and T. Two strands of DNA together form a double helix. The chemical and structural properties of DNA are the basis for how the genetic information that determines heredity is both encoded in genes (as a string of molecular "bases") and replicated by means of a template. The genetic information stored in DNA directs the synthesis of the thousands of proteins the cell needs. Changes in DNA (mutations) occur spontaneously at low rates. Some of these changes make no difference to the organism, but others have a variety of effects.

Understanding DNA makes it possible for scientists to manipulate genes to create new combinations of traits and new varieties of organisms. DNA is isolated from cells by breaking the cells and adding chemicals that precipitate the DNA. DNA electrophoresis, a method for working with known samples and markers to match DNA, separates DNA fragments based on size.

KEY VOCABULARY	
amino acid	gel electrophoresis
base pair	gene
cell	hydrogen bond
chromosome	isolation
deoxyribonucleic acid (DNA)	nucleotide
DNA	replication
double helix	sugar–phosphate backbone

Reproduction

Heredity is the passing of genetic traits from one generation to the next. Through selective breeding and genetic modification of organisms, people have significantly transformed the genetic makeup of all sorts of populations. Selective breeding develops organisms with desirable traits by influencing the phenotypes and genotypes of offspring. Studying the results of sexual reproduction of a model organism, such as corn, provides information about the behavior of genes and the relationship between genotype and phenotype.

Asexual reproduction produces genetically identical offspring from a single parent through mitosis. Mitosis is the process by which replicated chromosomes divide and, following cytokinesis, form two identical daughter cells.

Sexual reproduction produces offspring with genes from both parents. Fertilization occurs when a sperm and an egg unite in sexual reproduction. This produces an offspring with two copies of each chromosome, one from the paternal parent and one from the maternal parent. Gametes—sperm in males and eggs in females—contain half the number of chromosomes found in the somatic cells of the same organism. Gametes are formed through meiosis, which creates four haploid sex cells, each containing only one copy of each kind of chromosome. The independent segregation of chromosomes during meiosis is the basis for traits that exhibit independent assortment. As a result of independent segregation and crossing over during meiosis, one individual produces an almost limitless variety of gametes. Abnormalities in chromosome number from errors occurring in gamete production often result in loss of viability or abnormal development of affected offspring. A karyotype is a graphic tool that allows geneticists to visualize the chromosomes of a cell and to check for certain abnormalities.

KEY VOCABULARY

asexual reproduction	heredity
centrioles	karyotype
centromere	law of independent assortment
chromatid	meiosis
crossing over	mitosis
cytokinesis	nondisjunction
daughter cell	parent cell
diploid	selective breeding
gamete	sexual reproduction
haploid	somatic cell

Phenotype/Genotype (Gene Expression)

According to the laws of simple dominance, dominant traits will appear in the phenotype of an organism, while recessive traits are masked by the presence of a dominant trait. Dominance is not always complete. Incomplete dominance refers to the blending of two traits, while codominance refers to the expression of both traits in a heterozygote. From pedigrees scientists infer the genetic mechanism of inheritance of single-gene traits.

Punnett squares are models of the transmission of alleles from one generation to the next. They predict the phenotypes and genotypes of a cross between two parents for one or more traits that are not linked. A Punnett square demonstrates the possible phenotypic and genotypic results of a cross and how likely it is that each genotype and phenotype will occur from that cross.

Evolution: Maintaining Diversity

THERE IS GREAT VARIETY within and between the earth's ecosystems. Each ecosystem differs from others in its varieties of species, genetic makeup of its species, and the evolutionary relationships of species. All of these levels of variation comprise the earth's biodiversity.

This biodiversity is the product of billions of years of evolution. Ecologists and evolutionary biologists study the evolutionary processes that produce biodiversity, what caused the subtle and dramatic shifts that occurred in the past, and how biodiversity might change in the future. Conservationists often focus on understanding the biodiversity of an area in order to establish priorities for conservation of species. They and other scientists are also concerned with how human activities affect biodiversity.

In this unit you will investigate the levels of biodiversity, and the evolutionary processes that increase, decrease, or maintain biodiversity. You will also examine humans' social, environmental, and economic influences on biodiversity, and make recommendations for which forest area on a fictitious island should receive funds for conservation.

414

1 Biodiversity and Sustainability

TALK IT OVER • 1–2 CLASS SESSIONS

OVERVIEW

Student groups play a game involving ways that biodiversity and sustainability are connected. Each student manages one ecosystem on an island. They are challenged to build up a sustainability score that is calculated from the environmental, social, and economic points that they collect as a result of decisions they make and events that occur. Students see how some of their decisions alter the biodiversity of their ecosystem. They also find that the biodiversity of the ecosystem influences the outcomes of decisions and events.

KEY CONTENT

1. Biodiversity encompasses variability between and within ecosystems, between species, and within a species' gene pool as evidenced by genetic diversity. Biodiversity is closely linked to sustainability.

2. Ecosystem services are the benefits that people obtain from ecosystems, including natural resources and processes that humans rely on for survival. Examples of ecosystem services include income generation; soil protection; materials derived for food, medicine, and shelter; water purification; carbon removal; and pollution control.

3. Protected areas are sections of land and sea especially dedicated to the maintenance of biological diversity and of natural and associated cultural resources. They are usually managed by government agencies or nonprofit organizations.

4. Sustainability is the ability to meet the needs of the present without endangering the ability of future generations to meet their own needs. The three underlying pillars of sustainability are the environment, the economy, and society.

MATERIALS AND ADVANCE PREPARATION

For each group of four students

  4 sets of 26 Species Cards—one for each ecosystem
      set of 18 Event Cards
  4 Protected Area Cards
      set of 50 transparent, colored plastic Money Chips
      set of 50 opaque, colored plastic Social Chips
      number cube*

For each student

      Student Sheet 1.1, "Biodiversity Challenge Rules"
      Student Sheet 1.2, "Species Card Record"
      Student Sheet 1.3, "Sustainability Scores"
      Student Sheet 1.4, "Biodiversity Challenge Reflection"

TEACHING SUMMARY

Getting Started

- Discuss with students their ideas about ecosystems, biodiversity, and sustainability.

Doing the Activity

- Students play the game.

Follow-up

- Students discuss the results of the game and some of the world's biodiversity hotspots.

- Students learn about the trade-offs associated with a decision.

- Explain the purpose of SEPUP Analysis Questions.

BACKGROUND INFORMATION

Biodiversity

The United Nations declared 2010 to be the International Year of Biodiversity. On a broad level, biodiversity refers to the variety of life on this planet, but it is a more complex concept than that. Biodiversity encompasses variability between and within ecosystems, between species, and within a species as evidenced by genetic diversity.

Sustainability

For a situation or activity to be sustainable all three of the pillars must be strong. In practice, it is difficult to attend to all three of these areas, and it often happens that when one or more improves the others suffer. For example, cutting down trees in a forest may create jobs and provide a source of income to individuals and the community. It may well, however, damage the environment by removing food sources and habitat for forest organisms and exposing the soil to erosion. The level of harm may be minimal or extreme, depending on the practices employed in cutting down and removing the trees and how the rate of removal compares to the rate of replanting. Biodiversity is tied to sustainability because practices that reduce biodiversity may weaken aspects of sustainability. Examples of such practices include overfishing, logging, and activities that produce pollution.

Ecosystem Services

Wood obtained from cutting down trees is an example of an ecosystem service, which may be described as the benefits that people and nonhuman species obtain from ecosystems. Other examples would be the natural materials people take for food and medicine, and possibly such less obvious ones as the aesthetic beauty of an area, water purification, carbon removal, and pollution control. Deriving services from an ecosystem presents a sustainability challenge but does not always entail an environmental cost. In the Ecology unit of *Science and Global Issues*, ecosystem services are defined as the natural resources and processes that humans rely on for survival. In this unit, the definition is expanded to include those services that human and non-human species benefit from, which includes those that they rely on for survival, such as clean air and water, and those not needed for survival, such as the beauty or educational value of an area.

Protected Areas

One approach to ecosystem management involves designating an area as protected. The United Nations Environment Programme (UNEP) defines a protected area as an area of land or sea in which the biological diversity and the natural and cultural resources are protected from human disruption and maintained through governmental or other means. Protected areas include national parks and reserves. In some places, private landowners have declared an area as protected. In some protected regions, such as some privately owned areas of forests in the United States, a logging company may be allowed to cut down trees, but it must adhere to government standards for maintaining resources and biodiversity.

GETTING STARTED

1 ◆ This symbol represents an opportunity to elicit students' experiences or ideas that will help you direct your instruction. Sometimes you will be able to build on students' ideas and different perspectives, while at other times you will uncover ideas that are inconsistent with scientific explanations (but perhaps consistent with common reasoning). The Teaching Suggestions often provide strategies that you can use to uncover and address these ideas.

Ask students to describe ecosystems that they are familiar with. Guide the discussion to ensure that it includes local and distant, and large and small ecosystems. Introduce the variety of ecosystems as an example of biodiversity, and expand the conversation to include other forms of biodiversity, such as species and genetic diversity. Ask students to compile a list of the benefits that humans derive from ecosystems and the events or activities that threaten ecosystems. At this stage do not go into too much detail regarding the items on the list of the benefits, but plan on returning to it at the end of the activity and at various points in the unit. Finally, discuss sustainability and what it might mean with regard to a human community and to an ecosystem. If the students do not mention them, make sure to introduce the three pillars of sustainability: the economy, society, and the environment.

---

1 Biodiversity and Sustainability

1 **I**N THE WORLD'S many ecosystems—whether desert valleys, coral reefs, riverbanks, or backyard gardens—are unique assortments of species. The species vary in numbers and in how closely or distantly related they are to one another. Also within each species are variations in the genetic compositions of individuals. The combination of these levels of variability is referred to as **biological diversity** or more commonly, **biodiversity.**

Biodiversity is a characteristic of many ecosystems on Earth.

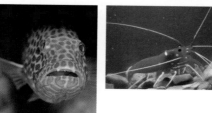

Ecologists and evolutionary biologists study the biodiversity in ecosystems and how it changed in the past and might change in the future. They examine how environmental factors, including human activities, influence biodiversity and how the sustainability and biodiversity of an area are linked. **Sustainability** is the ability to meet a community's present needs without compromising the ability of future generations to meet their own needs. Some conservationists track the levels of biodiversity in ecosystems in an effort to establish priorities for saving threatened species. One of their approaches is to identify and focus on hotspots, which are areas with a large number of endemic species that are experiencing an extraordinary loss of habitat. **Endemic** species are those that are found exclusively in one area.

In this activity you will examine the biodiversity on the fictitious island of Kapikua and explore some of the factors affecting biodiversity. You will be responsible for managing one ecosystem on the island. Your decisions and responses to events will have consequences for the many species and people in and around your ecosystem.

Challenge

▶ How are the biodiversity of an ecosystem and the sustainability of human communities related?

MATERIALS

FOR EACH GROUP OF FOUR STUDENTS

4   sets of 26 Species Cards—one for each ecosystem
    set of 18 Event Cards
4   Protected Area Cards
    set of 50 transparent, colored plastic Money Chips
    set of 50 opaque, colored plastic Social Chips
    number cube

FOR EACH STUDENT

Student Sheet 1.1, "Biodiversity Challenge Rules"
Student Sheet 1.2, "Species Card Record"
Student Sheet 1.3, "Sustainability Scores"
Student Sheet 1.4, "Biodiversity Challenge Reflection"

DOING THE ACTIVITY

2 In this activity, students will work in groups of four and in pairs to examine biodiversity in four ecosystems.

Review as necessary the characteristics of the four areas on the island. Define montane as growing in or inhabiting a mountain area.

Procedure

2   1. The map below shows the island of Kapikua, which is located near the equator. There are four major ecosystems on the island. After reading the information about the four ecosystems, have each group member choose one to manage. The ecosystems are:

Tropical Montane Cloud Forest

This ecosystem is in the higher altitudes of the mountain range running through the island. It is densely forested but the trees are generally much smaller than those found in the lowland rainforest. The air is always damp from the clouds and fog that envelop the area.

Lowland Tropical Rainforest

This area is a mix of primary and secondary forest. The primary forest is mainly undisturbed and consists of well-spaced tall trees that let little light through to the forest floor. The secondary forest has grown where sections of the primary forest were previously cleared. It has smaller trees that create a dense and tangled jungle environment.

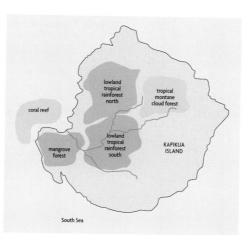

THE ISLAND OF KAPIKUA

417

625

3 Allow students time to read Student Sheet 1.1, "Biodiversity Challenge Rules," and to ask clarifying questions. Have each student look at a Species Card. Go through the information on the cards, paying particular attention to the levels of genetic diversity for the various populations of a particular species. Ask the class to speculate how having a higher or lower genetic diversity might influence a population over time. If students are unable to answer this question now, make sure that you return to it after they have finished playing the game, when the answer should have become much clearer. Tell students to shuffle the Species Cards well before selecting eight cards. It is important that each student records the types of cards and genetic diversity information on Student Sheet 1.2, "Species Card Record," before starting the game. They will make comparisons with this information at the end of the game.

FOLLOW-UP

4 Begin the discussion by asking students to examine how the sustainability scores recorded on Student Sheet 1.3, "Sustainability Scores," changed over the course of the game. Expand the discussion to include the tensions created by trying to balance the three pillars of sustainability. More information on these three pillars is on the *Science and Global Issues* page of the SEPUP website *(sepuplhs.org/sgi)*. Analysis Question 3 formally introduces ecosystem services. To assist the discussion, refer back to the list generated by the class at the start of the activity. Return to the question of how having a greater or lesser genetic diversity might influence a population over time. Students should be able to state that a greater genetic diversity is beneficial for a population because it gives the population a better chance for survival if the environment changes. Ask students whether anyone used a Protected Area card and, if so, what the advantages and disadvantages were. Discuss with the class whether it would be possible to

---

Mangrove Forest

This is an area of mangrove trees and shrubs along the coast where the forest floor is muddy and often covered by brackish water. There exist in this forest varied living conditions for the organisms that inhabit the ecosystem.

Coral Reef

This region lies just offshore from the mangrove forest and close to where the island's largest river flows into the sea. Here the ocean is shallow and much of the reef is easily accessible to swimmers and divers.

2. Once you have determined which ecosystem you will manage, read Student Sheet 1.1, "Biodiversity Challenge Rules." If you did not draw at least two forest or two coral Species Cards, exchange a different Species Card for either a forest or a coral Species Card. If you have questions, discuss them as a group before asking your teacher.

3 3. Before you begin playing the game, make a list of your eight species on Student Sheet 1.2, "Species Card Record." You will also record your species cards at the end of each round on this sheet.

4. Look at the information on your cards, and note on Student Sheet 1.2, "Species Card Record," any relationships you see between the species on the cards. For example, an organism of one species may rely on an organism of another species for food or shelter. These relationships will be important as you play the game.

5. On Student Sheet 1.3, "Sustainability Scores," calculate and record your initial sustainability score. You will recalculate this score at the end of each round and at the end of the game.

6. Play the game for the three rounds indicated in the Biodiversity Challenge Rules. Your goal is to finish with as high a sustainability score as possible.

7. Follow the instructions at the end of Student Sheet 1.1, "Biodiversity Challenge Rules," to adjust your third-round sustainability score to produce a final score.

4 8. Follow your teacher's directions for discussing this activity with the class.

5 9. Follow your teacher's directions for discussing the hotspots on the map at the end of this activity.

---

have a protected area from which ecosystem services were derived. Finally, discuss how the sustainability of an area was related to its biodiversity. Include examples of game play where an ecosystem showed increased resilience as a result of greater biodiversity (some of the Event Cards set up such situations). Decide if you would like students to fill out Student Sheet 1.4, "Biodiversity Challenge Reflection," in class or as homework.

Question 4 on Student Sheet 1.4 is an opportunity for students to identify the trade-offs of a decision about their ecosystem. One of the goals of *Science and Global Issues* is to teach students that

- decisions often involve trade-offs.

- identifying trade-offs involves analyzing evidence.

Explain to students that in this unit they will make several decisions about biodiversity. In this activity students must decide what are the trade-offs of decisions they make about their ecosystem. In a decision involving trade-offs, it is important for students to understand that a perfect choice is often not possible. It is possible, however, to recognize and analyze the trade-offs associated with each decision. For example, when asked, "Paper or plastic?" at a store checkout counter, most shoppers make the choice quickly. But there are several trade-offs attached to choosing paper or plastic. A shopper who chooses paper may do so to avoid generating plastic waste. In requesting the paper bag though, they are contributing to deforestation. In comparison, the shopper who chooses the plastic bag because it has stronger handles is accepting the trade-off that the plastic bag is made from petroleum-based materials. Neither choice is particularly beneficial for the environment, and both choices have a downside. Identifying the trade-offs helps clarify the reasoning that is being applied to make a decision, and the strength of the evidence relevant to making the most informed decision.

---

6 *Analysis*

1. What levels of biodiversity did you investigate in this activity?

2. Describe how the levels of biodiversity you investigated changed within your ecosystem on Kapikua.

3. **Ecosystem services** can be broadly defined as the benefits received from ecosystems, including natural resources and processes that humans and other species rely on for survival. What types of ecosystem services did your group encounter in the game?

4. Give examples of relationships you observed between ecosystems. Cite one of those examples to explain why what happened in one ecosystem affected others.

5. How is the sustainability of a region tied to its biodiversity?

6. **a.** Describe how the biodiversity of the ecosystems in your group changed during the game.

   b. How might the biodiversity of various regions of the earth have changed in the past?

   c. How might the biodiversity of various regions of the earth change in the future?

7 KEY VOCABULARY

biodiversity	hotspot
biological diversity	sustainability
ecosystem services	trade-off
endemic	

419

To further explore trade-offs, brainstorm with the class a list of decisions they make every day that involve trade-offs. Choose one and talk through the associated trade-offs of deciding one way or another. This practice will familiarize students with ways of identifying and considering trade-offs for this and subsequent activities.

5 Instruct students to review the map in the Student Book showing the world's biodiversity hotspots and the information provided for four of the hotspots. Depending on your classroom goals, you may instruct students to access the *Science and Global Issues* page of the SEPUP website *(sepuplhs.org/sgi)*, where there is a similar map of the biodiversity hotspots and more information about four

hotspots. Have students compare and discuss the hotspots for them to learn more about the hotspots' characteristics.

6 Point out to students that each activity in this book includes Analysis Questions to help guide them in their learning, provide ways for them to synthesize what they learned in the activity, and, in many cases, extend class discussion on the activity's connection to personal and global issues and sustainability.

All questions identified in this Teacher's Edition as assessment questions are to be completed individually.

7 This box lists the key vocabulary developed in this activity. When words are formally defined in an activity, they appear in bold type in the list. Encourage students to use these words when answering the Analysis Questions. Also, during informal and formal discussions listen for these words, and see if students are applying them correctly. Decide how you will support students' understanding of the vocabulary—perhaps with a student glossary, or setting up a word wall. For more suggestions on ways to develop students' understandings of and proficiency with scientific vocabulary, see the Vocabulary section of the Teacher Resources III: Literacy.

SAMPLE RESPONSES

1. Diversity between ecosystems, diversity between species, and genetic diversity within species.

2. Students' answers will vary but should reference changes related to the number of species, and fluctuations in the total genetic diversity in a particular population.

3. Students' answers will vary, but most students should have encountered opportunities to derive income and/or employment. Other examples might include soil protection, protection from storms, and sources of food.

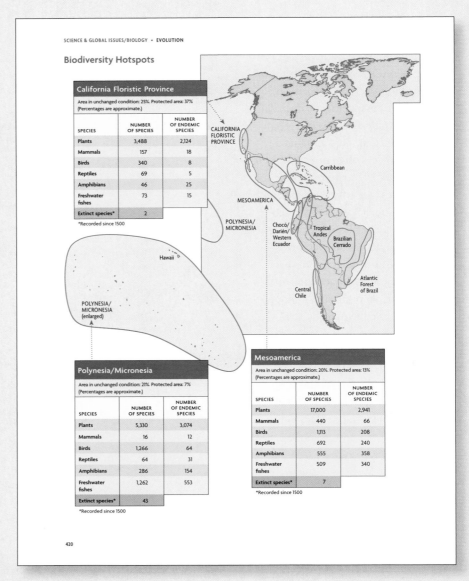

SCIENCE & GLOBAL ISSUES/BIOLOGY • EVOLUTION

Biodiversity Hotspots

California Floristic Province

Area in unchanged condition: 25%. Protected area: 37%
(Percentages are approximate.)

SPECIES	NUMBER OF SPECIES	NUMBER OF ENDEMIC SPECIES
Plants	3,488	2,124
Mammals	157	18
Birds	340	8
Reptiles	69	5
Amphibians	46	25
Freshwater fishes	73	15
Extinct species*	2	

*Recorded since 1500

Polynesia/Micronesia

Area in unchanged condition: 21%. Protected area: 7%
(Percentages are approximate.)

SPECIES	NUMBER OF SPECIES	NUMBER OF ENDEMIC SPECIES
Plants	5,330	3,074
Mammals	16	12
Birds	1,266	64
Reptiles	64	31
Amphibians	286	154
Freshwater fishes	1,262	553
Extinct species*	43	

*Recorded since 1500

Mesoamerica

Area in unchanged condition: 20%. Protected area: 13%
(Percentages are approximate.)

SPECIES	NUMBER OF SPECIES	NUMBER OF ENDEMIC SPECIES
Plants	17,000	2,941
Mammals	440	66
Birds	1,113	208
Reptiles	692	240
Amphibians	555	358
Freshwater fishes	509	340
Extinct species*	7	

*Recorded since 1500

420

4. As groups played the game they likely saw changes in one ecosystem affecting other ecosystems. The specific examples they cite will depend on the Event Cards that they turned over. Answers might include the following: building a tea plantation in the tropical montane cloud forest increased runoff to the other ecosystems; and removing parts of the coral reef or mangrove forest reduced protection from major storms, such as hurricanes, for most communities on the island.

5. The sustainability of a region seems to be higher when the biodiversity is higher. Although the relationship between the two is not simple, it becomes clear that when the biodiversity of a region becomes low it becomes less sustainable.

6. a. Students' answers will vary. Some students will have managed to increase the biodiversity of their ecosystems, some will have changed little, and some will have seen a reduction in biodiversity. The changes to biodiversity will be influenced by the decisions the students made and by circumstances outside their control, such as weather, disease, and what happened in other ecosystems.

   b. Biodiversity fluctuated as species evolved and extinctions occurred. Individual regions may have experienced dramatic changes in biodiversity, with some regions (such as dead zones in the ocean) seeing major declines in biodiversity.

c. There are many threats to biodiversity in various regions.
These include overfishing,
development, more people,
climate change, and pollution.
How individuals, communi-
ties, and governments control
these threats will greatly influence biodiversity.

REVISIT THE CHALLENGE

Review sustainability and its components, biodiversity, and types of ecosystem services.

Generate with the class ideas about
how sustainability, biodiversity, and
ecosystem services are related.

Since this is the first activity of the
"Evolution: Maintaining Diversity"
unit, make sure to discuss how biodiversity changes over short and
long time spans.

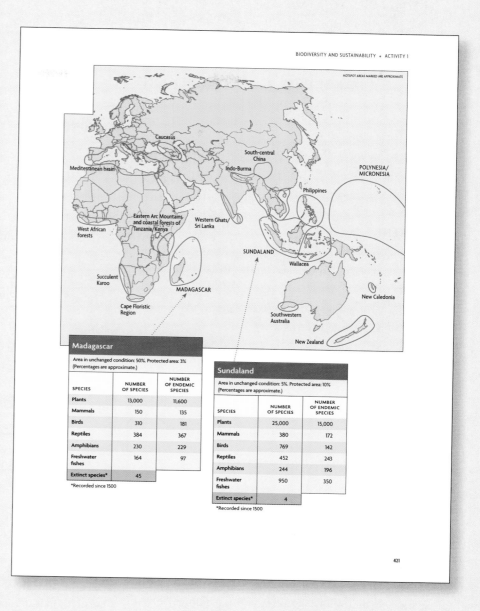

HOTSPOT AREAS MARKED ARE APPROXIMATE

Madagascar

Area in unchanged condition: 50%. Protected area: 3%
(Percentages are approximate.)

SPECIES	NUMBER OF SPECIES	NUMBER OF ENDEMIC SPECIES
Plants	13,000	11,600
Mammals	150	135
Birds	310	181
Reptiles	384	367
Amphibians	230	229
Freshwater fishes	164	97
Extinct species*	45	

*Recorded since 1500

Sundaland

Area in unchanged condition: 5%. Protected area: 10%
(Percentages are approximate.)

SPECIES	NUMBER OF SPECIES	NUMBER OF ENDEMIC SPECIES
Plants	25,000	15,000
Mammals	380	172
Birds	769	142
Reptiles	452	243
Amphibians	244	196
Freshwater fishes	950	350
Extinct species*	4	

*Recorded since 1500

421

2 Human Activities and Biodiversity

TALK IT OVER • 1–2 CLASS SESSIONS

OVERVIEW

Students read scenarios that describe various human activities that affect the diversity of ecosystems, species, and populations.

KEY CONTENT

1. Such human activities as acquisition of resources, urban growth, and waste disposal accelerate rates of natural change.
2. Three levels of biodiversity are ecosystem diversity, species diversity, and genetic diversity.
3. Human activities often cause biodiversity to increase or decrease.

KEY PROCESS SKILLS

1. Students develop conclusions from evidence.

MATERIALS AND ADVANCE PREPARATION

For the teacher

Transparency 2.1, "Status of Living and Extinct Taxa"
Scoring Guide: GROUP INTERACTION (GI)
Group Interaction Student Sheet 2, "Developing Communication Skills"

For each student

Scoring Guide: GROUP INTERACTION (GI) (optional)
Group Interaction Student Sheet 2, "Developing Communication Skills" (optional)

Masters for Group Interaction Student Sheets are in Teacher Resources II: Diverse Learners. Masters for Scoring Guides are in Teacher Resources IV: Assessment.

TEACHING SUMMARY

Getting Started

- Students determine what human activities are contributing to certain species' endangerments and extinctions.

Doing the Activity

- (LITERACY) Introduce the use of a science notebook.
- Students complete a chart about the effects of human activities on biodiversity as they read related scenarios.
- Introduce the SEPUP 4-2-1 cooperative learning model.

Follow-up

- The class discusses the types of human activities that affect three levels of biodiversity.

BACKGROUND INFORMATION

Humans' Impact on Biodiversity

Today, as in the past, people have a huge impact on biodiversity. Many recent extinctions have been caused by human actions. The passenger pigeon and Bali tiger became extinct due to habitat loss and hunting. There are several hypotheses about what led to the extinction of the golden toad in Costa Rica, including climate change, pollution, fungi or parasites, and UV-B radiation. Scientists estimate that hundreds of thousands of species are at risk of extinction today. Scientists determine the rate of extinction of species in several ways. One method is to measure the rate at which species are moving from threatened to endangered to extinct status as recorded by the International Union for Conservation of Nature (see reference on next page). These measures show that current rates of extinction are faster than any recorded in human history. Some scientists think such evidence means the earth is undergoing a sixth mass extinction. Since Earth's biodiversity provides so many valuable goods and services to humans, and biodiversity is important for the health and well-being of ecosystems, these extinctions will likely have adverse consequences for humans' social and economic well-being. Biodiversity ensures that ecosystems will be sustained into the future in part through evolution. Even though biodiversity eventually recovers after a mass extinction, it takes millions of years.

The IUCN Red List

It is impossible to conserve all of the species at risk of extinction. The International Union for Conservation of Nature (IUCN) Red List is a comprehensive inventory of the global conservation status of all plants and animals, and it has helped guide conservation efforts for threatened species. The criteria IUCN uses in evaluating the risk of extinction of plants and animals include the rate of decline, population size, area of geographic distribution, and degree of population and distribution fragmentation.

REFERENCES

International Union for Conservation of Nature. Summary statistics. Retrieved March 2010 from www.iucnredlist.org/about/summary-statistics.

GETTING STARTED

1 Project Transparency 2.1, "Status of Living and Extinct Taxa." Ask students what types of human activities they think may be contributing to species extinctions. Accept all answers, which are likely to include pollution, land development, and forest clearing. Share with the class that the top five human activities or consequences of their activities that threaten biodiversity are habitat loss and degradation, overharvesting, introduction of nonnative species, global climate change, and pollution. Tell students that in this activity they will look at some of these human activities and their effects.

DOING THE ACTIVITY

2 (LITERACY) Explain to students that as they conduct activities they will record data, observations, hypotheses, conclusions, and thoughts in their science notebooks. Keeping a science notebook helps them track data, note questions as they arise in investigations and discussion, and build science-writing skills. Decide how you would like students to record their work in each of the activities in this unit. For recommendations and more information, see the Science Notebooks section of Teacher Resources III: Literacy.

3 (GI ASSESSMENT) Activities in *Science and Global Issues* use a 4–2–1 cooperative learning model. Groups of four students share certain materials, pairs of students in the groups work together and discuss issues, and each student is responsible for recording ideas, observations, and thoughts. Throughout this unit, students will engage in small-group work and discussions. Good group communication skills will assist them in gaining a better understanding of content and having more meaningful discussions that support their learning. You may wish to use Group Interaction Student Sheet 2, "Developing Communication Skills," which gives students suggestions for communicating well when in a group. Encourage students to work within their groups, with their partners, and with the other pair in their groups to solve problems and answer questions. Collaboration is essential for developing new ideas and gaining a better understanding of scientific concepts. In this activity, students will work individually and in groups to discuss scenarios about various human effects on biodiversity. If necessary, explain to students your expectations for successful group effort. Give all students a copy of the GROUP INTERACTION (GI) Scoring Guide, and ask them to keep it with their science notebooks, as they

---

2 Human Activities and Biodiversity

1 **T**HERE ARE THREE general levels of biodiversity on earth. **Ecosystem diversity** is the variation within and between ecosystems. **Species diversity** is the number of species that exist in an area. **Genetic diversity** is the variation in the genes within a population of organisms.

In this activity, you will look at some examples of how human activities have altered the biodiversity of groups of taxa. **Taxa** (singular **taxon**) are levels of classification, for example species or genus.

Challenge

▶ How do humans alter the biodiversity of groups of taxa?

Human Activities that Affect Biodiversity

HABITAT DESTRUCTION
Humans change natural habitats through such activities as agriculture, building, mining, forestry, and pollution.

INTRODUCED SPECIES
Humans intentionally or accidentally move species from their native locations to new areas. When an introduced species causes or is likely to cause harm to the environment, the economy, or human health, the species is considered an invasive species.

OVEREXPLOITATION
Humans harvest animals or plants for ecosystem services, such as for food, medicine, lumber, collecting, and trading. The harvesting is considered overexploitation when the rate of harvest exceeds the ability of the population to recover.

Clearcutting of the Zambian rainforest.

Japanese beetles were accidentally introduced into the United States in 1916, and have since been severely destructive to turfgrass and ornamental plants.

So many striped narrow-headed softshell turtles have been taken from the wild for food and the international pet trade that natural populations are at risk.

422

will refer to it several times in this unit, and throughout *Science and Global Issues*. Let them know that you will use this throughout the unit at specific times to provide feedback on their work within their groups of four and with their partners. Take this opportunity to explain your expectations for group effort, and to discuss as a class what successful group work looks like. For more information on scoring how well students work together, see Teacher Resources IV: Assessment. For more information about ways to support group interactions see the Facilitating Group Interaction section of Teacher Resources II: Diverse Learners.

4 This activity describes three levels of biodiversity that are affected by five human activities. To ensure that students learn about all of these, assign the first six scenarios in the order shown in the chart below. You may decide to assign one pair in the group to read the first three scenarios, and the other pair to read the next three. Then have them discuss the scenarios with their groups. Alternatively you can assign one of each of the first six scenarios to a group, and have the groups share the information they recorded on the chart with the class. You may wish to assign the last two scenarios for homework. If so, begin the next class period with a discussion of the two scenarios. Instruct students to fill out the chart in their groups of four to document the type of human impact described in the scenarios, and which of the three types of biodiversity it alters.

5 A sample chart is shown at right.

Procedure

2
3

1. In your science notebook, copy the following chart. Give it an appropriate title.

Scenario	Type(s) of human impact	Type(s) of biodiversity altered

4 2. Follow your teacher's directions for which scenario(s) to read.

5 3. Work by yourself to read your assigned scenario(s). As you read, fill in the columns on the chart.

4. In your group, take turns summarizing your assigned scenario(s). As you listen, fill in the columns on the chart for each scenario that you did not read.

DISRUPTION OF NETWORKS

Ecosystems encompass a network of interdependent interactions. If the population of one species declines or goes extinct, that affects others in the network. An example of a network that could be disrupted is a food web.

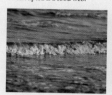

A harmful algal bloom causes illness or death in fish, seabirds, marine mammals, and humans who eat seafood contaminated with a neurotoxin from the algae. Algal blooms also reduce the oxygen levels in bodies of water.

BREEDING AND CLONING

People breed and clone populations of other organisms for various purposes. In doing so they might, for example, decrease genetic diversity in species of edible plants to create uniformly desirable crops.

A geneticist checks an ear of experimental corn for genetic changes.

423

Sample Student Response to Procedure Step 3–4

Scenario	Type(s) of human impact	Type(s) of biodiversity altered
Borneo rainforest	habitat destruction	ecosystem, species
Potato	breeding, cloning	genetic
Cichlids	invasive species, network of interactions	ecosystem, species
Dodo birds	overexploitation, introduced species	species, genetic (possibly)
Florida panthers	habitat destruction	genetic
Domestic dogs	breeding	genetic
Flying foxes	habitat destruction, overexploitation, network of interactions	ecosystem, species (possibly)
Elephant seals	overexploitation	genetic

Vast amounts of rainforest in Borneo were cleared to plant oil palm trees.

The Rainforests of Borneo

From an airplane above the island of Borneo, you can see the sudden divide between the rainforest and the straight rows of oil palm trees that have displaced the forest.

Borneo is a large island of more than 427,000 sq km (165,000 sq mi) between the South China and Java seas. On it are more than 15,000 known species of plants and some of the tallest tropical rainforests in the world. The rainforests are filled with an array of animals, including some that glide as they leap from tall trees, such as flying lizards, flying frogs, and flying snakes. Two species of gibbons and eight species of monkeys inhabit and climb in the trees. Sun bears, clouded leopards, elephants, orangutans, and rhinoceroses also live in and roam the rainforest. Even today scientists continue to discover species on the island that were never seen by other scientists before.

The greatest threat to the biodiversity of Borneo is forest destruction. Over the past two decades, approximately 40 million acres of forest have been cleared. Parts of the forests were cleared to plant palm trees, the fruits of which produce oil for cooking, body lotions, and fuel. The forests have also been extensively logged for timber to use for building and making paper. At the rate at which the forests of Borneo are being cut, the risk of current and future loss of biodiversity on the island is high.

The Potato in Ireland

After the potato was brought to Ireland from Spain in the 17th century, the Irish found they could grow more food in a smaller area with less labor when they planted just one variety: the lumper potato. That potato turned out to be a good source of nutrition and became a staple crop for Irish peasants. Like other living organisms, however, the potato is susceptible to microbes that cause disease, and lumpers are particularly susceptible to the fungus *Phytophthora infestans*, which causes potato blight. Making the Irish food supply more vulnerable, the lumper

In Ireland in the 1800s, potato blight killed whole crops of genetically identical lumper potatoes, causing widespread famine.

potatoes were all genetically identical to each other. In 1845, spores of the potato blight fungus were carried by the wind from England. A putrid stench hit the air as entire fields of potatoes died in just a few days.

While the potato blight reached all of Europe, only Ireland experienced devastating famine and suffering. One in eight Irish people died in three years.

Cichlids and Nile Perch

Within the last 200,000 years in Africa's huge Lake Victoria, more than 300 species of cichlid fish evolved to live in the various habitats in the lake. Some cichlids, such as tilapia, are edible, and some larger species are popular sport fishing prey. Genetic evidence suggests that the cichlids evolved from a common ancestor.

In the 1950s, the British government introduced the large Nile perch into the lake with the idea that the perch would provide the local people with a new protein source and a new commercial fishery.

Unfortunately, the perch ate the cichlids and other fish. Because cichlids were also fished along with the perch, introducing the perch appears to be the reason for the extinction of as many as 200 species of cichlids and the decline of other fish, such as catfish and lungfish.

a

b

When the Nile perch (a) was introduced into Lake Victoria, they ate the cichlids (b) and other fish that lived there.

In a further threat to the lake's biodiversity, the loss of the cichlid species that ate algae allowed the amount of algae in the lake to rise. Because algae consume oxygen, their abundance made it difficult for other small plants and animals in the lake to get enough oxygen for themselves. The Lake Victoria ecosystem is adjusting to these changes, but will not likely reach the level of biodiversity that existed before the introduction of Nile perch.

The Dodo Bird

The small Indian Ocean island of Mauritius was once home to populations of the large, flightless dodo bird, which had evolved over several million years on the island. Mauritius is isolated, and because they had little competition from other organisms the dodos had freely fed on fruit that had fallen to the ground. Those dodos with the ability to store large amounts of fat in times when food was scarce were better able to survive and reproduce. Eventually, over generations, the dodos increased in size. Flightlessness also evolved. As plant eaters in an environment with no predators, the inability to fly would have had no effect on the dodo's ability to survive. In the 16th and 17th centuries, Portuguese and Dutch explorers sailed to the island. The flightless dodos could not flee from humans who hunted them for food and for their eggs. The sailors also brought with them pigs, monkeys, and rats that fed on the dodos' eggs and chicks, and perhaps even adult dodos. On a small island, the relatively small dodo population could not survive under these changed conditions. In a small population, the genetic diversity of the population is relatively low. When genetic diversity is low, there is a low probability that any individual in the population will have the trait(s) required for survival and reproduction if the environment changes. Eighty years after humans arrived, dodos became extinct.

Dodo fossil bones confirm that the bird was flightless.

Florida Panther

By the 1950s, the once-large panther population of the south-eastern United States had been hunted to near extinction because of the threat people thought they posed to humans, livestock, and other animals. Today, urban and agricultural development and resulting habitat loss have decreased the panthers' range to only 5% of what it originally was. In 2009, a record number of 16 Florida panthers were killed by cars. With fewer than 100 panthers total remaining in southern Florida, this is a significant loss to the endangered panther population. Florida panthers are found in forested areas, including the mixed swamp, pine, and hardwood forests of the Everglades.

The Florida panther originally inhabited Florida, Louisiana, Arkansas, Mississippi, Alabama, Georgia, and parts of Tennessee and South Carolina. Between 1991 and 2003, more than 728,000 hectares (1.8 million acres) of forest in southern Florida were destroyed, and approximately 17,700 km (11,000 mi) of public roads were developed.

As people took over more and more land the panther population in Florida became isolated by habitat loss. Their isolation prevented them from breeding and exchanging genes with other panther populations. The inbreeding has led to reduced fertility, heart abnormalities, and infectious diseases in the population. In 1995, eight female panthers from Texas were introduced into the Florida population in an effort to help it recover. However, evidence suggests that so far this strategy has had limited success.

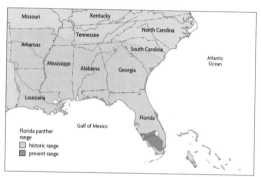

This depiction of the historic and current ranges of the Florida panther population shows how severely their habitat has been reduced.

427

Domestic Dogs

Domestic dogs are members of the subspecies *Canis lupus familiaris*. They are the result of thousands of years of dog breeding that began about 14,000 years ago when humans first domesticated the gray wolf, *Canis lupus*. The wolf populations in various parts of the world were made up of genetically different individual wolves. As wolves that interacted socially with humans became part of human communities, people took notice of their natural variations and the behavioral traits in their offspring that appeared to be inherited. Soon people were breeding wolves for particular desired traits, such as abilities for hunting, herding, hauling, or protecting their masters. Over centuries of such artificial selection, the descendants of the wolves became what we recognize as dogs.

Today there are hundreds of breeds of *Canis lupus familiaris*, from golden retrievers and poodles to chihuahuas and Pekingese lap dogs to pit bulls and rottweilers. Each breed has specific characteristics selected by the human breeders. For example, golden retrievers were bred to assist hunters by retrieving game. Because they are intelligent and sociable, they have also become popular as family pets. For

a

b

c

d

After gray wolves (a) were domesticated by humans, they were bred over centuries to produce hundreds of kinds of modern dogs (b–d).

decades the art of dog breeding has been big business, with mating of dogs of the same breed to produce dogs for show or superior performance in certain tasks. Now there is a trend to mate one breed with desirable traits to another with other desirable traits. The media has labeled the newly created mixed breeds "designer dogs," and some people are willing to pay thousands of dollars for such a puppy. The labradoodle, for example, is a mix of labrador retriever and poodle. While not all of the offspring in a litter have the exact same mix of traits, labradoodles' desired traits include a friendly, loyal disposition and a nonshedding coat.

Labradoodle

Flying Foxes

Some of the most important pollinators and seed dispersers of plants in the South Pacific islands are flying foxes, which are actually bats with ears, eyes, and snout comprising what looks like the face of a fox. Flying foxes are mammals that can weigh up to 1 kg (2.2 lbs).

Flying foxes feed on nectar, blossoms, pollen, and fruit. Reproduction of more than 79% of the plants of the Samoan islands is dependent on the flying fox for seed dispersal or pollination. In turn, the plants support much of the animal

The endangered flying fox bat is an important pollinator.

FOLLOW-UP

6 Ask for student volunteers to share their groups' ideas about the activities and impacts of humans on both themselves and other species. Bring out the idea that humans interact with a variety of species, often affecting the biodiversity of the species at the ecosystem, species, and genetic levels.

SAMPLE RESPONSES

1. a. The Borneo rainforest, flying foxes, and cichlid fish

    b. The Borneo rainforest, dodo birds, and cichlid fish

    c. Potatoes, dogs, northern elephant seals, and Florida panthers

2. a. Habitat destruction from clearing forests for planting oil palm might decrease the diversity of the Borneo rainforest ecosystem. Hunting in the Samoan island ecosystem has removed thousands of flying foxes, which are important pollinators for plants that other animals rely on for resources such as food or shelter. Putting Nile perch into Lake Victoria changed the lake ecosystem diversity because it caused cichlid populations to decline. Since some cichlids eat algae, the amount of algae in the lake has increased.

    b. The species diversity is lowered when the rainforest is cleared in Borneo because so many species rely on the rainforest to live. The number of species that lived on the island of Mauritius before humans arrived went down by one when the dodo bird went extinct, but the number of species increased with the introduced species brought in by humans. Two hundred cichlids in Lake Victoria became extinct after a new species, the Nile perch, was introduced.

---

diversity on the island and provide ecosystem services for humans. The wild banana is an example of a tree that largely depends on flying foxes to spread the pollen from one tree or one banana flower to another. Because of their important role in pollination and seed dispersal, the flying fox population is crucial for the maintenance of the Pacific island ecosystem. Local people depend on the wild banana for food and as a source of fiber to make textiles, rope, and paper.

A great threat to flying foxes, however, is people's taste for exotic foods. Each year from 1975 to 1990, between 8,000 and 29,000 flying foxes were hunted to supply the luxury food market. The bats are also hunted for their medicinal properties and sport.

Populations of flying foxes are especially vulnerable to destruction by hunters and other pressures because most females do not begin reproducing until they are one-to-two-years old. Once they start reproducing, they give birth to only one off-spring per year. The flying fox is classified as endangered under the United States Endangered Species Act, and cannot be imported into this country.

Northern Elephant Seals

Hundreds of thousands of northern elephant seals once lived in the Pacific Ocean with a range that spanned from the north in Alaska and British Columbia to the south in California. They are so named for their large size and the large nose that suggests an elephant's trunk. Male elephant seals grow to a weight of approximately 2,300 kg (5,000 lbs), and a length up to 4 m (14 ft), while mature females grow to weigh around 635 kg (1,400 lbs), and to be up to 3 m (11 ft) long.

Northern elephant seal

430

---

c. When people in Ireland limited the genetic diversity of potatoes, they put their whole crops at risk of disease, and when disease hit, the potatoes died, leading to the death of many people who relied on potatoes for food. The genetic makeup of the dog population changed compared to the wolves when the gray wolf was bred by humans for desirable domestic characteristics, but it isn't clear if the genetic diversity has changed. People hunted the northern elephant seals so heavily that the population got very small. Although the number of elephant seals is now strong, the whole population can be traced back to just one male who mated with females, meaning the genetic diversity is low. Habitat destruction caused the Florida panther population to shrink. Because they live in an isolated habitat in southern Florida, panthers have inbred, and now the population has illnesses and very low genetic diversity.

3. a. When one or more species in an area go extinct, the species diversity in that area will decrease unless other species migrate into or are introduced into the area.

    b. When the genetic diversity of a species is low, there is less chance that an individual will have the trait(s) that increases the probability of survival if the environment changes. This puts the species more at risk of extinction.

4. Students' answers will vary depending on their perspectives. Some might say that we only need to be concerned with species that affect us either positively (providing ecosystem services) or negatively (for example, the introduction or loss of the species leads to a disease). Others will say that we need to help protect any species that we can because biodiversity is valuable and those species may play important roles in the ecosystem even if they don't affect us directly.

REVIST THE CHALLENGE

Review the three types of biodiversity that students examined in this activity: ecosystem, species, and genetic. Review the idea that people affect the biodiversity of species on the ecosystem, species, and genetic levels, causing the three levels to increase or decrease. Some human activities that can affect biodiversity include habitat destruction, introduced species, overexploitation, disruption of networks, and breeding and cloning.

Elephant seals spend most of their time in the ocean but come ashore regularly to molt, breed, and give birth on land, making them a much easier target for hunters than whales. From 1820 to 1880, whale and seal hunters slaughtered whole colonies of elephant seals to make oil from their blubber. The blubber harvesting was so extensive that the species was nearly wiped out. In fact, estimates of their remaining population numbered from 20 to 100 individuals from the late 1880s to 1900. Scientists describe such a severe but temporary reduction in population size as a bottleneck.

Beginning in the early 1900s, the Mexican and United States governments protected the elephant seals with a ban on their hunting, and their numbers gradually increased. Today, astonishingly, there are more than 100,000 northern elephant seals. Of some concern to conservationists, however, is that the current seal population has been traced through genetic testing back to just one male who survived to reproduce with females. This means the genetic diversity is very low. But so far, at least, the low genetic diversity has not hindered the growth of the elephant seal population.

6 *Analysis*

1. For which scenario(s) did humans alter
    a. ecosystem diversity?
    b. species diversity?
    c. genetic diversity?

2. Explain how humans changed the ecosystem, species, and genetic diversity of the groups you identified in question 1.

3. What is the relationship between extinction and
    a. species diversity?
    b. genetic diversity?

4. Do you think it is important for humans to be aware of how we alter the genetic and species diversity of groups of organisms? Explain.

KEY VOCABULARY	
biodiversity	**species diversity**
ecosystem diversity	taxa
genetic diversity	taxon

EXTENSION

Instruct students to find examples of human effects on biodiversity in their communities, in the media, or in other sources. This is also an opportunity to take students outside (for example, to a field on school property) to observe examples of human effects on biodiversity. You may wish to assign students to make observations as homework.

3 Geologic Time

MODELING • 1–2 CLASS SESSIONS

OVERVIEW

Students are introduced to the vast time span of the earth's history and to the division of the history into geologic time periods based on major events in the evolution of life. Students convert the periods of geologic time to the scale of a football field and place key events on this timeline to help them understand how life has evolved since earth originated 4.5 billion years ago.

KEY CONTENT

1. The geologic timeline reflects the vast time scale since earth originated.

2. Earth was formed approximately 4.5 billion years ago. Life began on earth approximately 4.3 billion years ago.

3. Multicellular life originated relatively recently in geologic time, approximately 640 million years ago.

4. Most key events in the evolution of life occurred in relatively recent geologic time.

KEY PROCESS SKILLS

1. Students take measurements, collect, and record data.

MATERIALS AND ADVANCE PREPARATION

For the class
25 sheets of poster board or chart paper*

For the teacher
Transparency 3.1, "The Geologic Time Scale"
Scoring Guide: UNDERSTANDING CONCEPTS (UC)
Scoring Guide: COMMUNICATION SKILLS (CS)

For each pair of students
Student Sheet 3.3, "Geologic Event paper strips"
pair of scissors*
calculator*

For each student
Student Sheet 3.1, "Ideas about Evolution"
Student Sheet 3.2, "Geologic Time and Major Events"
Scoring Guide: UNDERSTANDING CONCEPTS (UC) (optional)
Scoring Guide: COMMUNICATION SKILLS (CS) (optional)

Not supplied in kit

Teacher's Note: *If you do not have a football field, mark off 100 yards on any playing field on your school's property, in the school's gymnasium, or in a hallway.*

You will need to make 25 poster-sized signs, one for each of the 19 geologic eras, periods, and epochs listed in the Student Book, and one for each of the six geologic events and the times they occurred as follows:

Earth originated: 4,500 mya
Earliest fossil record of prokaryotes: 3,500 mya
Oxygen levels in atmosphere increase: 3,500–2,500 mya
Earliest eukaryote fossils: 2,500 mya
Earliest mammals in fossil record: 200 mya
Earliest Homo erectus *fossils: 1.8 mya*

These signs will be placed on the football field to show time periods and key events.

Masters for Scoring Guides are in Teacher Resources IV: Assessment.

TEACHING SUMMARY

Getting Started

- Elicit students' ideas about geologic time and key events in biological evolution.

Doing the Activity

- (LITERACY) Students participate in an Informal Meeting of the Minds related to Student Sheet 3.1, "Ideas about Evolution."

- Students represent the 4.5 billion years of earth's history on a football field and place major evolutionary events along the scale.

Follow-up

- Introduce the SEPUP Assessment System.

- (UC, CS ASSESSMENT) Discuss students' ideas about geologic time, and review the conversions with which they demonstrated geologic time and events on the football field.

BACKGROUND INFORMATION

Scientists have divided the earth's history into a series of time periods referred to as the geologic time scale. The boundaries of the time periods are defined by the first appearance or the disappearance of certain fossils in the record, and thus vary greatly in length. Scientists estimated the date range for each time period using radiometric dating technology (to be described in Activity 6, "Evidence from the Fossil Record"). As new fossils are discovered and radiometric dating technologies continue to improve, these estimated dates are likely to be adjusted.

GETTING STARTED

1 ◆ Begin by drawing a line on the board that is labeled as shown at the bottom of the page. If necessary, explain that the abbreviation bya is billions of years ago, and mya is millions of years ago. Ask students to sketch the timeline in their science notebooks and label where along this timeline they think the following events occurred:

- First cells preserved in the fossil record

- Dinosaurs became extinct.

- "Ardi," a skeleton observed in the fossil record, who lived in Ethiopia.

If students do not know about Ardi, tell them that Ardi is short for *Ardipithecus ramidus,* a female skeleton that was discovered with fossils from other *Ar. ramidus* individuals 15 years ago in Ethiopia. Explain that Ardi provides evidence about the evolution of humans. If you wish, have students discuss their ideas in pairs.

Ask for student volunteers to share their ideas about the events on the time scale with the class. Tell students that they will be learning more about geologic time and Earth events in this activity. They will revisit their ideas at the end of the activity.

DOING THE ACTIVITY

2 ◆ (LITERACY) Distribute Student Sheet 3.1, "Ideas about Evolution." Instruct students to record their initial ideas about whether each statement is correct or incorrect in the "Before" column and to explain their reasoning.

---

3 Geologic Time

1 **T**HE EARTH'S HISTORY spans 4.5 billion years. Scientists use the terms **deep time** and **geologic time** interchangeably when describing this vast time scale. They have distinguished historical eras, or ages, in geologic time, such as the Archaean era and Proterozoic era. The eras are further divided into periods, such as the Cambrian period or Silurian period, and epochs based on when major changes in plants and animals occurred. Scientists learned about these changes by observing fossils. All of the periods of the earth's history together make up the geologic timeline.

It may be difficult to visualize just how long a billion years is, yet knowing about this immense span of time has been central to understanding the origins and evolution of life on the earth. In this activity, you will develop a scaled model to help you visualize geologic time and the history of life during that time.

Challenge

▶ What are the key events of geologic time?

The Burgess Shale in the Canadian Rockies in British Columbia is a rock formation that accumulated during the Middle Cambrian period approximately 500–550 million years ago. The fossils found there are some of the most diverse and well-preserved in the world. Many of the fossils are from organisms that lived on the sea floor.

432

Conduct an Informal Meeting of the Minds. Direct students to find a partner from another group and discuss their initial ideas about which statements are accurate and which are not accurate. Encourage students to cite evidence from a past science class or reliable source to support their ideas and to ask questions of each other. Circulate around the room as students discuss. This is an opportunity to informally assess students' current knowledge about evolution. Ask pairs to summarize their

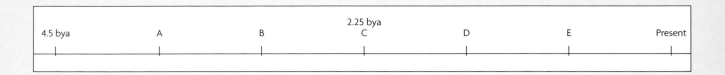

discussions with the class. Tell the class that they are sharing their initial ideas about evolution and that when they revisit these ideas throughout the unit they may revise and, if necessary, correct their ideas about each statement.

3 Distribute Student Sheet 3.2, "Geologic Time and Major Events," to each student. Project Transparency 3.1, "The Geologic Time Scale." Instruct students to copy the example football-field time scale conversions shown on the transparency. You may wish to work through an example conversion with the class as appropriate. Place the present time at 0 yards, and represent 4.5 billion years as a distance of 100 yards from the present. Working backward in time, each time mark is converted by calculating its ratio to 4.5 billion years ago and multiplying it by the 100-yard length of the football field. When times are given in mya, 4.5 billion is represented as 4,500 mya.

Example: The Pleistocene era began 1.8 mya.

1.8 mya ÷ 4,500 mya × 100 yds = 0.04 yds.

Have students complete Procedure Step 3. As they work, check to see that they are correctly converting geologic time into the appropriate distances on the football field. Sample answers for Student Sheet 3.2 with the event/eras, periods, and epochs labeled in blue are shown at the end of this activity.

MATERIALS

FOR EACH PAIR OF STUDENTS
set of 6 Geologic Event paper strips
scissors
calculator

FOR EACH STUDENT
Student Sheet 3.1, "Ideas about Evolution"
Student Sheet 3.2, "Geologic Time and Major Events"

Procedure

2 1. Review the statements on Student Sheet 3.1, "Ideas about Evolution."

2. Follow your teacher's instructions for responding to and discussing the statements on Student Sheet 3.1.

3 3. With your partner, examine the information on Student Sheet 3.2, "Geologic Time and Major Events," and the chart below. Convert each geologic time period from millions of years ago (mya) into yards on a football field, and record both the time in mya and the era/event, period, or epoch on the Student Sheet.

The Geologic Time Scale

GEOLOGIC ERA OR EVENT	GEOLOGIC PERIOD	GEOLOGIC EPOCH	TIME (MYA)
Earth is formed	—	—	4,500
Archean	—	—	4,300
Proterozoic	—	—	2,500
Paleozoic	Cambrian	—	542
Paleozoic	Ordovician	—	488
Paleozoic	Silurian	—	444
Paleozoic	Devonian	—	416
Paleozoic	Carboniferous	—	359
Paleozoic	Permian	—	299
Mesozoic	Triassic	—	251
Mesozoic	Jurassic	—	200
Mesozoic	Cretaceous	—	145
Cenozoic	Tertiary	Paleocene	65
Cenozoic	Tertiary	Eocene	55.8
Cenozoic	Tertiary	Oligocene	33.9
Cenozoic	Tertiary	Miocene	23
Cenozoic	Tertiary	Pliocene	5.3
Cenozoic	Quaternary	Pleistocene	1.8
Cenozoic	Quaternary	Recent (Holocene)	0.01

433

4 Distribute a sheet of Geologic Event paper strips to each pair of students, and instruct them to cut them into event strips and complete Procedure Step 4. After students have recorded the geologic events on Student Sheet 3.2, "Geologic Time and Major Events," tell the class that you and they will be going to the actual football field to observe the geologic timeline and events.

5 Before that, if you wish, project Transparency 3.1, "The Geologic Time Scale," to review conversions with students. Write in the remaining conversions on the transparency. A completed time scale is shown below right.

Explain to students that the next part of the activity will help them visualize where events fall along geologic time. Take students out to the football field. Ask them to bring Student Sheet 3.2, "Geologic Time and Major Events," with them to mark the conversions on the field. Explain that the 100-yard field represents 4.5 billion years or 4,500 million years, just as it does on the Student Sheet. The 0-yard mark represents today. Ask students where a person would stand to represent 4.3 billion years, or 4,300 million, years ago—the beginning of the Archean era. Have a student volunteer stand at 95.6 yards. This part of the activity is an opportunity to discuss the difficulty that most people have in understanding how long a million years is in terms of a human lifespan, yet how short it is in terms of the earth's age. In the context of deep geologic

---

4. Collect the sheet showing six Geologic Events, and with your partner, cut it into six Geologic Event strips. Read the information on the strips, and on Student Sheet 3.2, "Geologic Time and Major Events," arrange them where you think each occurred in geologic time. Once you have decided on an order, use a pencil to record the placement on the Student Sheet.

5. Follow your teacher's instructions for observing on an actual football field the events in geologic time that you recorded in Step 4.

6. Observe your Geologic Event paper strips again. Using your experience on the football field, record on Student Sheet 3.2, "Geologic Time and Major Events," the correct time placement of the six geologic events you were given. In your science notebook, record any changes you made to your original order.

7. Now record the following events on the timeline on Student Sheet 3.2, "Geologic Time and Major Events":

- Starting 500 mya: first vertebrates in fossil record
- Starting 416 mya: first insects in fossil record
- Starting 230 mya: first dinosaurs in fossil record
- Starting 144 mya: mass extinction, including dinosaurs

8. Look at the following diagrams, which are evolutionary trees showing relationships between taxa. Based on the trees, add the following events to the timeline on Student Sheet 3.2, "Geologic Time and Major Events":

- First seed plants in fossil record
- First reptiles in fossil record
- The extinction of pterosaurs

The Geologic Time Scale

GEOLOGIC ERA OR EVENT	GEOLOGIC PERIOD	GEOLOGIC EPOCH	TIME (MYA)	DISTANCE ON A FOOTBALL FIELD (YDS)
Earth is formed	—	—	4,500	100
Archean	—	—	4,300	95.6
Proterozoic	—	—	2,500	55.6
Paleozoic	Cambrian	—	542	12.0
Paleozoic	Ordovician	—	488	10.8
Paleozoic	Silurian	—	444	10.0
Paleozoic	Devonian	—	416	9.2
Paleozoic	Carboniferous	—	359	8.0
Paleozoic	Permian	—	299	6.6
Mesozoic	Triassic	—	251	5.6
Mesozoic	Jurassic	—	200	4.4
Mesozoic	Cretaceous	—	145	3.2
Cenozoic	Tertiary	Paleocene	65	1.4
Cenozoic	Tertiary	Eocene	55.8	1.2
Cenozoic	Tertiary	Oligocene	33.9	0.8
Cenozoic	Tertiary	Miocene	23	0.5
Cenozoic	Tertiary	Pliocene	5.3	0.1
Cenozoic	Quaternary	Pleistocene	1.8	0.04
Cenozoic	Quaternary	Recent (Holocene)	0.01	0

time over the course of the earth's history, 200 million years (represented by the relatively short 4.4 yards between 95.6 and 100) is an extremely short time. There are several ways to organize the class so that all of the students can observe the geologic time scale on the football field. You might assign 19 students to each hold one of the signs labeled with one of the 19 periods and epochs shown in the Student Book, and instruct them to stand at the appropriate locations on the field. Then distribute to six students one sign each that is labeled with the six events that they placed on the Student Sheet, and the actual time that they occurred, as shown below. Alternatively you might ask students to place the signs for the time periods and events on the ground at the appropriate places on the field, and have the class walk up and down the field to observe the timeline and events. Then you may also have students stand back at a certain distance so they can see the entire timeline.

- **Earth originated**
  4,500 mya, 100 yds

- **Earliest fossil record of prokaryotes**
  3,500 mya: 77.8 yds

- **Oxygen levels in atmosphere increase**
  starting 3,500 mya and up to 2,500 mya:
  77.8–55.6 yds

- **Earliest eukaryote fossils**
  2,500 mya: 55.6 yds

- **Earliest mammals in fossil record**
  200 mya: 4.4 yds

- **Earliest *Homo erectus* fossils**
  1.8 mya: 0.04 yds

6 Sample answers for Student Sheet 3.2, "Geologic Time and Major Events," with the events recorded in red are shown at the end of this activity.

7 Return to the classroom, and discuss with students how difficult it is to grasp time scale of billions (or even millions) of years. Discuss how the football field model illustrates this concept by showing the span of human life and other events compared to the age of the earth.

Instruct students to begin Procedure Step 7. Sample answers for Step 7 are shown below:

- **Starting 500 mya**
  first vertebrates in fossil record: 11.1 yds

- **Starting 416 mya**
  first insects in fossil record: 9.2 yds

- **Starting 230 mya**
  first dinosaurs in fossil record: 5.1 yds

- **Starting 144 mya**
  mass extinction, including dinosaurs: 3.2 yds

8 Students will work with some simple evolutionary trees in Procedure Step 8. The dates and conversions of the events are as follows:

- **First seed plants in fossil record**
  approximately 380 mya: 8.4 yds

- **First reptiles in fossil record**
  approximately 330 mya: 7.3 yds

- **The extinction of pterosaurs**
  approximately 64 mya: 1.4 yds

FOLLOW-UP

9 (UC, CS ASSESSMENT) Students' written work for Analysis Question 1 may be scored with the UNDERSTANDING CONCEPTS (UC) Scoring Guide. This is as an opportunity to introduce the SEPUP assessment system. Provide all students with a UC Scoring Guide, and ask them to keep it with their science notebooks, as they will refer to it several times in this unit and throughout the *Science and Global Issues* course. Explain to the class that you will use the UC Scoring Guide to provide feedback on the quality of their work. Let them know that you will use their writing from Analysis Question 1 to model how the Scoring Guide works.

Begin by pointing out the scoring levels 0–4, and review the criteria for each score. Explain that the scores are based on the quality of their responses and do not correspond to letter grades. A Level-3 response is a complete and correct response. A Level-4 response signifies that the student has both achieved and exceeded the acceptable level of response. Let students know that you would like them to strive to improve by at least one level in later activities. At first, many students will write Level-2 responses, and they should strive to achieve Level-3 responses.

As a class, discuss what a Level-3 response would include. A complete and correct response would include a description of what distinguishes the periods of geologic time. The major events noted should include single-celled organisms, increased oxygen levels, eukaryotic evolution, and mammals. You may develop a Level-3 exemplar with the class or share with students the Level-3 response shown on the next page. Point out the elements that make the example a Level-3 response, and discuss how a Level 1 and a Level 2 are different. Ask students for ideas about

how to improve the Level-3 response to make it a Level 4. Analysis Question 1 may also be scored with the COMMUNICATION SKILLS (CS) Scoring Guide. Distribute a copy of the CS Scoring Guide, and review the guidelines. Tell the class your expectations for satisfactory work.

To begin a discussion, ask students what patterns they see in the changes of life through geologic time. A pattern they should notice is the recent appearance of mammals and reptiles. If they do not bring it up, make sure to emphasize this to students. Remind them that for the vast majority of time on earth, unicellular organisms were the only form of life. Also, discuss two common misconceptions students might have, if they do not

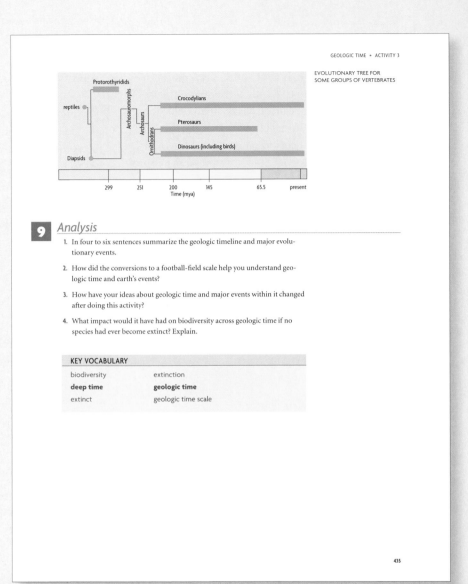

9 *Analysis*

1. In four to six sentences summarize the geologic timeline and major evolutionary events.

2. How did the conversions to a football-field scale help you understand geologic time and earth's events?

3. How have your ideas about geologic time and major events within it changed after doing this activity?

4. What impact would it have had on biodiversity across geologic time if no species had ever become extinct? Explain.

KEY VOCABULARY

biodiversity	extinction
deep time	**geologic time**
extinct	geologic time scale

435

bring them up: 1) that the origin of life occurred close to the time of the origin of the earth; and 2) that early humans and dinosaurs coexisted (a misconception they may have acquired from cartoons or other popular media). The timelines should show that fossil evidence proves these ideas to be inaccurate. Revisit the three events that students placed on the timeline at the beginning of the activity:

- **First cells observed in the fossil record**
  3,500 mya or 77.8 yds on a football field

- **Dinosaurs became extinct**
  65 mya or 1.4 yds on a football field

- **Ardi observed in the fossil record**
  approximately 4.4 mya or 0.1 yds on a football field

SAMPLE RESPONSES

1. (UC, CS ASSESSMENT) A complete and correct response will include a description of what distinguishes the periods of geologic time. The major events should include single-celled organisms as the first life forms to evolve, increased oxygen levels, eukaryotic evolution, and mammals.

   Sample Level-3 Response:
   The geologic timeline divides earth's history into periods based on the evolution and extinction of major groups of organisms. Each period does not necessarily span the same amount of time. During much of geologic time, only single-celled organisms, which were the first life forms to evolve on earth, were present. Oxygen levels in the atmosphere increased 2,500 million years ago, and during that same time, the earliest eukaryotes evolved. Mammals came about in fairly recent geologic history (251 million years ago) compared to single-celled organisms. Many groups of organisms, including humans, originated in very recent geologic time.

2. Students are likely to say that a concrete model with everyday conversions helped them visualize a million and a billion years as vastly longer than human lifetimes or even the existence of humans as a species.

3. Students' answers will vary. Some might say that they originally thought that mammals, including humans, appeared on Earth shortly after it originated. Some might say they had thought that dinosaurs and humans lived at the same time. Others might say that a million years seemed like an incredibly long time, but in geologic time, it is actually very short.

4. Students' answers will vary. Many will say that there would be more diversity because every species would still be alive or that the overall level of biodiversity would stay the same, but the type of biodiversity would change as time went on. Others might argue that there would be less biodiversity because the earlier life forms, if they hadn't gone extinct, would consume all of earth's resources including food, space, and water, leaving no resources for more recently evolved life forms, such as mammals.

REVISIT THE CHALLENGE

By now, students should understand that key events in geologic time were the evolutions or extinctions of major groups of organisms, and that geologic time periods are determined by these key events, rather than set numbers of years. For example, single-celled organisms appeared relatively early at 3.5 billion years ago, but by no means near the very beginning of the 4.5 billion-year life span of Earth. Multicellular life evolved much later, at 2.5 billion years ago, and mammals and humans evolved relatively recently. Students should also be able to state that geologic time is a vast amount of time that spans billions of years since the earth originated. The appendix of the Student Book has a complete geologic time scale with major evolutionary events.

Geologic Time and Major Events

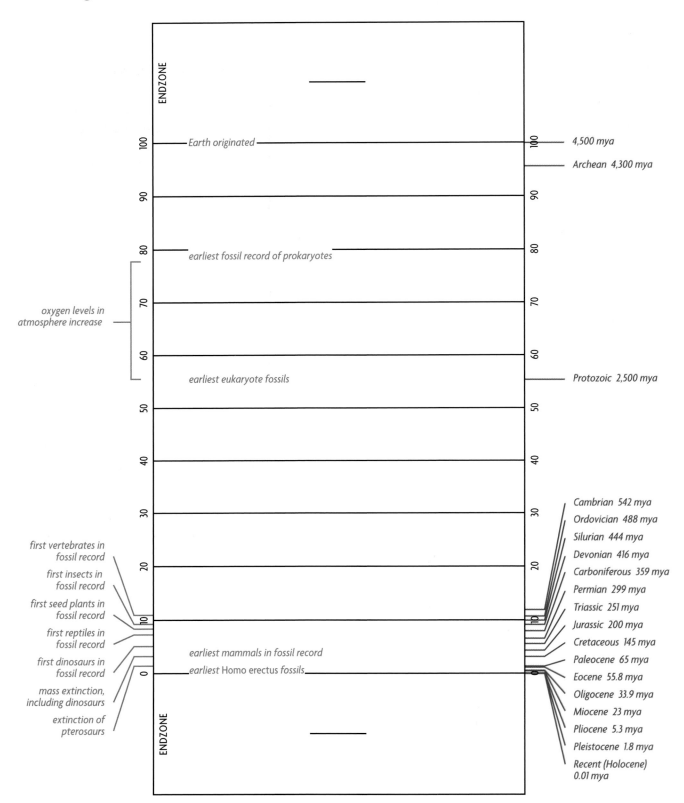

ENDZONE

100 — Earth originated ———————————————— 100 — 4,500 mya

———————————————— Archean 4,300 mya

90 90

80 — earliest fossil record of prokaryotes 80

oxygen levels in
atmosphere increase

70 70

60 60 — Protozoic 2,500 mya

— earliest eukaryote fossils

50 50

40 40

Cambrian 542 mya
30 30 Ordovician 488 mya
Silurian 444 mya
Devonian 416 mya
first vertebrates in
fossil record
20 20 Carboniferous 359 mya
first insects in
fossil record
Permian 299 mya
first seed plants in
fossil record
Triassic 251 mya
10 10 Jurassic 200 mya
first reptiles in
fossil record
Cretaceous 145 mya
first dinosaurs in
fossil record
earliest mammals in fossil record
Paleocene 65 mya
0 earliest Homo erectus fossils 0 Eocene 55.8 mya
mass extinction,
including dinosaurs
Oligocene 33.9 mya
Miocene 23 mya
extinction of
pterosaurs
ENDZONE Pliocene 5.3 mya
Pleistocene 1.8 mya
Recent (Holocene)
0.01 mya

4 Darwin and the Development of a Theory

READING • 1–2 CLASS SESSIONS

OVERVIEW

Students read about Charles Darwin and how his own research and ideas that were emerging from others' work led to his theory of natural selection as the mechanism for evolution. They are introduced to the key principles of natural selection and to Darwin's story as an example of the development of a scientific theory.

KEY CONTENT

1. Natural selection is a key part of the evolution of diverse taxa from common ancestors.

2. Darwin developed the theory of evolution by natural selection by putting together his own observations and ideas with the findings and ideas of other naturalists, geologists, and an economist.

3. Scientific theories are based on natural and physical phenomena.

4. Scientific theories are well established and highly reliable explanations.

5. Scientists usually build on earlier knowledge and are influenced by other experts and their society and culture.

6. Occasionally, a scientific advance has important long-lasting effects on science and society because of its explanation of natural phenomena. The theory of biological evolution by natural selection is an example of such an advance.

KEY PROCESS SKILLS

1. Students make accurate interpretations, inferences, and conclusions from text.

MATERIALS AND ADVANCE PREPARATION

For the teacher

Transparency 4.1, "Natural Selection and Evolution"

Transparency 4.2, "Timeline of Ideas Leading Up to and Following Darwin's Work"

Literacy Transparency 2, "Read, Think, and Take Note" (optional)

For each student

Student Sheet 4.1, "Scientists, Ideas, and Events that Influenced Darwin"

3 sticky notes*

Masters for Literacy Transparencies are in Teacher Resources III: Literacy.

TEACHING SUMMARY

Getting Started

• Discuss the intellectual culture of the 1700s and 1800s, during the time of Darwin's work.

Doing the Activity

• (LITERACY) Students follow the "Read, Think, and Take Note" strategy as they complete the reading.

Follow-up

• The class discusses the basic principles of evolution by natural selection and the people and ideas that influenced Darwin as he developed his ideas.

GETTING STARTED

 Begin by telling students that up through the 18th century, most scientists thought that the earth was a few thousand years old and that each species was created independently of others. But the late 1700s and 1800s were a time of enlightened thought about philosophy and nature, and the old ideas began to change. For example, around 1788, Georges-Louis Leclerc, Comte de Buffon (usually known as Buffon), proposed that species were not fixed, and that humans and apes shared a common ancestor, based on his observations of the similarities between them. Explain that Darwin was influenced by these ideas and by the ideas of many others, as well as by his own experience.

DOING THE ACTIVITY

2 (LITERACY) The literacy strategy "Read, Think, and Take Note" is an opportunity for students to record thoughts, reactions, or questions on sticky notes as they read. The notes serve to make concrete the thoughts arising in their minds and as prompts to generate conversation or written explanations. Throughout this unit and the rest of *Science and Global Issues* you will see multiple opportunities for students to employ and become comfortable with this strategy. Explain to students that through these literacy strategies they are learning the ways in which proficient readers think while reading. Display Literacy Transparency 3, "Read, Think, and Take Note," for students to refer to. Look for additional occasions for students to apply this strategy when reading text. For more information on "Read, Think, and Take Note," see Teacher Resources III: Literacy.

4 Darwin and the Development of a Theory

1 **STARTING IN THE** 1830s, British naturalist Charles Darwin suggested and developed some ideas about evolution that revolutionized the field of biology. **Biological evolution**, or **evolution**, is a change in the genetic composition of a population that gives rise to new life forms from common ancestors. Darwin's thinking was influenced by the ideas of several other people who worked before and during his time.

Challenge

▶ How did Darwin build on his and others' work to develop his ideas about natural selection and evolution?

MATERIALS

FOR EACH STUDENT
3 sticky notes
Student Sheet 4.1, "Scientists, Ideas, and Events that Influenced Darwin"

Procedure

1. As you read, follow the "Read, Think, and Take Note" strategy. To do this:

2
- Stop at least three times during the reading to mark on a sticky note your thoughts or questions about the reading. Use the list of guidelines on the next page to start your thinking.
- After writing a thought or question on a sticky note, place it next to the passage in the reading that prompted your note.
- Discuss with your partner the thoughts and questions you had while reading.

Charles Darwin

436

Read, Think, and Take Note: Guidelines

As you read, from time to time, write one of the following on a sticky note :

- Explain a thought or reaction to something you read
- Note something in the reading that is confusing or unfamiliar
- List a word that you do not know
- Describe a connection to something you learned or read previously
- Make a statement about the reading
- Pose a question about the reading
- Draw a diagram or picture of an idea or connection

2. After finishing the reading, complete the diagram on Student Sheet 4.1, "Scientists, Ideas, and Events that Influenced Darwin."

Reading

Before Darwin

In the early 1800s, naturalists had begun to consider the idea that species of living things are not fixed, a revolutionary idea at the time. Instead, they suspected, species have undergone changes ever since they first evolved on earth.

In France, Jean-Baptiste Lamarck was one of the naturalists considering changes in species. In 1809 (the year Charles Darwin was born), Lamarck published *Zoological Philosophy*, a book that presented one of the first theories of evolution. He suggested that when the environment changes, organisms must also change in response if they are to survive. He favored a mechanism for evolution proposed by earlier scientists that was based on use and disuse of organs. He stated that, for example, if giraffes continually stretched their necks to reach high treetops for food, their necks could lengthen over their lifetime, and their offspring could inherit these changes. If an animal did not use a particular organ, the organ would become smaller from one generation to the next or disappear entirely. Lamarck's theory would say, for example, that because snakes could slither through the grass, the legs of snake species gradually became smaller and smaller.

Lamarck was ignored or attacked by most of his colleagues for his theory of use and disuse because he had no evidence for his mechanism, and many of his ideas were pure speculation. Today, his theory is not accepted because scientists' investigations of heredity have shown that acquired characteristics (characteristics that develop during life, that are not inherited), such as strong muscles due to exercise, are not passed through from the body to the genes, and are not, therefore, passed on from parents to offspring.

437

Darwin's Observations on the Galapagos Islands

In 1831, one of Darwin's college professors recommended him to Captain Robert Fitzroy to join the voyage of the HMS Beagle, a survey ship that would travel all over the world. Appreciating Darwin's education and impressed by his wealthy background, Fitzroy accepted the 22-year-old Darwin on board.

While at sea Darwin read the first volume of Charles Lyell's recently published *Principles of Geology.* The main point of Lyell's book was that the geology of the earth in its present form helps explain the geologic past. Lyell proposed that large-scale geologic change results from small changes over extremely long periods of time. For example, the slow erosion of rock over many years can lead to the formation of a canyon. In addition, he, as had others, thought that the earth was much older than several thousand years.

Over the five years of the voyage, Darwin observed and collected a variety of animals, plants, and fossils to bring back to England. His work on the voyage included explorations on land in South America where he noted geological formations, and several weeks studying the organisms on the Galapagos Islands, about 970 km off the coast of Ecuador. Those 10 islands, as Darwin observed, were all formed from volcanic rocks and all had similar soil, climates, elevation, and size. He also noticed that the plants and animals on the islands had adapted to all kinds of environments.

Darwin's observations of plants and animals on the Galapagos Islands made him wonder about the origins of their similarities and differences.

Darwin made extensive observations of the Galapagos plants and animals. He wondered why the species on each island differed from each other but were much more like each other than species elsewhere.

Among the organisms Darwin brought back to England were the now-famous Galapagos finches. Darwin had collected a number of birds that he assumed were blackbirds, grosbeaks, and woodpeckers because they varied so much in beak structure, tails, and body form. Showing his collection to England's bird experts, he was surprised to learn that his birds were all members of 13 closely related species of finches. He had seen one group of finches often climbing around the flowers of cactus trees, while another group tended to flock together and feed on seeds on the ground. For each species of finch the birds' beaks were suited to the food sources available on the island they lived on. Although Darwin examined many other groups of organisms, including mockingbirds and tortoises, the finches became best known because they showed how a diverse group of species could evolve through natural selection from a common ancestor that originated on the mainlands.

Darwin observed biodiversity in many groups of organisms as he developed his ideas about natural selection, including the Galapagos finch (a), Galapagos mockingbird (b), and the Galapagos tortoise (c).

a

b

c

Variety and Artificial Selection through Breeding

Back in England as he thought about the patterns of organisms on the islands—different from and yet similar to those on the mainland—Darwin began to develop his ideas about biodiversity. From pigeon breeders he learned that selective breeding could be used to produce a great variety of pigeons in a relatively short period of time. A breeder would cage two individual pigeons with a desirable trait together to mate in order to obtain offspring that inherited and reinforced that trait. These improved offspring were then selected for further breeding, and the breeder would continue the process for generations. Meanwhile, another breeder would be mating his pigeons for another desirable trait. People had applied such artificial selection for thousands of years in breeding better crops and animals. Dogs, cows, corn, and tulips are just some of the organisms modified by humans through selective breeding.

Darwin became so fascinated with this that he began to breed pigeons at his home. In observing characteristics of tails, heads, beaks, and necks, he was once again astonished by the variety he could bring out among the pigeons, an astonishment similar to when he understood the variations among finches on the Galapagos. He also learned that if he crossbred varieties of pigeons, some offspring would resemble the birds he first started with when he began breeding. Darwin considered how this great variety might arise in nature. He wrote in his autobiography:

> After my return to England, it appeared to me that by following the example of Lyell in *Geology*, and by collecting all facts which bore in any way on the variation of animals and plants under domestication and nature, some light might be thrown on the whole subject. I soon perceived that selection was the keystone of man's success in making useful races of animals and plants. But how selection could be applied to organisms living in a state of nature remained for some time a mystery to me.

Darwin's breakthrough came in reasoning that the selection produced artificially by humans might occur in all sorts of species, as a result of changes in the environment. Also in his autobiography he wrote:

> In October 1838, that is, fifteen months after I had begun my systematic inquiry, I happened to read for amusement Malthus on Population, and being well prepared to appreciate the struggle for existence which everywhere goes on from long-continued observation of the habits of animals and plants, it at once struck me that under these circumstances favorable variations would tend to be preserved, and unfavorable ones to be destroyed. The result of this would be the formation of new species. Here, then, I had at last got a theory by which to work.

Darwin learned from pigeon breeders how selective breeding can produce a variety of pigeons.

Thomas Malthus

A BRITISH ECONOMIST who proposed in an essay in 1798 that human population growth will always exceed the amount of food available to feed the population, Malthus argued that the geometric growth of the human population would lead to starvation and suffering by the poorer members of society. He suggested that individuals in the population compete with each other for limited resources. Those successful in competing would survive, while those who failed were doomed to starvation. ∎

The Origin of Species

Darwin spent the next 20 years gathering more facts for the theory of natural selection. While he planned to write a large work on the theory, he spent time on many other projects as well. In 1858, however, another world-traveling naturalist, Alfred Russel Wallace, sent Darwin a summary of his own theory of evolution in which he drew conclusions similar to Darwin's. Wallace requested that Darwin, who was a respected naturalist, send the paper to the Linnaean Society, a group of influential naturalists of the day. Through Lyell and others, a meeting of the Linnaean Society was organized to present both men's work together. Soon after, in 1859, Darwin published his thorough and detailed explanation of natural selection in his book *On the Origin of Species.*

In *On the Origin of Species,* Darwin laid out his evidence that all living species change through a series of steps, as characteristics slightly more favorable to surviving in a particular environment are preserved successively over time. An accumulation of enough of these changes would give rise to a new species. In addition to recognizing that all species diverge and change through evolution, Darwin proposed that these changes take place through what he called **natural selection.** He reasoned that if breeders could use artificial selection to create dramatic changes in species over short periods of time, natural processes could lead to change over very long periods. As Darwin saw it, natural selection explained the differences in closely related species. The Galapagos finches provided an example of how an original small population could evolve into a number of different species. Because they are most closely related to South American finches, it appears that these finches first arrived on the islands from the mainland, perhaps as a result of storms that blew them off course.

Likely scattered among the 10 islands, individuals in the population encountered new food sources and habitats, which differed from island to island. The beaks of individual finches from the mainland would have had a certain amount of variation in their shapes and sizes. Those individuals with beaks that could feed easily on available food sources survived longer, reproducing more offspring that inherited the genes for similar traits. Over an unknown number of generations, this resulted in finches with different beaks in different habitats, depending on whether the type of food available was seeds, insects, or fruit. Long, pointed beaks, for example, were well suited for digging seeds out of cactus fruits. Short, wide beaks were best for eating seeds from the ground. Thin, sharp beaks were suited to catching insects. At the same time, other changes in characteristics, such as body size, tail shape, and behavior were also accumulating in the populations. Gradual accumulations of these changes through natural selection eventually led to the separation of a population into different species.

Alfred Russel Wallace

CONSIDERED THE CO-DISCOVERER of natural selection, Alfred Russel Wallace is also known for his accomplishments in the field of biogeography. One of his key contributions was to divide the world into seven major biogeographical areas. The name "Wallace's Line" was given to the divide between Southeast Asia and the Australia and New Zealand region because the plants and animals in the two areas were very different even though they were geographically close to one another. ∎

441

657

FOLLOW-UP

3 Review the ideas essential to understanding the mechanism of natural selection. Transparency 4.1, "Natural Selection and Evolution," will guide this discussion. First, for natural selection to occur, there must be heritable variation in the population. These variations might have been present in the population for a very long time, or might occasionally have arisen through mutations. If students studied the "Genetics: Feeding the World" unit of *Science and Global Issues*, they should be aware that mutation, recombination resulting from crossing over during gamete formation, and sexual reproduction lead to genetic variation within a population. In the case of the Galapagos finches, the ancestral finches must have had variations in their beaks, bodies, and tails. Second, there must be competition for the environmental resources needed for survival. Emphasize that Darwin extended Malthus' ideas about competition for resources in the human population to all species. This competition must lead to differential reproduction such that individuals with traits favorable to surviving in an environment produce more off-spring than those without those traits. Over relatively short periods of time natural selection leads to population changes, and over longer time periods it can lead to more significant changes that in turn lead to speciation and eventually the development of major new forms. Have students complete the diagram on Student Sheet 4.1, "Scientists, Ideas, and Events that Influenced Darwin." Many students will need to first discuss the reading before completing this diagram. They are asked to identify three key influences on Darwin's thinking about the reasons for the diversity of life. Ask students what Darwin might have been thinking about during his voyage. Students' responses might include: Darwin's observations during the voyage of the Beagle, his previous reading of Lamarck and other scientists' work suggesting that species are not fixed, and Lyell's ideas about geological or "deep" time. Then have students identify and describe four factors that influenced Darwin when he returned to England and that led him to develop and pub-

---

In *The Descent of Man*, published in 1871, Darwin identi-fied another mechanism for evolution, which he called sexual selection. **Sexual selection** refers to differential reproduction resulting from variation in the ability to obtain mates. For example, female peacocks tend to pref-erentially mate with males that have showy tail feathers. Darwin distinguished this type of selection from natural selection because these features are not necessarily adap-tive for the conditions of life; they promote reproductive success in a very different way that in some cases may even conflict with natural selection. For example, the showy tail display of a male peacock attracts potential female mates leading to increased reproduction, but may also attract predators, reducing survival.

Darwin's famous work drastically changed the field of biology. His story reflects how science progresses and theories are developed. Theories are complex and require support from a large body of evidence from many independent sources. **Evidence** is information used to support or refute a claim. Darwin made careful observations and thought about the patterns he saw while also thinking about ideas he learned by reading and talking to other scientists. His breakthrough came in putting these ideas together and providing a detailed description for how natural selection and sexual selection could give rise to diverse life forms from common ancestors. Since its development, a large body of evidence has been gathered to support the theory of natural selection, which provides a logical, scientifically tested explanation for the evolution of life.

Analysis

3

1. Look carefully back at the reading and write a five-to-eight sentence sum-mary about who influenced Darwin's thinking and how they did so.

2. What did you learn from Darwin about how a scientific theory is developed?

3. **a.** What kinds of traits evolve through natural selection? Give a few examples.

   b. What kinds of traits do not evolve through natural selection? Give a few examples.

KEY VOCABULARY	
biological evolution	natural selection
evidence	sexual selection
evolution	theory

lish the theory of evolution by natural selection. A sample completed diagram is provided at the end of this activity.

You may want to point out that although Darwin and other scientists of his time assumed that parents pass on heritable traits to their offspring, he and his contemporaries did not necessarily understand the mechanisms of genetics. Mendel's work on genetics and the principles of heredity were not published until several years after Darwin published *On the Origin of Species*. While Darwin knew that biological inheritance was essential to evolution, he did not know the details of the genetic processes involved. Finally, ask students how Darwin's story illustrates the establishment of a scientific theory. Responses should include that scientists work with their own observations and research, ideas and evidence provided by other scientists and experts in other fields, and their cultural and social environment. In Darwin's case, for many years he thought the scientific and social environment was such that his ideas would be dismissed or ridiculed. In fact he put off writing his book—until he realized that another scientist might publish first. Emphasize that Darwin's achievement involved putting together his own observations and ideas with those of others to develop and elaborate significant and revolutionary new ideas about evolution. This led to the theory of evolution by natural selection.

Extensive evidence has continued to validate the theory of natural selection and established it as a highly reliable explanation supported by a vast and growing body of evidence. You may wish to contrast theories with hypotheses, which are tentative-and-testable statements that are either supported or not supported by observational evidence. In the next two activities, students will explore some of the evidence for evolution of whales, and will be introduced to the difference between a theory and a hypothesis.

SAMPLE RESPONSES

1. Darwin was familiar with the ideas of Lamarck and others that species evolve, or change. While on his voyage, he observed many plants and animals, noting that many seemed to be closely related to but clearly different from nearby species. He also read the work of Lyell, who proposed that the earth was much older than people thought. When Darwin returned to England, he learned that plant and animal breeders were able to make major changes in organisms over very short periods of time through the selection of desired variations. This led him to the idea that natural processes might also lead to changes in taxa over longer time frames. His reading of Malthus's work led him to think that competition for environmental resources could be the reason for survival of those organisms most suited to the environment. He called this process natural selection, because it was the natural environment, rather than human activity, that led to differential reproduction and changes in populations of organisms.

2. A scientific theory is developed using ideas from scientists and experts, and a large body of evidence.

3. a. Only inherited traits can evolve through natural selection. Students' examples will vary, but may include such traits as coat color, body size, or speed because they can help an organism hide from or evade predators.

   b. Traits that cannot evolve through natural selection are traits that cannot be inherited. Students' examples will vary but may include such traits as a loss of a limb from an accident or weight gain from lack of exercise.

REVISIT THE CHALLENGE

Project Transparency 4.2, "Timeline of Ideas Leading Up To and Following Darwin's Work." Review the historical timeline of thought before, during, and after Darwin developed the theory of evolution by natural selection. Discuss the way scientists use the word theory in contrast to the way it is sometimes used in daily conversation. For scientists a theory is a well established and highly reliable explanation of a natural phenomenon, supported by numerous observations, experimental findings, and logical reasoning from the observations and findings. A hypothesis is a tentative (not final) and testable idea that may eventually be accepted or rejected based on scientific evidence and logical reasoning.

Scientists, Ideas, and Events that Influenced Darwin

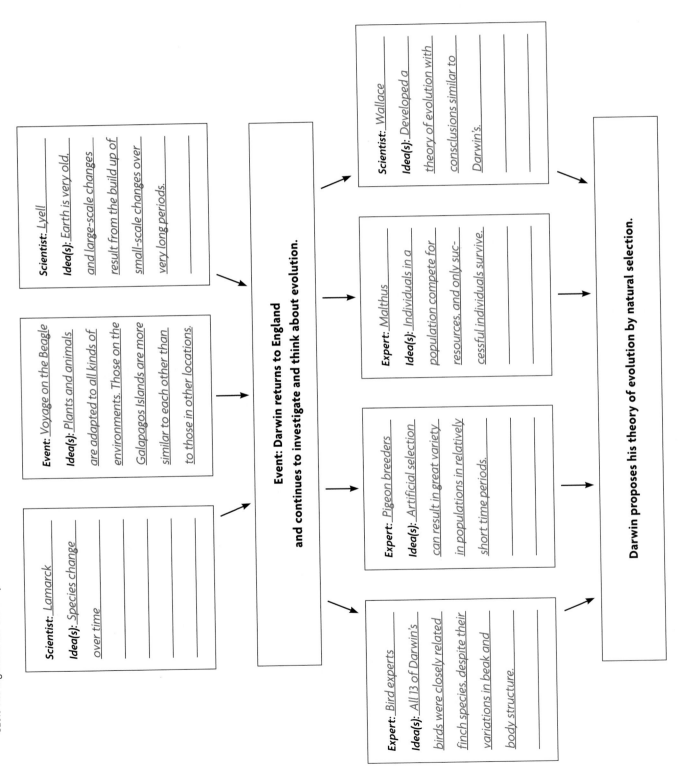

Scientist: _Lyell_
Idea(s): _Earth is very old, and large-scale changes result from the build up of small-scale changes over very long periods._

Event: _Voyage on the Beagle_
Idea(s): _Plants and animals are adapted to all kinds of environments. Those on the Galapagos Islands are more similar to each other than to those in other locations._

Scientist: _Lamarck_
Idea(s): _Species change over time_

Event: Darwin returns to England and continues to investigate and think about evolution.

Scientist: _Wallace_
Idea(s): _Developed a theory of evolution with conslusions similar to Darwin's._

Expert: _Malthus_
Idea(s): _Individuals in a population compete for resources, and only successful individuals survive._

Expert: _Pigeon breeders_
Idea(s): _Artificial selection can result in great variety in populations in relatively short time periods._

Expert: _Bird experts_
Idea(s): _All 13 of Darwin's birds were closely related finch species, despite their variations in beak and body structure._

Darwin proposes his theory of evolution by natural selection.

5 Using Fossil Evidence to Investigate Whale Evolution

INVESTIGATION • 1–2 CLASS SESSIONS

OVERVIEW

Students examine seven illustrations of fossil skeletons of modern whales and their extinct ancestors. The fossils, along with stratigraphic representations, provide evidence with which students trace the evolution of whales.

KEY CONTENT

1. Species are related by descent from common ancestors.

2. The theory of natural selection is a scientific explanation for the fossil record of ancient life forms.

KEY PROCESS SKILLS

1. Students communicate and defend a scientific argument.

2. Students develop conclusions from evidence.

MATERIALS AND ADVANCE PREPARATION

For the teacher

Transparency 5.1, "Complete Whale Fossil Chart"
Transparency 5.2, "Whale Evolutionary Tree"

For each pair of students

set of 5 Fossil Skeleton cards, B, K, M, O, and T
2 additional Fossil Skeleton cards, A and D

For each student

Student Sheet 5.1, "Whale Fossil Chart"
Student Sheet 5.2, "Whale Evolutionary Tree"
Student Sheet 3.2, "Geologic Time and Major Events," from Activity 3

Teacher's Note: *If your students completed the SEPUP Issues and Life Science course, they may have done an activity similar to this one. Whale evolution is an important example of macroevolution and how paleontologists study evolution with fossil evidence. If your students did that activity, have them work through this version quickly, or just review it with them to set the foundation for investigating additional examples of macroevolution in Activity 6, "Evidence from the Fossil Record."*

TEACHING SUMMARY

Getting Started

• Introduce the question of how modern whales evolved.

Doing the Activity

• Students group whale and whale ancestor skeletons according to similarities and differences.

• Students organize the skeletons into a possible evolutionary sequence.

• Students use the claims, evidence, and reasoning argumentation to determine the placement of skeletons A and D.

Follow-up

• The class discusses the placement on the tree of skeletons A and D and what the branching points on a tree show.

BACKGROUND INFORMATION

Cetacean Evolution

While many people view evolution as a progression from taxa found in the sea to land taxa, there are quite a few instances where a lineage of land taxa evolved into sea taxa. The aquatic mammals—pinnipeds (seals, sea lions, and walruses), sirenians (manatees, dugongs, and the recently extinct Stellar's sea cow), and cetaceans (whales, dolphins, and porpoises)—all have land-dwelling ancestors. In fact, the pinnipeds are not completely aquatic and provide an example of an intermediate state during the transition from land to water.

Whales, dolphins, and porpoises make up the order Cetacea, which includes 40 genera of living cetaceans and approximately 140 genera of known extinct cetacean ancestors. The cetacean evolutionary tree, shown on Transparency 5.2, "Whale Evolutionary Tree," illustrates the relationships of the various extinct whale ancestors to the whales that exist today. Many of the scientific names of whale ancestors contain the root "cet" to indicate that these animals are related to modern cetaceans.

Animals recognizable as modern whales have been swimming the earth's seas and rivers for at least 1 million years. Their mammalian characteristics (milk production, lungs, maintenance of internal body temperature, and vestigial hair) and forelimb structure have long suggested a terrestrial origin, and now DNA evidence supports the origin. In the 1990s, fossils were unearthed that allowed the whale lineage to be traced back 55 million years to ancestors that were relatively small land-dwelling mammals. The skeleton reconstructions shown on the Fossil Skeleton Cards are from ancestral whales for which the fossil evidence allows complete drawings to be made with confidence. There are numerous other partial skeletons of other whale ancestors intermediate in age to the ones appearing in this activity, but to simplify the evidence for students, only skeletons with obvious evidence of transitional features were included.

There are two suborders of modern whales: the Odontoceti, or toothed whales, and the Mysticeti, or baleen whales. Both groups are predators that feed on other animals, but they have different feeding methods and anatomies. Toothed whales eat fish, crabs, and squid, and, in the case of orcas, seals, birds, turtles, and many other aquatic animals. Baleen whales eat mostly krill. Toothed whales include porpoises, dolphins, orcas (killer whales), narwhals, and sperm whales. Baleen whales, such as humpback, gray, fin, and blue whales, have huge mouths spanned by large sieves made of keratin that strain zooplankton from the seawater. Available evidence suggests that the toothed whales and the baleen whales descended from the same group of aquatic ancestors, the dorudontids.

The shift in habitat from land to shallow water to open ocean involved many adaptations, which occurred in large part over the 20 million years between about 55 and 35 million years ago. Note that because of the incompleteness of the fossil record, the exact time these adaptations evolved cannot be pinpointed. Similarly, the branch points indicated on Transparency 5.2, "Whale Evolutionary Tree," are only approximate inferences. These adaptations included a shift of the nostrils backward and upward on the skull associated with the lengthening of the jaws, appearance of coverings for the nostrils, streamlining of the body shape, reduction and loss of the hind limbs, transformation of the forelimbs into flippers, addition of tail flukes, modification of ears and eyes, loss of most hair, and the thickening of body fat to form a layer of insulating blubber. In general, the features of a fossil that most clearly show whether an ancestor of an aquatic mammal lived on land or in the water are those skeletal features related to breathing, hearing, and locomotion.

Modern whales have no external hind limb. Some have no pelvic or hind limb bones at all, and others have very small ones that are disconnected from the rest of the skeleton and are vestigial (except as attachment points of genital muscles). On the other hand, whale forelimbs have large, flattened out, paddle-like bones, modified for use as flippers. Whales also have adaptations to their ears for underwater hearing, and a blowhole on the top of the head instead of a nose between their eyes and mouth.

Ancestors of Modern Whales

The descent of modern whales is, so far, traced to a now-extinct group called dorudontids, with diversifying forms seen among modern cetaceans evolving during the past 35 million years. Dorudontids were about 6 m (20 ft) long and proportionally more like dolphins than whales. They had a long snout with many sharp, triangular teeth, and their forelimbs were small, flattened flippers. The rear limbs were only about 10 cm (4 in) long. They may have spent some of their time on land, perhaps for mating. Dorudontids lived during the same time period as the basilosaurids (between about 41 and 35 million years ago), and those two groups share a common ancestor, one of the protocetids.

Basilosaurids probably inhabited all oceans of the world. These enormous animals—possibly up to 25 m (80 feet) long—had snake-like bodies with very small hind legs and a pelvis, resembling mythical sea serpents more than modern whales. Their long jaws (approximately 1.5 m or 5 ft) contained cone-shaped teeth in the front, which caught and held prey, and triangular-shaped teeth in the rear of the mouth for slicing prey. Basilosaurids most likely ate fish, squid, and their own smaller cousins, the dorudontids. Basilosaurids appear to have left no descendants.

Dorudontids and basilosaurids were descendants of the small, seal-like protocetids. While no complete protocetid skeletons have yet been found, they appear to have been a widespread group, evolved to a mostly aquatic existence. These creatures had small yet well-developed forelimbs and hind limbs, which may have allowed them to waddle on land. However, they also had a detached pelvis (poorly suited to supporting the body's weight on land), powerful tails, and an inner ear adapted for underwater hearing. Protocetids were probably quick and agile hunters who preyed on smaller sea creatures. Some species had nostrils above the eyes, but none had the blowhole characteristic of modern whales.

Ambulocetids, the ancestors of protocetids, had large hind limbs and probably filled an ecological niche similar to that of modern crocodiles, which they may have resembled in form. Their fossilized skeletons have been found only in rocks of the Indian subcontinent that were formed in near-shore environments. Ambulocetids could move both on land and in water. The pelvis, like that of modern land-dwelling mammals, was fused to the backbone. They probably ambushed their prey in shallow, near-shore waters, attacking with their strong jaws and large teeth. The *Ambulocetus natans* (meaning "walking whale that swims") was about the size of a sea lion— 3 m (10 ft) long and about 300 kg (650 lbs)—and probably swam similarly to a modern otter, using large hind limbs as paddles. Ambulocetids fossil representatives are about 49-million-years old.

Remingtonocetids, an odd group of animals that lived at about the same time as ambulocetids, appear to have left no descendants. Similar to ambulocetids in their large hind limbs, they differ in having smaller eyes, long and slender snouts, and widely separated ears. The ears might have been adaptations for enhanced hearing to locate prey.

Ambulocetids and remingtonocetids appear to be descendants of the earliest known whale ancestors, the pakicetids, fossils of which first appear in rocks found in Pakistan and formed around 55 million years ago. Although thought to have spent considerable time in the water, pakicetids had four fully developed legs to support their weight on land, as well as nostrils and ears typical of land mammals. Their skeletons are very similar to those of an extinct group of land mammals called mesonychids, which are thought to be a sister group to the ancestor of whales. Fossil evidence suggests that whale ancestors of that time were most likely members of a larger, less well-defined group of hoofed land mammals called paraxonians.

Claims, Evidence, and Reasoning

The claims, evidence, and reasoning approach to scientific argumentation used in this activity is based on the argumentation model first developed by Stephen Toulmin, and adapted by researchers investigating argumentation in the context of inquiry-science classrooms (see for example McNeill et al., 2006 below).

REFERENCES

Culotta, Elizabeth. (Winter 1996). It's a long way from Ambulocetus: The whales' journey to the sea. *Pacific Discovery* 14–18.

Gould, Stephen Jay. (1995). *Dinosaur in a haystack: Reflections in natural history.* New York: Crown Publishers, Inc.

Kellogg, Remington. (1936). *A review of the Archaeoceti.* Washington: Carnegie Institution.

McNeill, K. L., Lizotte, D. J, Krajcik, J., & Marx, R. W. (2006). Supporting students' construction of scientific explanations by fading scaffolds in instructional materials. *Journal of the Learning Sciences 15(2)*, 153–191.

Thewissen, J., ed. (1998). The emergence of whales: Evolutionary patterns in the origin of Cetacea. New York: Plenum Press.

Thewissen, J. G. M. & Bajpai, S. (December 2001). Whale origins as a poster child for macroevolution. *BioScience 51(12)*, 1037–1049. Retrieved July 2010 from http://www.thisviewoflife.org/references/papers/Thewissen%20and%20Bajpai%202001-%20Whale%20Origins.pdf.

Zimmer, Carl. (1998). *At the water's edge.* New York: Simon and Schuster.

GETTING STARTED

1 ◆ Begin by writing the words fish and mammals on the board. Ask students what characteristics individuals in each group have. Write those on the board. Likely responses for fish will include cold-bloodedness, gills, and fins. Likely responses for mammals will include warm-bloodedness, milk production and nursing of their young, and lungs. If students bring up that fish reproduce with eggs, tell them that all fish come from eggs, but that in some fish the eggs hatch internally and in others the eggs hatch externally. Ask students which group they think whales belong in. Most students will know that whales are mammals. If not, explain that whales maintain a constant internal body temperature, produce milk, nurse their young, have lungs, and are classified as mammals. Tell students that in this activity they will examine fossil evidence to investigate part of the evolutionary history of whales, much as paleontologists have done, to understand how whales evolved as mammals that live in water.

---

5 Using Fossil Evidence to Investigate Whale Evolution

1 LIVING ORGANISMS SOMETIMES leave behind physical evidence of themselves in rock, ice, tar, amber, or volcanic ash when they die. When this evidence is preserved over geologic time, it creates a **fossil.** In this activity you will use fossil evidence to investigate the evolution of whales.

Challenge

▶ How does fossil evidence determine the relationships of whale ancestors and their descendants?

Modern whales include the toothed whales, and the baleen whales. The sperm whale (a) is a toothed whale, and the humpback (b) is a baleen. This whale fossil (c), found in the northern Caucasus, Russia, dates from approximately 10 million years ago.

443

DOING THE ACTIVITY

2 Pass out sets of five Fossil Skeleton Cards, M, K, T, B, O, to each pair of students. Note that this Step is initially open-ended and that there is no single "right" answer based on the information so far. Further evidence will be made available when students reach Procedure Step 9.

Students are asked to group the skeletons into two groups of two and three skeletons. The group containing Skeleton M should be referred to as Group 1; this allows students to compare data tables easily. Most students will place M, K, and T in one group and B and O in the other.

3 If students need help distinguishing characteristics within groups and between groups, review with them an example using apples and oranges. Ask students what are the similarities between different types of apples and between different types of oranges. Then ask what are the similarities between apples and oranges.

A sample chart and Venn diagram for Procedure Steps 2 and 5 are shown below.

SCIENCE & GLOBAL ISSUES/BIOLOGY • EVOLUTION

MATERIALS

FOR EACH PAIR OF STUDENTS
  set of 5 Fossil Skeleton cards, B, K, M, O, and T
  2 additional Fossil Skeleton cards, A and D
FOR EACH STUDENT
  Student Sheet 5.1, "Whale Fossil Chart"
  Student Sheet 5.2, "Whale Evolutionary Tree"
  Student Sheet 3.2, "Geologic Time and Major Events," from Activity 3

Procedure

2

1. Compare the first set of five skeleton cards B, K, M, O, and T. With your partner, based on similarities you observe, group the skeletons into two sets, one with two cards and one with three. Name the set of skeletons containing skeleton M Group 1, and name the other set Group 2.

3

2. Create a data table in your science notebook for recording the following information:
   • Which skeletons you put into Groups 1 and 2
   • Five similarities and five differences within each group

3. In your science notebook, copy the Venn diagram shown below.

4. Discuss the similarities within each group. Record them on the Venn diagram in the areas where the circles do not overlap.

5. Write down as many similarities as you can between Group 1 and Group 2. Record the similarities between the groups on the Venn diagram in the space where the two circles overlap.

6. From the similarities and differences you noticed among all of the skeletons, arrange the cards vertically in the order you think each first appeared in geologic time, assuming M was found in the deepest rock layers of the earth. Place skeletons either in a single line or in a branched pattern from a common ancestor, depending on your observations.

   Hint: If there is a skeleton that doesn't seem to fit into a single-line arrangement, place it off to the side, next to the line.

444

Sample Student Response: Procedure Step 2

	Similarities	**Differences**
Group 1 skeletons (M, K, T)	• *vertebrates* • *All have tails, four limbs, jaws, and eye sockets.*	• *jaws/snouts (shape of head)* • *length of tail* • *T has shorter front limbs and both back and front limbs look flipper-like.* • *shape of pelvis* • *nearness of heel bones and body to the ground* • *straightness of legs*
Group 2 skeletons (B, O)	• *vertebrates* • *All have long tails, fins, similar jaws, and flat heads.*	• *relative size of head to body* • *presence/absence of teeth* • *number of ribs* • *presence/absence of hind limb bones* • *curvature of spinal column*

Sample Student Response: Procedure Steps 4–5

Group 1 (M, K, T): *vertebrates with tails of various lengths, four limbs*

Overlap: *all have heads (jaws, eye sockets), tails, and ribs*

Group 2 (B, O): *vertebrates with long tails, fins, flat heads*

4 Explain to students that in this activity they will follow a system of scientific argumentation that can be helpful in evaluating scientific ideas and constructing scientific explanations. Explain that while scientists do not always agree, scientific argumentation or scientific argument is different than the more common use of the word argument as a disagreement. Scientific argumentation is based on evidence and reasoning. In this system, a proposed idea or conclusion is referred to as a claim. The data or facts that support the claim are the evidence. The process of thinking and making inferences, connections, and conclusions to reach a claim based on the evidence is the reasoning. Emphasize that some claims are supported by extensive evidence and logical reasoning, while at the other extreme some claims are poorly supported by evidence or are based on faulty reasoning. Scientists evaluate proposed ideas (claims) based on the quality and quantity of evidence and on the reasoning that connects the evidence to the claim.

Explain to students that they will follow this approach to scientific discussion and argument to explain the placement of whale skeletons A and D on the tree. The following is a sample student response for the claim, evidence, and reasoning for the placement of A and D.

Claim

A is placed between K and T, and D is placed between T and B.

Evidence

A still has four limbs, but the front and back limbs are beginning to look a bit flipper-like. It is lower to the ground than K. It also has a large head for its body.

D has smaller hind legs than T, a slightly smaller head compared to its body than T, and a flatter spine than T.

---

7. Record your arrangement of the skeletons in your science notebook. Write a brief description of the reasoning behind your placement.

8. Obtain Student Sheet 5.1, "Whale Fossil Chart," which has more information. With that information rearrange your skeleton cards if necessary. Record any changes in your science notebook.

9. Obtain Student Sheet 5.2, "Whale Evolutionary Tree." Copy that tree into your science notebook below your arrangement of the skeletons. Record any similarities and differences you notice between the tree you copied and the arrangement you described in Step 7.

4 10. Obtain the two other cards A and D. With your partner, observe the cards and discuss where to place them on your arrangement. Record your placement of A and D on the tree you drew in your science notebook. Enter the following:

- A claim: your conclusion about the most logical placement of A and D on the tree
- Evidence: the evidence you gathered that supports the claim
- Reasoning: how the evidence you gathered supports the claim

5 11. Go back to the geologic timeline you constructed in Activity 3, "Geologic Time." On Student Sheet 3.2, "Geologic Time and Major Events,"

- record whale evolution at the appropriate time it began.
- mark the time span in which whale evolution occurred.

6 *Analysis*

1. What types of skeletal changes occurred during whale evolution?

2. What change (or transition) in habitat did whales' ancestors make?

3. Which fossil organism in whale evolution do you think was the first to live mostly in water? Explain your claim with evidence and reasoning.

4. Explain the changes in the skeletons during the transition in habitat, according to the theory of natural selection.

5. **a.** Explain what is happening at the region of the tree where remingtonocetids are observed.

   b. What can you infer remingtonocetids looked like based on the other information you have on the tree?

KEY VOCABULARY	
evidence	evolutionary tree
evolution	**fossil**

445

Reasoning

Since A's four limbs are beginning to look flipper-like and it is lower to the ground than K, it seems logical to place it next to K. Since A's limbs are not as flipper-like and it is not as low to the ground as T, it should be placed between K and T.

D should go between T and B because it has smaller hind legs compared to T, but B has no hind legs. D also has less curve in the spine compared to T but more curve than B.

5 Students should record whale evolution from approximately 55 mya to approximately 35 mya. Remind students that these times are estimates using available fossil evidence.

FOLLOW-UP

6 ⊕ ✓ Project Transparency 5.1, "Complete Whale Fossil Chart," showing the complete strata data for the whale fossils. Instruct students to observe the data and check their placement of A and D. Tell students that they will next investigate in the same way that paleontologists do with these kind of data. Give students a few minutes to discuss the data and modify their trees in their science notebooks. Also, instruct students who modified their trees to write an explanation for what evidence led them to modify their placements of A and D. Ask student volunteers to explain their placements of A and D on the tree. They will likely describe the same line of reasoning that paleontologists would: that fossils in lower strata are older than those in upper strata. The evidence supports the sample student claim that A is placed between K and T, and does not support the placement of D between B and T.

Then, project Transparency 5.2, "Whale Evolutionary Tree." Write in the correct placement of fossils A and D. A sample Student Sheet 5.2 is shown at the end of this activity.

Tell students to make any corrections to the tree they drew in their science notebook if necessary. Ask them what they think is happening at the branching point of T, B, and D. The protocetids are the common ancestor for basilosaurs and dorundontids, which diverged into two separate lineages. The basilosaur lineage went extinct, and the dorundontids led to the origin of whales. Next ask which lineage on this tree was the first to go extinct. Mesonychids were the first because the lineage branches off (diverges) and ends the furthest back in geologic time.

As you discuss Analysis Question 1, introduce students to the term vestigial structures to describe the reduced pelvic bones in whales. Explain that vestigial structures do not currently serve a useful function in the species, but are remnants of structures that did serve a function in earlier ancestors. Vestigial structures that are present in two species are evidence that they share a common evolutionary ancestry.

Instruct students to write a claim, and give evidence and reasoning for their claim in answering Analysis Question 3. Analysis Question 4 is an opportunity for a Quick Check assessment of students' understanding of the process of natural selection. A demonstration of complete understanding will incorporate the three factors that drive natural selection: heritable variation, competition for environmental resources, and differential reproduction.

SAMPLE RESPONSES

1. External hind limbs were lost, and those bones were either greatly reduced or lost entirely. The skull changed size and shape in various ways. Forelimbs evolved into fins. The tail elongated due to the reduced pelvis and lost external hind limbs, and the tail vertebrae became thicker and larger. Some students might notice a much more subtle change, which is that the enlarged neck vertebrae shrank, an indication that there is no advantage to having powerful neck muscles that support the weight of the head under water.

2. The early ancestors of whales lived on land. At some point, the descendants moved into a water habitat. They had characteristics that enabled them to live in the shallow-water environment.

3. *Claim:*

   Either B or D was the first to live mostly in water.

   Evidence:

   They either lost their hind limbs or those limbs and pelvis were greatly reduced. The tail lengthened with large vertebrae, and the forelimbs became fins. The neck vertebrae shrank.

   Reasoning:

   B and D show characteristics for swimming and life in water, such as large vertebrae in the tail and fin-like forelimbs. They also lack characteristics for life on land, such as attached pelvis and hind limbs and large neck vertebrae.

4. ✓ Originally, there was genetic variation in the ancestor population. Although they lived on land, some had larger back legs and some had smaller back legs. Those with smaller back legs survived better because it was easier for them to swim in their transition to a water habitat, and they could catch more food. They could also escape from predators more easily, which was especially important when they were young. These whale ancestors lived to produce more young, and passed on to them the heritable trait of smaller back legs. With each generation, more whale ancestors survived with smaller back legs and a better ability to swim. Over many, many generations, the average size of the back legs in the population decreased. At the same time, the forelimbs became more flipper-like and the pelvis was attached to the backbone.

5. a. The ambulocetids branched into two lineages: the remingtonocetids and the protocetids. The remingtonocetids eventually became extinct, while the protocetids continued to evolve and branch into two more lineages, the basilosaurs and the dorudontids.

   b. Based on the physical characteristics of their ancestral ambulocetids and the related protocetids, the remingtonocetids probably had long tails, legs with feet (not webbed), and teeth. It most likely could not live in water.

REVISIT THE CHALLENGE

Review with students how paleontologists use fossil evidence to investigate the evolution of whales. Analysis Question 4 serves as a good summary of the process. Bring out the idea that while fossils of all of the transitional whales may never be found, by focusing on transitional features of fossils that are found from the same line of descent, scientists can piece together evidence and logical conclusions about the evolution of whales. Students will be reading more about this in the next activity.

Whale Evolutionary Tree

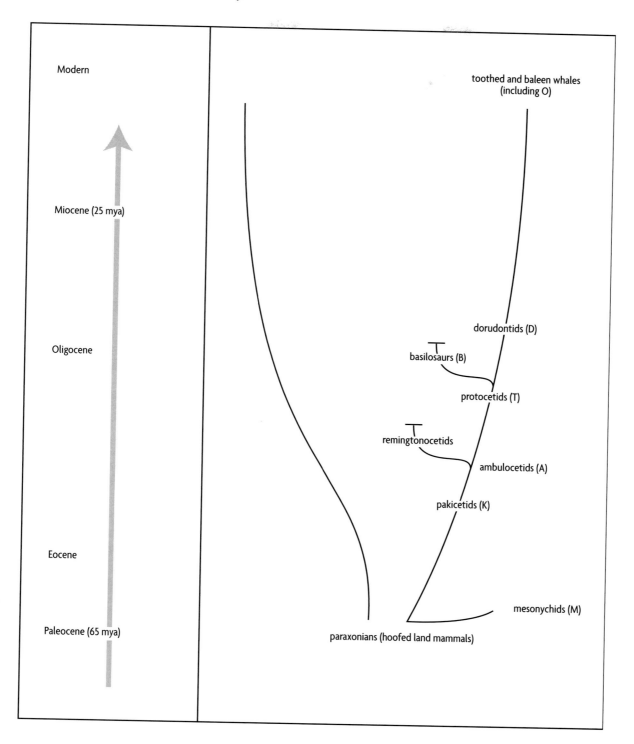

Evidence from the Fossil Record

READING • 1–2 CLASS SESSIONS

OVERVIEW

Students read about how scientists interpret evidence in the fossil record, including the use of stratigraphy and radiometric dating to determine the ages of fossils. The work of paleontologists investigating the evolution of tetrapods from fish provides an example of how fossil evidence contributes to our understanding of macroevolution.

KEY CONTENT

1. Stratigraphy is based on the idea that older rock strata are found beneath strata that were formed more recently.

2. Fossils in lower strata are generally older than fossils found in upper strata.

3. Scientific theories are well established and highly reliable explanations. Hypotheses are tentative and testable statements that eventually might be supported or refuted by observational evidence.

4. From fossils scientists have developed and tested hypotheses for how major taxa, such as tetrapods, evolved.

5. In the absence of transitional fossils, scientists focus on transitional features in fossils—key features that demonstrate the evolutionary changes that resulted in macroevolution.

KEY PROCESS SKILLS

1. Students make accurate interpretations, inferences, and conclusions from text.

MATERIALS

For each student
    Student Sheet 3.1, "Ideas about Evolution," from Activity 3

TEACHING SUMMARY

Getting Started

• Review whale evolution.

Doing the Activity

• (LITERACY) Students read about the fossil record, how fossils are dated, and fish–tetrapod evolution.

• Students revisit the statements on Student Sheet 3.1, "Ideas about Evolution."

Follow-up

• Review the importance of the fossil record in providing evidence for evolution.

BACKGROUND INFORMATION

Tetrapods evolved from a group of fleshy-finned bony fish called sarcopterygians, distinct from the ray-finned fish (actinopterygians), whose descendants comprise nearly all living bony fish. The lungfish and coelacanth are the only living fleshy-finned fish. *Acanthostega* and *Ichthyostega* are sometimes referred to as early tetrapods, but they are referred to as fleshy-finned forms in this activity because they are not true tetrapods. Tetrapods (Tetrapoda) formally include all living tetrapods (amphibia, reptiles, mammals, birds) and their most recent common ancestor.

GETTING STARTED

1 Ask students to open their science notebooks to the whale evolutionary tree that they created in the last activity. Review with them the importance of fossils in determining the evolutionary history of whales. Point out that in the last activity they investigated similarities and differences in fossil ancestors to develop hypotheses for the lineage leading to evolution of modern whales. Then, they used the information about where in the earth's layers the fossils were found to support or modify their hypotheses. Tell students that they will be reading about how scientists determine the age of fossils to help them understand the evolutionary history and relationships of taxa. They will also read about fossils' roles in the study of another lineage: that leading to the evolution of tetrapods (four-limbed animals) from fleshy-finned ancestors.

---

6 Evidence from the Fossil Record

1 THE **FOSSIL RECORD** includes all of the fossils that have existed in the 4.5 billion years of earth's history—whether they have been discovered or not. Fossils may be bones, teeth, shells, footprints, or prints of other structures. Fossils form in several ways. An organism might have been preserved in ice, tar, amber, or volcanic ash. An organism's footprints or parts, such as leaves and feathers, might be preserved in rocks if the environmental conditions did not destroy them first. Paleontologists, the scientists who study the fossil record, use several methods to figure out when a fossil formed. The structures and ages of fossils provide evidence for macroevolution—the formation of major new groups of organisms. Fossil evidence has helped scientists figure out how such groups as dinosaurs, birds, and mammals evolved.

Challenge

▶ How do scientists interpret evidence in the fossil record?

MATERIALS

FOR EACH STUDENT
Student Sheet 3.1, "Ideas about Evolution," from Activity 3
Student Sheet 3.2, "Geologic Time and Major Events," from Activity 3

This fossil worm from the Burgess Shale lived in the Middle Cambrian era, approximately 500 million years ago. The worm lived in burrows in sediment on the seabed.

446

DOING THE ACTIVITY

2 The reading is supported with a literacy strategy called Stopping to Think, which helps students process the information they read. Stopping to Think questions focus students' attention on important ideas they encounter in the text. These questions do not require a written response and are different from the Analysis Questions found at the end of the activity. For more information on this strategy, Teacher Resources III: Literacy.

3 Students should mark the period of fish-to-tetrapod evolution between 380 and 375 million years ago, in the Middle Devonian period.

4 ◆ Sample answers to Student Sheet 3.1, "Ideas about Evolution," are shown at the end of this activity. Monitor students' ideas and have them reflect on how they may be changing each time students add to Student Sheet 3.1.

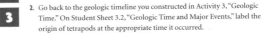

Procedure

2 1. When reading, answer the Stopping to Think questions in your mind.

3 2. Go back to the geologic timeline you constructed in Activity 3, "Geologic Time." On Student Sheet 3.2, "Geologic Time and Major Events," label the origin of tetrapods at the appropriate time it occurred.

4 3. Go back to the statements on Student Sheet 3.1, "Ideas about Evolution," from Activity 3. Add information from this activity or a previous activity to support whether any of the statements are correct or incorrect.

Reading

Determining the Age of a Fossil

Paleontologists rely mainly on two methods to determine the age of the earth and the ages of rock layers and the fossils they contain. With stratigraphy, they determine the sequence of events, such as the formation of particular rock layers. With radiometric dating, they determine how many years ago rock layers and fossils formed.

Stratigraphy is the study of rock layers. Rock layers form from lava flows or from sediments. As hot lava spills over an area and cools, it becomes a layer of hard rock. Sediment layers form from small particles of rock and soil that settle and build up over millions of years. Most sediment forms from ash or small particles of rock that have been worn away by ice, water, or wind. Sediment layers are softer than hardened lava and often contain many fossils. As sediment layers build up, their weight creates pressure that squeezes them into solid rock. Layers of lava and of compressed sediments are called **strata**. Stratigraphy is based on the logical reasoning that deeper strata and the fossils found in them are older, while upper strata and the fossils they contain formed more recently.

Some of the sediments that make up the layers of the Grand Canyon in Arizona were transported by wind and water from the Appalachian Mountains in eastern North America.

447

5 Some strata form when hot lava cools. Other strata form when sediment particles carried by air, water, or ice fall to the surface of the earth or the bottom of the body of water. As a layer of particles builds up over time, its weight compresses it into a solid.

The fossils formed at the same time the strata formed.

About 200 years ago, scientists observed that certain layers of rock in different geographic areas contained similar characteristic fossils. This observation led scientists to the idea that these layers of rock and the fossils preserved in them formed at the same time. The geologic timeline you studied in Activity 3, "Geologic Time," divides geologic time into periods based on the presence or absence of various kinds of fossils in rock strata.

STOPPING TO THINK 1

5

> *How do strata form?*
> *What is the relationship between strata and the fossils that formed in them?*

Stratigraphic dating provides the relative ages of rock layers and the fossils within them. Interpreting evidence from stratigraphy requires an understanding of geology. For example, wind and water might erode strata and uncover deeper layers. The movement of the earth's surface from an earthquake might tilt or uplift the strata, which breaks the sequence of the layers. Paleontologists consider these factors when interpreting stratigraphic evidence.

With **radiometric dating** scientists estimate not only the order of rock layer and fossil formation, but how many years ago rock layers and fossils formed. It is based on the decay of radioactive atoms of certain elements. For example, radioactive carbon is trapped in fossils in sedimentary rock layers. Organisms take up radioactive carbon-14 when they are alive. After they die, the radioactive carbon decays. Carbon-14 has a half-life of 5,730 years, which means that half of the carbon-14 present in an organism when it dies will have decayed in 5,730 years. The graph below shows how the fraction of carbon-14 remaining indicates the age of the fossil. Measuring carbon-14 is accurate in determining dates up to 50,000–60,000 years ago. For fossils older than that, the amount of carbon-14 remaining can no longer be measured accurately.

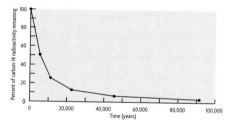

DATING FOSSILS USING CARBON-14

6 Scientists analyze the percentage of a radioactive element in the fossil or nearby rock to determine how many years have passed since the rock layer and the fossil within it formed.

To figure out the dates of older samples, scientists work with other radioactive isotopes, such as potassium and uranium. These radioactive elements are trapped in igneous rock layers that formed as molten lava cooled, and they have longer half-lives. The table below shows how these radioactive elements provide a clock that tells the ages of rock layers.

Atomic Half-lives and Radiometric Dating		
RADIOACTIVE ELEMENT	HALF-LIFE (YEARS)	USEFUL RANGE (YEARS)
Carbon-14	5,730	< 60,000
Potassium-40	1.26 billion	100,000–4.5 billion
Uranium-238	4.5 billion	2 million–4.5 billion

STOPPING TO THINK 2

6 *How does information from radioactive data help to determine the age of a fossil?*

Studying Fossils to Determine the Origin of Tetrapods

Paleontologists primarily study fossils. They learn a lot about extinct species by directly observing the fossils and determining how old they are. From fossils they also infer the habitats and behavior of previous organisms.

One of the most fascinating evolutionary puzzles paleontologists have studied is the macroevolution of terrestrial tetrapods from marine fish. **Terrestrial tetrapods** are the four-limbed mammals, reptiles, amphibians, and birds that live on land. In the late 19th century, paleontologist Edward Cope proposed that tetrapods evolved from aquatic vertebrates that had fleshy fins with structural similarities to limbs. These fleshy-finned organisms were similar to the coelacanth and lungfish alive today. But the details of the evolution of tetrapods remained mostly unknown, including the timeframe of the events. Until 1987, the fossil evidence was based on two forms, *Eusthenopteron* and *Ichthyostega*. They were not "fishes" as we think of them today; they were distinct from the true ray-finned fishes such as tuna and trout. Rather, they were fleshy-finned forms, whose limbs and fins were covered with fleshy muscle, like our hands and the hands of all tetrapods. *Eusthenopteron* and *Ichthyostega* are not tetrapods, but they are on the line to tetrapods, as shown in the tree on the next page.

449

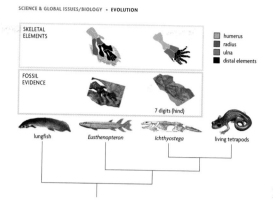

Edward Cope's hypothesis, shown as an evolutionary tree

You have probably seen a drawing of an organism, such as a lungfish, crawling out of water onto land. Scientists were curious about whether this was how tetrapods evolved. Did a fish propel itself onto land with its fins and then evolve limbs? Or did tetrapods evolve in an aquatic environment? *Eusthenopteron* and *Ichthyostega* did not provide evidence to answer these questions.

Since the late 1980s, scientists have found fossils that have helped them figure out the sequence of events leading to the divergence of the tetrapods. They have sequenced the fossils by a process similar to the one you used in Activity 5, "Using Fossil Evidence to Investigate Whale Evolution." Stratigraphy and radiometric dating helped them determine the age of fossils they discovered. A particularly important fossil is the skeleton of *Acanthostega*, discovered in East Greenland in 1987. This organism had legs and feet, but it lacked other body parts associated with life on land. Its legs did not have ankles strong enough to support its weight on land; instead, they were like paddles. And while it had both lungs and gills, its rib cage was too short to prevent the chest cavity from collapsing when on land.

Acanthostega changed the thinking about events leading to life on land. It suggested that aquatic organisms evolved such features as lungs and legs with feet in the shallow-water environments along coastal margins during the Devonian period. Scientists hypothesized that these features allowed hunting, mating, and perhaps laying eggs in low-water areas of tangled vegetation. According to this hypothesis, the lungs and legs were later co-opted in new evolving species for life on land. **Co-opted features** are those that evolved to serve one function, and later evolved through natural selection to perform a new function.

7 Scientists previously hypothesized that taxa crawled from water onto land and then evolved features for life on land. *Acanthostega* suggested that aquatic organisms evolved lungs and feet while living in shallow water, and these features were later co-opted for life on land.

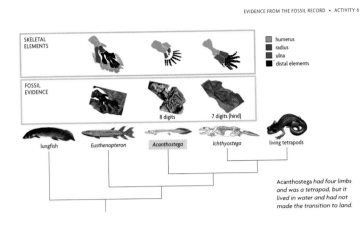

EVIDENCE FROM THE FOSSIL RECORD • ACTIVITY 6

Acanthostega had four limbs and was a tetrapod, but it lived in water and had not made the transition to land.

STOPPING TO THINK 3

7 *How did Acanthostega change scientists' thinking about the evolution of tetrapods?*

As scientists continued hunting for fossils all over the world, they discovered more fish-like tetrapods and tetrapod-like fishes. These examples began to fill in branches of the evolutionary tree between *Eusthenopteron* and *Acanthostega*. They also suggested that tetrapods originated 380–363 million years ago, in the Middle Devonian time period. In 1999, a team of scientists set out to hunt for fossils in rock layers they knew had formed between 380 and 363 million years ago. They chose an area of the Canadian Arctic that paleontologists had not searched before. This was an ideal place to search because no buildings, roads, or trees covered the rock layers. After seven years, in 2006, the team announced their headline-making discovery of *Tiktaalik*, a 375-million-year-old fleshy-finned fossil. *Tiktaalik* had the scales and gills of other aquatic vertebrates, but it had lungs too, like other fleshy fins including the lungfish and coelacanth. It had a tetrapod-like head and the beginnings of a neck. Its fleshy fins had thin ray bones for paddling in water, but stronger interior bones for support, much like those in tetrapods. Because of its clear transitional features, *Tiktaalik* is humorously nicknamed "the fishapod," but in fact it is only one in a series of forms in the transition to land.

451

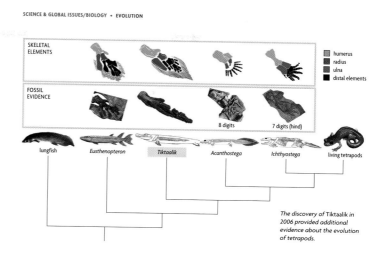

The discovery of Tiktaalik *in 2006 provided additional evidence about the evolution of tetrapods.*

Transitional Fossils

Such fossils as *Tiktaalik, Acanthostega,* and *Ichthyostega,* have helped scientists understand and explain the evolutionary stages that led to the origin of tetrapods and life on land. Fossils that show the intermediate state between an ancestor and its descendants are sometimes called transitional fossils. Transitional fossils that have not been discovered have been referred to as "missing links." This term is misleading, because scientists do not expect that a given fossil will be the direct ancestor of another. At best it may be a distant cousin, but it will have many of the features that the undiscovered direct ancestors did have. Thus, the fact that a perfectly transitional fossil has not been discovered does not mean that the taxon did not exist.

Scientists expect that many direct and distantly related transitional fossils will never be found for several reasons. First, some organisms or body parts of organisms do not form fossils well. Second, the environmental conditions or natural geologic processes may have prevented fossil formation or destroyed fossils before they could be found. Third, only a tiny fraction of existing fossils will ever be found because many are buried under ice caps or are so far underground that they are impossible to reach. And finally, finding fossils is difficult, slow, and costly in areas that have harsh weather conditions. Despite these obstacles, many transitional fossils have been found since the 1800s. These include fossils in lines of descent that led to reptiles, birds, and mammals.

8 A transitional fossil shows characters of an intermediate taxon between an ancestor and its descendant.

Scientists expect that some fossils will never be found because some organisms or body parts of organisms do not form fossils well, environmental conditions or geologic processes might have prevented fossil formation or destroyed the fossils, or they are located in areas that are extremely difficult or impossible for humans to reach.

FOLLOW-UP

9 Review that the fossil record contains fossils from taxa that have lived over 3.5 billion years of the earth's 4.5-billion-year history. Therefore, it is an extremely valuable bank of evidence for scientists to access when they are trying to understand the history of the ancestry of life on earth. Stress that stratigraphy helps scientists determine the order of events and relate the history of life to other changes taking place on earth, while radiometric dating (sometimes called radioactive dating) helps them estimate how many years ago these events took place.

8

STOPPING TO THINK 4

What makes a fossil a transitional fossil?
What are the reasons scientists expect there to be gaps in the fossil record?

Transitional Features

Because many transitional fossils are unlikely to be found, many evolutionary biologists focus on **transitional features,** those specific features of fossils that show the intermediate state between an ancestor and its descendants. This approach is based on the idea that, even though nobody finds the single direct ancestor leading to a group of organisms, someone may find other organisms that have branched from the same line of descent. By studying the features of these organisms, scientists can put together a picture of the evolution of features that led to major new groups of organisms.

Although not all fossils are likely to be found, there is abundant fossil evidence to show that evolution occurs. And, as shown by the origin of tetrapods, the work of scientists has reconstructed the steps by which major transitions occurred. This has led to a better understanding of the process of evolution.

9

Analysis

1. Based on what you know about the geologic timeline and the formation of the earth, explain which fossils would be newer and older in the various layers of rock in the Grand Canyon.

2. Explain why Cope's ideas about the evolution of tetrapods were considered a hypothesis and not a theory.

3. **a.** What new hypothesis was suggested for the evolution of tetrapods following Cope's original hypothesis?

   b. Explain the evidence that led to the hypothesis you described in (a).

KEY VOCABULARY	
co-opted features	**stratigraphic dating**
evolution	**stratigraphy**
fossil record	**terrestrial tetrapods**
macroevolution	**transitional features**
radiometric dating	transitional fossils
strata	

453

Paleontologists' research on the evolution of tetrapods from fleshy-finned fish (formally called sarcopterygians) provides a good example of how scientists develop, test, and refine hypotheses. Cope's original hypothesis that tetrapods evolved from fish was first supported by limited evidence—the fossils of *Eusthenopteron* and *Ichthyostega*. But since the late 1980s, scientists have found additional examples that both support Cope's original hypothesis and provide additional information for reconstructing the evolutionary transition from fish to tetrapod. *Acanthostega* led to a new hypothesis: that limbs evolved before tetrapods moved onto land. The search for additional fossils and the example of *Tiktaalik* demonstrate how scientists seek additional evidence to support or refute a hypothesis. *Tiktaalik* and other recently discovered transitional fossils provide additional evidence in support of the hypothesis that limbs evolved before tetrapods moved onto land.

SAMPLE RESPONSES

1. The fossils in the lower layers formed earlier and are older. As you go up to higher layers, the fossils formed more recently and are younger.

2. Cope's ideas were considered a hypothesis because they could be tested with observational evidence, in this case, fossils. When new fossils were discovered, the hypothesis for the evolution of tetrapods from fish was supported. However, a new hypothesis for the details of the evolution was developed.

3. a. The new hypothesis was that limbs evolved before tetrapods moved onto land.

    b. *Acanthostega* was discovered, which had legs and feet, but not strong ankles to support its weight on land. Instead, its legs were paddlelike. It had lungs and gills, but the rib cage was too short to prevent the chest cavity from collapsing when the animal was on land.

REVISIT THE CHALLENGE

Review the methods for dating fossils—stratigraphic and radiometric dating—and the challenges involved in finding fossils. Stress that stratigraphy determines the order of events, but radiometric dating is needed to estimate dates in thousands, millions, or billions of years ago. Discuss the misleading nature of the term "missing links," if it is used to imply that transitional taxa did not exist or that scientists expect to find the direct ancestor of a particular form. Emphasize that although many more fossils are likely to be discovered in future years, providing further evidence for the evolution of taxa, fossils of other organisms will likely never be found. While fossils are useful evidence for the character(s) distributed among living taxa, they also provide evidence for rates and processes of evolution. Finally, distinguish hypotheses about the details of specific transitions from the overall theory of evolution, which is supported by abundant evidence. Although all details of fish-to-tetrapod evolution are not known, all evidence supports the evolution of tetrapods from fleshy-finned fish (sarcopterygians), which were the ancestors of modern fleshy-finned fish (lungfish and coelacanth) and modern terrestrial tetrapods.

Ideas about Evolution

Statement 1: *Evolution is a climb up a ladder of progress with taxa always getting bigger and better.*

Before doing any activity, I think *the statement is correct:* Yes ☐ No ☐ *because* _____

Activity Number	After doing these activities, I think		
	Statement is correct:	**Evidence and reasoning:**
5 and 6	Yes ☐ No ☒	*Fish, whales, and tetrapods did not get bigger and better; they changed as features were selected for in the environment.*
	Yes ☐ No ☐	
	Yes ☐ No ☐	

Statement 2: *The theory of evolution by natural selection is supported by a large body of scientific evidence.*

Before doing any activity, I think *the statement is correct:* Yes ☐ No ☐ *because* _____

Activity Number	After doing these activities, I think		
	Statement is correct:	**Evidence and reasoning:**
6	Yes ☒ No ☐	*The fossil record contains a lot of information about evolutionary changes over geologic time, such as the evolution of whales and tetrapods.*
	Yes ☐ No ☐	
	Yes ☐ No ☐	

Ideas about Evolution (continued)

Statement 3: *Natural selection is not a random process.*

Before doing any activity, I think the statement is correct: Yes ☐ No ☐ because _____

Activity Number	After doing these activities, I think	
	Statement is correct:	**Evidence and reasoning:**
	Yes ☐ No ☐	_____ _____ _____
	Yes ☐ No ☐	_____ _____ _____
	Yes ☐ No ☐	_____ _____ _____

Statement 4: *Evolution is a process by which taxa choose to adapt to their environment.*

Before doing any activity, I think the statement is correct: Yes ☐ No ☐ because _____

Activity Number	After doing these activities, I think	
	Statement is correct:	**Evidence and reasoning:**
5 and 6	Yes ☐ No ☒	*Whales and tetrapods did not choose to adapt. Features that allowed for increased survival and reproduction were selected for and passed on.*
	Yes ☐ No ☐	_____ _____ _____
	Yes ☐ No ☐	_____ _____ _____

Ideas about Evolution (continued)

Statement 5: *Evidence suggests that humans and apes share an evolutionary ancestry.*

Before doing any activity, I think *the statement is correct:* Yes ☐ No ☐ *because* _____

Activity Number	After doing these activities, I think	
	Statement is correct:	Evidence and reasoning:
	Yes ☐ No ☐	
	Yes ☐ No ☐	
	Yes ☐ No ☐	

7 The Phylogeny of Vertebrates

INVESTIGATION • 1–2 CLASS SESSIONS

OVERVIEW

Students study a data matrix of shared derived characters to create a tree for a group of vertebrates. Given additional morphological evidence, they decide which of three tree hypotheses is consistent with the evidence provided.

KEY CONTENT

1. The millions of species of plants, animals, and microorganisms that live on earth today are related by descent from common ancestors.

2. Modern biological classifications show how taxa are related based on similarities that reflect their genealogical relationships.

3. Shared derived characters as evidence of common ancestry determine where to place taxa on a tree.

4. Scientific hypotheses are tentative-and-testable statements that are either supported or not supported by observational evidence.

5. Morphological evidence, such as forelimb structure and function, combined with other evidence leads scientists to hypothesize the evolutionary relationships of taxa on a tree.

6. Scientific explanations must adhere to criteria such as the application of appropriate evidence, consistently logical reasoning, and basis in accepted historical and current scientific knowledge.

KEY PROCESS SKILLS

1. Students interpret data.

2. Students construct explanations based on knowledge and reasoning.

MATERIALS AND ADVANCE PREPARATION

For the teacher
Transparency 7.1, "Taxonomy"
Transparency 7.2, "Vertebrate Forelimbs"
Transparency 7.3, "Homology and Analogy"
Transparency 7.4, "Vertebrate Tree"
Transparency 7.5, "Hypotheses for Vertebrate Phylogeny"

For each pair of students
set of seven Vertebrate Cards
set of seven Forelimb Skeleton Cards
colored pencils*

For each student
Student Sheet 7.1, "Evidence in Anklebones"
Student Sheet 3.1, "Ideas about Evolution," from Activity 3

TEACHING SUMMARY

Getting Started
- Review shared characters, and introduce a character matrix.

Doing the Activity
- Students observe vertebrate forelimbs as evidence for common ancestry.

- Students construct a tree from a character matrix and determine which of three tree hypotheses is most consistent with the evidence provided.

- Students revisit the statements on Student Sheet 3.1, "Ideas about Evolution."

Follow-up
- ✓ The class discusses the three tree hypotheses for the evolutionary relationships of six vertebrates.

BACKGROUND INFORMATION

Classification

Swedish scientist Carolus Linnaeus (1707–1778) developed a binomial system of classification in which all living things were placed into a genus and species. As other scientists adopted and improved on Linnaeus's two-part taxonomy, an internationally accepted seven-level system developed, which is known today as the Linnaean system. The largest grouping was the kingdom, followed by a subgroup, the phylum, followed by the successively smaller subgroups of class, order, family, genus, and species. Another higher level of classification, the domain, was introduced in 1990. The chart below shows the classification for a sample set of taxa.

While a rose was still called a rose in common language, to the scientists studying plants, rose could refer to any one of 100–150 plants in the same genus. The Linnaean system allowed them to classify specific roses, such as *Rosa canina, Rosa stellata,* and *Rosa rugosa.* Linnaeus had combined two previous schools of thought about classification, which were classification by dividing into smaller groups and classification by observing similar characteristics and grouping by relationship. The seven-level system was, however, inherently flawed and arbitrary in that scientists accepted the existence of seven levels without investigation.

Recent Classification Strategies

Charles Darwin (1809–1882) took ideas about order in nature in a new direction. He developed a classification system based on phylogeny (common ancestry), rather than morphology. His focus was on variation among individuals, natural selection, and descent with modification. Darwin recognized the heritability of characteristics and proposed that resemblances between species were due to characteristics inherited from common ancestral species. He looked at certain inherited characteristics—homologues—to identify common ancestry and to reconstruct evolutionary history. Unlike his predecessors, Darwin stated that classifications should be based on ancestry or genealogy alone.

Evolutionary Trees as Scientific Representations

German biologist Willi Hennig (1913–1976) proposed a way to classify living things genealogically in a method called either phylogenetic systematics or cladistics. Systematics is an analytical approach to understanding the diversity and relationships between living things based on shared derived characters rather than overall similarity. Systematists have in the past studied the fossils and the form and structure of an organism and its parts (morphology), and biochemical similarities or homologies as the bases for inferring relationships among taxa. The advent of molecular biology allowed systematists to add molecular data sets, including sequences of proteins and DNA and RNA, to compare taxa.

As new information becomes known and considered with all other available evidence, scientists might move taxa from one group to another on the evolutionary tree. Although scientists sometimes use the Linnaean system of classification for convenience, evolutionary biologists avoid it because the rankings are arbitrary and not based on evolutionary relationships.

Biological Classification

LEVEL	NORTHERN RED OAK TREE	MOUSE	E. COLI	HOUSE CAT	HUMAN	CHIMPANZEE
Domain	Eukarya	Eukarya	Bacteria	Eukarya	Eukarya	Eukarya
Kingdom	Plantae	Animalia	Eubacteria	Animalia	Animalia	Animalia
Phylum	Magnoliophyta	Chordata	Proteobacteria	Chordata	Chordata	Chordata
Class	Magnoliopsida	Mammalia	Gamma Proteobacteria	Mammalia	Mammalia	Mammalia
Order	Fagales	Rodentia	Enterobacteriales	Carnivora	Primates	Primates
Family	Fagaceae	Muridae (superfamily, Muroidea; subfamily, Murinae)	Enterobacteriaceae	Felidae	Hominidae	Hominidae
Genus	*Quercus*	*Mus*	*Escherichia*	*Felis*	*Homo*	*Pan*
Species	*Quercus rubra*	*Mus musculus*	*Escherichia coli*	*Felis domesticus*	*Homo sapiens*	*Pan troglodytes*

Homologies and Analogies

Because evolutionary trees are hypotheses about the evolutionary relationships of taxa, the characters that scientists identify to construct a tree must be reliable indicators of common ancestry. Shared characters are divided into two categories: homologous and analogous. Homologous characters are defined by evolutionary biologists as those that are shared by a species or a group of species and their common ancestor.

Homologous characters are further subdivided into shared derived and shared ancestral characters. Shared derived characters are unique to a lineage and the common ancestor and therefore help to define evolutionary relationships. Forelimbs are an example of a shared derived character. Shared ancestral characters are found in the common ancestor, but only in some of its descendants, making them less reliable than shared derived characters for showing common ancestry. For example, giraffes, hippopotamuses, and whales share a common ancestor that had legs and a neck, but only giraffes and hippos have legs and a neck; whales do not.

Analogous characters are shared by species, but are not present in their common ancestor. Analogous characters result from convergent evolution, which means that they evolved by natural selection independently but with similar selection pressures. Bird and bat wings are homologous as forelimbs, but analogous as wings. The wings are analogous because fossil evidence suggests that bird and bat wings were not inherited from a common winged ancestor. You can tell the wings are analogous by looking at the major differences in their structures. For example, bat wings have flaps of skin stretched between the bones, while birds' wings extend along the limb and are covered with feathers. A close look at the relationships between birds, bats, and other tetrapods show that wings evolved independently, as shown below.

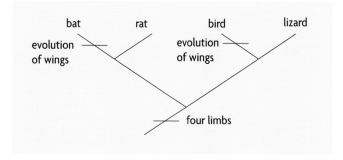

GETTING STARTED

1 Write the words strawberry, apple, and orange on the board. Add the word "fruit" next to each. Ask students by what specific physical characteristic in these fruits we could classify them into two groups. One characteristic is that strawberries have external seeds, and oranges and apples have internal seeds. Write "external seeds" next to "fruit" for the strawberry, and "internal seeds" next to "fruit" for the apple and orange. Next ask students what physical characteristic distinguishes an orange from an apple.

Students might say that oranges have a peel or are segmented. Record the distinguishing characteristic next to internal seeds for the orange.

Tell students that physical characteristics such as these used to classify the fruits serve as data for one method of classifying objects or organisms. In this activity they will apply physical data based on common ancestry to make hypotheses—in the form of evolutionary trees—about the classification of taxa. The trees are branched diagrams that show the evolutionary relationships of taxa.

---

7   The Phylogeny of Vertebrates

1 **K**NOWLEDGE OF THE evolutionary history and relationships of groups of species helps scientists and conservationists understand the biodiversity of an area. Such information helps conservationists decide where and how to focus their efforts.

To understand the relationships of groups of species, scientists have devised various systems for classifying species. Some classification systems compare the observable characteristics of organisms, such as their physical structures, reproduction capabilities, and embryological development, and then assign the organism to a taxon. The higher-level taxa are those above the species level. Above species, starting at the highest, taxon classifications descend in this order: kingdom, phylum, class, order, family, and genus.

There are limitations, however, to classifying taxa based on their physical characteristics alone. That system raises several questions. For example, which similarities and differences are the most important to consider? Should whales be classified as fishes because they have flippers and live in the water? Or are whales mammals because they maintain a constant body temperature and produce milk?

Modern classification, therefore, is based on phylogenetics, which is the study of the evolutionary relationships among taxa. In a phylogenetic study, scientists work with specific characteristics, often called characters. A **character** is a recognizable structure, function, or behavior of an organism. A **homologous character,** or **homology,** is shared by taxa and their common ancestor. For example, all vertebrates and their common ancestor have a vertebral column. Homologous characters provide information about common ancestry, which is more reliable evidence for classifying organisms than their physical similarities and differences or ecological roles.

In the taxon classification system, the domestic cat's classification levels are:

Kingdom: Animalia
Phylum: Chordata
Class: Mammalia
Order: Carnivora
Family: Felidae
Genus: Felis
Species: F. domesticus.

454

If students are not familiar with biological taxonomy based on the system of seven levels of classification, you may wish to show Transparency 7.1, "Taxonomy," to introduce the word and the Linnaean system. Taxonomy is the science of identifying characteristics that may be used to classify groups of organisms. Remind students that the term taxon describes any level of classification in the hierarchy from domain to kingdom, phylum, class, order, family, genus, and species. While some everyday names of organisms—such as ginkgo, human, and sugar maple—refer to species, others refer to higher taxa, such as oak trees (the genus *Quercus*), birds (the class Aves), or bacteria (the domain Prokarya).

This is also a good time to introduce or review the binomial system of nomenclature, by which the genus and species name describe a particular species. For example, the chim-

panzee's scientific name is *Pan troglodytes*. Point out that the genus name is capitalized and both are italicized in this system. For a shorthand version of a name, scientists denote the genus with a capital first letter with a period followed by the full species name. For example, the chimpanzee is *P. troglodytes*.

Explain that in the past, taxonomy focused on observable characteristics of organisms, such as their structure or morphology, method of reproduction, and embryological development. Modern taxonomy is based on evidence about the evolutionary relationships between types of organisms. As scientists learn more about living organisms, additional evidence, including extensive molecular evidence, is moving taxonomy away from the seven-level classification system.

DOING THE ACTIVITY

2 Distribute the cards, and monitor students' work as they complete Part A. The chart below shows sample student answers for Procedure Steps 1 and 2.

When students have completed Part A, project Transparency 7.2, "Vertebrate Forelimbs," and explain that the forelimbs they observed are an example of a shared derived character, which means they are unique to all the members of a clade and their common ancestor.

Sample Student Response to Procedure Steps 1 and 2

	Similarities	Differences
Vertebrate Cards	All forelimbs are used for movement. All have joints.	Some forelimbs are used for swimming. Some are used for walking on land. The shapes and lengths are different.
Forelimb Skeleton Cards	All have a humerus, radius, ulna, and carpals. All have similar positions and structures.	Sizes and shapes of bones differ. Numbers of carpels differ.

Homologies are shared by the common ancestor and some or all of its descendants. Those homologies shared by all populations of a single species or group of species descended from a common ancestor are called **shared derived characters.** Therefore, they are very important in determining relationships. To find shared derived characters, scientists examine large amounts of evidence, such as fossil, physical, and molecular (proteins, chromosomes, DNA) data. Scientists then construct an **evolutionary tree,** or tree, which is a branched diagram for classifying taxa. A tree represents a hypothesis about the evolutionary relationships of taxa.

In this activity you will examine the forelimbs of some vertebrates. You will then look at additional shared derived characters to determine which tree hypothesis best supports the evolution of vertebrates.

Challenge

▶ How do you test a tree hypothesis for a group of taxa?

MATERIALS

FOR EACH PAIR OF STUDENTS
  set of seven Vertebrate Cards
  set of seven Forelimb Skeleton Cards
  colored pencils

FOR EACH STUDENT
  Student Sheet 7.1, "Evidence in Anklebones"
  Student Sheet 3.1, "Ideas about Evolution," from Activity 3

Procedure

Part A: Comparing Vertebrate Forelimbs

It is often difficult to determine if shared characters are also derived characters. One way scientists approach this is to compare the position and structures of the characters.

1. With your partner, observe the forelimbs of the animals shown on the Vertebrate Cards. A forelimb is a front limb of an organism, such as the front leg of a horse, the arm of a human, or the wing of a bird. In your science notebook, record the similarities and differences you observe in the forelimbs of the seven organisms. For example, observe the function, such as walking or flying, the shape, and the number of digits (toes, fingers), if any.

---

3 The evidence to support this is that the positions and structures of the parts of the forelimb skeletons are similar in all of the species. The statement in Procedure Step 3 is accurate because forelimbs are shared derived characters between the species, and, therefore, must have been present in their common ancestor. Explain that the forelimbs all have the same basic structures and bone parts, but have been modified through natural selection for different functions.

Next, point out to students that while they might have noticed similarities in the functions and shapes of the forelimbs in the Vertebrate Cards, function and overall shape alone do not mean the organisms have shared derived characters. Use the example of bird and bat wings. Project Transparency 7.3, "Homology and Analogy." It might seem like the wings of birds and bats are homologous because they serve the same function. However, the wings of birds and bats are not homologous because they were not present in the most recent common ancestor of birds and bats. If you examine fossils and the physical characteristics of the wings themselves, there are clues that the wings did not arise from a common ancestor that had wings. For example, a bird's wings are covered with feathers, while a bat's wings are made up of flaps of skin that are stretched between the bones. The wings evolved independently to serve the same function. Explain that bird and bat *forelimbs* are homologous as defined by evolutionary biologists, but bird and bat forelimbs as *wings* are analogous. An analogous character is one that is shared but was not present in the most recent common ancestor. Instead, an analogous character for two species evolved independently in similar environments.

4 Direct students' attention to the character matrix in the Student Book. Explain that a character matrix helps to construct an evolutionary tree, which is a system for classifying taxa. Start at the bottom of the matrix with the vertebral column. Explain that all of the taxa shown at the top of the chart are vertebrates and, as their name reflects, have the shared derived character of a column of vertebrae. Therefore, the number one is noted in the bottom row for the vertebral column for each organism to show that it has that character. Explain that as you move up the rows of the matrix, organisms are separated from one another sequentially, based on whether or not they share specific derived characters. And, as you move up the rows of the matrix from the bottom, you see that fewer and fewer organisms have the character. Often, the character in the topmost row of the matrix is unique to one taxon.

Ask students which organisms have forelimbs or modified forelimbs. All but the lamprey have forelimbs or modified forelimbs as noted by the "0" in the row labeled "forelimbs" for "lamprey." Next, project Transparency 7.4, "Vertebrate Tree." Explain to students that they will use the character matrix to begin constructing a tree for the organisms. With a marker add forelimbs to the tree above the lamprey, and add the frog to the first branch just above it. A sample drawing is shown below.

---

2. With your partner, look at the Forelimb Skeleton Cards, showing all of the bones in the forelimbs of the organisms. In your science notebook, record the similarities and differences you observe between the skeletal structures of the forelimbs of the organisms. For example, note the types, positions, and structures of the bones and joints.

3
3. In your group, discuss and explain how the forelimb evidence supports the following statement:

All of the taxa share a common ancestor that had forelimbs with similar structures. The taxa gradually evolved as certain features enabled them to take advantage of opportunities in their environment.

Part B: Creating Trees with Evidence

4
4. With your partner, examine the table below, which shows a matrix of characters for a set of species, including the forelimbs for some of the vertebrates you investigated in Part A (0 = absent, 1 = present). Follow your teacher's instructions to construct an evolutionary tree in your science notebook for the six taxa in the matrix. Be sure to label the characters from the matrix and the names of the organisms on your tree.

Character Matrix for Six Vertebrates

CHARACTER	LAMPREY	FROG	BIRD	WHALE	PIG	HUMAN
Pelvic remnants (small portion of what was once a whole pelvis)	0	0	0	1	0	0
Body hair	0	0	0	1	1	1
Amniotic egg	0	0	1	1	1	1
Forelimbs	0	1	1	1	1	1
Vertebral column (backbone)	1	1	1	1	1	1

5
5. Were any of the taxa difficult to place on the tree? List them, and explain why they were difficult to place.

6
6. When scientists construct evolutionary trees, they sometimes need to gather more evidence to determine the most likely placement of each organism they are studying. Obtain Student Sheet 7.1, "Evidence in Anklebones." This is one of many examples of evidence used to determine the evolutionary relationships of mammals. Record your observations of the positions, shapes, and parts of the bones.

456

A sample completed ladder for Procedure Step 4 is shown below.

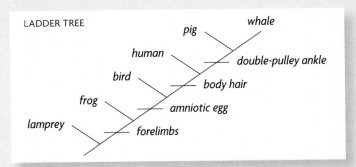

LADDER TREE

Discuss with students that evolutionary trees can be drawn in two formats: tree and ladder. The tree format is preferred because it more accurately reflects the branching of descendants from common ancestors. The ladder format can be misleading because it suggests progress up a ladder, that the taxon at the end is more complex, or that one taxa "evolves into" or "comes from" another. However, when first learning to draw trees, some people find it easier to draw a ladder first and convert the ladder to a tree as shown below.

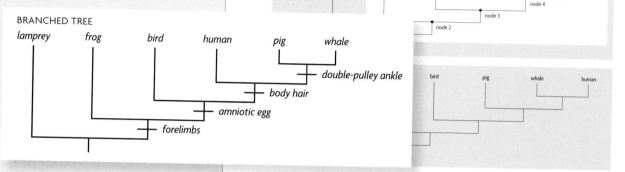

BRANCHED TREE

lamprey   frog   bird   human   pig   whale

double-pulley ankle

body hair

amniotic egg

forelimbs

5 With the information provided on the matrix for this activity, students will not be able to distinguish the whale, pig, and human.

6 Before students complete Procedure Step 6, discuss which part of the tree was difficult to determine. Explain that when scientists are uncertain of where to place taxa on a tree, they examine additional characters. Tell students that they will have additional character evidence to determine the hypothesis that best supports the evidence.

7. Work by yourself to examine the three evolutionary tree hypotheses shown below. Decide which tree is consistent with the characters in the matrix and the anklebone evidence. In your science notebook, copy the tree you decided on. Then, write a four-to-six sentence explanation for which tree hypothesis you chose.

lamprey   frog   bird   CLADE   whale   pig   human

node 5

node 4

node 3

node 2

bird   pig   whale   human

lamprey   frog   bird   human   whale   pig

HYPOTHESIS 3

8. Go back to the statements on Student Sheet 3.1, "Ideas about Evolution," from Activity 3. Record information from this activity to support whether any of the statements is correct or incorrect.

457

Project Transparency 7.5, "Hypotheses for Vertebrate Phylogeny." Explain that evolutionary trees are considered hypotheses because they are tentative-and-testable explanations for evolutionary relationships and common ancestry based on the available evidence in the form of characters. Students will determine which of the three tree hypotheses is best supported by the available evidence. Explain that, like any hypothesis, a tree hypothesis may change if additional evidence or other logical reasoning emerges to explain the relationships of the species.

While pointing out tree features on the transparency, explain to students how to read an evolutionary tree. The root of the tree represents the ancestor and the tips represent the descendants of the ancestor. A node is a place on the tree where a single lineage branches into two or more lineages. The node represents the characteristics of a common ancestor. The nodes lead to tips that represent descendent groups. A group that includes a common ancestor (node) and all of its descendants is called a clade. Two groups on a tree that share a more recent common ancestor represented by a node are more closely related to one another than they are to groups that share a more distant common ancestor. For example, in Hypothesis 1, the frog and bird are more closely related to one another than they are to the lamprey because the frog and bird share a more recent common ancestor, represented by node 2. Frogs, birds, and lampreys share a more distant ancestor farther back in time, represented by node 1.

The relationships shown on trees provide information about the bio-diversity of the groups in the tree. A cluster of more closely related groups is most likely less biodiverse than a set of taxa that are spread out across the tree. For example, a group made up of the whale, pig, and human taxa is less diverse than a group made up of the lamprey, bird, and human taxa. Distribute copies of Student Sheet 7.1, "Evidence in Anklebones," to each student for Procedure Step 6.

7 The following is a sample response for Procedure Step 7:

From the evidence in the character matrix and the ankle evidence, I think Hypothesis 3 is the most consistent with all of the evidence. The shared derived characters show evidence for the separation and grouping of the lamprey, frog, and bird. The data matrix did not give enough information to separate out the grouping of the whale, pig, and human. Based on the ankle evidence, the whale and pig share a more recent ancestor than either does with human. The evidence for this is the double-pulley ankle that whales and pigs share, with two trochleas. Humans have a single-pulley ankle with just one trochlea.

If students are confused about whether or not whales have ankles, explain that the ankle evidence came from a whale ancestor that had hind limbs with ankles and a pelvis. Modern whales evolved to no longer have hind limbs with ankles or a pelvis. Stress that these are examples of the many shared derived characters scientists observe in constructing tree hypotheses. Stress that some tree hypotheses are so strongly supported by the evidence that they are generally accepted by the scientific community. Other tree hypotheses are more tentative.

8 ◆ Sample student responses to Procedure Step 8 are shown on the sample Student Sheet 3.1, "Ideas about Evolution," at the end of this activity.

---

9 *Analysis*

1. How would fossil evidence provide additional support for the statement in Step 3?

2. A **clade** is a group on an evolutionary tree that includes a common ancestor and all of its descendants. Draw a box around one clade in the tree from Step 7.

3. Based on the tree you chose:

   a. Which are more closely related to humans: birds or frogs? Support your answer with evidence.

   b. Which are more distantly related to birds: humans or lampreys? Support your answer with evidence.

   c. Which group shares a more recent common ancestor with whales: pigs or humans? Support your answer with evidence.

4. Based on the portion of a tree shown below, what can you say about the relationship of taxa X to horses and humans?

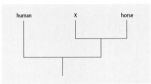

KEY VOCABULARY	
character	hypothesis
clade	node
evidence	phylogenetics
evolutionary tree	**shared derived character**
homologous character	taxa
homology	taxon

458

FOLLOW-UP

9 ✓ Project Transparency 7.5, "Hypotheses for Vertebrate Phylogeny." Review with students that the tree that best represents the evidence in the character matrix and the anklebones is Hypothesis 3, which shows the whale and pig branching from a more recent common ancestor. Review with students that in Activity 5, "Using Fossil Evidence to Investigate Whale Evolution," they worked in the same way that paleontologists do, analyzing fossil skeleton evidence to understand how whales evolved as mammals that live in water. In this activity, they observed additional skeleton evidence in the anklebones of pigs, humans, and a whale ancestor. This is one piece of evidence that supports the evolution of whales as mammals. Because pigs (mammals) and the whale ancestor share a double-pulley ankle, and other derived characters are not shared with humans, this supports the hypothesis that they share a more recent common ancestor that also had the double-pulley ankle. If you wish, explain that a double-pulley ankle bone has two deep grooves, one on each end. Another bone fits into these grooves to form a sliding joint. A single-pulley ankle bone has only one groove.

Analysis Questions 3 and 4 are Quick Check assessments of students' understanding of how to read and interpret evolutionary trees.

SAMPLE RESPONSES

1. The fossils provide additional evidence of shared characters present in all the taxa with forelimbs, supporting the hypothesis that the forelimbs were inherited from a common ancestor.

2. One possible answer follows.

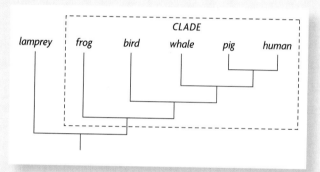

3. a. ✓ Birds are more closely related to humans because they share a more recent common ancestor with humans than humans do with frogs.

    b. Lampreys are more distantly related to birds than humans because birds and lampreys share a more distant common ancestor than do birds and humans.

c. Pigs share a more recent ancestor with whales because they have in common more shared derived characters such as the double-pulley ankle bone.

4. ✓ Taxa X is more closely related to horses than it is to humans because X shares a more recent common ancestor with horses that it does not share with humans.

REVIST THE CHALLENGE

Review with students how evolutionary trees are constructed from evidence of shared derived characters. Remind them that in this activity they focused on shared derived characters that were or are physical characteristics of the organisms, but that shared derived characters are also based on DNA or other molecular evidence. Point out that physical and molecular evidence is also obtained from fossils. Scientists look at many shared derived characters when they are constructing evolutionary trees. Trees show the evolutionary relationships of groups of organisms, and are the current method for classifying them.

Emphasize that trees are considered hypotheses because they are tentative-and-testable explanations for evolutionary relationships and common ancestry based on the available evidence. Some tree hypotheses are so strongly supported by the evidence that scientists do not dispute them. An example is the tree that shows that dinosaurs are the evolutionary ancestors of birds. Other tree hypotheses may change if new evidence or logical reasoning explains the relationships of the species.

Ideas about Evolution

Statement 1: Evolution is a climb up a ladder of progress with taxa always getting bigger and better.

Before doing any activity, I think the statement is correct: Yes ☐ No ☐ because _____

Activity Number	After doing these activities, I think	
	Statement is correct:	Evidence and reasoning:
5 and 6	Yes ☐ No ☒	Fish, whales, and tetrapods did not get bigger and better; they changed as features were selected for in the environment.
	Yes ☐ No ☐	
	Yes ☐ No ☐	

Statement 2: The theory of evolution by natural selection is supported by a large body of scientific evidence.

Before doing any activity, I think the statement is correct: Yes ☐ No ☐ because _____

Activity Number	After doing these activities, I think	
	Statement is correct:	Evidence and reasoning:
6	Yes ☒ No ☐	The fossil record contains a lot of information about evolutionary changes over geologic time, such as the evolution of whales and tetrapods.
7	Yes ☒ No ☐	Fossil and character data from living taxa, and molecular data are used to construct evolutionary trees to determine the branching order on trees and show common ancestry.
7	Yes ☒ No ☐	Physical evidence supports the natural selection and common ancestry of vertebrates.

©2010 The Regents of the University of California

Ideas about Evolution (continued)

Statement 3: *Natural selection is not a random process.*

Before doing any activity, I think the statement is correct: Yes ☐ No ☐ because _____

Activity Number	After doing these activities, I think	
	Statement is correct:	**Evidence and reasoning:**
	Yes ☐ No ☐	
	Yes ☐ No ☐	
	Yes ☐ No ☐	

Statement 4: *Evolution is a process by which taxa choose to adapt to their environment.*

Before doing any activity, I think the statement is correct: Yes ☐ No ☐ because _____

Activity Number	After doing these activities, I think	
	Statement is correct:	**Evidence and reasoning:**
5 and 6	Yes ☐ No ☒	*Whales and tetrapods did not choose to adapt. Features that allowed for increased survival and reproduction were selected for and passed on.*
	Yes ☐ No ☐	
	Yes ☐ No ☐	

(continued on next page)

Ideas about Evolution *(continued)*

Statement 5: *Evidence suggests that humans and apes share an evolutionary ancestry.*

Before doing any activity, I think *the statement is correct:* Yes ☐ No ☐ *because* _____

Activity Number	After doing these activities, I think	
	Statement is correct:	**Evidence and reasoning:**
	Yes ☐ No ☐	
	Yes ☐ No ☐	
	Yes ☐ No ☐	

8 Studying Hominids

INVESTIGATION • 2–3 CLASS SESSIONS

OVERVIEW

Students examine fossil and molecular evidence to determine the evolutionary relationships between apes and extinct and modern humans. They read additional information about the evolution of the human lineage.

KEY CONTENT

1. The millions of species of plants, animals, and microorganisms that live on earth today are related by descent from common ancestors.

2. The theory of natural selection and its evolutionary consequences provides a scientific explanation for the fossil record of ancient life forms and the striking molecular similarities found among diverse species of living organisms.

3. Scientists apply fossil and molecular data to develop hypotheses for how major taxa, such as the hominids (African apes and humans), evolved.

4. Evolutionary biologists and paleontologists focus on transitional features in fossils—those key features that demonstrate the evolutionary changes that resulted in macroevolution.

5. Scientific explanations must adhere to such criteria as the application of appropriate evidence, consistently logical reasoning, and basis in accepted historical and current knowledge.

KEY PROCESS SKILLS

1. Students develop conclusions from evidence.

2. Students communicate and defend a scientific argument.

3. Students make accurate interpretations, inferences, and conclusions from text.

MATERIALS AND ADVANCE PREPARATION

For the teacher
Transparency 8.1, "Vertebrate Phylogeny"
Transparency 8.2, "Skull Measurements"
Scoring Guide: UNDERSTANDING CONCEPTS (UC)

For each group of four students
set of six Cranium Diagrams

For each pair of students
metric ruler*
protractor*
sticky notes*

For each student
Student Sheet 8.1, "Cranium Comparisons"
Student Sheet 3.1, "Ideas about Evolution," from Activity 3
Scoring Guide: UNDERSTANDING CONCEPTS (UC) (optional)

Masters for Scoring Guides are in Teacher Resources IV: Assessment.

Make one copy of each of the six Cranium Diagrams for each group of four students. If you have access to castings of real hominid skulls, use them in addition to or in place of the diagrams.

TEACHING SUMMARY

Getting Started

- The class reviews the anklebone evidence they observed to help them determine the evolutionary ancestry of whales, pigs, and humans.

Doing the Activity

- Students analyze cranium data for members of the hominid family.

- (LITERACY) Students read about other evidence scientists have gathered about the evolution of the human lineage.

- Students revisit the statements on Student Sheet 3.1, "Ideas about Evolution."

Follow-up

- The class discusses the tree showing the relationship between humans, chimpanzees, and gorillas.

BACKGROUND INFORMATION

Taxonomy for Apes and Humans

Greater knowledge of genetics has led to a better understanding of the taxonomy of the hominoids, which include all apes and humans. The hominoids comprise three families: the Hylobatidae (gibbons and siamangs), Pongidae (orangutans), and the Hominidae (humans, and the African apes (gorillas, chimpanzees, and bonobos). The Hominidae family is divided into three subfamilies: gorillas, chimpanzees (including the closely related bonobos), and hominins (humans both living and extinct). This taxonomy is a revised classification of the "hominids." Previously, hominids referred to humans and their extinct bipedal ancestors. Now it refers to humans and the African apes, and hominin refers to only humans and their bipedal ancestors.

Genetic Data as Evidence for Evolution

Over the past few decades, the understanding of genetics has revolutionized biochemistry, molecular biology, evolutionary biology, and all other areas of biology. As scientists developed methods for accurately sequencing the nucleotides that make up the DNA of living species, they applied these sequences to determine the evolutionary relationships between taxa.

While all DNA is made of the same four nucleotides—thymine, adenine, guanine, and cytosine—mutations cause changes in the specific sequences that make up genes. Mutations are limited in that there are only certain kinds of changes that can happen, but random in that they happen anywhere in the genome and that any base can change. The more time that passes, the more likely DNA is to change due to mutations. Therefore, the more closely related two taxa are to each other, the more similar their DNA will be.

Even though mutations occur in all DNA, scientists have found that some genes tolerate mutation better than others, which means that their function is not as greatly affected by these random mutations. Because of this, genes evolve at different rates. Those genes that tolerate more change evolve more quickly and those that are impaired by change evolve more slowly.

The average rate at which a specific gene evolves is called its molecular clock. For example, the genes for three proteins—cytochrome c, hemoglobin, and fibrinopeptides—all have different clocks. Cytochrome c evolves slowly because it interacts very specifically with large macromolecules to perform its function in cellular respiration. Minuscule changes may make cytochrome c lose its function and affect processes that are vital for the organism's survival. Hemoglobin evolves at an intermediate rate because it only interacts with oxygen and a few very small molecules in performing its function of carrying oxygen through the blood. Even with some changes, hemoglobin can still carry out its function. Fibrinopeptides evolve fairly quickly because they can continue to carry out their role in blood clotting despite most amino acid changes.

Evolutionary scientists examine the molecular clock for two primary purposes: to determine the evolutionary relationship between taxa, and to determine how long ago in geologic time two taxa that shared a common ancestor began to diverge from one another. For example, suppose you wanted to examine the divergence of birds and mammals. The difference in the sequence for cytochrome c in a chicken, and in such mammals as pigs, horses, cows, sheep, and rabbits is approximately 9%. Because there is so little difference in the protein for chicken and mammals, the divergence of birds and mammals happened relatively more recently.

GETTING STARTED

1 Project Transparency 8.1, "Vertebrate Phylogeny." Review with students the example of a character that separates humans from whales and pigs, which they learned about in Activity 7, "The Phylogeny of Vertebrates." A whale ancestor and pigs share a double-pulley ankle, while humans have a single-pulley ankle. Tell students that in this activity they will examine in more detail the human lineage and the evidence for the evolution of the human lineage.

8 Studying Hominids

1 IN **ACTIVITY 5,** "Using Fossil Evidence to Investigate Whale Evolution," you were working with evidence for the evolution of the whale lineage. A **lineage** is a series of populations of a single species or several species descended from a common ancestor. On an evolutionary tree a branch represents a lineage.

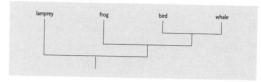

Each line shown on this tree for vertebrates is a lineage.

The evolution of another lineage supported by a growing body of evidence is the one that led to humans. In this activity, you will examine some of the evidence about the species that make up hominids, which include humans and apes.

A Neanderthal fossil skeleton.

459

DOING THE ACTIVITY

2 Before students begin, project Transparency 8.2, "Skull Measurements," which shows the gorilla skull. On the transparency demonstrate how to draw the lines and take the various cranium measurements:

- First, a horizontal line is drawn across the skull with the line touching the bottom of the eye socket.

- Second, a vertical line is drawn that just touches the front-most part of the eye socket.

- Third, a line is drawn from the middle of the upper incisors upward to the front of the brow ridge and continuing until it intersects with the vertical line that was already drawn.

- Finally, a line is drawn that touches the top of the brow ridge and the most protruding part of the forehead.

Transparency 8.2, "Skull Measurements," shows the angles resulting from the drawing of these lines. The transparency also illustrates the location of the upper incisors and molars for measuring the length of the upper jaw.

3 Monitor students' progress as they work through Procedure Step 3, and answer questions when necessary.

4 Sample answers to Student Sheet 8.1, "Cranium Comparisons" are shown at right.

Challenge

▶ How do biologists study the evolutionary relationships of hominids?

MATERIALS

FOR EACH GROUP OF FOUR STUDENTS
set of six Cranium Diagrams

FOR EACH PAIR OF STUDENTS
metric ruler
protractor
sticky notes

FOR EACH STUDENT
Student Sheet 8.1, "Cranium Comparisons"
Student Sheet 3.1, "Ideas about Evolution," from Activity 3
Student Sheet 3.2, "Geologic Time and Major Events," from Activity 3

Procedure

Part A: Physical Evidence for Human Ancestry

2 1. With your group, compare the six cranium diagrams. Record in your science notebook similarities and differences you observe.

3 2. Group the six organisms according to how closely related you think they are based on the similarities and differences you recorded in Step 1. Write your groupings in your science notebook.

4 3. Obtain Student Sheet 8.1, "Cranium Comparisons." Observe the characteristics shown on the chart, and record the information in the appropriate column. Measure lengths with a ruler, and measure angles with a protractor.

Note: Diagrams 1, 2, and 3 already show the lines you will measure. For diagrams 4, 5, and 6 you will need to draw the lines that you will then measure.

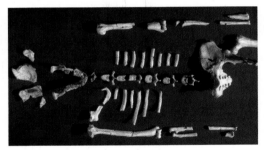

The skeleton of "Lucy" provides evidence about the evolution of the human lineage.

460

Sample Student Response: Student Sheet 8.1, "Cranium Comparisons"

Skull number	Angle of face from incisors to brow ridge	Angle of forehead	Length of upper jaw (cm) (from back molars to between two front incisors)	Volume of braincase (cm³)
1	30°	63°	8.9	500–700
2	30°	66°	6.1	300–500
3	15°	40°	5.9	750–1,250
4	4–5°	50°	5.4	1,300–1,750
5	10°	36°	5.4	1,000–1,700
6	21°	61°	6.7	410–530

5 Some possible patterns for the cranium data are as follows:

- For the angles of the face and forehead and length of the upper jaw, 1, 2, and 6 are in order from largest to smallest/shortest.

- For the angle of the forehead and length of the upper jaw, 4, 3, and 5 are in order from largest to smallest/shortest.

- Generally, 1, 2, and 6 have larger angles on the forehead and face and longer upper jaw compared to 3, 4, and 5.

- Skulls 1, 2, and 6 have a smaller braincase volume compared to 3, 4, and 5.

- There is a general pattern of larger face/forehead angles and longer upper jaw, paired with a smaller braincase volume.

When students have completed Procedure Step 4, tell them the names of the six organisms. Instruct them to write in their science notebooks the names that correspond with the numbers. The names are shown at right.

6 (LITERACY) When students have completed the reading, instruct them to refer to their sticky notes from the "Read, Think, and Take Note" strategy and discuss in their groups any points of confusion or questions that came up as they read. Encourage them to work together to make meaning of the text. You may wish to hold a class discussion about words and sentences that students thought were difficult.

7 If you wish, stop after students have completed Part A and discuss student conclusions about the six organisms. Many students will likely group skulls 1, 2, and possibly 6 as more similar to each other than they are to skulls 3, 4, and 5. Based on the information given, some students may hypothesize that 1, 2, and 6 are likely to be more closely related and possibly ancestors of 3, 4, and 5. In addition, 3, 4, and 5 are likely to be more closely related to each another.

The following appears in an inset reproduction of the student page:

5 4. Examine your observations from Step 3. Record any patterns in the data that suggest changes over time.

6 5. Complete the reading, "Natural Selection in the Human Lineage," on the following pages to learn more about the ape and human lineages. As you read, follow the " and Take Note" strategy, using the sticky notes as you did in previous activities.

7 6. Based on your data and the information in the reading, what conclusions can you draw about the relationships between the six species?

Part B: Molecular Evidence for Human Ancestry

8 7. The box below shows a portion of the amino acid sequence for hemoglobin in humans, chimpanzees, and gorillas. Sketch a tree hypothesis suggested by the amino acid data and the information you gathered in Part A. Label the root of the tree "common ancestor."

> **Amino Acid Sequence Data**
>
> **HUMAN**
> MVHLTPEEKSAVTALWGKVNVDEVGGEALGRLLVVYPWTQRFFESFGDLSTPDAVMGNPKVKAHGKKVLGAFSD
> GLAHLDNLKGTFATLSELHCDKLHVDPEN **F** RLLGNVLVCVLAHHFGKEFTPPVQAAYQKVVAGVANALAHKYH
>
> **CHIMPANZEE**
> MVHLTPEEKSAVTALWGKVNVDEVGGEALGRLLVVYPWTQRFFESFGDLSTPDAVMGNPKVKAHGKKVLGAFSD
> GLAHLDNLKGTFATLSELHCDKLHVDPEN **F** RLLGNVLVCVLAHHFGKEFTPPVQAAYQKVVAGVANALAHKYH
>
> **GORILLA**
> MVHLTPEEKSAVTALWGKVNVDEVGGEALGRLLVVYPWTQRFFESFGDLSTPDAVMGNPKVKAHGKKVLGAFSD
> GLAHLDNLKGTFATLSELHCDKLHVDPEN **K** RLLGNVLVCVLAHHFGKEFTPPVQAAYQKVVAGVANALAHKYH

9 8. Go back to the statements on Student Sheet 3.1, "Ideas about Evolution," from Activity 3. Record on it information from this activity to support whether any of the statements is correct or incorrect.

Cranium Comparisons

Skull number	Scientific name	Common name
1	Gorilla gorilla	Gorilla
2	Pan troglodytes	Chimpanzee
3	Homo erectus	—
4	Homo neanderthalensis	"Neanderthal"
5	Homo sapiens	Modern human
6	Australopithecus boisei	"Lucy"

461

---

8 The molecular evidence comes from the complete sequence for the hemoglobin beta chain, made of 104 amino acids. There is just one amino acid difference in the gorilla's sequence compared to the human's and chimpanzee's. Scientists have investigated the sequences of other proteins and found more differences between gorilla and human, and gorilla and chimpanzee compared to human and chimpanzee.

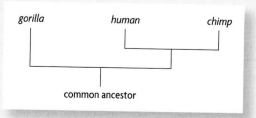

common ancestor

9 ✦ Sample student responses to Student Sheet 3.1, "Ideas about Evolution," are shown at the end of this activity. Review students' ideas and have them reflect on what they have learned.

Students will label the hominid divergence at approximately 4.5–5 million years ago.

FOLLOW-UP

10 (UC ASSESSMENT) Analysis Question 1 is an opportunity to assess students' understanding of how genetic evidence shows evolutionary relationships. Review the UNDERSTANDING CONCEPTS (UC) Scoring Guide with the class, and tell students your expectations for satisfactory work. Hold a class discussion about where students placed the human, chimpanzee, and gorilla on the tree.

✦ This is also an opportunity to review the organization of a tree with nodes representing the common ancestor and the divergence (branching) of lineages. If students placed all three taxa in a straight line, this indicates a misconception about tree organization or the concepts of common ancestry and direct descent. For example, students might think that some taxa "change into" or "evolve into" another taxa. All of the evidence in this activity leads to a tree hypothesis that humans, chimpanzees, and gorillas share a common ancestor. Humans and chimps are more closely related by a more recent ancestor that gorillas do not share. Be sure to emphasize that the tree shows common ancestry but not direct descent. In other words, humans are not directly descended from gorillas, chimps, or apes, but they do share a common ancestor with these other primates.

Analysis

10 1. Suppose you analyzed the DNA sequences for a number of DNA segments in humans, chimpanzees, and gorillas, and you collected the data in the table below:

DNA Sequences in Humans, Chimpanzees, and Gorillas	
DNA COMPARISON	SEQUENCE DIFFERENCE (%)
Human–chimpanzee	1.24
Human–gorilla	1.62
Chimpanzee–gorilla	1.63

Explain how these data are related to the amino acid data from Part B and how they explain the evolutionary relationship between humans, chimps, and gorillas.

2. Based on the portion of the hominid tree from Procedure Step 7, how would you respond to someone who claims that

   a. scientific evidence suggests that humans descended from chimps and gorillas?

   b. scientific evidence suggests that humans, gorillas, and chimpanzees share an evolutionary ancestor?

3. How does the scientific process you followed in this activity reflect the way that scientists ask and answer questions about the natural world?

KEY VOCABULARY	
evidence	hominid
evolutionary tree	**lineage**

SAMPLE RESPONSES

1. (UC ASSESSMENT) A complete and correct response will explain how the DNA data are consistent with the amino acid data, and what this tells about how closely related gorillas, chimps, and humans are, based on their common ancestry.

Sample Level-3 Response

The DNA data are consistent with the amino acid data, showing a bigger difference between humans and gorillas, and chimpanzees and gorillas, than humans and chimpanzees. This suggests that humans and chimps are more closely related to one another than either is to gorillas, and that they share a more recent common ancestor.

2. a. The claim is incorrect. The molecular data suggest that humans and apes share a common ancestor, not that humans descended from apes.

    b. The claim is correct. The physical evidence and genetic evidence suggest an evolutionary ancestor.

3. Students' answers will vary. Sample responses include that scientists make observations from various lines of evidence, including physical and molecular data. They look for patterns of similarities and differences in the lines of evidence to make hypotheses about evolutionary relationships. If new evidence comes along, they determine if the hypothesis is still valid.

READING

Natural Selection in the Human Lineage

MODERN HUMANS (*Homo sapiens*) are classified as members of the family Hominidae, as are gorillas and chimpanzees. Evidence suggests that the human and chimpanzee lineages split approximately 5 million years ago as shown in the tree below.

Scientists are still gathering evidence that would allow them to reconstruct the early history of the hominids. The fossil and DNA data they have collected, however, suggest that the adaptation for walking upright on two legs (bipedalism) defines the divergence of the human lineage. The chart above summarizes the locomotion methods for the six hominid species that you are investigating in this activity.

Locomotion Methods for Six Hominid Species	
SPECIES	LOCOMOTION
Gorilla gorilla (gorilla)	Knuckle walking most of the time and bipedal walking for short distances
Pan troglodytes (chimpanzee)	Knuckle walking most of the time and bipedal walking for short distances
Australopithecines boisei ("Lucy," extinct)	fully bipedal
Homo erectus (extinct)	fully bipedal
Homo neanderthalensis ("Neanderthal," extinct)	fully bipedal
Homo sapiens (modern humans)	fully bipedal

There are several physical characters that allow for full-time upright walking in humans:

- Humans have larger vertebrae to carry the weight of the upper body.
- The point at which the spinal cord enters the skull is near the center of the cranium, which allows the head to balance on top of the spine.
- The human pelvis is positioned for greater balance while walking. The structure of the human foot includes a weight-bearing platform and a shock-absorbing arch.

(Continued on next page)

TREE HYPOTHESIS FOR PRIMATES

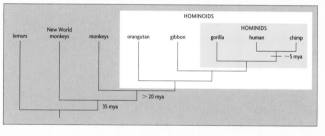

463

REVISIT THE CHALLENGE

Review with students the evidence behind the hypothesis explaining the evolution of the human lineage, including the cranium data and environmental data. Explain that new evidence about the evolution of the human lineage is still being discovered. For example, the "Ardi," fossil is 1.2 million years older than Lucy, and the discoverers hypothesize that Ardi is a hominin, which would place human evolution earlier than previously hypothesized. Some scientists have proposed that Ardi pre-dates the splitting of the human and ape lineages. Only additional evidence will resolve this question. This is another opportunity to stress to students that, while more hominin fossils are likely to be discovered, others will never be found. Also, the details of the evolution of humans might remain hypotheses because new evidence is still being discovered. However, the overall process of evolution, including the evolution of the human lineage, is supported by a large body of evidence.

(Continued from previous page)

As new fossil and DNA evidence is discovered, scientists evaluate hypotheses for the evolution of bipedalism by natural selection. There is evidence to suggest that early hominins (living humans and extinct bipedal ancestors) had both the character for bipedal motion and the character in quadrupeds (taxa with four-legged locomotion) for grasping when moving in trees. A 4.4 million-year-old fossil, called "Ardi," had features for walking on two legs on the ground and grasping when moving in the trees. Ardi's pelvis was structured to support large hind limb muscles for climbing, resulting in a walk without the side-to-side gait of a chimpanzee. Ardi had big toes spread out from the rest for climbing, like those of an ape. She had an additional bone inside a tendon in the big toes that made them more rigid, and suitable for walking. These characters, which indicate Ardi was capable of foraging in the grasslands and climbing trees, provide clues about the evolution of bipedalism and the environment in which the human lineage might have evolved. Additional evidence will help scientists understand more clearly the factors that led to the divergence of the human lineage from its ancestors. ■

Ideas about Evolution

Statement 1: Evolution is a climb up a ladder of progress with taxa always getting bigger and better.

Before doing any activity, I think the statement is correct: Yes ☐ No ☐ because _____

Activity Number	After doing these activities, I think	
	Statement is correct:	Evidence and reasoning:
5 and 6	Yes ☐ No ☒	Fish, whales, and tetrapods did not get bigger and better; they changed as features were selected for in the environment.
	Yes ☐ No ☐	
	Yes ☐ No ☐	

Statement 2: The theory of evolution by natural selection is supported by a large body of scientific evidence.

Before doing any activity, I think the statement is correct: Yes ☐ No ☐ because _____

Activity Number	After doing these activities, I think	
	Statement is correct:	Evidence and reasoning:
6	Yes ☒ No ☐	The fossil record contains a lot of information about evolutionary changes over geologic time, such as the evolution of whales and tetrapods.
7	Yes ☒ No ☐	Fossil and character data from living taxa, and molecular data are used to construct evolutionary trees to determine the branching order on trees and show common ancestry.
7	Yes ☒ No ☐	Physical evidence supports the natural selection and common ancestry of vertebrates.

Ideas about Evolution (continued)

Statement 3: *Natural selection is not a random process.*

Before doing any activity, I think *the statement is correct:* Yes ☐ No ☐ *because* _____

Activity Number	After doing these activities, I think	
	Statement is correct:	**Evidence and reasoning:**
	Yes ☐ No ☐	
	Yes ☐ No ☐	
	Yes ☐ No ☐	

Statement 4: *Evolution is a process by which taxa choose to adapt to their environment.*

Before doing any activity, I think *the statement is correct:* Yes ☐ No ☐ *because* _____

Activity Number	After doing these activities, I think	
	Statement is correct:	**Evidence and reasoning:**
5 and 6	Yes ☐ No ☒	*Whales and tetrapods did not choose to adapt. Features that allowed for increased survival and reproduction were selected for and passed on.*
	Yes ☐ No ☐	
	Yes ☐ No ☐	

Ideas about Evolution (continued)

Statement 5: *Evidence suggests that humans and apes share an evolutionary ancestry.*

Before doing any activity, I think *the statement is correct:* Yes ☐ No ☐ *because* _____

Activity Number	After doing these activities, I think	
	Statement is correct:	**Evidence and reasoning:**
8	Yes ☒ No ☐	DNA and protein evidence suggests that humans and chimpanzees share a more recent common ancestor than either does with gorillas. All of these lineages share a common ancestor.
8	Yes ☒ No ☐	Physical evidence (cranium data) suggests an evolutionary ancestry.
	Yes ☐ No ☐	

Studying Lineages for Conservation

INVESTIGATION • 1–2 CLASS SESSIONS

OVERVIEW

Students read about Madagascar, which is a biodiversity hotspot. They then investigate an evolutionary tree of lemurs and rank four areas on the island for conservation priority based on phylogenetic diversity.

KEY CONTENT

1. The millions of species of plants, animals, and microorganisms that live on earth today are related by descent from common ancestors.

2. Modern biological classifications show how taxa are related based on similarities in their genealogical lineages.

3. Phylogenetic diversity demonstrates the relationships of lineages to one another through time.

4. Phylogenetic diversity provides information for people to make sustainable conservation decisions.

5. Sustainability is closely linked to biodiversity.

KEY PROCESS SKILLS

1. Students examine data to identify trends and relationships.

2. Students develop conclusions from evidence.

3. Students make accurate interpretations, inferences, and conclusions from text.

MATERIALS AND ADVANCE PREPARATION

For the teacher
Literacy Transparency 3, "Read, Think, and Take Note"
Scoring Guide: EVIDENCE AND TRADE-OFFS (ET)

For each student
sticky notes*

Scoring Guide: EVIDENCE AND TRADE-OFFS (ET) (optional)

Masters for Literacy Transparencies are in Teacher Resources III: Literacy. Masters for Scoring Guides are in Teacher Resources IV: Assessment.

TEACHING SUMMARY

Getting Started
• Review ecosystem, species, and genetic diversity.

Doing the Activity
• (LITERACY) Students read a case study about Madagascar and the lemurs endemic to Madagascar.

• Students examine an evolutionary tree of lemurs in order to determine the phylogenetic diversity of lemurs in four areas on Madagascar.

Follow-up
• (ET ASSESSMENT) Students rank four areas on Madagascar for conservation priority and consider the role of phylogenetic diversity in making sustainable conservation decisions.

BACKGROUND INFORMATION

Conserving Biodiversity

Most scientists agree that conservation efforts should focus on ecosystems that have the highest biodiversity, which is measured by the genetic diversity within a single species, the numbers of different species, and the variety of ecosystems in a given area. Biodiversity is also measured by phylogenetic diversity, which shows the relationships of entire lineages through time. The evolutionary tree for lemurs in this activity is based on actual phylogenetic data for the lemurs in Madagascar, which is published in the reference at the end of this section. The varying lengths of the branches on the tree do not represent extinctions as they do in some evolutionary trees.

Some of the areas where biodiversity or the potential for biodiversity is considered to be the highest are in biodiversity hotspots. These hotspots tend to be located in tropical areas near the equator for several reasons: there is a smaller range of climates, making the growing season longer to produce a rich variety of plant species; the geography often has canopies, subcanopies, and mountains of varying altitudes, which all create more niches; there is greater competition among species, which leads to more specialization; and there is higher biomass productivity as a result of more direct sunlight that allows for more photosynthesis.

REFERENCES

Horvath, J., Weisrock, D., Embry, S. L., Fiorentino, I., Balhoff, J. P., Kappeler, P., Wray, G. A., Willard, H., & Yoder, A. D. (2008). The development and application of a phylogenomic toolkit: Resolving the evolutionary history of Madagascar's lemurs. *Genome Research, 18(3)*, 489–499. Retrieved July 2010 from http://genome.cshlp.org/content/18/3/489.full.pdf+html.

GETTING STARTED

1 Review the three types of biodiversity—ecosystem, species, and genetic diversity—that students investigated in previous activities. If appropriate, instruct students to go back to the scenarios in Activity 2, "Human Activities and Biodiversity." Tell students that in this activity, they will learn about a fourth level of biodiversity: phylogenetic diversity.

9 Studying Lineages for Conservation

1 IN PREVIOUS ACTIVITIES you examined the evidence for the evolution by natural selection of the whale and human lineages. You also learned how evolutionary trees show the pattern of the relationships of lineages to one another through time. This variation between taxa on a tree is called **phylogenetic diversity.** Of great value to conservationists when they consider sustainable conservation measures, trees show which lineages are either rich or limited in species diversity. Trees also illustrate which lineages are ancient or unusual.

The island of Madagascar, off the east coast of Africa, is a biodiversity hotspot where conservationists are focusing on phylogenetic diversity. As you have learned, biodiversity hotspots have both a high number of endemic species and extraordinary habitat loss. Of immediate concern is the welfare of lemurs, which are found only in Madagascar and the Comoro Islands nearby.

Suppose you are a member of a team of conservationists that must prioritize conservation efforts on Madagascar. The map on the next page shows the areas on the island that are being considered for protection, the lemur species that live in those areas, and the parks and reserves already established on the island.

Challenge

▶ How does evidence about phylogenetic relationships assist evolutionary biologists and conservationists in making sustainable conservation decisions?

MATERIALS

FOR EACH STUDENT
sticky notes

The ring-tailed lemur is one of the best-known lemurs, because of its long tail with black and white rings.

465

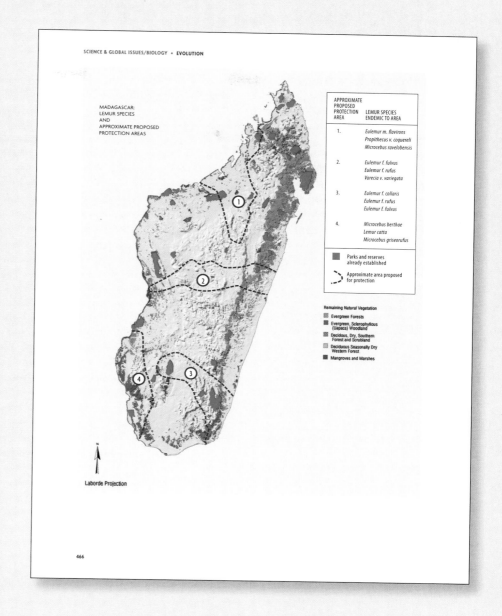

SCIENCE & GLOBAL ISSUES/BIOLOGY • EVOLUTION

MADAGASCAR:
LEMUR SPECIES
AND
APPROXIMATE PROPOSED
PROTECTION AREAS

APPROXIMATE PROPOSED PROTECTION AREA	LEMUR SPECIES ENDEMIC TO AREA
1.	*Eulemur m. flavirons*
	Propithecus v. coquereli
	Microcebus ravelobensis
2.	*Eulemur f. fulvus*
	Eulemur f. rufus
	Varecia v. variegata
3.	*Eulemur f. collaris*
	Eulemur f. rufus
	Eulemur f. fulvus
4.	*Microcebus berthae*
	Lemur catta
	Microcebus griseorufus

Parks and reserves already established

Approximate area proposed for protection

Remaining Natural Vegetation
Evergreen Forests
Evergreen, Sclerophyllous (Uapaca) Woodland
Decidous, Dry, Southern Forest and Scrubland
Deciduous Seasonally Dry Western Forest
Mangroves and Marshes

N

Laborde Projection

466

DOING THE ACTIVITY

2 (LITERACY) If necessary, project Literacy Transparency 3, "Guidelines for Read, Think, and Take Note." Consider holding a class discussion about students' thoughts and questions about the Reading after they have discussed them in pairs in Procedure Step 2.

3 Sample student responses for the descriptions of the phylogenetic diversity of the lemurs are summarized in the table below.

Sample Student Response: Procedure Step 3
Phylogenetic Diversity of Lemurs

Area	Phylogenetic diversity
1	Lemurs in three genera spread out across the tree in three families.
2	Lemurs in two genera are in the same family.
3	Lemurs are all in one family in the Eulemur genus, and located fairly closely on the tree.
4	Lemurs in two families and two genera

Procedure

2

1. Read the case study about Madagascar on the following pages to learn more about the island.

2. Discuss with your partner the thoughts and questions you had while reading.

3

3. The tree shown below was assembled with genetic evidence for the lemur taxa of Madagascar. In your science notebook, describe the phylogenetic diversity of the lemurs in each area that is being considered for wildlife protection.

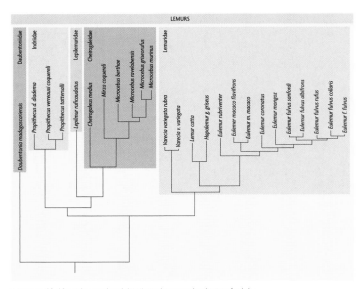

SOURCE: Modified from Julie Horvath et al., (2008) "Development and application of a phylo-genomic toolkit: Resolving the evolutionary history of Madagascar's lemurs."

467

FOLLOW-UP

4 (ET ASSESSMENT) Analysis Question 2 is an opportunity to apply the EVIDENCE AND TRADE-OFFS (ET) Scoring Guide to assess students' ability to use evidence for prioritizing conservation and to identify trade-offs. Distribute copies of the ET Scoring Guide. Project a transparency of the ET Scoring Guide, and review the standards for a Level-3 response.

Hold a class discussion about students' suggested ranking for conserving the lemurs on Madagascar. Most students will rank the areas from highest priority to lowest in this order: Area 1, Area 4, Area 2, and Area 3, which follows the level from highest to lowest of the phylogenetic diversity in each area. Some students might say that the lemurs in Area 2 are more diverse than those in Area 4 because they look more spread out across that part of the tree than the lemurs that make up Area 4. If so, remind them that lemurs that are classified in a separate family are likely to be more diverse because they share a more distant common ancestor and, therefore, are more distantly related.

Next, explain that when biodiversity is conserved, the sustainability of the ecosystem is conserved. This is because biodiversity serves as the raw material on which natural selection works. If there is no biodiversity or there are very low levels of biodiversity, the populations are more likely at higher risk of reduction or extinction should their environment change. Also, groups located closer to the base or root of a tree often have a higher conservation priority because they are likely more ancient or unique lineages. Phylogenetic diversity is important to examine because it gives a broad picture of the pattern of biodiversity across lineages over time.

4 Analysis

1. Why is phylogenetic diversity important when making conservation decisions?

2. **a.** How would you prioritize the four areas suggested for conservation on Madagascar? Consider evidence from the activity to rank them, and explain your reasoning.

   b. Suppose you have enough funds to protect the area that you assigned the highest priority in your ranking. What are the trade-offs of your decision?

3. What other information would you need for making the most informed and sustainable conservation decision?

KEY VOCABULARY	
endemic	**phylogenetic diversity**
evidence	species diversity
evolutionary tree	trade-off
hotspot	tree
lineage	

468

SAMPLE RESPONSES

1. Phylogenetic diversity is important to consider because it shows the relationships of lineages. By looking at the relationships you can tell which lineages are older, more unusual, or have more or less species diversity.

2. (ET ASSESSMENT) A complete and correct Level-3 response will explain the reasoning for the rankings based on phylogenetic diversity as evidence, and explain the trade-offs.

Sample Level-3 Response

a. I would rank the following from highest to lowest: Area 1, Area 4, Area 2, Area 3. Area 1 is the highest priority because there are three genera of lemurs spread out across the tree in three families. Area 4 is the next highest because there are lemurs from two families and two genera. Area 2 ranks third because the lemurs are in two genera, but the same family. Area 3 gets the lowest priority because the lemurs are in the same family and the same genus.

b. The trade-offs of conserving Area 1, where there is the highest phylogenetic diversity are that lemurs in two genera, *Varecia* and *Lemur,* would not be conserved because they do not live in Area 1. This is important because each genus is only represented in one area. Also, in Area 1 there is only one species in the *Eulemur* and *Microcebus* genera, while in other areas at least two species of *Eulemur* and *Microcebus* are present. If either of these genera are especially important for the ecosystem, or for ecosystem services, or are rare, they can be best conserved by focusing on the areas where more of them are represented rather than by focusing on Area 1.

3. Students' answers will vary. Sample responses include knowing what other species besides lemurs live there, what ecosystem services are provided by the areas, whether any of the species have an important ecological role, and whether any lemurs are present in especially low population numbers.

CASE STUDY

Madagascar

SINCE 1953, the island of Madagascar has lost approximately half of its forest cover. The lemurs, which live primarily in forests and depend on trees for shelter and food, are severely affected by forest loss.

Deforestation in Madagascar

GEOGRAPHIC LOCATION AND ECOSYSTEMS

Madagascar is the largest of a series of islands in the Indian Ocean off the southeast coast of Africa. Madagascar became an island approximately 160 million years ago when it broke away from the African continent. Over many millions of years, and through the movement of the earth's plates, it drifted about 400 km to the southeast of Africa.

Madagascar has a variety of ecosystems. Hills and rice-growing valleys occupy a central plateau region. There are several montane forest areas ranging from an altitude of approximately 2.4 km to 2.9 km (8,000–9,000 ft). The highest mountain on Madagascar is in the northern area and rises 2,876 km (9,436 ft) above sea level. In the west are dry forests, swamps, and grassy plains, and the eastern coast and lowlands on the island are mostly wet evergreen rainforest. Along the eastern coastline is a reef that is rich with marine life. The southern areas of the island are mostly dry desert forests.

UNIQUE AND THREATENED BIODIVERSITY

Thousands of species of organisms have evolved on the island that are not present on the nearby African continent or anywhere else in the world. Some of these endemic species were living on the land that became the island when it broke away from the African continent. Others, such as the ancestors of lemurs, migrated to the island after it split away. Isolated over many generations, the thousands of species evolved into different species from those living on the continent. Madagascar's species diversity is shown in the table at left.

(Continued on next page)

Species Diversity on Madagascar		
SPECIES	TOTAL NUMBER OF SPECIES	NUMBER OF ENDEMIC SPECIES
Plants	13,000	11,600
Mammals	150	135 (51 are threatened)
Birds	310	181
Reptiles	384	367
Amphibians	230	229
Freshwater fishes	164	97
Extinct species*	45	

*Recorded since 1500

469

REVISIT THE CHALLENGE

Review the importance of phylogenetic diversity in showing an overall pattern of biodiversity across lineages. Students should be able to state that biodiversity, which can be measured at the phylogenetic, ecosystem, species, or genetic level, is an important indicator of the sustainability of an area.

(Continued from previous page)

LEMURS

Lemurs living on the island today are of various sizes and colors and are classified into five families. One of their ecological roles is dispersing the seeds from the fruits they eat, which ensures steady growth of new plants. The five lemur families and their genera are described in the table at right.

HUMAN IMPACTS

Approximately 2,000 years ago, humans made their way on boats to Madagascar. Today Madagascar is inhabited by approximately 21 million people, and the population is growing by 3% annually. The source of livelihood for more than 90% of Madagascar's residents is the resources from the forests, such as the wood from cutting down the trees. As of today most of Madagascar's forests have been cut down or burned to make space for dwellings, crops, and livestock, leaving only 15% of the island forested. Because lemurs live almost exclusively in the forests, they are threatened by the forest destruction. Other human impacts on lemur populations are hunting and collecting. From their arrival on the island until the early 1960s, when it became illegal to keep or kill lemurs, people hunted them for food. All of the largest lemur species eventually became extinct.

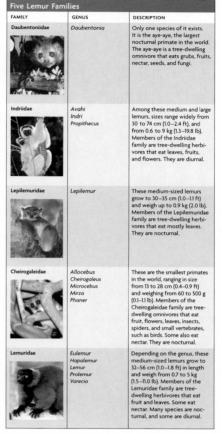

Five Lemur Families

FAMILY	GENUS	DESCRIPTION
Daubentoniidae	*Daubentonia*	Only one species of it exists. It is the aye-aye, the largest nocturnal primate in the world. The aye-aye is a tree-dwelling omnivore that eats grubs, fruits, nectar, seeds, and fungi.
Indriidae	*Avahi* *Indri* *Propithecus*	Among these medium and large lemurs, sizes range widely from 30 to 74 cm (1.0–2.4 ft), and from 0.6 to 9 kg (1.3–19.8 lb). Members of the Indriidae family are tree-dwelling herbivores that eat leaves, fruits, and flowers. They are diurnal.
Lepilemuridae	*Lepilemur*	These medium-sized lemurs grow to 30–35 cm (1.0–1.1 ft) and weigh up to 0.9 kg (2.0 lb). Members of the Lepilemuridae family are tree-dwelling herbivores that eat mostly leaves. They are nocturnal.
Cheirogaleidae	*Allocebus* *Cheirogaleus* *Microcebus* *Mirza* *Phaner*	These are the smallest primates in the world, ranging in size from 13 to 28 cm (0.4–0.9 ft) and weighing from 60 to 500 g (0.1–1.1 lb). Members of the Cheirogaleidae family are tree-dwelling omnivores that eat fruit, flowers, leaves, insects, spiders, and small vertebrates, such as birds. Some also eat nectar. They are nocturnal.
Lemuridae	*Eulemur* *Hapalemur* *Lemur* *Prolemur* *Varecia*	Depending on the genus, these medium-sized lemurs grow to 32–56 cm (1.0–1.8 ft) in length and weigh from 0.7 to 5 kg (1.5–11.0 lb). Members of the Lemuridae family are tree-dwelling herbivores that eat fruit and leaves. Some eat nectar. Many species are nocturnal, and some are diurnal.

CONSERVATION ACTIONS

In 2003, to the delight of conservationists and evolutionary biologists around the world, Madagascar tripled the area it had designated for conservation. Today 46 areas protected from human activities make up approximately 2.7% of the land on Madagascar. These areas include national parks, nature reserves to conserve ecosystems, and special reserves to conserve particular species. In some areas, ecotourism has provided valuable income to the people of Madagascar. Ecotourism is a term for travel to natural areas to view animals and plants in their habitats. In many regions this has created jobs for local people, whether in transporting, feeding, housing, or guiding tourists, or guarding the protected areas.

Sustainability Factors Related to Madagascar's Forests		
SOCIAL	ECONOMIC	ENVIRONMENTAL
Cutting down trees provides jobs and wood for building, furniture-making, and other endeavors. People work as tour guides, and in hotels and restaurants in areas where there is ecotourism.	Forests provide coffee, vanilla, cocoa, and other economic resources. Ecotourism in conserved areas provides income to people who live on the island.	Forests are destroyed to clear land for planting crops, such as sugar cane and sweet potatoes, for raising livestock, and to make space for building. Forest destruction affects species that live on the island.

SUSTAINABILITY

The table above summarizes the factors that affect the sustainability of the island of Madagascar. ■

10 What Is a Species?

INVESTIGATION • 3–4 CLASS SESSIONS

OVERVIEW

In this activity students learn about the biological species concept in defining species and how it provides information about where new species are in the process of separation from closely related species. Students then investigate the factors that lead to reproductive isolation of species.

KEY CONTENT

1. Species evolve over time. The millions of species that live on the earth today are related by descent from common ancestors.

2. Taxa are classified in a hierarchy of groups and subgroups based on genealogical relationships.

3. The broad patterns of behavior exhibited by animals have evolved by natural selection as a result of reproductive success.

4. Scientists have found that the original definition of species as groups of organisms with similar morphology does not reflect underlying evolutionary processes.

5. The biological species concept defines a species as a population of individuals that actually or can potentially interbreed in nature to produce fertile offspring.

6. Scientific explanations must adhere to criteria such as the application of appropriate evidence, consistently logical reasoning, and basis in accepted historical and current scientific knowledge.

KEY PROCESS SKILLS

1. Students communicate and defend a scientific argument.

2. Students apply evidence and reasoning to formulate a logical claim for where populations are in the process of speciation.

MATERIALS AND ADVANCE PREPARATION

For the teacher

> Scoring Guide: GROUP INTERACTION (GI)
> Scoring Guide: UNDERSTANDING CONCEPTS (UC)

For each group of four students

> set of 14 Species Pairs Cards
> set of 8 Reproductive Barrier Cards
> chart paper* (optional)
> markers* (optional)

For each student

> Student Sheet 10.1, "Supporting a Scientific Argument" (optional)
> Scoring Guide: GROUP INTERACTION (GI) (optional)
> Scoring Guide: UNDERSTANDING CONCEPTS (UC) (optional)

*Not supplied in kit

Decide in advance if you will hand out Student Sheet 10.1, "Supporting a Scientific Argument," or have students record this information in their science notebooks.

Masters for Scoring Guides are in Teacher Resource IV: Assessment.

TEACHING SUMMARY

Getting Started

- Students write their understanding of the concept of a species.

Doing the Activity

- Review the claim, evidence, and reasoning approach of the activity and, with the class, apply it to examples in the Student Book.

- Students make claims based on evidence and reasoning about where in the process of separation species are from one another.

- (GI ASSESSMENT) Students sort pairs of species based on the barriers to reproduction that isolate them and prevent gene flow.

- (LITERACY) Students write definitions in their own words for the types of isolation, and conduct an Informal Meeting of the Minds to discuss their definitions.

Follow-up

- (UC ASSESSMENT) Discuss the biological species concept as providing a snapshot of where two populations are in the process of separation.

- The class discusses factors that might lead to speciation.

GETTING STARTED

1 ◆ Begin the activity by writing the following three questions on the board.

a. What is a species?

b. Some examples of species are:

_____.

c. How do biologists decide if two populations are of the same or different species?

Tell students to write the questions and their answers in their science notebooks or, if you would like to collect and read their answers, on an index card or piece of paper. Students' answers will provide you with formative assessments for you to determine what students already know and to adjust your instruction if necessary. For example, if most students were introduced to taxonomy in middle school and know that a species is the most fundamental unit of classification, you need not emphasize this concept.

Some students are likely to say a species is a group of organisms that share some common characteristics. Their examples are likely to vary widely, and some may be at a higher level of classification than the species level. Oak trees, for example, are members of a genus that includes several hundred species. Everyday examples of two species are the domestic dog and domestic cat. Others that students might mention are humans and chimpanzees. Students are likely to say that biologists decide whether organisms are in the same or different species based on their appearance. However, some may have been introduced to the idea that members of the same species are able to mate and produce fertile offspring, possibly citing the example of the mating of horses and donkeys to produce sterile mules. Stress that early classification systems focused on the observable characteristics of organisms, but modern systems do not.

10 What Is a Species?

1 THINK ABOUT THE many different types of organisms you see in a typical day. In addition to humans, you might see mammals such as dogs and cats; birds such as robins and pigeons; insects such as ants and flies; and plants ranging from dandelions to oak trees. On a farm or at the zoo or aquarium, you would see even more examples.

The original idea of different types, or species, of organisms was based on the observable differences in their appearances. A species was defined as a group of organisms with similar physical characteristics. Beginning in the late 1700s, species became the basic unit of classification.

As scientists learned more about evolution and the causes of differences among groups of organisms, their ideas about species changed. Scientists now know that some populations of organisms that appear identical are in fact different species, and others that appear different are the same species. The original species concept was replaced by concepts that focus on evolutionary relationships.

There are now several alternative definitions for species. In this activity, you will explore the **biological species concept.** This method of defining a species is based on whether the organisms actually or can potentially breed with each other to produce fertile offspring. If they can, they are of the same species. This approach gives evolutionary biologists and conservationists a snapshot of where species are in the process of separation from one another. The classification of populations into the same or separate biological species may affect their conservation status. For example, if two populations are determined to be in separate species, it is more likely that both will be considered for protection.

The pickerel frog (a) and moor frog (b) are two species of frogs in the Rana genus.

472

Other species concepts are applied in other fields of biology. For example, evolutionary biologists use a phylogenetic species concept, which defines a species as a distinct lineage and reflects the evolutionary relationships among taxa.

Challenge

▶ How do new species separate from existing species?

MATERIALS

FOR EACH GROUP OF FOUR STUDENTS
set of 14 Species Pair Cards
set of eight Reproductive Barrier Cards

BACKGROUND INFORMATION

The Biological Species Concept

ACCORDING TO THE biological species concept, a **biological species** is all of the populations of individuals that actually or can potentially breed with each other in nature to produce fertile offspring. The result of this interbreeding is movement of genes, called **gene flow,** throughout the species. Members of the same species share a common group of genes—a **gene pool**—and a common evolutionary history. Should members of different populations mate but produce no or no fertile offspring or very rarely breed with each other even when present in the same location, they are considered different biological species.

OTHER WAYS TO CATEGORIZE SPECIES

The biological species concept is straightforward, but it turns out that there are a number of areas where it is not helpful. For example, many species, such as bacterial species, do not reproduce

sexually. The concept also does not fit many plant species that cross-breed under natural or artificial conditions. Also, the concept cannot be applied to fossil organisms because their breeding cannot be observed.

Nevertheless, the biological species concept gives scientists a snapshot of the evolution of new species in many groups of plants and animals. As you review the examples on the following pages, keep in mind that the populations that share a common gene pool are most likely in the early stages of separation from one another. This is likely to be the case if individuals in the two populations meet the following two conditions:

· They usually breed together if they meet in the wild.

· Their breeding produces offspring able to produce their own offspring. ■

DOING THE ACTIVITY

2 Remind students that they applied the claim, evidence, and reasoning approach to scientific argumentation in Activity 5, "Using Fossil Evidence to Investigate Whale Evolution." Review this approach to scientific discussion and argumentation. Explain to students that they will take this approach in determining where in the process of separation species are from one another (early, mid, or late). To do this, they must first have a working concept of what a species is.

Stress that the biological species concept differs from the original concept for defining species, and it stresses the importance of successful reproduction in the wild and the sharing of a common set of genes, or gene pool.

3 If you would like students to enter their work on optional Student Sheet 10.1, "Supporting a Scientific Argument," distribute it now.

4 Work through as many examples as necessary with the class until you think students are ready to work on them more independently. As you work together, be sure students understand the following about the parts of scientific argument:

The claim portion is a statement about the placement of species as early, mid, or late in the process of separation as follows:

- Early means they are either still one species, or that they have just begun separation.

- Mid means they are separating.

- Late means they are at the end of separation, and they have most likely split into two species.

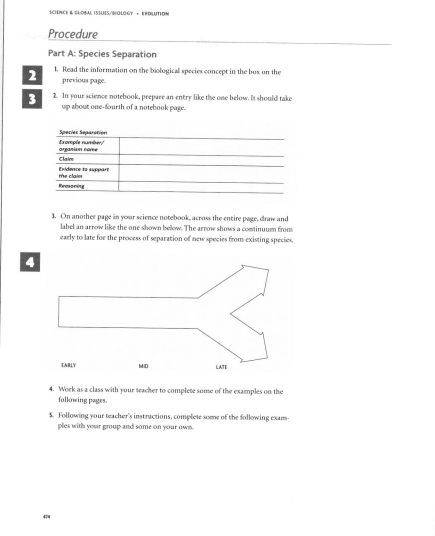

Note that this is a continuum, and students may wish to use designations such as early–mid or mid–late if the evidence is incomplete or inconclusive. The evidence portion of argumentation for these examples refers to what happens with mating and offspring. In the reasoning setup, students should include a statement about how the mating and offspring results affect the exchange of genes and sharing of a common gene pool, which indicates where in separation the species are likely to be. This reasoning relies on the biological species concept and ties the evidence back to the claim.

5 Next, instruct students to work in groups to complete enough examples to give them adequate practice applying the claim, evidence, and reasoning approach to species separation. Circulate around the room, and determine whether you need to review students' ideas before they complete the remaining assigned examples independently. Sample answers follow.

Example 1: Red and Purple Sea Urchins

Claim: Late

Evidence: The eggs can be fertilized in the lab, but the embryos do not survive.

Reasoning: Even though the eggs can be artificially fertilized, the offspring do not survive. Therefore, they cannot exchange genes and share a common gene pool, and they have most likely split.

Example 2: Eastern and Great Plains Narrowmouth Frogs

Claim: Mid

Evidence: Even though they might encounter each other, the two frogs usually do not choose to mate with their own kind based on mating call.

Reasoning: Since they usually do not breed, they are not exchanging genes and sharing a common gene pool, and are further along in separation as a result.

Example 3: Northern and California Spotted Owls

Claim: Early–mid

Evidence: The owls' ranges overlap, and they can breed to produce fertile offspring, but rarely do so.

Reasoning: Because they can breed and produce fertile offspring, they can exchange genes and share a common gene pool, even if rarely. This means they must be early to midway in the separation process.

---

5 6. In your science notebook, record each of the following:

- The example number and the name of the organisms
- Your claim: a statement about what stage of separation the species are in
- Place the names of the organisms at the appropriate stage of separation (early, mid, late) along the arrow you drew in Step 3.
- Your evidence: the information available about the mechanism of the separation between species
- Your reasoning: an explanation of the mechanism of separation that supports your claim. Refer to the biological species concept to explain each species' stage in the separation process.

7. Repeat Step 6 for all of your assigned examples.

The Separation of Species

EXAMPLE 1

Red and Purple Sea Urchins

Red and purple sea urchins live in shallow ocean waters along the eastern Pacific coast from Alaska to Mexico. The sperm of one of these organisms fertilizes the eggs of the other only in the laboratory, where scientists mix the eggs with much higher concentrations of sperm than are likely in the wild. The embryos produced, however, do not survive beyond the very early stages of development. ■

Red sea urchins

Purple sea urchins

475

Example 4: Horses and Donkeys

Claim: Late

Evidence: They can breed but do not produce fertile offspring. Sometimes female mules breed with horses or donkeys and do produce live offspring.

Reasoning: If they breed, there are offspring, but the offspring are always infertile. Therefore, they cannot exchange genes and share a common gene pool and have most likely split.

Example 5: Dogs and Wolves

Claim: Early

Evidence: Dogs and wolves do mate and produce fertile offspring.

Reasoning: If dogs and wolves can mate to produce fertile offspring, they can exchange genes and share a common gene pool, which means they are one species or early in separation.

Example 6: Midas Cichlid and Arrow Cichlid Fish

Claim: Late

Evidence: The cichlids do not mate in the wild, and their offspring by selective breeding do not live.

Reasoning: If they do not mate in the wild and the offspring of controlled breeding do not live, they have most likely split, and there is no exchange of genes or common gene pool.

Example 7: Blue and Red Cichlid Fish

Claim: Early–mid

Evidence: The fish do not breed in nature, but can be bred in a lab to produce fertile offspring.

Reasoning: The fish can breed to produce fertile offspring. And, they are very similar to each other. This means they share a common gene pool, and they are likely to be one species or early in the separation process.

Example 8: Green Lacewings

Claim: Early–mid

Evidence: If mated in a lab, the lacewings produce fertile offspring. They look identical, but small genetic changes resulting in a different mating signals make them unlikely to breed in the wild.

Reasoning: If the lacewings are mated, they exchange genes and share a common gene pool. But they also have a different mating signal, making them likely to be in a relatively early stage of separation.

Example 9: Copper-resistant and Copper-tolerant Yellow Monkey Flowers

Claim: Early–mid

Evidence: When scientists cross the plants many die early, but some live.

Reasoning: If some of the plants live, those few can exchange genes and share a common gene pool, which means they are not as separated as they would be if they couldn't.

Example 10: Orchids

Claim: Late

Evidence: The orchids flower on different days and cannot be bred to produce hybrids.

Reasoning: If the orchids cannot reproduce fertile offspring in nature or in the lab they cannot exchange genes or share a common gene pool, which means they have most likely split.

A sample response arrow is shown below.

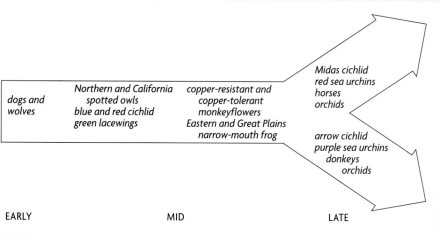

EXAMPLE 2

Eastern and Great Plains Narrowmouth Frogs

The eastern narrowmouth frog's range extends along the east coast of the United States from the Carolinas to Florida and west into parts of Oklahoma and Texas, where it lives in moist areas. The Great Plains narrowmouth frog's range is from Baja California in Mexico to eastern Texas, eastern Oklahoma, and northern Missouri, where it lives in drier regions. These two types of frogs occasionally breed naturally in the areas where they overlap, but the fertility of their offspring is not known. Most of the time the frogs select mates of their own type, perhaps because of differences in their mating calls. The two groups of frogs are distinguished by their colors. ■

*Great Plains narrow mouth frog (top),
Eastern narrow mouth frog (bottom)*

EXAMPLE 3

Northern and California Spotted Owls

Northern spotted owls range from northwestern California to western Oregon, Washington, and Canada. California spotted owls are found in the Sierra Nevada from northern to southern California. The two owl populations overlap in parts of northern California. Field observations and genetic evidence suggest that when birds of each type come into contact they have bred and produced fertile offspring. These offspring have a hybrid (mixed) genetic makeup. However, this cross-breeding is rare. Northern and California spotted owls show some differences in appearance and genetics. ■

EXAMPLE 4

Horses and Donkeys

A female horse and a male donkey can mate to produce a mule. Horses have 64 chromosomes, while donkeys have 62. The mule is born with 63 chromosomes that cannot divide evenly, and this makes mules sterile. Although there are some cases of female mules breeding successfully with male horses or donkeys to produce live but infertile offspring, there are no known cases of male mules breeding successfully with female mules, donkeys, or horses. ■

The mule is the sterile offspring of a horse and a donkey.

EXAMPLE 5

Dogs and Wolves

There is great variety among domesticated dogs, which were bred from wolves approximately 10,000 years ago. Most dogs can breed with one another and have puppies that show a mix of the traits of the parent dogs. For example, a breeder of designer dogs can mate a boxer and a poodle to produce a boxerdoodle. Dogs from different breeds often mate to produce a mixed breed dog, commonly called a mutt. Dogs can also breed with wolves to produce fertile offspring. These mixed offspring can reproduce with similar dogs, other dog breeds, or wolves. Genetic analysis reveals very little difference between dogs and wolves. Wolves are much more similar genetically to dogs than to coyotes. ■

EXAMPLE 6

Midas Cichlid and Arrow Cichlid Fish

Scientists are studying two types of cichlid fish in a volcanic lake in Nicaragua. The Midas cichlid is a bottom-feeder, has a wide body, and eats algae. The arrow cichlid has a slender body for swimming and eats winged insects. The two types of fish select mates of their own kind, and fail to reproduce live offspring when people try to breed them. ∎

Arrow cichlid (top),
Midas cichlid (bottom)

EXAMPLE 7

Blue and Red Cichlid Fish

Two very similar types of cichlid fish live in Lake Victoria in Africa. One is blue, and the other is red. Females of these two types prefer mates of the same color, and in nature these two types of fish do not breed. However, in a lab, when they are put in lighting conditions where they cannot see the color of the other fish, they will freely mate with fish of the other color. In these lab conditions, the females would now mate with either color male, and produce fully fertile offspring. ∎

EXAMPLE 8

Green Lacewings

Two populations of lacewings that look identical and live in the same locations do not mate in the wild because they have different mating signals. Female lacewings exhibit a strong preference in the wild for males with a similar mating signal. Genetic analysis suggests that the changes in mating signal result from changes in just a small number of genes, but that these changes prevent the mating of males and females with different mating signals. When mated in the laboratory, offspring of these two types of lacewings are fertile. ■

EXAMPLE 9

Copper-resistant and Copper-tolerant Yellow Monkey Flower

Copper is toxic to most plants. However, scientists have observed a few plants that have developed a tolerance for copper. One of those is the yellow monkey flower. When scientists crossed copper-tolerant plants with plants sensitive to copper, many of the hybrid plants did not survive. In early growth stages, their leaves turned yellow and they died soon after. ■

EXAMPLE 10

Orchids

Three populations of orchids each flower at different times of the year for just a single day. Therefore, even though these orchids grow in the same tropical forest area, there is no chance that members of one population will fertilize the other in the wild. ■

6 (GI ASSESSMENT) Distribute a set of 14 Species Pair Cards to each group of four students. Inform students that this activity asks them to demonstrate their ability to work together in their groups to complete the Procedure. If necessary, distribute copies of the GROUP INTERACTION (GI) Scoring Guide. Review the guidelines for the GI Scoring Guide.

7 Tell students to work through Procedure Steps 9–11. Groups should work together to organize the cards and record the groupings they have formed. Most importantly, they should note the common barrier to reproduction by which they formed each of the groupings of species. If students are having problems, suggest that they select only one criterion to begin their sorting, but allow them to work as independently as possible.

8 Hold a brief class discussion about how groups classified the barriers to reproduction, and named their groupings. Allow members of each group to briefly show their classifications and describe the choices they made. You might also provide chart paper and markers for students to display their systems. Highlight the similarities and differences between the systems that the different groups used by listing them on the board or overhead.

Do not hand out the sets of Reproductive Barrier Cards, which represent the groupings scientists put together, to each team until Procedure Step 13. Explain that scientists look for patterns in their observations and make the kinds of observations students made to group the barriers to reproduction that are described on the cards.

Part B: The Formation of New Species

Evolutionary biologists focus on the question of how new species and other taxa evolve. As you have learned, two populations that have different physical characteristics might still belong to the same species if they can interbreed to produce fertile offspring and do so in nature. This interbreeding allows gene flow, with the two populations sharing a common gene pool.

How do new species evolve? According to the biological species concept, two populations must be reproductively isolated. Reproductive isolation is caused by several kinds of barriers. Once they become reproductively isolated, the two populations will no longer share a common gene pool. Each population will change independently of the other as a result of selection by the different environments. Eventually the two populations could evolve into two separate species.

6 8. With your group, spread the Species Pair Cards out on a table.

7 9. Examine the information on each card carefully, noting the barriers to reproduction between the two species described on the card.

10. Sort the cards into groups based on the barriers to reproduction. Work with your group to agree on a name that describes each kind of barrier. While doing so,

   • listen to and consider the explanations of your group members.

   • if you disagree, explain how and why you disagree.

11. In your science notebook, write the title: Our Groupings. Beneath this title, list the groups that you created and the names you picked to describe each group. Be sure to record which species pairs belong to each group.

8 12. Following your teacher's instructions, your team will present your groupings to the class. As you look at other students' groupings, observe the similarities and differences between their systems and yours. Discuss your observations with your team members.

13. Your group will receive eight Reproductive Barrier Cards from your teacher. Each card represents a barrier that leads to reproductive isolation of related species. Based on the information on the Reproductive Barrier Cards place each Species Pair Card under a Reproductive Barrier Card.

14. Record this new set of groupings in your science notebook under the title Scientific Groupings.

9 15. List the isolating mechanisms you examined in this activity. Write a definition for each mechanism in your own words.

10 16. List the two types of reproductive isolation in this section, and describe them in your own words.

SUGGESTED ANSWERS

Habitat isolation: Garter snakes, insects

Behavioral isolation: Meadowlarks, fireflies, blue and red cichlids

Geographic isolation: Squirrels

Temporal isolation: Lacewings, orchids

Mechanical isolation: Flowering plants, damselflies

Gametic isolation: Purple and white sea urchins

Hybrid sterility: Lions and tigers, horses and donkeys

Reduced hybrid viability: Frogs

9 Suggested definitions for the types of isolation follow.

Behavioral isolation: Mating songs or signals are too different for potential mates to recognize, or the animals have different courtship rituals.

Habitat isolation: Two species live in the same area but in slightly different habitats, such as in or on different parts of the same plant.

Temporal isolation: The two species breed at different times of the year.

Mechanical isolation: The two species do not have the anatomical structures necessary for mating.

Gametic isolation: Sperm and eggs cannot interact.

10 (LITERACY) Sample definitions for the two types of reproductive isolation follow.

Hybrid sterility: Members of species can mate, but their offspring are sterile.

Reduced hybrid viability: Two species can mate, but the offspring do not live long enough to reproduce their own offspring.

When students have completed Procedure Step 15, conduct an Informal Meeting of the Minds. Direct students to find a partner from another group and to discuss their definitions for the types of barriers, citing an example or two for each. Circulate around the room as students talk. Ask pairs to share their definitions with the class. You may wish to have them learn the scientific names for the different barriers, but it is more important that they can describe them, how they work, and give an example or two. If you wish, assign this task as homework. Begin the next class period with a review of the information.

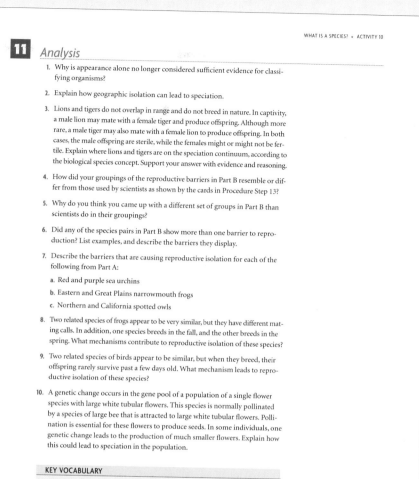

11 *Analysis*

1. Why is appearance alone no longer considered sufficient evidence for classifying organisms?

2. Explain how geographic isolation can lead to speciation.

3. Lions and tigers do not overlap in range and do not breed in nature. In captivity, a male lion may mate with a female tiger and produce offspring. Although more rare, a male tiger may also mate with a female lion to produce offspring. In both cases, the male offspring are sterile, while the females might or might not be fertile. Explain where lions and tigers are on the speciation continuum, according to the biological species concept. Support your answer with evidence and reasoning.

4. How did your groupings of the reproductive barriers in Part B resemble or differ from those used by scientists as shown by the cards in Procedure Step 13?

5. Why do you think you came up with a different set of groups in Part B than scientists do in their groupings?

6. Did any of the species pairs in Part B show more than one barrier to reproduction? List examples, and describe the barriers they display.

7. Describe the barriers that are causing reproductive isolation for each of the following from Part A:

   a. Red and purple sea urchins

   b. Eastern and Great Plains narrowmouth frogs

   c. Northern and California spotted owls

8. Two related species of frogs appear to be very similar, but they have different mating calls. In addition, one species breeds in the fall, and the other breeds in the spring. What mechanisms contribute to reproductive isolation of these species?

9. Two related species of birds appear to be similar, but when they breed, their offspring rarely survive past a few days old. What mechanism leads to reproductive isolation of these species?

10. A genetic change occurs in the gene pool of a population of a single flower species with large white tubular flowers. This species is normally pollinated by a species of large bee that is attracted to large white tubular flowers. Pollination is essential for these flowers to produce seeds. In some individuals, one genetic change leads to the production of much smaller flowers. Explain how this could lead to speciation in the population.

KEY VOCABULARY

biological species	**gene flow**
biological species concept	**gene pool**
evidence	species

481

FOLLOW-UP

11 (UC ASSESSMENT) Analysis Questions 2 and 3 are an opportunity to apply the UNDERSTANDING CONCEPTS (UC) Scoring Guide to assess students' understanding of geographic isolation and speciation. Review the UC Scoring Guide, and tell the class your expectations for satisfactory work.

As you discuss the activity and the answers to the Analysis Questions, emphasize to students that for some of the examples there is a fair amount of grey area for scientists who are trying to determine where in speciation the populations are. This illustrates why the biological species concept is considered just a snapshot of what is going on with speciation. Stress the growing emphasis in the field of classification on the importance of the evolutionary relationships among taxa, using the phylogenetic species concept. Discuss also the importance in science of applying evidence and logical reasoning in making claims from which to build arguments and explanations. Discuss some of the examples. Ask students if they felt the information they were given in this activity provided the evidence to make a solid claim. Note that in some cases, evidence about breeding success was not provided because it is not available. Missing evidence affects the certainty of a claim. Emphasize the importance of logical reasoning, which requires an understanding of the appropriate concept(s), in this case the biological species concept, and the development of reasonable connections and inferences between the evidence and the concept.

In regard to species conservation introduce the importance of where in the process of separation from one another two populations are. In the United States the Endangered Species Act (ESA) protects species and subspecies, and in the case of vertebrates, it may also protect "distinct population segments" that are considered significant in relation to the entire species. Thus, the species or subspecies designation of a population may determine whether it gets ESA protection if the animal is threatened.

Ask students to volunteer to list the factors that lead to speciation. They should be able to mention all of the types that were given on the Reproductive Barrier Cards in Part B. Write those on the board. Ask students what all of these types of barriers have in common. Discuss the idea that all of these are barriers that keep populations apart and no longer able to breed. This means they can no longer exchange genes with one another. As this activity demonstrates, there are more barriers than just geographic isolation that may keep populations from reproducing. Some barriers occur even if the two populations live in the same area. For example, two populations that live in the same area might have different mating seasons or mating calls. Also, geographic isolation alone is not always enough to lead to speciation. Some populations might still mate and produce live offspring if they are brought together after being geographically isolated.

FOLLOW-UP

SAMPLE RESPONSES

1. Scientists concluded from evolutionary evidence that some species that look identical are different species and others that appear different are the same species.

2. (UC ASSESSMENT) A complete and correct response will include a description of the types of geographic features that can stop gene flow, prevent the sharing of a gene pool, and lead to the separation of species.

Sample Level-3 Response

Two populations can get separated by physical features on earth such as the formation of mountains, canyons, rivers, or glaciers. Or a population moves far away from the original population. This could stop gene flow between the populations, prevent them from sharing a common gene pool, and lead to speciation.

3. (UC ASSESSMENT) A complete and correct response will explain the placement of lions and tigers on the speciation continuum, and cite evidence and reasoning from the biological species concept to support the answer.

Sample Level-3 Response

Lions and tigers are late in the speciation process, but not completely separate. The evidence for this is that they do not produce fertile male offspring even when mated in captivity, while some female offspring are fertile. According to the biological species concept, the offspring of a biological species are fertile, so lions and tigers, with the exception of some female offspring, do not meet this part of the definition of a biological species.

4. Students' answers will vary, but should be based on students' recognition of differences between their systems and the system illustrated on the Reproductive Barrier Cards. For example, some students may have classified as behavioral isolation the two species of damselflies as species that cannot mate because the males cannot hold onto the females. These students may have interpreted the holding on as a behavior that may be part of a courtship ritual of some type rather than as a result of mechanical isolation.

5. Students may suggest they do not have as many examples as scientists do, or that they lumped or split categories differently than scientists.

6. Lions and tigers show both geographic isolation and hybrid sterility.

7. a. Reduced hybrid viability

   b. Behavioral isolation

   c. Geographic isolation

8. Behavioral (the different mating calls) and temporal (mating at different times)

9. Reduced hybrid viability

10. The change could lead to the need for different pollinators because of mechanical isolation. If the pollinator of one group cannot pollinate the other group (and vice versa) due to differences in the size of the flowers, these two groups of organisms will become reproductively isolated, even though they grow in the same area.

REVISIT THE CHALLENGE

Review these key points about species separation and the biological species concept:

- To be of the same species two populations must be able to breed and choose to breed when they come in contact. If they do not breed successfully, there cannot be a flow of genes from one population to the other and the populations will not share a gene pool. This means they are reproductively isolated, and therefore, likely to be later in separation from one another.

- All species are continually in the process of separation from one another. For some species the biological species concept determines a snapshot of where on the continuum of separation they are.

- When female offspring of hybrids between two populations are fertile but males are not (as in the case of mules), the offspring are not considered to be fully fertile, and the horses and donkeys are considered to be late in separation. Again, this is because gene flow cannot continue freely between the horse and donkey populations. In this case, the mules are essentially a dead end, and cannot continue a lineage of offspring.

- There are a variety of factors that lead to speciation.

11 Natural Selection

MODELING • 1–2 CLASS SESSIONS

OVERVIEW

Students work with a computer simulation to model how new species evolve as a result of natural selection when populations encounter new environments, whether as a result of environmental change or migration. They also investigate the process of extinction.

KEY CONTENT

1. Adaptive radiation is the relatively rapid evolution from a common ancestor of multiple species that occupy newly available environments.

2. Natural selection and reproductive isolation lead to speciation in new environments.

3. For natural selection to occur in a population there must be heritable variation among individuals, competition for resources needed for survival, and differential survival and reproduction.

4. Extinction occurs when the environment changes. Less diverse populations have fewer variations that might enhance survival in new environments and are at greater risk of extinction.

MATERIALS AND ADVANCE PREPARATION

For the teacher
Transparency 4.1, "Principles of Natural Selection"

For each pair of students
computer with Internet access*

For each student
Student Sheet 11.1, "Natural Selection"
(available online only: see note top right)
Student Sheet 3.1, "Ideas about Evolution" from
Activity 3

Not supplied in kit

Note: *Student Sheet 11.1, "Natural Selection," is found only on* the Science and Global Issues *website* (sepuplhs.org/sgi). *Sample student answers are also available on the website. Both are located in the teacher's section. Arrange for computers with Internet access for the day(s) students do this activity. Go to the* Science and Global Issues *page of the SEPUP website to access the simulation. You may want to bookmark this site for students. Make sure the browsers and supporting software are current and can properly run the simulation.*

TEACHING SUMMARY

Getting Started

- Review natural selection.

Doing the Activity

- Students investigate the natural selection of a population that colonizes new environments on an island.

- Students revisit the statements on Student Sheet 3.1, "Ideas about Evolution."

Follow-up

- The class discusses how the populations evolved by natural selection.

GETTING STARTED

1 Project Transparency 4.1, "Principles of Natural Selection." Review with students that the natural selection of a population requires both heritable variation among the individuals and competition between individuals for the environmental resources needed for survival. This leads to differential survival and reproduction and, over many generations, to an accumulation of changes in the traits of a population. Review with students that heritable traits are those that are determined at least in part by genes. Some heritable traits, such as coat color in mice, are determined by just one or a few genes. Other traits, such as body size, are determined by a number of genes as well as environmental factors, such as availability of food. Nonheritable traits are those that cannot be inherited, such as larger muscles developed through weightlifting, or the absence of a limb due to an accident.

11 Natural Selection

1 EVERY ENVIRONMENT ON earth changes. These changes might be gradual or fairly sudden results of geologic events, changes in climate, or human activities. When environmental changes occur, natural selection of populations living in the affected areas is likely to follow. Organisms also encounter new environments when they migrate. Both environmental changes and newly available environments can lead to the evolution of new species.

In a new environment a species splits into two lineages, and speciation continues in repeated cycles. Sometimes the evolutionary change is relatively rapid, and other times it is slower. An **adaptive radiation** is the relatively rapid evolution from a common ancestor of multiple species that occupy newly available environments. Adaptive radiation contributes to the biodiversity of an area as new species evolve over relatively short periods of time.

The evolution of honeycreepers on the Hawaiian Islands is a striking example of adaptive radiation. It occurred over 200,000–300,000 years after the arrival of the first ancestors.

482

DOING THE ACTIVITY

2 All directions for the simulation are on Student Sheet 11.1, "Natural Selection." Circulate around the room, and monitor students as they work through the computer simulation.

FOLLOW-UP

3 ◆ Sample student responses to Procedure Step 2 are shown on the sample Student Sheet 3.1, "Ideas about Evolution," at the end of this activity. Discuss with students whether and how their ideas have changed.

4 Discuss the changes that occurred in the populations of birds in the various areas of the island. Emphasize that both random and nonrandom events influence the natural selection of populations. The random events are the specific mutations and recombinations that arise in a population and lead to genetic variation. The nonrandom events are the selection of favorable traits in a given environment. While there are random elements, the overall process of evolution by natural selection is nonrandom because of the specific selection of variations that result in greater fitness in a given environment. If genetic variation in the population is low, the population is at greater risk of extinction because there is less chance that some will have characteristics that will allow them to survive and reproduce if there is a change in the environment.

Challenge

▶ How does natural selection lead to speciation?

MATERIALS

FOR EACH PAIR OF STUDENTS
computer with Internet access

FOR EACH STUDENT
Student Sheet 11.1, "Natural Selection"
Student Sheet 3.1, "Ideas about Evolution," from Activity 3

Procedure

2 1. Visit the *Science and Global Issues* page of the SEPUP website at *sepuplhs.org/sgi*. With your partner, go to "Natural Selection," and follow the simulation.

3 2. Go back to the statements on Student Sheet 3.1, "Ideas about Evolution." Record information from this activity to support whether any of the statements are correct or incorrect.

4 ### Analysis

1. A few of the individuals in the population that first inhabited each area on the island started out with variations in beak shape and size, body size, color, and breeding season. What biological processes caused some individuals to have these variations?

2. Describe the three conditions that are required for natural selection to take place in a population.

3. **a.** What conditions can lead to extinction?
   b. How does extinction lead to the evolution of new taxa?

4. Explain in evolutionary terms why a high level of biodiversity increases the likelihood that a species or ecosystem would be sustainable.

KEY VOCABULARY	
adaptive radiation	mutation
evolution	natural selection
extinct	species
extinction	taxa

483

SAMPLE RESPONSES

1. The variations resulted from mutation or recombination.

2. The conditions that are required for natural selection are heritable variation in individuals, competition for resources needed for survival, and differential survival and reproduction.

3. a. Some of the conditions that can lead to extinction include effects of human activities, natural disasters, such natural processes as erosion, and diseases.

   b. Extinction of a population opens up new environments for other species to migrate into. In the new environment, some individuals might have traits that increase their fitness, and natural selection will lead to speciation.

4. Greater biodiversity increases the likelihood that a species or ecosystem is sustainable because in a new or changed environment, there are more likely to be variants that are fit for that environment and that can pass on the fit trait or traits to the next generation.

REVISIT THE CHALLENGE

Students should understand that natural selection acts on favorable heritable variations that exist among the individuals in a population for a given environment. Speciation results over long periods of time after a population colonizes a new environment, and natural selection and reproductive isolation take place. Adaptive radiation is the relatively rapid evolution from a common ancestor of multiple species that occupy newly available environments. Extinction is likely to occur if there is no genetic variation present in the individuals in a population for selection to act on.

Ideas about Evolution

Statement 1: *Evolution is a climb up a ladder of progress with taxa always getting bigger and better.*

Before doing any activity, I think *the statement is correct:* Yes ☐ No ☐ *because* _____

Activity Number	After doing these activities, I think	
	Statement is correct:	**Evidence and reasoning:**
5 and 6	Yes ☐ No ☒	*Fish, whales, and tetrapods did not get bigger and better; they changed as features were selected for in the environment.*
11	Yes ☐ No ☒	*The birds changed but they did not get bigger or better. For example, their beak shape may have changed. Also, each population of birds had individuals with various forms of the traits; some were well suited to the environment and others were not.*
	Yes ☐ No ☐	

Statement 2: *The theory of evolution by natural selection is supported by a large body of scientific evidence.*

Before doing any activity, I think *the statement is correct:* Yes ☐ No ☐ *because* _____

Activity Number	After doing these activities, I think	
	Statement is correct:	**Evidence and reasoning:**
6	Yes ☒ No ☐	*The fossil record contains a lot of information about evolutionary changes over geologic time, such as the evolution of whales and tetrapods.*
7	Yes ☒ No ☐	*Fossil and character data from living taxa, and molecular data are used to construct evolutionary trees to determine the branching order on trees and show common ancestry.*
7	Yes ☒ No ☐	*Physical evidence supports the natural selection and common ancestry of vertebrates.*

Ideas about Evolution (continued)

Statement 3: Natural selection is not a random process.

Before doing any activity, I think the statement is correct: Yes ☐ No ☐ because _____

Activity Number	After doing these activities, I think	
	Statement is correct:	Evidence and reasoning:
11	Yes ☒ No ☐	The selection of certain traits of the birds was not random. It was specific to the traits that already existed in the birds and increased their probability of survival in the environment.
	Yes ☐ No ☐	
	Yes ☐ No ☐	

Statement 4: Evolution is a process by which taxa choose to adapt to their environment.

Before doing any activity, I think the statement is correct: Yes ☐ No ☐ because _____

Activity Number	After doing these activities, I think	
	Statement is correct:	Evidence and reasoning:
5 and 6	Yes ☐ No ☒	Whales and tetrapods did not choose to adapt. Features that allowed for increased survival and reproduction were selected for and passed on.
11	Yes ☐ No ☒	Natural selection works on the genetic variation that exists in a population. Some individuals have the variation that increases the probability of survival, and some do not. The traits are inherited or due to mutations that the organism does not choose or try to get.
	Yes ☐ No ☐	

Ideas about Evolution (continued)

Statement 5: *Evidence suggests that humans and apes share an evolutionary ancestry.*

Before doing any activity, I think *the statement is correct:* Yes ☐ No ☒ *because* _____

Activity Number	After doing these activities, I think		
	Statement is correct:	Evidence and reasoning:	
8	Yes ☒ No ☐	DNA and protein evidence suggests that humans and chimpanzees share a more recent common ancestor than either does with gorillas. All of these lineages share a common ancestor.	
8	Yes ☒ No ☐	Physical evidence (cranium data) suggests an evolutionary ancestry.	
	Yes ☐ No ☐		

12 The Genetic Basis of Adaptation

MODELING • 1–2 CLASS SESSIONS

OVERVIEW

Students work with a model to investigate the changes in gene frequency in a population of mice after an environmental change occurs. They record data for both the genotypes and the phenotypes of the mouse population over several generations. They relate the changes to the effects of natural selection on gene frequencies in the mouse population.

KEY CONTENT

1. Natural selection acts on existing genetic variability in a population.

2. Genetic variation occurs naturally in a population due to mutation and recombination of genetic material.

3. Genes store genetic information that interacts with environmental factors to determine the traits, or phenotypes, of organisms.

4. Environmental changes may lead to natural selection of traits that were previously rare, but enhance fitness in the new environment.

5. Over many generations the gene for a selected trait becomes increasingly common in the population.

KEY PROCESS SKILLS

1. Students graph and analyze data.

MATERIALS AND ADVANCE PREPARATION

For the teacher

Transparency 12.1, "Mice in a Light Granite Environment"
Transparency 12.2, "Mice in a Dark Lava Bed Environment"

For each group of four students

8-sided number cube
9-oz plastic cup*
8   D cards
8   d cards

For each pair of students

colored pencils*

For each student

Student Sheet 12.1, "Changes in the Gene Pool of a Mouse Population"
Student Sheet 3.1, "Ideas about Evolution," from Activity 3
graph paper*

Not supplied in kit

Distribute to each group one cup containing a pool of 8 D cards and 8 d cards to use as needed throughout the model.

TEACHING SUMMARY

Getting Started

• Discuss the links between mouse coat color, the environment, and survival of the mice.

Doing the Activity

• Introduce the inheritance of coat color in rock pocket mice.

• Students model the microevolution of coat color in the mouse population.

• ✓ Students graph the alleles for the mouse generations they modeled.

• ✓ Students revisit the statements on Student Sheet 3.1, "Ideas about Evolution."

Follow-up

• The class pools and discusses the results.

BACKGROUND INFORMATION

Rock Pocket Mice

The model in this activity is based on the rock pocket mice that live in the deserts of the southwestern United States. The gene responsible for light and dark coat color in the rock pocket mouse is called Mc1r, the melanocortin-1 gene. Researchers at the University of Arizona found that this gene follows a simple dominant–recessive pattern of inheritance. Light-colored mice have two copies of the recessive allele for the light coat color, and dark-colored mice have either one or two copies of the dominant allele for the dark trait. Most rock pocket mice are light colored and live in a dry desert environment. However, several dark populations are found in the basalt lava beds in Arizona, which formed 1.7 million years ago. Due to genetic variation, some individuals in the dark populations are light-colored, and some individuals in the light populations are dark-colored.

For information about rock pocket mouse evolution on the lava beds, see the link on the *Science and Global Issues* page of the SEPUP website *(sepuplhs.org/sgi)*.

Genetics

Upper- and lower-case letters are commonly used to represent the dominant and recessive alleles for a trait determined by one gene. For example, an upper-case $\underline{D}$ would represent the dominant dark coat color trait in rock pocket mice, and a lower-case d would represent the recessive light coat color trait. Upper case letters are underlined so that upper case is always easily distinguishable (e.g. $\underline{S}$ and s). An individual with the dd genotype is referred to as homozygous recessive, and its phenotype for coat color is light. Individuals with genotypes of either $\underline{DD}$ (homozygous dominant) or $\underline{D}$d (heterozygous) will exhibit the dark phenotype for coat color.

During gamete formation, only one of the two alleles present in a parent mouse is passed on in each gamete (sperm or egg). During fertilization, the resulting zygote receives one allele from each parent. Thus, each offspring has two alleles, one from each parent, for the gene for coat color. These alleles determine the offspring's genotype for coat color.

Genetic Diversity

Genetic diversity refers to allele diversity in an entire genome across a population. While most traits are determined by more than one gene, in this activity, students look at a simplified model of the genetic diversity of just a simple one-gene, one-trait inheritance in a population.

GETTING STARTED

1 Project Transparency 12.1, "Mice in a Light Granite Environment." Give students three seconds to count as many light mice as they can. Mention that before a volcanic eruption, most of the mice in the region were naturally light colored. Then show Transparency 12.2, "Mice in a Dark Lava Bed Environment," which illustrates the environment that formed after a volcanic eruption. Again, give students three seconds to count as many light mice as they can. Just as it was easier for them to see more light mice against a dark background, it is easier for predator owls to see and catch light mice against a dark background than against a light one.

Ask students to predict what eventually is likely to happen to the population in the darker environment. The mouse population as a whole is likely to become darker colored as more individuals with dark coats survive the predators and reproduce. Inform students that the model they will be working through in this activity will simulate what is likely to happen over several generations to the population at the genetic level.

---

12 The Genetic Basis of Adaptation

1 **T**HROUGHOUT THIS UNIT you have studied environmental and evolutionary influences on biodiversity. In the previous activity, you observed how some species evolve in a relatively short period of time, adapting to newly available environments and contributing to the biodiversity of an ecosystem. A **biological adaptation**, or **adaptation**, is an inherited characteristic that favors the survival or reproduction of an organism, and is the result of natural selection.

Some evolutionary biologists study how environmental and evolutionary changes affect populations at the genetic level. Scientists studying the rock pocket mouse, *Chaetodipus intermedius*, have found that changes in the coat colors of mouse populations illustrate the genetic mechanism of natural selection. The coat color of a rock pocket mouse is an example of an adaptation.

Light and dark-colored rock pocket mice on light granite.

In this activity you will model genetic changes in a population of rock pocket mice as a result of natural selection.

Challenge

▶ How did a change in the environment lead to genetic changes in populations of the rock pocket mouse?

484

5 Circulate around the room, and monitor students' progress as they work through the model for all of the genotypes in the generations students modeled. Then collect each group's totals on a chart. Instruct students to record and add up the totals on the chart for all of the groups in the class. If there is no obvious trend toward a higher proportion of D alleles and a lower proportion of d alleles, or the class is not convinced of the trend, instruct students to follow Procedure Steps 3–9 to complete three, four, or five additional generations until the trend becomes clear. Then add the class's totals for the additional generations to the data already collected on the chart.

6 ✓Procedure Steps 13 and 14 are a Quick Check assessment of students' ability to organize data in a graph.

7 ◆ Sample responses to the statements on Student Sheet 3.1, "Ideas about Evolution," that apply to this activity and Activities 9–11 are shown at the end of this activity.

---

9. Now assume the class represents a population of mice. Randomly choose another student from the class to work with in this round. Follow Steps 3–7 for your surviving mouse and the surviving mouse of your partner to determine the genes for a litter of eight offspring in Generation 3. When you need a number cube, use one at a nearby table. Record on Student Sheet 12.1, "Changes in the Gene Pool of a Mouse Population," the genotype and phenotype of each offspring.

10. Repeat Steps 3–9 with another randomly chosen student from the class until you have completed five generations on the Student Sheet.

11. Work with your group of four to add up the following for each generation. Your teacher will collect each group's totals to compile the class data for the following:

- The number of each allele present in only the mice that reproduced (the mice that were circled).
- The number of light- and dark-colored mice present in each generation, including living, dead, and reproducing.

5 12. In your science notebook, make a chart like the one below. Follow your teacher's directions to record the information for the class for all of the generations.

Generation	Number of D alleles in parent mouse population	Number of d alleles in parent mouse population	Total number of light-colored offspring mice	Total number of dark-colored offspring mice

6 13. On one side of a sheet of graph paper, draw a line graph with a colored pencil showing the number of D alleles present in each of the mouse generations you modeled. Be sure to label the axes. With a different-colored pencil draw a line graph on the same set of axes to show the number of d alleles present in each generation.

14. In colored pencil draw a second line graph to show the number of light-colored mice present in each of the generations you modeled. Be sure to label the axes. With a different-colored pencil draw a line graph on the same set of axes to show the number of dark-colored mice present in each generation.

7 15. Go back to the statements on Student Sheet 3.1, "Ideas about Evolution," from Activity 3. Record information from this activity and any previous activity to support whether any of the statements are correct or incorrect.

FOLLOW-UP

8 ✓The population of mice for the class will most likely be made up of all (or almost all) dark individuals (DD and Dd). Ask students how this population of mice compares to the population that they began with. In the beginning, there were more light than dark mice in the population, and the allele that produces the dark color was less common in the gene pool. Over five or more generations in the dark environment, the population changed, so that the population included mostly dark mice. Stress that individual mice did not change from light to dark over their lifetimes, nor did the mice get "better" in the dark environment. Instead the population changed as the darker mice were more likely to survive in the dark lava environment, reproduce, and pass on the trait for dark coat color to their offspring. Note that the changes in the rock pocket mouse population are an example of microevolution, which is small-scale evolutionary change that results in changes in the proportion of genes in a population.

Ask students why genetic diversity was important to the survival of the mice in the dark environment. They should be able to explain that if there had been no genetic diversity for the coat color gene, meaning the presence of both D and d alleles, the mouse population in the dark environment would have quickly decreased and might have eventually died out. Ask students to describe the genetic diversity of the current mouse population. It may be very low if very few mice still have a recessive allele for the light color, but it is likely that some alleles remain in the population. Ask students to suggest why this diversity might help the mice survive in the future. If the environment changes again, to a light environment, for example, there is a higher probability that light individuals in the population will survive.

Tell students that the model of changes in one gene for coat color in this activity is a simplified model of genetic diversity. Most traits are determined by multiple genes, and genetic diversity generally refers to the diversity of the entire genome across a population.

Discuss the role of fitness and reproductive success in natural selection. In this case, the light-colored individuals were less fit in (not as well suited to) the dark environment, and they were reduced in numbers through natural selection. As the light mice die and fail to reproduce offspring, the dd genotype is gradually reduced in the population. Explain to students that this illustrates how natural selection acts on the phenotypes of individuals, which in turn affects the genotypes and phenotypes of the next generation. As natural selection proceeds, the pattern of gene frequencies and phenotypes of the entire population of individuals changes.

Next ask students how scientists who study such processes as natural selection use models. Models help scientists predict what may happen to the gene pool of a population as the result of environmental changes.

Ask students if there is anything they would change in the model that would improve its accuracy. Students might suggest that it is unrealistic that no individuals migrated into or out of the area. It also may be unrealistic that nearly all of the dd and none of the Dd or DD mice died each generation, given that other factors, such as health and speed, might affect survival. Finally, it was not realistic that only one of the surviving mice in each generation

went on to reproduce (students used a number cube to determine which one reproduced successfully in order to make the model manageable).

You may wish to conclude the activity by showing a video animation of rock pocket mouse evolution. See the link on the *Science and Global Issues* page of the SEPUP website (*sepuplhs.org/sgi*).

Analysis Question 1 is a Quick Check assessment of students' understanding of how the mouse population changed and the role that genetics played in the change. This is the place to emphasize that it is the phenotype, not the genotype that is selected for by the environment in natural selection. Also, genetic diversity must be present for natural selection to occur.

SCIENCE & GLOBAL ISSUES/BIOLOGY • EVOLUTION

7 Analysis

1. Explain how a change in the environment led to selection for:
   a. genetic changes in the population of mice over several generations.
   b. phenotypic changes in the population of mice over several generations.
2. Did the evidence provided by your model match your prediction? Explain.
3. What aspects of natural selection were modeled in this activity?
4. What eventually would have happened in the mouse population if all of the mice had the genotype dd when the volcanic eruption occurred in their area?

KEY VOCABULARY

adaptation	evolve
allele	gene
biological adaptation	genetic diversity
evolution	

488

(continued on next page)

SAMPLE RESPONSES

4. If all of the mice were dd with a light coat, there would

their science notebooks any differences they notice between groups' evaluations.

This is an opportunity for you to review each group's evaluation to assess whether they have corrected any misconceptions about evolution. For statement 5, tell students that while they looked at just the crania evidence for the organisms and a portion of the molecular evidence, there are other skeletal and molecular data that scientists examine to track the evolution of the hominids. If there are any statements for which students still hold misconceptions, discuss them, and bring out the evidence from the unit that supports whether the statement is accurate or inaccurate. Encourage students to discuss the statements in terms of the evidence from Student Sheet 3.1, "Ideas about Evolution," that they collected throughout the unit.

FOLLOW-UP

5 (UC, CS ASSESSMENT) Analysis Question 1 is an opportunity to introduce students to the COMMUNICATION SKILLS (CS) Scoring Guide. Distribute copies of the CS Scoring Guide, and tell the class your expectations for satisfactory work. It is also an opportunity to assess students' understanding of evolutionary concepts. Review the Understanding Concepts (UC) Scoring Guide with the class, and tell students your expectations for satisfactory work.

---

5 *Analysis*

1. Choose one of the five statements from Student Sheet 3.1, "Ideas about Evolution." Write a short evaluation of the statement. Include in it

   • the statement you are evaluating and whether the statement is scientifically correct or incorrect.

   • an explanation of the evidence and reasoning from the unit that supports whether the statement is correct or incorrect.

   KEY VOCABULARY

adaptation	evolution
evidence	natural selection

   499

SAMPLE RESPONSES

1. (UC, CS ASSESSMENT) A complete and correct response should include:

   - A summary of the statement being evaluated and whether the statement is correct or incorrect.

   - An explanation of the evidence from the unit to support whether the statement is correct or incorrect.

Sample Level-3 Response

I am evaluating Statement 3: Natural selection is a not a random process. Scientists have gathered evidence to support this statement. The evidence includes the evolution of species, such as the Galapagos finches and the rock pocket mice. There are elements of natural selection that are random, namely mutations and recombination of genes during reproduction. However, the process of selection of the most fit individuals in an environment is not random. Finches with beaks that were most fit, or suitable, for using the available food sources survived and reproduced more successfully. Rock pocket mice with dark coats were more fit for a dark environment. Because they could better hide from owls they survived, reproduced, and passed on the trait for dark coat color to their offspring.

REVISIT THE CHALLENGE

Review that throughout the unit, students had the opportunity to experience firsthand that all scientific knowledge is subject to change as new evidence becomes available. For example, students had this experience in Activity 5, "Using Fossil Evidence to Investigate Whale Evolution," and in Activity 8, "Studying Hominids," when they modified their ideas based on new information. In addition to their first-hand experience, students read about an example of scientists changing their explanations as they gathered fossil evidence about the evolution of terrestrial tetrapods. Scientific explanations must be based on appropriate evidence, reasoning, and accepted historical and current knowledge. This activity reinforced the theory of evolution as a well-established and highly reliable explanation for the origins and diversity of life. While new evidence about the evolution of specific lineages is still being discovered, the overall processes of the theory of evolution and, in some cases, the evolution of specific lineages, are supported by a large body of evidence.

Ideas about Evolution (continued)

Statement: *Evidence suggests that humans and apes share an evolutionary ancestry.*

Before doing any activity, I think the statement is correct: Yes ☐ No ☐ because _____

Activity Number	After doing these activities, I think	
	Statement is correct:	**Evidence and reasoning:**
8	Yes ☒ No ☐	*DNA and protein evidence suggests that humans and chimpanzees share a more recent common ancestor than either does with gorillas. All of these lineages share a common ancestor.*
8	Yes ☒ No ☐	*Physical evidence (cranium data) suggests an evolutionary ancestry.*
	Yes ☐ No ☐	

15 Conservation of an Island Biodiversity Hotspot

TALK IT OVER • 1–2 CLASS SESSIONS

OVERVIEW

Students read about four forest areas being considered for conservation on the island of Kapikua, and use the information to make an initial recommendation for which forest area should have the highest conservation priority. Then students analyze the phylogenetic diversity for the endemic primates on the island, and apply the additional evidence to reexamine their recommendation for conservation.

KEY CONTENT

1. Science is a social enterprise, but alone it only indicates what can happen, not what should happen. The latter involves human decisions about the use of knowledge.

2. Human activities can cause biodiversity to increase or decrease. Such human activities as acquisition of resources, urban growth, and waste disposal accelerate rates of natural change in organisms and ecosystems.

3. The millions of different species of plants, animals, and microorganisms that live on earth today are related by descent from common ancestors.

4. Evolutionary trees show evolutionary ancestry.

5. Biodiversity is measured on phylogenetic, species, and genetic levels.

KEY PROCESS SKILLS

1. Students consider and evaluate multiple perspectives.

2. Students interpret data.

3. Students take a position and support it with evidence.

MATERIALS AND ADVANCE PREPARATION

For the teacher

Scoring Guide: COMMUNICATION SKILLS (CS)
Scoring Guide: EVIDENCE AND TRADE-OFFS (ET)

For each student

Literacy Student Sheet 2a, "Writing Frame—Evidence and Trade-offs," (optional)
Scoring Guide: COMMUNICATION SKILLS (CS) (optional)
Scoring Guide: EVIDENCE AND TRADE-OFFS (ET) (optional)

Masters for Literacy Student Sheets are in Teacher Resources III: Literacy. Masters for Scoring Guides are in Teacher Resources IV: Assessment.

TEACHING SUMMARY

Getting Started

- Students review the benefits that people derive from ecosystems.

Doing the Activity

- Students read about the four forest areas under consideration for conservation on Kapikua.

- Students write an initial recommendation for which forest area should receive conservation priority.

- Students analyze the phylogenetic data for four forest areas on Kapikua and use this evidence to reexamine their initial ideas about which area should be conserved.

Follow-up

- (LITERACY) The class conducts a Walking Debate about which forest area should be conserved.

- (ET, CS ASSESSMENT) Students write a summary recommendation for which forest area should be conserved.

BACKGROUND INFORMATION

The length of the branches of a tree often reflects the amount of evolutionary change that has occurred within the lineage represented by the branch. Longer branches represent more evolutionary change. Taxa that share a more recent common ancestor on fairly short branches are most likely less diverse than taxa that share a more distant common ancestor and are on longer branches. Even more diverse is a set of taxa along branches that are dispersed across the tree because they represent more distant ancestry.

GETTING STARTED

1 Ask students to go back to the list they compiled at the beginning of Activity 1, "Biodiversity and Sustainability," of the benefits that humans derive from ecosystems. Ask for student volunteers to share the benefits they recorded. Likely examples will include food, shelter, and building materials. Review that the benefits people obtain from ecosystems are referred to as ecosystem services. Explain that sustainable conservation decisions are complex because there are social, environmental, and economic considerations, and conflicting viewpoints on priorities. Conservationists must also take into account both the interests in ecosystem services and the biodiversity of an area.

15 Conservation of an Island Biodiversity Hotspot

1 THE GOVERNMENT OF *Kapikua wants to expand biodiversity conservation efforts on the island. The government has two goals: 1) to protect the overall biodiversity and sustainability of the island ecosystem, and 2) to protect the endemic primates that live in the forests on the island. The endangered primates are unique and very sensitive to habitat changes. This puts them at a higher risk of extinction. The primates have also become a well-known attraction for ecotourists from around the world. The government has enough funds to fully support conservation at only one of four forest areas being considered for conservation. You are a member of the conservation team that will advise on which area should get full conservation support.*

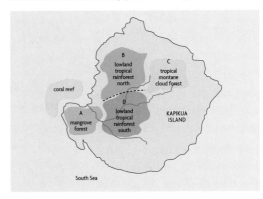

THE ISLAND OF KAPIKUA

In this activity you will learn more about each of the four areas and select one for conservation. You will use additional evidence from an evolutionary tree for the primates to decide which area should be conserved.

Challenge

▶ Which of four areas should receive priority for conservation?

DOING THE ACTIVITY

2 A sample completed chart is shown on the next page.

Procedure

Part A: Four Possible Conservation Areas

1. With your group, assign to each student one of the four forest areas under consideration for conservation. Work by yourself to read below and on the next pages the summary of your assigned area.

2. In your science notebook, make a chart like the one shown below. Fill in the chart for your assigned forest area.

Forest area	Economic outcomes if conserved	Social outcomes if conserved	Environmental outcomes if conserved	Benefits of conserving the area	Trade-offs of conserving the area

2 3. Present a summary of your forest area to the members of your group. As your group members present the information about their forest areas, complete the chart.

Area A: Mangrove Forest

UNIQUE CHARACTERISTICS

The mangrove forest on the island is dense with stilt mangrove trees and shrubs that grow in brackish coastal swamps. The roots of the mangrove trees filter the salts out of seawater. They also filter silt and nutrients from river water, allowing clear water to flow to the nearby coral reef. The vegetation serves an important role in the coastal area as a buffer to protect the nearby shoreline villages from hurricanes and other storms. The vegetation also prevents erosion along the riverbanks. Mangroves provide food and shelter to a variety of organisms.

CONSERVATION CONSIDERATIONS

In recent years, partly because of mangrove forest degradation, the inland areas of the island have been damaged by flooding from severe storms that have blown in. Almost all of the buildings and houses in one village were lost to the flooding. The villagers lost their crops and homes, and had to move to other areas.

Mangrove Forest	
LAND AREA TO BE CONSERVED (%)	3
NUMBER OF ENDEMIC SPECIES IN THE AREA	14
NUMBER OF ENDEMIC SPECIES THREATENED	7

501

Sample Student Response: Procedure Steps 2–3
Forest Conservation Areas

Forest area	Economic outcomes if conserved	Social outcomes if conserved	Environmental outcomes if conserved	Benefits of conserving the area	Trade-offs of conserving the area
Mangrove	Ecotourism would provide jobs and revenue for the island. Fishermen who earn income from catching and selling fish and shrimp might receive less income.	Ecotourism would provide jobs, income, and enjoyment. Fishermen may have to move or find other types of work. Catch limits would affect a food source for people on the island.	Dense vegetation serves as a barrier to flooding from storms for inland villages. Mangrove forests prevent erosion, filter water that flows to the coral reef, and provide food and shelter to a number of organisms. 14 endemic and 7 threatened endemic species would be protected. 3% of land area would be conserved.	Ecotourism Area would continue to provide buffer from storms. Filters water and preserves coral reef Provides food and shelter for organisms	Limited boating and fishing would negatively affect the fishermen and would reduce an island food source.
Lowland tropical rainforest north	Lost income, jobs, and sustainable, desirable coffee crop	Lost income, jobs, and sustainable, desirable coffee crop Loss of a sustainable commodity that people worldwide enjoy	Area is biodiverse. 135 endemic and 10 threatened endemic species would be protected. 3% of land area would be conserved.	This would conserve only a small percentage of remaining land, but the area has a fair amount of biodiversity.	Coffee harvesters would not be able to harvest, causing lost profit and jobs for a relatively small number of people.
Lowland tropical rainforest south	Percentage of pharmaceutical profits would go back to island. Ecotourism to primate protection and public education center would provide jobs to island residents and income.	Plants used for pharmaceutical research could lead to products that could save millions of lives. Primate and public education center would provide enjoyment and education to ecotourists and islanders.	Larger area than northern rainforest and most biodiverse forest area on island Kapok trees provide highway system for tree-dwelling mammals. Primate center might reduce their risk of extinction. 254 endemic and 75 threatened endemic species would be protected. 7% of land area would be conserved.	Profit from pharmaceuticals for the company A percentage of the profit would go to the island. Pharmaceuticals would save lives. Protects a diverse area and tree-dwelling mammals that depend on the trees for highway	Primate and public education center would require the construction of roads and facilities, which could affect the environment.
Tropical montane cloud forest	Reduced profit for tea company because it could not expand its plantation No new jobs on plantation In times of drought other agricultural jobs and crops might be saved by irrigation from cloud forest waters.	Tea is a desirable commodity worldwide. The plantation would not provide new jobs. Cloud forest water provides source of power for people's homes.	Organisms that depend on the climate and water that is stored by the forest would be protected. 11 endemic and 5 threatened endemic species would be protected. 4% of land area would be conserved.	Organisms that depend on water and climate would be protected. Clean water source for drinking water for the island would be protected.	Loss of tea profit and jobs that would be generated from expansion of the plantation

If the area is conserved, the island government plans to offer limited permits at a reasonable cost for sustainable ecotourism to the area. For those who live on the island, ecotourism would provide jobs ranging from researchers and tour guides to restaurant waiters, cooks, hotel workers, drivers, and boat crewmen. People who make handicrafts and other goods also would earn money by selling their wares to tourists. Park fees would bring in revenue that would also contribute to the island's economy.

Currently, island residents have unlimited access to the mangrove forest for fishing and shrimping. Some fishermen have small businesses in which they sell their catch at local markets. Others fish for recreation or to feed their families. If the mangrove is conserved, a strict catch limit will be enforced in order to protect the food sources for a variety of organisms in the ecosystem. The new limits could force the local fishermen to downsize their businesses and reduce their income.

Area B: Lowland Tropical Rainforest North

UNIQUE CHARACTERISTICS

The lowland tropical rainforest is the most bio-diverse area on the island, although the northern region of the rainforest is less diverse than the southern region. The earliest settlers in the northern area introduced new plants and animals to provide sources of food, medicine, building materials, and decoration. They cleared land to plant agricultural crops, and hunted lizards and birds for additional food. Since the first settlers came to the area, logging, development, and agriculture have destroyed 95% of the northern region's forest.

Lowland Tropical Rainforest North	
LAND AREA TO BE CONSERVED (%)	3
NUMBER OF ENDEMIC SPECIES IN THE AREA	135
NUMBER OF ENDEMIC SPECIES THREATENED	10

CONSERVATION CONSIDERATIONS

A small family-run business harvests coffee from the plants they have grown in this forest area. The exported coffee is a desirable commodity for people in other countries, and it is marketed as some of the best quality and most sustainable in the world. It benefits the family and a small number of workers hired to help with the harvest. If the forest is designated for conservation, the family will no longer have access to the forest for their coffee. This would mean lost income, with family members and the small number of people employed by the business losing their jobs. However, the species that live in the remaining 3% of undeveloped area will be protected.

Area C: Lowland Tropical Rainforest South

UNIQUE CHARACTERISTICS

The southern region of the lowland tropical rainforest is the most biodiverse on the island. It is
larger than the northern region of the rainforest,
and because the earliest settlers remained mostly in
the northern region of the forest, this area was not
as severely deforested as the north. Medical research
scientists search for unique species in this area that
may provide substances for new medicines. A
number of tree-dwelling species depend on the
kapok trees as a highway that allows them to move
around the forest without having to travel on the
ground.

Lowland Tropical Rainforest South	
LAND AREA TO BE CONSERVED (%)	7
NUMBER OF ENDEMIC SPECIES IN THE AREA	254
NUMBER OF ENDEMIC SPECIES THREATENED	75

CONSERVATION CONSIDERATIONS

If this area were conserved, the vast biodiversity of
the area would be protected, including the plant
species central to pharmaceutical research and
product development. Research scientists would be
assigned permits to collect specimens in a sustainable manner from the area. Recently, a team of scientists was sent to the island to research a plant
found nowhere else that shows potential as a new
malaria treatment. If the treatment is successful, it
could save millions of lives. The research institute signed an agreement with the
Kapikua government that a percentage of the profit made from products containing substances from Kapikua plants will go back into the island economy.

If this area is conserved, the government plans to build a primate center to
research and protect the endemic primates that live in the island forests. This
center will also be the focus of a program to educate the public. Permits will be
available for ecotourists to visit the center to observe the primates and learn more
about them through tours and exhibits. However, the cost of the permits will be
much higher for this remote area than the cost to tour the mangrove forest. The
primate center and access for ecotourists will require the construction of roads
and facilities, which will be done in the most sustainable manner possible. For
island residents it will provide such jobs as tour guides, drivers, lab technicians,
and instructors.

Area D: Tropical Montane Cloud Forest

UNIQUE CHARACTERISTICS

The tropical montane cloud forest ecosystem plays an important role in the water cycle and climate on the island. Experiments have shown that cloud forests prevent the evaporation of precipitation far better than non-cloud forests do. The precipitation in the cloud forest is mostly in the form of fog, which condenses on the trees and drips onto the ground. The water soaks into the soil, where it is stored. Any excess runoff drains into stagnant water pools in the forest. The large water supply in the soil and the pools supports a wide variety of organisms.

Tropical Montane Cloud Forest	
LAND AREA TO BE CONSERVED (%)	4
NUMBER OF ENDEMIC SPECIES IN THE AREA	11
NUMBER OF ENDEMIC SPECIES THREATENED	5

CONSERVATION CONSIDERATIONS

Such human activities as logging and clearing the land to plant crops have degraded the cloud forest on Kapikua. This is a concern because during the dry season it is important that water from the cloud forest reaches the lower elevations where it is needed for irrigation, power generation, and drinking water. Recently, there have been reports of pollution problems with the water supply in another area of the island. Because of these reports, the government is concerned that in the future there will not be an adequate supply of clean water for the island. If conserved, the cloud forest would supply one source of clean drinking water.

Two decades ago, a corporation bought a portion of the cloud forest to develop a large tea plantation. The tea is highly desirable worldwide because the unique growing conditions give it a flavor that people love. Currently, there is a plan underway to expand the plantation to meet the growing demand for the tea. If the cloud forest is conserved, the tea plantation would not be permitted to expand, the company would not increase its profits, and no additional jobs for islanders would be created.

However, if the area were conserved, the risk of further adverse effects on the water cycle, climate, and organisms that depend on these resources would be reduced. For example, the fastigo whipping frog is a rare species that inhabits only the cloud forest. It lives in bushes close to shallow pools of standing water and breeds in the standing water. If the forest area is not conserved, the frog might be further endangered.

3 Ask for student volunteers to share with the class their initial recommendations for which forest area should be conserved and their reasons. A variety of opinions are likely to be expressed. A sample response follows.

I think the mangrove forest should be conserved. The mangrove forest would help to protect the villages from the risk of further flood damage that has destroyed almost all of one village in recent years. The conservation would include permits for sustainable ecotourism that would provide recreation and education to tourists and jobs to island residents.

4 Review with students what the lengths of branches and nodes on an evolutionary tree represent. Tell students that on the tree the nodes for the primates are numbered from most distant common ancestor (node 1) to most recent common ancestor (node 6).

A final column added to the chart in Procedure Steps 6 and 7 is shown at right.

FOLLOW-UP

5 (LITERACY) Extend the discussion and prepare students for a written assessment by conducting a Walking Debate (see the Literacy section of Teacher Resources III: Literacy). This strategy works best when the question or issue has no single correct answer. Designate one corner of the room as "Lowland Tropical Rainforest North," a second area of the room as "Lowland Tropical Rainforest South," a third area of the room as "Tropical Montane Cloud Forest," and a fourth area of the room as "Mangrove Forest." Have students stand in the place that they think is the area that should have the highest conservation priority on the island. If most of the students already agree on a particular option, assign some of them to the other options to foster

the skills of debate and evidence analysis. Tell students to take with them the chart they created in Procedure Steps 2 and 3 to refer to in the discussion. Have each group of students explain to the class why they chose that option. Once each group has explained its choice, allow time for students to ask clarifying questions. Then allow students to change their minds and move to another area.

After the Walking Debate, emphasize the tensions that arise when examining where to focus sustainable conservation efforts. There can be tension between stakeholders

---

CONSERVATION OF AN ISLAND BIODIVERSITY HOTSPOT • ACTIVITY 15

3 4. In your science notebook, write a brief summary for which forest area you would select for conservation based on the information you have so far. Explain your reasoning.

Part B: Evolutionary Tree Analysis

5. In your science notebook, add to the chart you created in Step 2 a column labeled "Phylogenetic diversity of primates."

4 6. With your group, compare the evolutionary tree below for each of the four forest areas. The tree shows evolutionary data for primate taxa that are endemic to the island. In the column you created in Step 5, record the number of the node that represents the most recent common ancestor for all of the primates collectively living in each of the four areas.

7. In the column you created in Step 5, describe the phylogenetic diversity of the primate species living in each forest area.

5 8. Conduct a Walking Debate as a way to share your ideas with the class about which forest area should have conservation priority. Your teacher will explain how to run the debate.

Forest Conservation Areas

Forest area	Phylogenetic diversity of primates
Mangrove	Most recent common ancestor is node 3.
	Moderately diverse
	Species share a relatively distant common ancestor
	Branches are longer than others.
Lowland tropical rainforest north	Most recent common ancestor is node 6.
	Not diverse
	Species share a relatively recent common ancestor, and branches are short.
Lowland tropical rainforest south	Most recent common ancestor is node 1.
	Very diverse
	Species are dispersed across the tree.
	They share the most distant common ancestor, and branches vary in length.
Tropical montane cloud forest	Most recent common ancestor is node 5.
	Not diverse, but slightly more diverse than lowland tropical rainforest north
	Species share a relatively recent common ancestor (but slightly more distant than B), and branches are short.

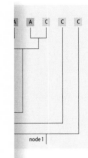

505

---

interested in ecosystem services versus those interested in biodiversity. For example, conservation in the cloud forest might allow for the maintenance of water storage and water sources needed for organisms to survive, but development, such as the expansion of a tea plantation, would not be permitted. However, sometimes the ecosystem services and biodiversity interests can both be met. For example, maintaining the biodiversity of an area rich in plant species that could be used for pharmaceuticals means that there is greater potential for finding the right plants for the products that could save many lives.

6 (LITERACY) (ET, CS ASSESSMENT)
Analysis Question 1 allows you to assess students' understanding of evidence and trade-offs with the EVIDENCE AND TRADE-OFFS (ET) Scoring Guide. Review the guidelines of the ET Scoring Guide, and tell the class your expectations for satisfactory work.

To help students summarize their positions you may wish to pass Literacy Student Sheet 2a, "Writing Frame—Evidence and Trade-offs." This sheet provides a literacy strategy known as a writing frame, which gives students a structure for communicating their ideas. More information about the writing frame literacy strategy is in Teacher Resources III: Literacy. You may want to assess students' written summaries on the writing frame with the COMMUNICATION SKILLS (CS) Scoring Guide. If necessary, pass out copies of the CS Scoring Guide, and tell the class your expectations for satisfactory work. Review sustainability indicators. If students had the "Sustainability" unit of the *Science and Global Issues* course, they were introduced to indicators. An indicator is an observation or calculation that shows the presence or state of a condition or trend.

---

6 *Analysis*

1. Which forest did you decide should be conserved? Cite at least three pieces of evidence to explain your reasoning, and state the trade-offs of your decision.

2. Describe three indicators you would recommend using to monitor the success of the conservation over the next 10 years if your recommendation from Question 1 were implemented. These indicators can be any observations that will help determine if the recommendation is successful.

3. What social, economic, and environmental elements of sustainability were involved in your considerations about which area should be conserved?

4. What scientific evidence influenced your considerations about which area to conserve?

KEY VOCABULARY	
biodiversity	lineage
ecosystem services	phylogenetic diversity
endemic	sustainability
evidence	taxa
evolution	taxon
evolutionary tree	trade-off
indicator	

When students have completed the Analysis Questions, ask them to think about which influenced them most as they prioritized the conservation areas: biodiversity or ecosystem services. Have them discuss their ideas in pairs or groups. Bring out the idea that sustainable conservation decisions involve both the ecosystem services provided by an area and the biodiversity of the area. Sometimes there is tension between the two, and sometimes they go hand in hand. The resolution of this tension is a large part of what conservationists discuss in order to come to the most sustainable conservation decisions.

SAMPLE RESPONSES

1. (ET ASSESSMENT) (CS ASSESSMENT) A complete and correct response will include a recommendation, three pieces of evidence from the information about the forest area and from the evolutionary tree analysis, including what the tree evidence tells about the diversity of the primates. It will also explain at least one trade-off of the decision.

    Sample Level-3 Response:

    I recommend that Forest C, the Lowland Tropical Rainforest South, should receive the conservation funds.

    My decision is based on the following evidence:

    First, the tree evidence shows that there is a great amount of biodiversity in the primates that live in the area. The primate species that live there are dispersed widely across the tree and have the most distant common ancestor. Three of the branches are the longest on the tree, which means there is probably a lot of evolutionary change in those lineages. Since evolution acts on genetic variation, this forest's populations are more likely to survive changes in the environment.

    Second, if the area is conserved, a primate and public education center will protect the endemic primates, and might help to reduce their risk of extinction.

    Third, if the forest is conserved, the plants that can be used for the research and development of pharmaceuticals and other products will be preserved. If successful, these products will help human health, possibly save lives, and bring profit back to the island.

    Some trade-offs of my decision are that to build the primate and public education center, roads and facilities must be constructed, and lots of people will visit the area. The building and visitation could disrupt the fragile habitat.

    Also, if the Montane Cloud forest is not conserved, there is a potential risk that the water quality of an island drinking water source will be affected.

2. To monitor the success of the conservation of the rainforest, I would recommend keeping a count of the total number of all species in the area, and a count of the number of offspring of the primate species in the populations. I would also recommend tracking the phylogenetic diversity of the primates.

3. The social elements were jobs and products such as pharmaceuticals that benefit human health, and the special tea that humans enjoy as a beverage. The economic elements were income to be made from products or services and jobs. The environmental elements were the effects on species, the percentage of land to be conserved, the number of endemic species, and the number of threatened endemic species.

4. The scientific evidence included the number of endemic and threatened endemic species living in each area, the information about the water storage and drainage to lower elevations in the cloud forest, the barrier to storms and water filtration by the vegetation in the mangrove, and the phylogenetic diversity of the primates on the evolutionary tree. There was also evidence about the overall health of an ecosystem, and the effect of one ecosystem on another, as in the case of the mangrove and coral reef.

REVISIT THE CHALLENGE

Students should be able to explain that conservation decisions are complex because they involve multiple perspectives, and social, economic, and environmental considerations. These include profits and jobs, materials and goods, recreation, education, the biodiversity of an area, and the percentage of threatened species in an area. Evolutionary trees help determine the phylogenetic diversity of an area, and, therefore, its sustainability. Since evolution depends on variation, the more biodiverse a population is, the more likely it is to survive an environmental change, and is more likely sustainable as a result. Sustainable conservation decisions involve both the ecosystem services provided by an area and the biodiversity of the area. Sometimes there is tension between the two, and sometimes they are complementary.

Unit Review: Evolution

Biodiversity and Sustainability

Biodiversity encompasses variability between and within ecosystems, between species, and within a species' gene pool as evidenced by genetic diversity. Biodiversity is closely linked to sustainability.

Human activities often cause biodiversity to increase or decrease. Such activities as acquisition of resources, urban growth, and waste disposal accelerate rates of natural change, and may lead to habitat loss, ecosystem destruction, or species extinctions.

Human activities may also diminish ecosystems services—the benefits that people and non-human species obtain from ecosystems. These include natural resources and processes that humans rely on for survival. Some examples of ecosystem services are materials derived for food, medicine, and shelter, water purification, carbon dioxide removal, and pollution control.

Protected areas are sections of land and sea especially dedicated to the maintenance of biological diversity and of natural and associated cultural resources. They are usually managed by governmental agencies or nonprofit organizations.

KEY VOCABULARY	
biodiversity	hotspot
biological diversity	indicator
ecosystem diversity	species diversity
ecosystem services	sustainability
endemic	trade-off
genetic diversity	

Geologic Time and the Fossil Record

Earth formed approximately 4.5 billion years ago. The geologic timeline reflects the vast time scale since Earth originated. It shows that life began on Earth approximately 4.3 billion years ago, and multicellular life originated relatively recently in geologic time, approximately 640 million years ago. Most key events in the evolution of life occurred in very recent geologic time.

From fossils scientists have developed and tested hypotheses for how major groups of organisms, such as tetrapods, evolved. Scientists use stratigraphy and radiometric dating to determine the ages of rock layers (strata) and the fossils within them. Stratigraphy is based on the idea that older rock strata are found beneath strata that were formed more recently. Fossils in lower strata are generally older than fossils found in upper strata. In the absence of transitional fossils, scientists focus on transitional features in fossils—key features that demonstrate the evolutionary changes that resulted in macroevolution.

KEY VOCABULARY	
co-opted features	geologic timeline
deep time	radiometric dating
extinct	strata
extinction	stratigraphic dating
fossil	stratigraphy
fossil record	terrestrial tetrapods
geologic time	transitional features
geologic time scale	transitional fossils

Darwin and the Theory of Natural Selection

The millions of species of plants, animals, and microorganisms that live on earth today evolved over many generations and are related by descent from common ancestors. Natural selection is the primary means by which diverse organisms evolve from common ancestors. Charles Darwin (1809–1882) developed the theory of evolution by natural selection by putting together his own observations and ideas with the findings and ideas of other naturalists, geologists, and an economist.

The theory of natural selection and its evolutionary results provide a scientific explanation for the fossil record of ancient life forms and the striking molecular similarities found among diverse species of living organisms. Natural selection acts on any trait—including physical, biochemical, or behavioral traits—that increases the probability of survival and reproduction. The broad patterns of behavior exhibited by animals have evolved by natural selection to ensure reproductive success.

Natural selection is not random. For natural selection to occur in a population there must be heritable variation among individuals, competition for resources needed for survival, and differential survival and reproduction. Natural genetic variation is the result of mutation and recombination in the individuals that make up a population. Based on environmental conditions, favorable traits that enhance survival are passed on during reproduction. As more individuals inherit the favorable trait(s), the population changes. Environmental changes can lead to natural selection of traits that were previously rare but now enhance fitness in the new environment. Adaptive radiation is the relatively rapid evolution from a common ancestor of multiple species that occupy newly available environments.

There is a large body of physical, molecular, and fossil evidence to support the natural selection theory of evolution.

KEY VOCABULARY	
adaptive radiation	natural selection
mutation	sexual selection

Phylogeny

Modern biological classifications show how organisms are related in a hierarchy of groups and subgroups based on similarities that reflect their genealogical relationships. Phylogenetic diversity results from the relationships of lineages to one another, and helps people make sustainable conservation decisions.

Evolutionary trees represent hypotheses for evolutionary ancestry. Shared derived characters determine where to place taxa on a tree. Evidence about structure, function, biochemistry, and behavior of taxa leads scientists to hypothesize the evolutionary relationships of taxa.

Scientists apply fossil and molecular data to develop hypotheses for how major groups of organisms, such as the hominids (African apes and humans), evolved. For example, fossil and genetic data suggest that humans and apes share a common ancestor. Chimpanzees and humans share a more recent ancestor than either does with gorillas. Evolutionary biologists and paleontologists focus on transitional features in fossils—those key features that demonstrate the evolutionary changes that resulted in macroevolution.

KEY VOCABULARY	
character	node
clade	phylogenetic diversity
evolutionary tree	phylogeny
hominid	shared derived character
homologous character	taxa
homology	taxon
lineage	

Processes and Outcomes of Evolution

Evolutionary processes led to the biodiversity of life, all of which is related by descent from a common ancestor. Evolution is the ongoing process by which traits favorable to living in a particular environment are selected for and passed on to offspring.

Microevolution is evolution on a small scale and results in changes in the proportion of genes in a population. Genes store genetic information that interacts with environmental factors to determine the traits, or phenotypes, of organisms. Natural selection acts on existing genetic variability in a population. Over many generations the gene for a selected trait becomes increasingly common in the population.

Species is the basic unit of classification. Scientists have found that the original definition of species as groups of organisms with similar structure, function, biochemistry, and behavior does not reflect underlying evolutionary processes. The biological species concept defines a species as a population of individuals that actually does or can potentially interbreed in nature to produce fertile offspring. Natural selection and reproductive isolation lead to speciation in new environments.

Adaptations are inherited characteristics that improve the survival and reproduction of an organism and are the results of natural selection. Adaptive characters include physical traits, behaviors, biochemical processes, or any other traits that enhance fitness and evolve through natural selection. Adaptations are the result of natural selection and do not occur over the lifetime of individuals.

Macroevolution is any change that occurs at or above the species level and is shaped by both speciation and extinction. Macroevolution leads to the large-scale patterns of biodiversity on earth.

Extinction occurs when the environment changes and a species is no longer fit for the new environment. Less diverse populations have fewer variations that might enhance survival in new environments and are at greater risk of extinction. The biodiversity at any time in earth's history depends on both the evolution of new taxa and the extinction of existing taxa.

KEY VOCABULARY

adaptation	fitness
adaptive character	gene
allele	gene flow
biological adaptation	gene pool
biological evolution	geographic isolation
biological species	macroevolution
biological species concept	mass extinction
evolution	microevolution
evolve	reproductive isolation
extinct	speciation
extinction	species
fit	

Inquiry and the Nature of Science

Scientific explanations must adhere to such criteria as application of appropriate evidence, consistently logical reasoning, and basis in accepted historical and current scientific knowledge. Scientific theories are based on natural and physical phenomena. Scientific theories are well-established and highly reliable explanations. Scientific hypotheses are tentative-and-testable statements that are either supported or not supported by observational evidence.

Science is a social enterprise, but alone it only indicates what can happen, not what should happen. The latter involves human decisions about the application of knowledge. Scientists usually build on earlier knowledge and are influenced by other experts and their society and culture. Occasionally, a scientific advance has important long-lasting effects on science and society because of its explanation of natural phenomena. The theory of biological evolution by natural selection is an example of such an advance.

KEY VOCABULARY	
evidence	theory
hypothesis	

Glossary

abiotic. Describes factors in an environment that are not, and have never been, living, including temperature, light, and precipitation. See also **biotic.**

active transport. Movement of a substance from lower to higher concentration through a protein carrier, requiring energy input usually provided by conversion of ATP to ADP.

adaptation. The change through natural selection of a population's physical, biochemical, or behavioral traits that better suit the population's environment.

adaptive radiation. The relatively rapid evolution from a common ancestor of multiple species that occupy newly available environments. Same as **biological adaptation.**

adenosine triphosphate (ATP). A small molecule that is the primary carrier of usable energy within the cell.

aerobic respiration. Reactions of cellular respiration that use oxygen to further break down the products of glycolysis, releasing energy in the form of ATP. See also **anaerobic respiration.**

allele. One of several forms of the same gene. A sexually reproduced organism has two alleles for each gene, one from each parent, which may or may not be the same form. See also **gene.**

amensalism. A symbiotic relationship in which one species is harmed, while the other species neither benefits nor is it harmed. See also **symbiotic relationship.**

amino acid. The basic building block of proteins; varying arrangements of 20 amino acids make up all natural proteins found in living organisms. See also **protein.**

anaerobic respiration. A form of cellular respiration that does not require oxygen, resulting in incomplete breakdown of sugars and generation of less usable energy than produced by aerobic respiration. See also **anaerobic respiration.**

antibiotic. A chemical substance that kills microorganisms and is used to treat infections.

aquaculture. The growing of fish and other aquatic species for human consumption.

asexual reproduction. Reproduction of genetically identical offspring from a single parent through mitosis. See also **mitosis, sexual reproduction.**

bacteria. A domain of single-celled prokaryotic organisms. While some cause infections in humans, others are harmless or even essential to human life.

base pair. Two nucleotides in double-stranded DNA connected by hydrogen bonds. See also **DNA, hydrogen bonds, nucleotides.**

binding site. A region on a protein or nucleic acid where other molecules attach, or bind. For example, an enzyme's substrate fits into a three-dimensional binding site on the enzyme.

biodiversity. The assortment of species on earth; within and between ecosystems; and the variation in the genetic composition of a species. Same as **biological diversity.**

biofuel. Fuel compounds, such as bioethanol and biodiesel, that are produced from renewable biological sources, such as corn.

biological adaptation. Same as **adaptation.**

biological diversity. Same as **biodiversity.**

biological evolution. Changes in the genetic composition of a population that eventually give rise to other diverse life forms. See also **evolution.**

biological species. The individuals of a population that breed or can potentially breed to produce fertile offspring. See also **species, species diversity.**

biological species concept. One definition of species as: a population or populations that can breed or potentially breed to exchange genes and produce fertile offspring.

biome. A large region classified by the interaction of the living organisms, climate, and geographical features.

biotic. Describes factors in an environment that are associated with living organisms. See also **abiotic.**

Calvin cycle. The series of light-independent, enzyme-catalyzed reactions that take place in the stroma of the chloroplast. During these reactions carbon dioxide combines with the hydrogen ions and electrons produced from water during light-dependent reactions. These reactions result in the production of the high-energy sugar glucose. See also **light-independent reactions.**

cancer. Any of more than 100 diseases that result when cells lose the normal controls that regulate their growth and division in the cell cycle. They may invade nearby tissues or spread to other locations in the body.

carbon cycle. The cycle in which carbon moves between reservoirs. See also **carbon reservoir.**

carbon footprint. The estimated amount of land and sea area (acres or hectares) that would be needed to completely absorb one person's carbon emissions. It is a subset of ecological footprint. See also **ecological footprint.**

carbon reservoir. A natural feature, such as a rock, a pinch of soil, or an organism, that stores carbon-containing molecules and exchanges them with other carbon reservoirs. See also **carbon cycle.**

carrier. An individual who carries a genetic trait for a disease but is not afflicted, usually identified through genetic testing. See also **trait.**

carrying capacity. The largest population of a species that an ecosystem can support long-term based on the resources available.

catalyze. The action of a catalyst, a chemical that speeds up a chemical reaction without being used up in the reaction.

causal relationship. An occurrence between two correlated events when one event (called the cause) directly produces another event (called the effect). In a causal relationship, the cause(s) alone produce the effect.

Page 350 TL Tom McHugh/Photo Researchers, Inc.; BR Herve Berthoule/Jacana/Photo Researchers, Inc.

Page 353 Lawrence Migdale/Photo Researchers, Inc.

Page 354 Biophoto Associates/Photo Researchers, Inc.

Page 361 ©Benjamin Lowy/Corbis

Page 362 Nigel Cattlin/Photo Researchers, Inc.

Page 363 Jack Dykinga

Page 368 University of California Agriculture and Environment

Page 372 TL National Human Genome Research; BR Maggie Bartlett, NIHGRI

Page 373 Patrick Landman/Photo Researchers, Inc.

Page 376 T Biology Pics/Photo Researchers, Inc. B Steve Gschmeissner/Photo Researchers, Inc.

Page 377 Biophoto Associates/Photo Researchers, Inc.

Page 382 L Inga Spence/Photo Researchers, Inc.; R Adam Jones/Photo Researchers, Inc.

Page 383 © Vasily Fedosenko/Reuters/Corbis

Page 386 Gustoimages/Photo Researchers, Inc.

Page 388 TR Veronique Leplat/Photo Researchers, Inc.; MR Wayne Nishijima, University of Hawaii at Manoa

Page 389 StockTrek/Getty Images

Page 393 Adrian Bicker/Photo Researchers, Inc

Page 400 T Martin Bond/Photo Reseachers, Inc.; B © Queen's Printer for Ontario, 2009. Reproduced with permission.

Evolution

Unit Opener Page 413 Nigel J. Dennis/Photo Researchers, Inc.

Page 415 TL Bjamla Ladic/Photo Researchers, Inc.; TR Art Wolfe/Photo Researchers, Inc.; MR E.R. Degginger/Photo Researchers, Inc.; BR Gregory G. Dimijian, M.D./Photo Researchers, Inc.; BL John Maraventano/Photo Researchers, Inc.

Page 422 BL Paal Hermansen/Photo Researchers, Inc.; BM Larry Landolfi/Photo Researchers, Inc.; BR Shekar Dattatri © Chelonian Research Foundation

Page 423 BL Alexis Rosenfeld/Photo Researchers, Inc.; BR Jack Dykinga/USDA Agricultrural Research Service

Page 424 Cede Prudente/Photo Researchers, Inc.

Page 425 TL, TR Nigel Cattlin/Photo Researchers, Inc.; MR Tom McHugh/Photo Researchers, Inc.; BR Mark Smith/Photo Researchers, Inc.

Page 426 Fox Photos/Getty Images

Page 427 U.S. Fish and Wildlife Service

Page 428 ML U.S. Fish and Wildlife Service; MR Jose Reynaldo da Fonseca/Wikimedia commons; BL Adam.J.W.C./Wikimedia commons; BR Paddy Patterson/Wikimedia commons

Page 429 TR Mark Taylor/Photo Researchers, Inc.; BL © How Hwee Young/Corbis

Page 430 Gerald C. Kelley/Photo Researchers, Inc.

Page 432 L. Newman & A. Flowers/Photo Researchers, Inc.

Page 436 Mary Evans/Photo Researchers, Inc.

Page 439 ML Ralph Lee Hopkins/Photo Researchers, Inc.; MR Francois Gohier/Photo Researchers, Inc.; B Jeanne White/Photo Researchers, Inc.

Page 440 William Munoz/Photo Researchers, Inc.

Page 441 Science Source/Photo Researchers, Inc.

Page 442 Steve Maslowski/Photo Researchers, Inc.

Page 443 BR RIA Novosti/Photo Researchers, Inc.; ML Francois Gohier/Photo Researchers, Inc.; BL Saul Gonor/Photo Researchers, Inc.

Page 446 Alan Sirulnkoff/Photo Researchers, Inc.

Page 447 National Park Service

Page 454 iStockphoto

Page 459 Philippe Plailly/Photo Researchers, Inc.

Page 460 Tom McHugh/Photo Researchers, Inc.

Page 465 Nigel J. Dennis/Photo Researchers, Inc.

Page 466 Courtesy of David R. Parks

Page 469 National Park Service

Page 470 From top in order: Alan & Sandy Carey/Photo Researchers, Inc.; Jacana/Photo Researchers, Inc.; Sidney Bahrt/Photo Researchers, Inc.; Nigel J. Dennis/Photo Researchers, Inc.; Millard H. Sharp/Photo Researchers, Inc.

Page 472 BL DEA/A. Calegari/De Agostini/Getty Images; BR Rod Planck/Photo Researchers, Inc.

Page 475 BL Peter Skinner/Photo Researchers, Inc.; BR Neil McDaniel/Photo Researchers, Inc.

Page 476 TR Suzanne L. Collins/Photo Researchers, Inc.; MR Phil A. Dotson/Photo Researchers, Inc.

Page 477 Fotosearch

Page 478 Courtesy of Ad Konings

Page 479 TR Jack Kelly Clark, courtesy University of California Statewide IPM Program; MR ©Steve Schoenig

Page 482 T Michael Ord/Photo Researchers, Inc.; B Peter LaTourrette

Page 489 BL Barbara Strnadova/Photo Researchers, Inc. BR Francois Gohier/Photo Researchers, Inc.

Page 492 National Fish and Wildlife Service

Page 493 BM Tom McHugh/Photo Researchers, Inc.; M Scott Camazine/Photo Researchers, Inc.; BR Vaughan Fleming/Photo Researchers, Inc.

Page 501 Jacques Jangoux/Photo Researchers, Inc.

Page 502 Nigel Cattlin/Photo Researchers, Inc.

Page 503 Nigel Cattlin/Photo Researchers, Inc.

Page 504 Fletcher & Baylis/Photo Researchers, Inc.